D1384131

STUDIES IN
PSYCHOSOMATIC
MEDICINE

STUDIES IN
PSYCHOSOMATIC
MEDICINE

AN APPROACH TO THE CAUSE AND
TREATMENT OF VEGETATIVE DISTURBANCES

By

FRANZ ALEXANDER, M.D.

and

THOMAS MORTON FRENCH, M.D.

with

CATHERINE L. BACON, M.D.

CLARENCE BERNSTEIN, JR., M.D.

LUDOLF N. BOLLMEIER, M.D.

MARGARET W. GERARD, M.D.

ROY R. GRINKER, M.D.

MARTIN GROTJAHN, M.D.

ADELAIDE M. JOHNSON, M.D.

HARRY B. LEVEY, M.D.

MAURICE LEVINE, M.D.

HELEN V. MC LEAN, M.D.

WILLIAM C. MENNINGER, M.D.

ALBRECHT MEYER, M.D.

MILTON L. MILLER, M.D.

SIDNEY A. PORTIS, M.D.

LEON J. SAUL, M.D.

LOUIS B. SHAPIRO, M.D.

CAREL VAN DER HEIDE, M.D.

GEORGE W. WILSON, M.D.

THE RONALD PRESS COMPANY · NEW YORK

2

PREFACE

The aim of this volume is to present comprehensive information concerning the new era of medicine that is designated by the term "psychosomatic." While it is designed primarily for medical men in the various specialties, and for psychiatrists, it should also be of interest to those laymen who seek to understand how body and mind work together to produce a certain state in the human organism.

It consists of a collection of papers based upon the psychoanalytic study of patients suffering from chronic disturbances of the vegetative organs. These were written individually or collectively by the Staff of the Chicago Institute for Psychoanalysis during the past sixteen years. Many of them are no longer readily available elsewhere. The more significant ones are here presented as a method of approach to the study of disease, its course and cure, an approach which uses all available sources of information—the observation of behavior, verbal communication, and bodily symptoms. They include a study of gastrointestinal disturbances, the first collective research of the Institute, which was a pioneer work in psychosomatic medicine.

The Institute's activities constitute one of the few consistent and systematic investigations in this field, and since these papers were first published, investigation in many of the same disorders has continued. From time to time new disease entities have been selected for study from the long list of ailments which plague mankind. It should be remarked, of course, that in view of the continuing investigations now being carried on, none of these papers should be regarded as the last word on the subject.

The papers have been classified according to type of somatic disturbance for the convenience of those who may be interested in some particular branch of psychosomatic medicine.

These studies have for the most part been presented first to scientific societies and then printed in scientific periodicals. For the courtesy of reprinting these articles we extend our thanks to the following publications and publishers: *The International Journal of Psycho-Analysis,* London; Columbia University Press, International Universities Press, *The American Journal of Orthopsychiatry, The Journal of Nervous and Mental Disease, The Psychoanalytic Quarterly, The Psychoanalytic Review, Psychosomatic Medicine,*

Research Publications of the Association for Research in Nervous and Mental Disease, The Nervous Child, all of New York; and *Psychosomatic Medicine Monographs,* Chicago.

HELEN ROSS, Administrative Director
Institute for Psychoanalysis, Chicago

September, 1948

INTRODUCTION

By FRANZ ALEXANDER, M.D.

The investigative studies presented in this volume cover a large territory; they are all concerned, however, with the emotional factors involved in the disturbance of the various vegetative functions. As in all scientific research, these studies are based on certain *fundamental postulates* and *operational concepts*. Though highly divergent phenomena are herein presented, the work achieves unity because of these underlying postulates and concepts, and because of a common basic orientation toward the field of psychiatry.

Fundamental Postulates

1. The disturbances of the vegetative functions are the results not of one but of a variety of etiological factors. Roughly, two categories of factors can be differentiated: organic and psychological. The vulnerability of an organ is determined by its hereditary constitution and by the environmental influences to which it has been exposed.

2. Organic factors must be studied and treated by somatic methods and emotional factors by psychological methods.

3. The relative importance of these two sets of factors varies from case to case within the same disease entity.

4. The attempt to single out certain diseases as psychosomatic is erroneous and futile. Every disease is psychosomatic because both psychological and somatic factors have a part in its cause and influence its course. This assumption is valid even for such specific infectious diseases as tuberculosis. Apart from exposure to the bacillus of Koch, the resistance of the organism is an equally important etiological factor in this disease. The resistance is also dependent upon the emotional state of the patient. We use the expression "psychosomatic" exclusively as a methodological concept; it is a type of approach in medicine: a simultaneous study and treatment of psychological and somatic factors *in their mutual interrelation*.

5. The emotional constellations which contribute to the disturbances of the vegetative organs are for the most part specific. It cannot be said that any emotion disturbs the function of any organ, but rather that there is an intimate affinity between certain emotional

states and certain vegetative functions, or, more precisely, between certain emotional constellations (nuclear conflicts) and somatic responses. A superficial study of emotional states is not enough to show this affinity. To establish the specific relationship requires long, refined, systematic investigations with the help of the psychoanalytic technique. Our studies were based on a simultaneous investigation of the somatic conditions made by specialists in the respective fields, and of psychoanalytic observations made both in briefer anamnestic explorations and prolonged therapeutic work.

Operational Concepts

1. The influence of psychological processes upon the functions of the body can be divided into three categories:

(a) *Voluntary behavior.* This type of behavior is called adaptive or integrated behavior; it is always motivated by goals.

(b) *Expressive innervations.* This type of behavior, exemplified by laughter, weeping, blushing, is a discharge phenomenon directed solely to relieve (express) specific emotional tensions. Sexual phenomena also belong to this category. Unlike (a), these expressions are not motivated by utilitarian goals.

(c) *Vegetative responses to emotional states.* These are adaptive responses of the vegetative functions to meet conditions to which the organism is exposed. In face of danger to the organism, the vegetative functions prepare for fight or flight by means of elevation of blood pressure, changes in the distribution of the blood in the different organs, mobilization of carbohydrates, etc.

The first two categories belong to the field of psychiatry. Disturbances of adequate integrated behavior and of normal expression of emotions are known as psychoneuroses, behavior disorders, and psychoses. The third category, however, consists in the failure of harmony between emotional states and vegetative responses, and therefore belongs to the borderland between psychiatry and other medical specialties. In this book we deal primarily with this type of disease, although there is some overlapping with the first two categories. An imbalance between outwardly directed behavior and the internal vegetative functions usually occurs in individuals who suffer from inadequate, unhappy interpersonal relations. In fact, the emotional component in vegetative disturbances is the result of a neurotic disturbance in the first or second category.

2. We differentiate between conversion symptoms and vegetative responses to emotions. "Conversion" we use in the original Freudian sense as the symbolic expression of emotions by bodily innervations, which represent the ideational content connected with the emotions and also relieve the emotional tension. It is an equivalent of emotional tension. Vegetative responses to emotions are those changes in vegetative functions which occur as an integral part of the emotional state. Elevation of blood pressure is a normal constituent characteristic of rage; it does not express or relieve rage. Gastric secretion belongs to the emotional state preceding nutrition; it is not a symbolic expression or a relief of hunger but a physiological component of the wish for food.

In this book we deal primarily with vegetative responses to disturbed emotional states, although here again there is some overlapping with conversion phenomena. Processes in nature do not follow the schematic formulae of textbooks.

3. We operate with the concept that organic diseases, based on altered morphology, may develop as the end result of functional disturbances.

In persons suffering from neurotic conflicts, normal expression of certain emotions is blocked because of repression or inhibition. This results in chronic emotional tensions such as anxiety, rage, or a dependent longing for help and care. Many vegetative disturbances are the results of such chronic emotional conflict situations. If functional disturbances due to emotional conflicts persist long enough in persons who have a somatic predisposition to them, gross morphological changes in the affected organs may result. The vegetative responses themselves are normal reactions to the underlying emotions, just as elevation of blood pressure is the normal cardiovascular response to rage. A peptic ulcer may result from chronic hyperfunction of the stomach; or malignant, irreversible hypertension based on arterial changes may result from prolonged essential hypertension of emotional origin. It is only the chronicity of these emotional states —due to inadequate expression—that constitutes the pathological nature of the condition.

It should be emphasized that the last two concepts—that there is a differentiation between conversion symptoms and vegetative sequelae and that chronic functional disturbances may lead to organic diseases based on an altered morphology—are not proposed as facts. They are operational concepts which have proved to be of great value in our investigations.

Basic Orientation

We consider the psychosomatic approach as the beginning of a new era in medicine. This is an orientation which attempts to understand diseases not as isolated local processes but as disturbances of the total coordination of organic processes. Because personality functions are precisely the highest coordinative activities of the organism, this new orientation includes the study of the participation of the total personality in the disease process. We are fully conscious of the temporary nature of our findings and formulations and of the need for continued study in these and related fields.

CONTENTS

PART I

GENERAL PRINCIPLES

PART II

DISTURBANCES OF THE GASTROINTESTINAL TRACT

ix

PART III

DISTURBANCES OF THE RESPIRATORY SYSTEM

PART IV

CARDIOVASCULAR DISTURBANCES

PART V

ENDOCRINOLOGY AND METABOLISM

CONTENTS

PART I
GENERAL PRINCIPLES

FUNDAMENTAL CONCEPTS OF PSYCHO-SOMATIC RESEARCH *

PSYCHOGENESIS, CONVERSION, SPECIFICITY

By Franz Alexander, M.D.

Although psychosomatic research is of recent origin, it deals with one of the oldest, if not *the* oldest, problems of scientific thought—with the mind-body problem. This may explain the heavy load of traditional concepts and assumptions which hamper its development. At first I shall take up the concept of *psychogenesis* in general, then that of *hysterical conversion* in particular, and finally the question of the *specificity* of emotional factors involved in somatic dysfunctions.

Psychogenesis

The question of psychogenesis is linked up with the ancient dichotomy: psyche versus soma. When the Journal of Psychosomatic Medicine was started our editorial staff felt that in the first issue some clear statement should be made about this confusing philosophical issue to discourage authors from writing endless discussions on this point. I quote from this introductory statement of the editors:

Emphasis is put on the thesis that there is no logical distinction between "mind and body," mental and physical. It is assumed that the complex neurophysiology of mood, instinct, and intellect differs from other physiology in degree of complexity but not in quality. Hence again divisions of medical disciplines into physiology, neurology, internal medicine, psychiatry, and psychology may be convenient for academic administration, but biologically and philosophically these divisions have no validity. It takes for granted that psychic and somatic phenomena take place in the same biological system and are probably two aspects of the same process, that psychological phenomena should be studied in their psychological causality with intrinsically psychological methods, and physiological phenomena in their physical causality with the methods of physics and chemistry (1).

In spite of this statement we will receive manuscripts in which the authors involve themselves in a hopeless struggle with this age-worn

* *Psychosomatic Medicine* V : 205-210, 1943.

problem. For example, an author gives an excellent description of the effect of psychological factors upon some clinical conditions, then becomes apologetic and tries to dodge the whole issue of psychogenesis by saying that one should not speak of psychogenesis but of the coexistence of certain psychological factors with certain physical symptoms.

It is important that the question of psychogenesis should be clarified, stating explicitly what is meant by it. First let us examine an example. In the case of emotionally caused elevation of the blood pressure, psychogenesis does not mean that the contraction of the blood vessels is effected by some nonsomatic mechanism. Rage consists in physiological processes which take place somewhere in the central nervous system. The physiological effect of rage consists of a chain of events—among them the elevation of blood pressure—in which every link can be described at least theoretically in physiological terms. The distinctive feature of psychogenic factors, such as emotions or ideas and fantasies, is that they *can* be studied also psychologically through introspection or by verbal communication from those in whom these physiological processes take place. An automobile climbing a hill has no sensation of effort, tiredness, or of a goal to reach. In contrast to a man-built machine, the organism climbing a mountain has an awareness of certain of its internal physiological processes in the form of effort, tiredness, discouragement, renewed effort, and so on. Moreover, man, in contrast to the animal organisms, is able to convey these internal sensations to others by verbal communication. Verbal communication is therefore one of the most potent instruments of psychology, and consequently also of psychosomatic research. When we speak of psychogenesis we refer to physiological processes consisting of central excitations in the nervous system which can be studied by psychological methods because they are perceived subjectively in the form of emotions, ideas, or wishes. Psychosomatic research deals with such processes in which certain links in the causal chain of events lend themselves, at the present state of our knowledge, more readily to a study by psychological methods than by physiological methods, since the detailed investigation of emotions as brain processes is not far enough advanced. My expectation is, however, that even when the physiological basis of psychological phenomena will be better known we will not be able to dispense with their psychological study. It is hardly conceivable that the different moves of two chess players can ever be more clearly understood in biochemical or neurophysiological than in psychological and logical terms.

Conversion

The concept of hysterical conversion, too, is closely related to the philosophical question of mind and body. The expression itself carries the connotation that a psychological process is transmuted into a bodily manifestation. Freud formulated the concept of conversion in the following way: "In hysteria the unbearable idea is rendered innocuous by the quantity of excitation attached to it being transmuted into some bodily form of expression, a process for which I should like to propose the name of 'conversion'" (20). Essentially an hysterical conversion symptom is nothing but an unusual innervation; it does not differ in principle from any other voluntary innervation or from such expressive movements as speech, laughter, or weeping. When we want to hit someone, our arms are brought into movement; when we speak, our ideas are converted into movements of the laryngeal muscles and of the lips and tongue. In laughter or weeping, also, an emotion finds bodily expression. It was unfortunate that Freud spoke, referring to hysterical conversion, of a "mysterious leap" from the psychic to the physiologic (19). In a conversion symptom like hysterical contracture, the "leap from the psychic into the somatic" is not more mysterious than in any of the common motor innervations such as voluntary movements or expressive movements, as laughter or weeping. The meaning of conversion symptom was originally very definite: a conversion symptom was a symbolic substitute for an unbearable emotion. It was assumed that the symptom relieved, at least to some degree, the tension produced by the repression of the unbearable emotion. It was considered a kind of physical abreaction or equivalent of an unconscious emotional tension. From the beginning Freud insisted that the repressed emotion ultimately can always be retraced to a sexual tension. Ferenczi made this even more explicit by postulating that a physical conversion symptom is always a kind of genitalization of that part of the body (15). I shall not enter into the discussion of the validity of the exclusively sexual origin of conversion symptoms at the present moment.

Repeated attempts have been made to extend the original concept of hysterical conversion to all forms of psychogenic disturbances of the body, even to those of the visceral vegetative organs. It was claimed that the essence of psychogenic disturbances is always the same. A repressed emotional tension finds expression through bodily channels. Whether it takes place in vegetative organs controlled by the autonomic nervous system or in the voluntary neuromuscular and sensory perceptive systems is a secondary matter. According to this concept, emotional hypertension is the conversion of repressed rage or some other emotion into a physical symptom—the elevation of blood pressure. The adherents to this concept even went so far as to say that a peptic ulcer might be considered a conversion symptom. Some repressed emotion, let us say some biting fantasies, find somatic expression in tissue changes of the stomach. In previous writings I have tried to demonstrate the grave error inherent in such superficial generalizations (2, 3, 7). I pointed out that the original concept of hysterical conversion is still an excellent and valid one if it is restricted to those phenomena on which it was originally based by Freud. At the same time I introduced the concept of another form of psychogenic process which is observed in vegetative disturbances, such as emotional hypertension, or in psychogenic organic conditions, such as peptic ulcers. Since these publications I have arrived at still more precise formulations which I should like to present on this occasion.

I still uphold my original suggestion that we restrict hysterical conversion phenomena to symptoms of the voluntary neuromuscular and the sensory perceptive systems, and differentiate them from psychogenic symptoms which occur in vegetative organ systems, the functions of which are under the control of the autonomic nervous system. The rationale of this distinction is about as follows: Hysterical conversion symptoms are substitute expressions—abreactions —or emotional tensions which cannot find adequate outlet through full-fledged motor behavior. For example, sexual excitation, which normally is gratified by intercourse, if repressed may find expression in some other motor innervation such as convulsions imitating the muscular movements of intercourse. Or anger, which cannot find expression through yelling, shouting, accusing, hitting, might lead to conversion symptoms in organs which are used for the legitimate expression of rage—the larynx or the extremities in the form of hysterical aphasia or paralysis. As Freud originally stressed it, these substitutive innervations never bring full relief; they are only attempts at relief; the symptoms express, at the same time, both the repressed emotion and its rejection. Just because they do not relieve the tension fully we have a pathological condition. The important issue, however, is that the emotional tension is at least partially relieved by the symptom itself. We deal with a different psychodynamic and physiological situation in the field of vegetative neuroses, although there are some similarities to the conversion symptoms. Here the somatic symptoms are not substitute expressions of repressed emotions, but they are normal physiological accompaniments of the symptom. For example, the emotional states of rage and fear are connected with a physiological syndrome consisting of such diversified vegetative processes as the stimulation of the adrenal system, mobilization of sugar, elevation of the blood pressure, changes in the distribution of blood which is squeezed out from the splanchnic area into the muscles, to the lungs, and to the brain. These physiological processes are normal corollaries of rage and fear; they do not relieve suppressed rage, but they accompany rage. They are the adjustment of the organism to definite tasks which it has to face in a dangerous situation, to fight or to flee. They are a utilitarian preparation and adaptation of the internal vegetative processes to a specific type of behavior which is requested from the organism. The elevated blood pressure or mobilization of sugar does not relieve the anger in the least; these symptoms do not appear in place of the emotional tension; they simply accompany the emotion of rage; they are an inseparable part of the total phenomenon which we call "rage." They are the systemic reaction of the body to rage. The chronicity of an emotional tension alone is what makes such a condition morbid. The nonneurotic individual is able to get rid of his rage by some legitimate expression. Some psychoneurotics can drain off the suppressed hostile feelings in compulsion symptoms. The hypertensive patient's pathology consists in the fact that he is under a constant or frequent, not repressed but unexpressed, emotional tension which is not drained either by psychoneurotic symptoms or by legitimate expression such as verbal or physical combat. He has not the relief that the angry man has of beating up his adversary or at least telling him what he has on his mind. The difference between conversion symptom and vegetative neurosis is now obvious. A conversion symptom is a symbolic expression of a well-defined emotional content —an attempt at relief. It is expressed by the voluntary neuromuscular or sensory perceptive systems whose original function is to express and relieve emotional tension. A vegetative neurosis like emotional hypertension is not an attempt to express an emotion, but is the physiological accompaniment of constant or periodically recurring emotional states.

The same conditions described in emotional hypertension can be applied readily to all other vegetative systems. Similarly, a gastric neurosis consisting of a chronic disturbance of the secretory and motor functions of the stomach is not the expression or drainage of an emotional tension but the physiological accompaniment of it. These patients want to be loved, to be taken care of, a wish to which they cannot give legitimate expression because of a neurotically exaggerated sense of shame or guilt; therefore they are under constant influence of these emotional tensions. The wish to be loved is deeply associated with the wish to be fed, since the nursing situation is the first one in which the child enjoys parental love and care. Because of early emotional associations, the chronic longing to be loved and taken care of is apt to stimulate the stomach functions. The stomach symptoms are the physiological corollaries of the passive state of expectation of receiving food. The disturbance of the secretory and motor functions of the stomach is not the substitute expression of an emotion, but the physiological counterpart of an emotion, namely, of the desire to be taken care of. The wish to be taken care of may be repressed and transformed into the wish to be nursed. This is not a conversion, however, but the substitution of one desire for another. Corresponding to this wish to be nursed are certain vegetative inner-vations which are not substitutes for the wish to be nursed but are the inseparable physiological sequelae. If the desire to be taken care of is satisfied, for example, through sanitorium treatment, the con-stant pressure of this wish may cease, and with it the stomach symp-toms may fully disappear. Neurotic stomach symptoms, however, are not conversions of a repressed longing for love into stomach symptoms; they do not appear in place of the emotions, but are the physiological concomitants of a chronic or periodic emotional ten-sion. Bulimia, in contradistinction to a stomach neurosis, may be considered as a conversion symptom. Here the wish to be loved, to be given things or to take things, is drained, that is to say, satisfied, at least to some extent by incorporating food. Eating becomes both a satisfaction and a symbolic substitute for being loved or being im-pregnated or for a biting aggressive attack. It fulfills all the require-ments of a conversion symptom. Asthma also has components of a hysterical conversion symptom, since it can serve as the direct ex-pression and partial substitute for a suppressed emotion such as the wish to cry. Breathing—although an automatic function—is also under the control of voluntary innervations. Acid secretion of the stomach, however, is not. Breathing is used in such expressive func-tions as speech and crying; stomach secretion may be a concomitant of an emotional state but is never used for its symbolic expression, as is speech or crying. Possibly there are mixed conditions in which both types of mechanism coexist. The psychodynamic background of most psychogenic skin disturbances is still very unclear, but it appears that in the skin both conversion mechanisms and vegetative neurotic symptoms may occur. The skin is partially a sensory per-ceptive but also a vegetative organ. Blushing is obviously a conver-sion symptom. On the other hand it is probable that the physio-logical mechanism in psychogenic urticaria follows the pattern of vegetative neuroses. Psychosomatic disturbances involving sphyncter functions both under autonomic and voluntary control, such as constipation, diarrhea, pollakiuria, urine retention, etc., represent a combination of hysterical conversion symptoms and vegetative neuroses.

Finally, peptic ulcer is neither a conversion symptom nor a vegetative neurosis. In some cases it is the somatic end result of a longstanding neurotic stomach dysfunction, but in itself has nothing whatever directly to do with any emotion. It is not the symbolic expression of a wish or a self-punishment. It is a secondary physiological end effect of a long-standing dysfunction. It is an organic disturbance which in many cases is the end result of a psychogenic functional disturbance, a vegetative neurosis of the stomach.

To summarize: It seems advisable to differentiate between hysterical conversion and vegetative neurosis. Their similarities are rather superficial: both conditions are psychogenic, that is to say, they are caused ultimately by a chronic repressed or at least unrelieved emotional tension. The mechanisms involved, however, are fundamentally different both psychodynamically and physiologically. The hysterical conversion symptom is an attempt to relieve an emotional tension in a symbolic way; it is a symbolic expression of a definite emotional content. This mechanism is restricted to the voluntary neuromuscular or sensory perceptive systems whose function is to express and relieve emotions. A vegetative neurosis consists of a psychogenic dysfunction of a vegetative organ which is not under control of the voluntary neuromuscular system. The vegetative symptom is not a substitute expression of the emotion, but its normal physiological concomitant. We assume that, corresponding to every emotional state, there is a certain distribution of vegetative innervations. When we have to fight or undergo physical exertion, the vegetative organs of digestion are relaxed, whereas the muscular system and the lungs are in a state of preparation. The emotional attitude accompanying and preceding food intake and digestion again is accompanied by a different distribution of vegetative tonus. In this instance the visceral organs become hyperemic, whereas the skeletal muscle tonus decreases and the concomitant drowsiness is the indication of a transitory anemia of the cortex. If these emotional states are chronically sustained, the corresponding vegetative innervations also become chronic. The circulatory system of the hypertensive behaves as if this person were ready to attack somebody at any moment. On the other hand, when the stomach neurotic breaks down under an excessive load of responsibility, he recoils from his habitual overactivity and assumes the vegetative mood of the state that accompanies digestion, to which his alimentary tract reacts with a continuous hyperactivity. This recoiling from exaggerated outward activity and strain we may call "vegetative retreat." It is a counter-coup phenomenon, a kind of exhaustion following sustained effort. According to all indications, an outward-directed active aggressive state is connected with a sustained excess of tonus of the sympathetic-adrenal system from which the individual, when exhausted, may retreat into the opposite attitude in which the tonus of the vagal-insular system is increased. This increased tonus of the parasympathetic system, possibly connected with a simultaneous relaxation of sympathetic-adrenal tonus, is what I denote by the expression "vegetative retreat." This may assume different forms consisting in some hyperactivity of visceral organs resulting from parasympathetic excitation such as hypersecretion and hypermotility of the stomach, diarrhea, or psychogenic hyperinsulinism (psychogenic hypoglycemia).[1] Possibly the condition described by Gowers as vagal attacks, which he considered as related to the epileptic seizure, is the most extreme example of a vegetative retreat (21).

Specificity

This brings us to the last crucial problem of psychosomatic research, the question of specificity, which I shall touch upon only briefly on this occasion. According to one school of thought, there is no specific correlation; any emotional tension may influence any vegetative system. The choice of the symptoms may depend upon the history of the patient and on his constitution; if he has a weak stomach, he has a stomach upset when he gets angry; if he has a labile vasomotor system, he might become a hypertensive under the influence of aggressions. Perhaps an early respiratory infection has made his lungs susceptible; then he will react to every emotional upset with an asthma attack. The other heuristic assumption, which has guided our investigative work in the Chicago Psychoanalytic Institute, is that the physiological responses to different emotional tensions are varied; that, consequently, vegetative dysfunctions result from specific emotional constellations. As I have emphasized, we know from human and animal experiment that different emotional states have their specific vegetative tonus. The vegetative syndrome which corresponds to rage and fear is definitely different from that

---

[1] In a number of patients with a so-called psychogenetic fatigue, Sidney A. Portis suggested that a possible physiological mechanism involved was that of hyperinsulinism. This resulted from a temporary or prolonged parasympathetic stimulation. Daily physiological doses of atropine by mouth brought about a cessation of the fatigue symptom. See Sidney A. Portis and Irving H. Zitman, A mechanism of fatigue in neuropsychiatric patients, *J. Amer. Med. Assn.*, 1943, 121.

of passive relaxation during digestion; a state of impatience or of tense attentiveness has bodily concomitants in vegetative and skeletal innervations different from those in a paralyzing state of panic. The vegetative concomitants of various emotional states are as different from each other as laughter from weeping—the physical expression of merriment from that of sorrow. It is therefore to be expected that just as the nature of the chronic unrelieved emotional state varies, so also will the corresponding vegetative disturbance vary. The results of current investigations are all in favor of the theory of specificity (4–7, 9–11, 13–14, 16–18, 22–32, 34).[2] Gastric neurotic symptoms have a different psychology from those of emotional diarrhea or constipation; cardiac cases differ in their emotional background from asthmatics. The emotional component in functional glycosuria has its own peculiarities, and there is good evidence that the emotional factor in glaucoma has again its specific features. This emotional specificity can be ascertained, of course, only by careful, minute observation for which the best method available is the prolonged interview technique of psychoanalysis. However, briefer but careful psychiatric anamnestic studies conducted by well-trained observers often reveal the specific personality factors involved in different types of cases. To what extent constitutional factors influence the picture, and to what extent a pre-existing organic pathology or sensitivity are responsible, are questions to be decided by further careful clinical studies.

Summary

1. An attempt is made to clarify the concept of psychogenesis.

2. The fundamental psychological and physiological differences between *conversion symptoms, vegetative neuroses,* and *psychogenic organic disease* are elaborated.

3. The problem of specificity of emotional factors in different vegetative neuroses is discussed. Evidence for the specificity of emotional factors is offered.

BIBLIOGRAPHY

1. Introductory Statement. *Psychosom. Med.,* 1939, **1**, 1.
2. ALEXANDER, FRANZ. Functional disturbances of psychogenic origin. *J. Amer. med. Assn.,* 1933, **100**, 469.
3. ALEXANDER, FRANZ. Critical discussion of the extension of the theory of conversion hysteria to the field of organic diseases. In *Medical value of psychoanalysis.* (2nd Ed.) New York: W. W. Norton & Co., 1936.

---

2 For a more complete literature concerning specific emotional factors I refer to Dr. H. F. Dunbar's book, *Emotions and bodily changes* (12) and different reviews published in the *Journal of Psychosomatic Medicine* (8, 33, 35, 36). See also Weiss and English, *Psychosomatic medicine,* Philadelphia: W. B. Saunders Co., 1943.

4. ALEXANDER, FRANZ. Emotional factors in essential hypertension. *Psychosom. Med.,* 1939, **1**, 173. (In this volume, page 289.)

5. ALEXANDER, FRANZ. Psychoanalytic study of a case of essential hypertension. *Psychosom. Med.,* 1939, **1**, 139. (In this volume, page 298.)

6. ALEXANDER, FRANZ. Gastrointestinal neuroses. In S. A. Portis (Ed.), *Diseases of the digestive system.* Philadelphia: Lea & Febiger, 1941.

7. ALEXANDER, FRANZ, AND CO-WORKERS. The influence of psychologic factors upon gastrointestinal disturbances: a symposium. *Psychoanal. Quart.,* 1934, **3**, 501. (In this volume, page 103.)

8. BRUSH, L. Recent literature relative to the psychiatric aspects of gastrointestinal disorders. *Psychosom. Med.,* 1939, **1**, 423.

9. DANIELS, G. E. Psychiatric aspects of ulcerative colitis. *New Engl. J. med.,* 1942, **226**, 178.

10. DEUTSCH, FELIX. Emotional factors in asthma and other allergic conditions. Paper read before the Assn. med. Social Workers, February, 1938.

11. DUNBAR, H. F. Psychoanalytic notes relating to syndromes of asthma and hay fever. *Psychoanal. Quart.,* 1938, **7**, 25.

12. DUNBAR, H. F. *Emotions and bodily changes.* (2nd Ed.) New York: Columbia University Press, 1938.

13. DUNBAR, H. F. Character and symptom formation. *Psychoanal. Quart.,* 1939, **8**, 18.

14. DUNBAR, H. F., WOLFE, T., AND RIOCH, N. The psychic component of the disease process in cardiac, diabetic, and fracture patients. *Am. J. Psychiat.,* 1936, **93**, 649.

15. FERENCZI, SÁNDOR. The phenomena of hysterical materialization. In *Further contributions to the theory and technique of psychoanalysis.* London: Hogarth Press, 1926. P. 89.

16. FRENCH, T. M. Psychogenic factors in asthma. *Am. J. Psychiat.,* 1939, **96**, 67.

17. FRENCH, T. M. Physiology of behavior and choice of neurosis. *Psychoanal. Quart.,* 1941, **10**, 561.

18. FRENCH, T. M., ALEXANDER, F., AND CO-WORKERS. Psychogenic factors in bronchial asthma. Part I. *Psychosom. Med. Monogr.,* 1941, **1**, No. 4. Part II. *Psychosom. Med. Monogr.,* 1941, **2**, No. 1 and No. 2. National Research Council, Washington, D. C.

19. FREUD, SIGMUND. *A general introduction to psychoanalysis.* New York: Boni & Liveright, 1920.

20. FREUD, SIGMUND. The defence neuro-psychosis (1894). In *Collected papers,* **1**, 59. London: Hogarth Press, 1924.

21. GOWERS, SIR WILLIAM. Vagal and vaso-vagal attacks. In *The border-land of epilepsy.* Philadelphia: Blakiston, 1907.

22. HILL, L. B. Psychoanalytic observations on essential hypertension. *Psychoanal. Rev.,* 1935, **22**, 60.

23. MENNINGER, K. A., AND MENNINGER, WM. C. Psychoanalytic observations in cardiac disorders. *Am. Heart J.,* 1936, **11**, No. 1.

24. MILLER, M. L. Blood pressure findings in relation to inhibited aggressions in psychotics. *Psychosom. Med.,* 1939, **1**, 162. (In this volume, page 316.)

25. MILLER, M. L. A psychological study of eczema and neurodermatitis. *Psychosom. Med.,* 1942, **4**, 82. (In this volume, page 401.)

26. MILLER, M. L., AND MCLEAN, H. V. The status of the emotions in palpitation and extrasystoles with a note on the effort syndrome. *Psychoanal. Quart.,* 1941, **10**, 545. (In this volume, page 333.)

27. MITTELMAN, B., WOLF, H. G., AND SCHARF, M. Emotions and gastroduodenal functions. Experimental studies on patients with gastritis, duodenitis, and peptic ulcer. *Psychosom. Med.,* 1942, **4**, 5.

28. SAUL, L. J. A note on the psychogenesis of organic symptoms. *Psychoanal. Quart.,* 1935, **4**, 476. (In this volume, page 85.)

29. SAUL, L. J. Psychogenic factors in the etiology of the common cold and related symptoms. *Int. J. Psycho-Anal.*, 1938, **19**, 451.

30. SAUL, L. J. Hostility in cases of essential hypertension. *Psychosom. Med.*, 1939, **1**, 153. (In this volume, page 345.)

31. SAUL, L. J. Some observations on the relations of emotions and allergy. *Psychosom. Med.*, 1941, **3**, 66. (In this volume, page 547.)

32. SAUL, L. J. The emotional settings of some attacks of urticaria. *Psychosom. Med.*, 1941, **3**, 349. (In this volume, page 424.)

33. STOKES, J. H., AND BERMAN, H. Psychosomatic correlations in allergic conditions: a review of problems and literature. *Psychosom. Med.*, 1940, **2**, 438.

34. VAN DER HEIDE, C. A study of mechanisms in two cases of peptic ulcer. *Psychosom. Med.*, 1940, **2**, 398. (In this volume, page 206.)

35. WEISS, E. Recent advances in pathogenesis and treatment of hypertension. A Review. *Psychosom. Med.*, 1939, **1**, 180.

36. WHITE, B. V., COBB, STANLEY, AND JONES, C. M. Mucous colitis. A psychological medical study of 60 cases. *Psychosom. Med. Monogr.*, 1939, **1**, No. 1. National Research Council, Washington, D. C.

PRESENT TRENDS IN PSYCHIATRY AND THE FUTURE OUTLOOK *

By Franz Alexander, M.D.

It is generally held that in all fields of human endeavor, the present can be understood only in the light of the past. This truism, needs, however, an important qualification. For example, in tracing back the development of scientific knowledge, it is important that we apply the evolutional perspective only to those developments which have a real historical continuity. In other words, in reconstructing the development of scientific knowledge, only those ideas and observations of the past—correct or fallacious—should be considered which actually contributed to the present state of knowledge. Unfortunately this principle is not always followed. The traditional introductory phrase in a scientific address, "Already the ancients knew of the existence of this or that," is far more often applied than is justified. For instance, in writing about the history of chemistry, an author who tells us that already the ancients knew of the existence of atoms and who then quotes Democritus bases his contention only on a linguistic coincidence. Dalton's atom and Democritus' atom have no relationship to each other. They resulted from entirely different mental operations. The main significance of Dalton's atom is that it is specific for each element and has a definite quantitative weight relationship to other atoms with which it enters into chemical compounds. Democritus' atom has none of these qualities. It is the result of exclusively deductive speculations. Only the word "atom" is common to them. It is, therefore, justified in the historical presentation of chemistry to start with Dalton and completely ignore Democritus, whose concepts actually did not contribute in the least to its development. Similarly, it is justified for Einstein to begin his book, *The Evolution of Physics,* with Galileo and disregard, for example, Aristotle, whose wrong ideas of motion, supported by his great authority, according to Einstein, not only did not contribute to the development of physics but actually retarded it. According to him the discovery and "the use of scientific reasoning by Galileo was

* From *Modern Attitudes in Psychiatry.* New York, Columbia University Press, 1946, pp. 61-89.

one of the most important achievements in the history of human thought, and marks the real beginnings of physics." [1]

The application of the scientific method in the field of psychiatry is of even more recent origin. In presenting the modern concepts of psychiatry, our historical obligation to pay tribute to the great men of the past is still more limited than in the case of physics or chemistry. Observations and ideas in psychiatry which have a real influence upon our present knowledge do not reach further back than 150 years, and most of our present knowledge has been developed only in the last 80 years. In psychiatry we are in the same fortunate position to which a young American lady tourist gave terse expression while inspecting an old church in Italy. The guide was describing the altar in his perfunctory manner:

"This center portion comes from the fourteenth century, the picture over to the left wing from the thirteenth century, and this sculpture dates back authentically to the twelfth century." At this moment I overheard the one young American lady whispering to her friend, "Gosh, I am glad we don't have so many centuries in America."

In psychiatry we are in a similar position. We may give credit to Pinel for introducing in 1793 a more humane attitude toward the insane, which marks the real beginning of the development of psychiatry. We may give credit even to Sydenham for some keen observations he made as early as 1682 concerning hysteria. However, even a merely descriptive systematic survey of the field of psychiatry is of quite recent origin. Kraepelin's system of psychiatry, published near the end of the last century, was the culmination of a period of careful clinical observations in which men like Kahlbaum, Wernicke, Babinsky, and others played a leading role. This descriptive type of psychiatry concerned itself mainly with the delineation of different disease pictures and their typical course. It developed during the last century, while psychiatric treatment, which is based on the knowledge of the nature and causes of mental disturbances, is evolving only at present before our eyes. These current efforts to achieve a causal understanding and cure of mental disturbances are widely varied; they cover a large range, from biochemical research to the psychodynamic and the sociological approaches. All of them are etiologically oriented and apply controlled methods of scientific observation and reasoning. This etiological orientation, the demand for understanding the causes and the nature of mental illness in contrast to the previous merely descriptive approach, is one of the most

---

[1] Einstein and Infeld, *The evolution of physics*. New York: Simon & Schuster, 1938, p. 7.

conspicuous features of present-day psychiatry. Concurrently, the mere custodial care of the mentally disturbed patient of former days is giving place to attempts at causal treatment.

The discussion of some phases of this new etiological orientation, as it affected both psychiatric theory and practice, is the purpose of this presentation.

The explanation of mental disorders first followed the same pathways which proved productive in other branches of medicine. Of fundamental importance was the recognition of the fact that mental activity is the function of the central nervous system. It is difficult to determine precisely when this basic fact was first established. In a vague fashion it was known to the ancient Greek physicians, but more concretely it was recognized only by the medical scientists of the eighteenth century. This knowledge opened the way to the anatomical and physiological study of the brain which served as the scientific basis of psychiatry. Psychiatry could now apply the principle of Morgagni, namely, that every disease consists in the local disturbance of an organ. This principle has been further refined by the development of histology, and has culminated in Virchow's cellular pathology which postulated that every disease is the result of disturbed cell function and can be recognized by the microscope in structural changes in the tissues of the affected organs.

Under the influence of this doctrine, in the second half of the last century, feverish investigative activities have sprung up in the field of the histological anatomy of the brain. Ramón y Cajal, Golgi, Nissl, Alzheimer, Apáthy, von Lenhossek and some others were the heroes of this period. Many of these great scientists were not psychiatrists but anatomists. Most of their contributions to the knowledge of the histological architectonics of the brain cannot even today be applied to the understanding of disturbed mental function. Their vision of constructing a bridge between brain and mind, between psychiatry as the science of disturbed mental activity and brain anatomy and physiology, has not at this time been accomplished. It appears as if the principle of Virchow would not prove so effective in the field of mental diseases as in other parts of medicine. The common major disturbances of the personality—the schizophrenic and manic depressive psychoses—which have been described by Kahlbaum, Kraepelin, Bleuler, and other great clinicians, could not be identified by the help of the microscope. Careful histological analyses of the brain of deceased psychotics who suffered from these disturbances did not reveal any, even minute, structural changes recognizable under the microscope. The medical man was then confronted with a tantalizing puzzle. The brain of a patient whose external behavior and emotional reactions conspicuously differed from those of the healthy person did not reveal any consistent deviations even under the most exacting scrutiny. And the same was true with many other psychiatric conditions such as the psychoneuroses and behavior disorders. To make this state of affairs even more aggravating, psychiatry's sister branch, neurology, succeeded at the same time in correlating the disturbances of many complex functions with disturbed anatomical structure. Such paramount functions of the personality as goal-directed coordinated movements or speech, when disturbed, often appeared in connection with structural changes in those parts of the nervous system which have been recognized as the seats of these functions. In other cases, not the brain centers but the nerve connection between these centers and the organs which they control was damaged. So it happened that while neurology, which dealt with isolated functions of the nervous system, developed into the most exacting diagnostical branch of medicine, psychiatry, which concerned itself with the highest integration of the various functions of the nervous system, came into the reputation of being a backward, undeveloped field. It was of some consolation that a few well-defined disturbances, such as general paralysis, long suspected to be caused by syphilis, could be explained from tissue damage in the central nervous system. When finally the syphilitic origin of general paralysis was proved beyond doubt by Noguchi and Moore, this discovery, more than anything else, aroused a new hope for advancing psychiatry eventually into the rank of the other medical specialties. The reason for this hope was not so much that Virchow's principle of cellular pathology had been vindicated in the field of psychiatry—because structural damage of the brain tissue was known for many years, not only in general paralysis but also in senile dementia and Alzheimer's disease—but the discovery by Noguchi of the microorganism, treponema pallidum, in the brain of the general paretic opened the way for the first time in the field of psychiatry for an etiologically oriented therapy.

The generally accepted classical pattern for etiology can be roughly summarized in the following causal sequence. A disease consists of the faulty functioning of an organ. This faulty functioning is based on a damaged cell structure which is recognizable under the microscope. The causes of the damage are various. The most important ones are infection, that is to say, the invasion of an organ by microorganisms, as in tuberculosis, or chemical agents, as in poisoning, or by mechanical causes, as in fractures or contusions. In addition, aging—this chronic disease of all living organisms—consisting in a progressive degeneration of the tissues, has also been recognized as an important causal factor of disease.

At the turn of the last century, certainly by 1913, with Noguchi's discovery, all these causative factors had been well established in the field of psychiatry. Concussions of the brain and hemorrhages causing mechanical pressure were examples of the mechanical causation of disturbed mental function; alcoholism and other toxic psychoses of the chemical etiology; and senile dementia, a well-defined condition based on the progressive degeneration of brain tissue as the result of aging. Finally, the postsyphilitic conditions of the nervous system, particularly general paralysis characterized by profound changes in the personality, were found due to syphilitic infection of the brain and could serve as a counterpart of the bacterial invasions of other organs, like tuberculosis of the lungs.

Now the psychiatrist could raise his head: He, too, was a physician who could approach his patient with laboratory methods of diagnosis and treatment. In this respect, Ehrlich's chemotherapy of postsyphilitic conditions was of particular significance. Up to that time psychiatry was a field in which for centuries the role of the physician consisted in custodial care, and, at the most, careful observation of the patient. Whatever therapy existed before was either based on magic, as in exorcism of evil spirits of the prescientific era, or was thoroughly ineffective, as electro- and hydrotherapy, so popular at the end of the last and at the beginning of this century. Ehrlich's chemotherapy of postsyphilitic conditions with salvarsan contributed more than anything else to the prestige of psychiatry. It was conceived as a real causal therapy which satisfied all the demands of modern medical philosophy. It was directed toward the elimination of the established specific cause of the disease, a pathogenic microorganism. The method was to apply a powerful chemical substance which was designed to leave the organism unharmed and to exterminate the pathogenic microorganism. Under the influence of this method, hopes ran high that soon the whole field of psychiatry would be conquered by the usual methods of medical research and therapy.

The therapeutic results with chemotherapy of general paralysis have turned out to be much less satisfactory than was expected at the beginning. It was later supplanted by the more effective fever treatment.

There were some other impressive discoveries which contributed to these hopes. The explanation of the symptoms of mental retardation in myxedema from a decreased function of the thyroid gland, and the remarkable cure of such cases by Horsley through transplantation of the thyroid gland, which was later substituted by oral medication of thyroid extract, was a classical example of the causal treatment of a psychiatric condition.

Hyperthyroidism was another disease in which mental symptoms could be influenced by biochemical and surgical methods. These two diseases, caused by glandular disturbances, showed beyond doubt that the endocrine glands have a definite influence upon mental processes. It was not unreasonable to hope that with the advancement of biochemistry, particularly with the intimate knowledge of the complicated interplay of the endocrine glands, the physiological causes of psychoses and psychoneuroses would be understood and made accessible to causal therapy.

Had it not been for the important group of schizophrenic disturbances in which a profound disintegration of the personality occurs without any discernible organic change, and for the even larger group of psychoneurotics, psychiatry in the second decade of this century would have seemed to have a good chance of becoming a branch of medicine equal to internal medicine, based on pathological anatomy and physiology, and open to the traditional methods of treatment. We shall see, however, that psychiatry not only did not fulfill these expectations, but also that the rest of medicine had to discard the exclusive somatic approach and borrow a new point of view from psychiatry. It was not, therefore, psychiatry that became converted to an exclusive organic point of view, but rather medicine began to adopt an orientation which originated in psychiatry. This is called the psychosomatic point of view. How all this happened is of particular interest for the understanding of the present trend in medical evolution, and will be the focus of our attention in the rest of this paper.

In spite of sporadic successes, such as the explanation and cure of general paralysis and myxedema with the traditional methods of medicine, the majority of psychiatric conditions, the schizophrenic psychoses as well as the psychoneuroses, stubbornly resisted all such efforts. In these cases no specific histological changes could be found. One began to regard these major disturbances of the personality, as well as the milder emotional disorders, as functional diseases, in contrast to general paralysis or senile dementia which are called organic because of the demonstrable histological changes in the brain tissue. This terminological differentiation, however, did not alter the embarrassing fact that these often extreme disintegrations of the psychic functions resisted all types of therapy used in other branches of medicine, such as pharmacological and surgical methods, and at the same time did not yield to any explanations along the traditional lines. Yet the rapid progress in the successful application of laboratory methods in the rest of medicine was so promising that the hope for a final understanding of all psychiatric disorders on an anatomical, physiological, and biochemical basis was not abandoned.

And thus, in all centers of medical research, the histopathological, bacteriological, and biochemical attempts at the solution of the problem of schizophrenia and other functional disturbances of the mind continued with unabated intensity when, in the last decade of the past century, a completely novel method of investigation and therapy was introduced by Sigmund Freud. It is customary to attribute the origin of psychoanalysis to the French School, to the hypnosis research of Charcot, Bernheim, and Liébeault. In his autobiographical writings Freud retraces the beginning of his ideas to influences received during his studies in the Saltpêtrière with Charcot, and later in Nancy with Bernheim and Liébeault. From the point of view of biography this is certainly a correct picture. From the point of view of the history of scientific thought the beginning of the psychodynamic approach must be credited to Freud himself.

As Galileo was the first to apply the method of scientific reasoning to the phenomena of motion, so Freud accomplished the same thing in the field of the study of human personality. Personality research, or motivational psychology as a science, begins with him. He was the first to adopt consistently the principle of strict determination of psychological processes and to establish the fundamental dynamic principles of psychological causality. After he discovered that a great part of human behavior is determined by unconscious motivations, and after he developed a technique by which unconscious motivations can be made conscious, he was able for the first time to demonstrate the strict determination of psychological processes. With the help of this new psychology the bizarre phenomena of psychotic and neurotic symptoms, as well as seemingly senseless dreams, could be understood as meaningful products of the mind. In the course of time many details and even some basic formulations of his theory have gradually lost their validity; what is permanent in his contribution is the method of observing human behavior and the type of reasoning he applied to its psychological understanding.

This is not the place to dwell upon the details of the psychoanalytic approach. Only the general import of these new concepts upon psychiatric and general medical thought will be discussed. The traditional view that disease consists in a local damage caused by a circumscribed injury—bacterial, mechanical, or chemical in nature— cannot be applied to diseases which develop as the result of the total reactions of the organism as a whole toward its environment. Except for aging, this theory of disease does not give recognition to the fact that the process of life itself—with its sustained strains and continuous wear and tear—may be an important source of disease. As in a machine, a local defect may develop from exaggerated use, so also in the human organism local defects may originate from increased or unbalanced functioning of one organ or of the organism as a whole. Although such conspicuous examples as hypertrophy of the heart resulting from excessive use, or degeneration of a paralyzed limb resulting from lack of use, were well known, the significant principle underlying this type of process has not been given sufficient and explicit recognition. It was particularly not recognized that not only may single organs be injured by excessive use or lack of use, more precisely by disturbed functions, but that the organism as a whole, through the injury of the integrating functions controlling total behavior, may become damaged during the ordinary process of living. It is a strange fact that while medicine became keenly aware of the importance of all kinds of localized, more or less accidental, damages caused by bacterial infection, chemical poisoning, or mechanical injury, it would not explicitly recognize—except in the obvious process of aging—those continuous taxations of the organism which are an almost unavoidable part of life itself.

The reasons for this lack of recognition are not hard to find. Medicine studied the organs and their functions as separate things; it became divided into specialties and forgot about the organism as a unit. It dealt with all the specific damages affecting separate organs, such as the lungs, the heart, the stomach, and neglected all those sources of disease which affect the organism as a whole during its struggle to overcome the hardships faced in the difficult business of living. These difficulties consist in assuring gratification to the subjective needs of the organism which require a constant adaptation to environmental conditions. This adaptation is the function of the central nervous system. In man we call this function "personality," which is but the sum of these integrated reactions of the total organism to its environment.

It is no wonder that this exclusively analytical period of medicine had no use for the study of the human personality and its disturbances. The great majority of personality disorders belongs to just that category of disease in which the causal factors do not consist of local injury but have their insidious origin in the repeated daily emotional influences to which the person is consistently exposed throughout the course of growing up—in the fears, resentments, rivalries, and all kinds of emotional frustrations which arise in everyday contacts with other human beings. These influences cannot be studied by the usual methods of medicine. They cannot be described in physiological terms, and their effect cannot be detected by palpation, by optical inspection either by the unaided eye or by the microscope, or by the thermometer. They can be studied only by methods specifically suited to the study of human relationships, that is to say, by psychological methods.

To supply such a method was the contribution of Freud. Psychoanalytic treatment was based on the understanding of the psychological causes of emotional disorders. It was a methodical, goal-directed treatment aimed at influencing morbid patterns of feeling by purely psychological means. As such it was foreign to contemporary medical philosophy and appeared to contradict its basic tenet of the living organism as a complicated physicochemical machine and the physician as the engineer of the body.

The followers of Freud organized themselves in an international association which remained isolated not only from medicine as a whole but also from psychiatry, and for a while it appeared that Freud's psychoanalysis, for reasons which I shall discuss later, would remain a foreign body sequestered at the borderline of medical science.

In spite of its extraterritorial status, the influence of psychoanalysis upon psychiatry has been most profound. Gradually the exclusive preoccupation of psychiatrists was shifted from the advanced, mostly uncurable psychotics, who represented the end phases of mental disintegration, to that larger group of emotionally maladjusted persons who formerly received little consideration from the medical profession. This large group of psychoneurotics proved accessible to psychotherapy, and as a result ambulatory psychiatry, in contrast to institutional psychiatry, has taken the leadership which it acquired because of its vigorous therapeutic orientation and particularly because of its contributions to a profound understanding of normal and morbid behavior.

Nevertheless it required fifty years for psychoanalysis to become incorporated into medical thought. The reasons for this long delay have been discussed repeatedly by a great many authors. They have pointed out that psychoanalysis undermined the most cherished self-deceptions of mankind about human nature, and that it provoked a particular resistance since it dealt frankly with the facts of sexual life in a cultural era of which sexual hypocrisy and sexual repression were perhaps the most outstanding attributes. Apart from these general cultural factors, a more specific cause of its rejection was that psychoanalysis introduced into medicine a discordant note, namely psychological motivations, in a period in which medicine was most proud of having become a laboratory science and in which the medical man liked to act in the role of the scientific engineer of the human body. Moreover, psychoanalysis represented an integrative point of view in a period in which medicine was most analytically minded. A last and least recognized reason for the slowness with which psychoanalysis was absorbed by medicine was that for a long time the investigative aspect of the psychoanalytic treatment outweighed the practical therapeutic orientation. Only recently have analysts begun to realize that their technique of treatment, particularly their whole therapeutic orientation, requires a thorough revision; that they need a more flexible procedure which can be adjusted to the particular needs of the tremendous variety of mental sufferers.

Finally, as the latest development, there are encouraging signs of a gradual reconciliation of the traditional medical and the new psychological approaches. There is a growing interest among physicians not only in the diseased heart, stomach, or liver, but also in the owner of these organs, the sick person himself. And thus psychiatry, the science of the diseased person, is becoming the concern of the whole medical profession.

The study of the total reactions of the organism, in contrast to the study of isolated functions, has received a new impetus from animal psychology. Taking their departure from the school of Pavlov, which dealt mainly with circumscribed conditioned reflexes, a vigorous group of animal experimenters in this country have succeeded in producing neurotic symptoms in animals by increasing the difficulties of certain tasks with which the animals were confronted if they were to satisfy their hunger. In these studies the investigator's interest was not directed toward the isolated parts of the animal organism, but toward the behavior of the whole animal. Let me throw more light upon the significance of this new integrative point of view by concrete examples. The problem of alcoholism is particularly apt to illustrate this issue.

In the traditional psychiatric discussion of chronic alcoholism, the main emphasis was laid upon a detailed description of symptoms which develop as a result of chronic alcoholic intoxication—the dilatation of the blood vessels of the face, fatty degeneration of the heart, cirrhosis of the liver, general emaciation, tremor, decrease of sexual potency, loss of moral standards, of pride, modesty, and will power, and the progressive deterioration of intellectual functions. Such a description gives a faithful picture of the various consequences of chronic intoxication in certain individuals. It gives also a rough etiological explanation of the symptoms which result from the toxic effects of alcohol upon the brain and the other organs. However, the real etiological problem of chronic alcoholism is not even touched by this approach. What made the victim an addict is not answered at all by a description of the secondary effects of his excessive drinking. Obviously the answer to the question requires motivational psychology, an approach entirely different from that used in the rest of medicine.

In the standard textbook of psychiatry this question as to the motivations responsible for chronic alcoholism has been treated, as a rule, in a short appendage to the precise psychiatric description of the secondary effects of alcohol. This appendage usually contained nothing but more or less useless generalities. Even in such an excellent text as that of Bleuler, after eleven pages of a highly technical and detailed description of the secondary toxic effects of alcohol, two pages on etiology follow, containing only generalities derived not from detailed, methodical observations but mostly from common sense. Among the etiological factors the greatest emphasis has usually been laid on heredity. Obviously this only dodges the etiological question. There are certainly no genes which carry over from one generation to another a specific longing for alcohol; what reasonably can be meant by heredity is the inheritance of certain personality traits, for example, a weak will or a lack of natural resistance against alcohol, qualities which may make a person a candidate for becoming an alcoholic later in life under certain specific conditions. This, however, is still but a circumvention of the issue, substituting for one unknown factor another. The mere fact that it is not unusual for a chronic alcoholic to lose his habit under changed circumstances of living renders highly unsatisfactory the hereditary etiology as a general explanation. It is certain that experiences of early and later life and external circumstances play an important role. To fill this obvious gap, the traditional textbook adds occasionally a few remarks about escapist tendencies, about the fact that alcohol helps the victim to forget and enables him to extricate himself temporarily from chronic emotional strain.

It must be clear to everyone that the causes of alcoholism can only be approached scientifically if cases are studied for the purpose of establishing those actual motivations which have driven the patient to become a drinker. Since drinking is a type of voluntary behavior, just as eating, taking a walk, gambling, or reading a magazine, its understanding requires the study of motivations. Such a motivational psychology, based on reliable observation and reasoning, is the precise contribution of psychoanalysis to the medical sciences.

As I said before, the assimilation of this motivational point of view into medical thought progresses with exasperating slowness because methods of psychological observation and reasoning, and, above all, the admission of motivation as a causative factor, have been regarded as foreign bodies in the system of medicine. Only very recently has there been a definite change in attitude characterized by a reconciliation of older and newer views. There are still obstacles which have to be cleared, consisting mostly of adherence to traditional modes of thought. Many physicians, even psychiatrists, still regard the motivational, that is to say psychological, explanations as incompatible with the organic. This can be clearly observed in relation to the puzzling problem of schizophrenia, which has thus far resisted every etiological approach whether of therapy or explanation. Here the organic and the psychological schools are in opposition to each other. The first school holds that real schizophrenia is an organic disease caused by endogenous factors, among which heredity seems to be most important; the second insists that schizophrenia is the ultimate outcome of those chronic emotional injuries which begin in early family life and continue through infancy and puberty until the outbreak of the manifest symptoms. While the organic school is unable as yet to locate any tangible significant changes within the organism, there is an unshakable belief among its followers that, with improved methods, certain biochemical changes will be discovered as the causative factors. The psychological school again considers all such attempts as futile; it hopes that with improved psychological study of life histories, specific emotional experiences responsible for the disintegration of the total personality may be unearthed. The psychological school at present has more to offer. Many case histories reveal extremely injurious family constellations—a consistent disturbance of early human relations, such as maternal rejection or paternal intimidation—which retard the development of emotional security without which no healthy personality can exist. This school assumes that the difference between this type of serious disturbance of personality and the milder forms of psychoneuroses is primarily a quantitative one. The ultimate causative factors are of the same nature in both types of disorders that comprise disturbed human relations; in the major psychoses these influences probably begin earlier, are more intense and consistent than in the milder cases of neuroses. The objection to this view is that in many cases the most careful studies of the life history of the schizophrenic patient cannot elicit any more severe or unusual experiences than those which one finds in milder psychoneuroses. In fact many mentally healthy persons have had extremely unfavorable childhoods, and yet seem to have escaped not only a psychosis but even milder forms of neuroses. In other words there is no simple correlation between the severity of a mental disturbance and the severity of the emotionally injurious experiences of the past. It seems, therefore, that some basic constitutional factor must be responsible for the difference in susceptibility to traumatic emotional influences. Freud and most of his followers admit that the constitutional factor is all important. On the other hand, the emotional constellations in the family are extremely complex. In a seemingly hopeless environment one favorable factor may be present; an understanding uncle, a helpful older sister, or nursery teacher may give the child emotional support and help him to withstand all the other extremely unfavorable influences. Therefore the followers of the psychological school justifiably insist that before constitutional factors are drawn in as explanation, the environmental influences should be exhaustively evaluated. Because the earliest emotional experiences in most cases cannot be reconstructed, an adequate evaluation of the relative influence of constitution versus later experiences is not possible. One thing, however, stands out: that the relative importance of these two sets of factors varies in individual cases. Some persons with inherited constitutional weaknesses become sick under almost every circumstance—favorable or unfavorable—while others with strong constitutions become sick only if exposed to extreme and consistent emotional injuries. In any case, constitutional predisposition will have to remain a very vague concept until it is definable in concrete terms of anatomy and physiology.

Constitution, however, is not the only factor with which the organic school in schizophrenia research concerns itself. It assumes a progressive disease process somewhere in the organism, possibly in the brain or in the lower portions of the nervous system or in the endocrine glands, a process which sometime in the future will be understood in physiological and chemical terms. Whenever seemingly consistent somatic deviations are reported in schizophrenics, the hope is aroused that now finally the schizophrenia riddle will be solved.

Gradually the fallacy of this whole controversy, the organic versus the environmental theory, is becoming apparent. The new light is coming from a rather unexpected quarter—the careful psychodynamic study of persons who are suffering from certain diseases of the vegetative organs—the stomach, bowels, heart, lungs, skin, and glands—diseases in which emotional factors have long been suspected as causative.

It is well known from everyday experience that emotions such as fear, anger, resentment, guilt, or embarrassment have definite physiological effects. The best-known examples are weeping, laughing, blushing, and losing bowel or bladder control under the influence of fear. All these examples are, however, transitory processes occurring in everyday life in all healthy persons. What the systematic psychosomatic studies have shown is that not only transitory physiological changes can be caused by emotions, but that sustained emotional strain may lead to chronic disturbances of physiological functions and in this way cause bodily diseases. They have shown that in widespread organic conditions (for example, ulcers of the stomach and duodenum, asthma, chronic high blood pressure) emotional tensions play an important causative role. These emotional tensions again arise from the disturbed human relations which have proved to play such an important part in psychoneuroses.

When these facts first became current the most common reaction of the medical man was bewilderment. These new ideas introduced a cleavage, a dualism, into medical thought. For the physician, emotions as causes of diseases meant a retrogression to prescientific, magical, animalistic beliefs, back to the old division of man into a body and soul. It was of little consolation that this rediscovered soul appeared now in a scientific garb, that it was being studied during office hours, in hospitals and psychological laboratories, and described with Greek and Latin technical expressions. It was still felt strange that such elusive things as thwarted hopes, resentments, fears, and emotional frustrations should be considered as the ultimate causes of such tangible disturbances in the body as a wound in the stomach wall or an increased secretion of hydrochloric acid or a prolonged contraction of the blood vessels. It was of little use that the psychoanalyst pointed to everyday facts within the reach of everybody's experience; for example, that such a complex emotional state as embarrassment does cause a tangible change in the body—blushing, due to the dilatation of the blood vessels in the cheek. The answer of the medical man was, "Well, blushing can be explained physiologically. This dilatation of the blood vessels in the cheek is caused by nerve impulses conducted from higher brain centers via the autonomic nervous system. What the psychologist or psychoanalyst calls 'embarrassment,' in the last analysis is *nothing but some physiological process in the brain.* This physiological process in the brain, which is conducted through the nervous pathways to the blood vessels of the cheek, is the only thing which merits scientific consideration."

This response is correct except for the statement "embarrassment is nothing but a process in the brain." Embarrassment certainly is a distinct process in the brain, but at the same time it is a subjective sensation which can be described in psychological terms and which also merits scientific consideration. In fact, at the present state of our knowledge, it can be described only in psychological terms. We do not know much about the nature of that assumed physiological process which takes place in the brain when a person feels embarrassment. However, embarrassment as a psychological phenomenon can be most precisely described by the person who blushes. The person can tell us—of course, only if he wants to—whether he was embarrassed because he lied, or because he was praised, or because he suddenly heard the voice of his sweetheart. It is obvious, therefore, that at present if we want to study scientifically the phenomenon of blushing, we do better if we examine its causes in psychological terms. We may hope that sometime in the future we shall also know the concomitant physiological processes, but even then it is an open question whether we shall dispense with our psychological understanding of embarrassment. For example: one person blushes when praised by the teacher in the presence of others because in childhood he had competed with his brother for parental approval, and remembering the illicit means by which he often obtained this approval he now feels guilty and ashamed. Could the most minute physiological description explain as much as does this psychological one? Even such a common process as blushing from embarrassment can only be understood fully in the light of the life history of the individual. The same is true for weeping or laughter. Only when we know what makes Mr. Smith so sensitive to certain human events can we understand why his eyes fill with tears over a sentimental scene in the movies, whereas Mr. Jones in the same situation remains completely composed. Only the history of Mr. Smith and Mr. Jones will explain to us how and why the one became highly sensitized on seeing an old, helpless man peering through a window at a happy family on a Christmas Eve, and why the other found the same scene trite and boring. Whether the most advanced brain physiology will ever be able to substitute for this type of knowledge is certainly an open question. It is difficult to imagine that it will.

Certain it is, however, that at the present state of our knowledge the factors which cause weeping, laughing, or blushing can only be described by using both psychological and physiological methods. The innervation of the tear gland in weeping, or the dilatation of the blood vessels in blushing, the conduction of the nerve influences from the brain cortex to the eyes and the cheek can only be described in physiological terms, whereas the causative emotions are definable only in psychological terms. And, similarly, the local processes which immediately cause the ulceration of the stomach or cause an asthmatic attack must be described in strictly physiological terms. The causative emotional tensions, on the other hand, must be described and understood in psychological terms. Omitting this psychological part of the whole process does not increase the scientific nature of our description. On the contrary, understanding the local mechanisms involved in the development of an ulcer or asthma is only half the story. Omitting the other half, the part which requires, at our present state of knowledge, psychological descriptions, would be to give up the most important aim of medicine, the understanding of causes. An appropriate use of psychological and physiological methods of description—each in its proper place—is the essence of the psychosomatic approach.

We may now return to our previous statement concerning the fallacy of the controversy of an organic versus a psychological explanation of schizophrenia. Applying the psychosomatic point of view to this tantalizing problem of medical research, we can reasonably assume that, with improved methods, we shall be able to discover consistent and relevant biochemical changes in the schizophrenic patient. At the same time, in view of what we know today about the typical life history of schizophrenics, we may also reasonably assume that these biochemical changes develop under the influence of emotional injuries. In fact certain rather consistent changes in the carbohydrate metabolism have been observed recently in schizophrenic patients. On the other hand it has been known for some time, both from Cannon's animal experiments and from clinical observations, that the carbohydrate metabolism is under the influence of emotions. The interrelation of biochemical changes and emotions is today beyond question. Emotional tensions through the autonomic nervous system do influence the body chemistry, and the changed body chemistry in turn reacts upon the emotional life. With the clear recognition of such mutual influences the cleavage between emotional and organic factors can be relegated to the past. Body chemistry and emotions do not represent two different sets of facts, one physical, the other mental. When we speak of emotions we refer always to definite physical processes in the brain, which, however, can be studied psychologically because these brain processes are perceived subjectively as emotions and can be communicated to others by the use of language. The combined biochemical and psychological approach is now only in its beginnings but will undoubtedly become the main trend of future research and therapy.

This progressive reconciliation of the psychological and somatic points of view for a while seemed to be interrupted by recent developments in the field of psychiatric therapy. I refer to the introduction of the method of shock treatment by insulin, metrazol, and, most recently, by electric current. In a sense the shock treatments did not follow the etiological orientation which characterized modern developments in psychiatry. They are not based on the understanding of the causes of the illness. On the contrary, the different forms of shock treatment, putting the patient in a transitory unconscious state characterized by violent so-called epileptiform convulsions, are entirely empirical. The beneficial effect upon certain types of patients cannot yet be explained satisfactorily. Both organic and psychological explanations have been offered, but without sufficient supporting evidence. For a while the old controversies about organic versus psychological explanation of mental illness were revived, and the organicists were inclined to see in shock therapy a vindication of their point of view. The problem of shock therapy at present is still in a state of confusion. As more and more cases are being followed up, evidence increases that with some exceptions we deal here with temporary remissions. For some unknown reason this violent treatment is able to produce in certain psychotic patients a temporary improvement, and in the group of involutional melancholia more lasting benefits. It would appear that by the metrazol and electric-shock treatments the imprint of causative emotional experiences upon the brain tissue may be blotted out. Temporary memory defects after electric-shock and metrazol treatment would seem to confirm this assumption. The personality make-up of the patients thus treated is not changed, however, and most of them become sick again some time after they return to the original traumatic conditions. In any case, those who think that the results of shock therapy support the organic explanation only reveal that they are still confused concerning the age-old pseudoproblem of body versus mind. Their reasoning is as primitive as would be the argument that cheerfulness is an organic process because it can be induced by the consumption of a chemical substance, alcohol. Cheerfulness obviously can also be introduced psychologically, for example, breaking the good news to a fearful student that he passed a difficult examination. Nevertheless cheerfulness consists certainly in a physiological brain process which can be induced both chemically by alcohol or psychologically by good news.

While the introduction of shock treatment appears as an episode of some theoretical and practical interest, another scientific development assumes a momentous significance for the future of psychiatry. I am referring to studies in cultural psychology paving the way for a field which may be called social psychiatry or, perhaps more aptly, preventive psychiatry. This development feeds from two sources: psychiatry on the one hand, and cultural anthropology and sociology on the other. Here we deal not primarily with the evaluation of past accomplishments but with future outlook.

The psychoanalytic approach is highly individualistic; it attempts to explain the patient's difficulties as a result of his past experiences, which are highly specific and different in each individual case. And yet certain experiences, certain basic conflict-situations, such as the Oedipus complex, are common to all cases. Freud and his followers were inclined to consider these basic emotional constellations as the manifestation of universal human nature; in other words, the manifestation of the basic biological structure of man. In particular, the conflict between what is called the ego, the organized portion of the personality, and the sexual drive was postulated not only as universal but as the ultimate cause of every neurosis. In the light of cultural anthropology—the comparative study of different cultures—these fundamental findings of psychoanalysis assume a new meaning. Such studies have shown that, although the sexual impulse in every culture is subject to rather complicated regulations, these regulations differ according to the local social structure. For example, taboos and marital laws are different in matriarchal and patriarchal societies.

The same is true in the expression of hostile feelings. The different attitude of the child toward paternal authority and ancestors in China and the United States is another example of opposite extiemes. These different cultural standards begin to exert their influence in earliest infancy; they pervade the whole emotional atmosphere of the family. Accordingly—as Linton, Kardiner, Bateson, and Mead have shown—the basic personality structure of the members of different cultures differs. In the light of these differences we begin to recognize that those emotional conflict situations, which have been discovered by European and American psychoanalysts, are not the manifestation of a universal human nature but are variations of human nature. This does not mean that such a fundamental emotional constellation as the Oedipus complex is only of local nature. Because of his biological dependency, every child in all cultures has a possessive attitude toward his mother and fear and hatred against all rivals. However, even this fundamental conflict situation has a local color in the different cultures. Accordingly its pathogenic significance may vary not only from family to family—this we always knew —but also from culture to culture. Furthermore, there can be no doubt that the extreme sexual repression of the Victorian era was responsible for the prominent role which Freud attributed to sexuality in the causation of neuroses. Sexuality acquired this significant role not because of some basic biological reasons, but because of the repressive method of handling its manifestations within the family and in public life during the Victorian period.

In our present days another nuclear emotional conflict stands out. It centers around emotional insecurity, a conflict between competitive ambition and stress upon individual accomplishment, and a deep longing for dependence and security. The ideals of individual initiative, endurance, and self-reliance, and of an adventurous enterprising spirit, are deeply rooted in the American cultural tradition derived from the days of unlimited opportunity. These old virile ideals are still alive, but their successful realization is becoming more and more difficult in our present complex interdependent society in which mammoth corporations, on the one hand, and the all-powerful trade unions, on the other, are desperately combining the great impersonal demons of our times: the inexorable laws of the business cycle and unemployment. This social atmosphere is the ideal breeding place of insecurity and the longing for dependence, both attitudes so diametrically opposite to the traditional love of freedom of spirit and action. And thus we recognize the central neurotic conflict of our present days—the conflict between individualistic ideals and a longing for order, security, and dependence.

Life in our machine age is becoming more and more complex. In our free and competitive society we are at one time both friends and rivals; we live in "antagonistic cooperation" with our fellow men. Though our democratic institutions require from us independence in judgment and action, many individuals never attain a state of inner security and so long for help and leadership. Fears and hostilities, frustrations and thwarted hopes, exaggerated ambitions and discouragement may lead to mental and nervous symptoms or to disturbed human relations.

This cultural point of view sharpens our eyes for detecting in the kaleidoscopic variety of emotional disturbances the common features determined by the milieu to which every person growing up in the same society is exposed. The recognition of these culturally determined factors in the development of personality and neuroses introduces into psychiatry the preventive point of view and represents the connecting link between healing and education. Changed cultural conditions require new, or at least modified, emotional patterns. Only if educational standards and ideals are appropriate to the existing conditions can the spread of neuroses be prevented. Education which belongs to conditions of the past leads to emotional disturbances. For example, stress upon individual accomplishments was more important in pioneer days than it is now in our highly industrialized civilization. Individual initiative and creative aspirations should not be discouraged, but should be directed also to the less-explored frontiers of scientific investigation and artistic creation.

Psychiatry began with custodial care for those totally incapacitated because of mental illness, and up to the last century its progress consisted chiefly in humanizing this care. The next step was to reach a better understanding of the nature of mental disturbances and thus to develop therapeutic measures. Now psychiatry is concerned not only with therapy but also with prevention. Large-scale prevention is essentially a problem of education which requires a keen understanding of the prevailing cultural patterns. To help the individual to adapt himself to these cultural patterns is the great practical task of dynamic psychology.

TRAINING PRINCIPLES IN PSYCHOSOMATIC MEDICINE *

By FRANZ ALEXANDER, M.D.

The first prerequisite of sound teaching in any field is the clarification of fundamental principles and concepts. The psychosomatic approach, although as old as medicine itself, has developed only very recently from bedside manner and medical art into a method which is based on controlled observations and scientific concepts. It is not surprising, therefore, that there is not yet general agreement even concerning fundamental questions. Limitation of time does not permit discussion of the whole question of psychosomatic teaching, research, and practice; I shall therefore limit myself to the definition of the field and a clarification of some controversial issues. These considerations may serve as a basis for sound teaching in this field.

The term "psychosomatic" is principally used in two ways: (a) referring to a method of approach in research and therapy, a method which can be applied in the whole field of medicine; (b) referring diagnostically to certain conditions which some authors (Haliday) call "psychosomatic affections." The first use of the term, which is entirely methodological, is sound and generally accepted; the second, which is diagnostic, is open to controversy.

In my opinion one should restrict the meaning of "psychosomatics" to the methodological principle. In the present phase of our investigative techniques, certain body functions and their disturbances can best be studied by psychological methods, while other functions can be approached only by physiological methods. In studying the totality of organic processes, both methods must be applied at the same time in order to account for the whole phenomenon. For example, stomach secretion as an isolated process in itself can be studied only by the methods of biochemistry; its nervous control, however, cannot be studied completely by physiological methods alone because the latter cannot adequately account for certain central (emotional) influences without utilizing psychological information. The fact that receptive dependent wishes mobilize stomach secretion cannot be ascertained by physiological methods alone because these wishes can-

* American Journal of Orthopsychiatry XV: 410-412, 1946.

not be identified by any existing physiological technique. *Theoretically,* emotional influences can be studied also as brain processes; *practically,* however, this will be possible only after physiological techniques have been developed by which different emotions can be identified.

The same considerations hold true for the study of the disturbances of physiological functions. The disturbance of stomach secretion, as is observed in peptic ulcers, might be caused by different factors, both central and local, emotional and dietary. At the present state of our knowledge, there is no method of appraising the quantitative proportions of these various local and central factors in each case. We have good reason to believe that the emotional factor plays a significant role in the majority of cases. Haliday, himself an ardent advocate of the concept of psychosomatic affection, in one of his recent articles refers to the peptic ulcer of chlorotic girls in which "physical" factors are important. Also in adult males and females the emotional and nonemotional factors vary in relative significance from case to case. Peptic ulcer is not a nosological entity, but a symptom caused by a multiplicity of etiological factors which vary in different cases. Postoperative stomach ulcers in cases of mid-brain tumor (Cushing) have an etiology different from that observed in chronic cases which develop as a result of emotional tensions. And even in the latter types, faulty dietary habits may be of etiological importance.

The same is true for the etiology of bronchial asthma in which both allergic and emotional factors are present and have a complimentary relationship to each other. The important fact is that the typical emotional factors which are found in certain organic diseases are present also in persons who show no organic symptoms. It is obvious, therefore, that emotional factors represent merely a category of factors which, only in combination with certain nonemotional factors, produce organic diseases. Psychosomatic affection, consequently, is an inappropriate concept: it implies the preponderance of emotional factors in certain affections, although the significance of emotional factors varies from case to case, and their relative importance in respect to coexisting nonemotional factors cannot be ascertained by our present investigative methods.

Ours is a very young field, and the scattered knowledge that we have does not allow us to accept such an arbitrary diagnostic classification. Evidence is rapidly growing that in almost all chronic diseases emotional factors play an important role. The importance of the emotional factor varies from patient to patient. This might be the case even in certain chronic infectious diseases. If the expression "psychosomatic disease" means the presence of emotional factors of etiological significance, the major part of diseases is psychosomatic. It is much more appropriate, therefore, to limit the concept of psychosomatics to the study of the psychological component in organic diseases and to the therapy which attempts to influence this psychological component. This orientation will put an end to the present-day confusion.

At present young physicians often express their desire to specialize in psychosomatic medicine. When urged to state concretely what they have in mind, it usually turns out to be a desire to specialize in the treatment of certain vegetative disturbances in which, in recent years, the etiological significance of emotional factors has been established. This obviously would lead to an anomalous specialization within medicine. Patients suffering from peptic ulcer, asthma, essential hypertension, disturbances of metabolism, and other conditions in which emotional factors play a role will need, in the future as in the past, both organic and psychological treatment at the same time. The organic treatment requires, as it always has, a thorough knowledge of the existing medical specialties; the psychotherapeutic approach requires a thorough knowledge of psychiatry. Cooperation of psychiatrists with the different medical specialists will remain the only sound approach. While psychiatric teaching will need to become more and more an integral part of the training of every physician, psychotherapy will have to remain a specialty requiring specific and thorough training, as does surgery.

PHYSIOLOGY OF BEHAVIOR AND CHOICE OF NEUROSIS *

By Thomas M. French, M.D.

It is an old and often repeated observation with which all analysts are familiar that a dream will frequently anticipate the onset of a somatic symptom or even of an organic illness. As an example I may cite from one of our asthma patients a dream which Dr. Helen McLean has placed at my disposal.

The patient, a 46-year-old, rather inarticulate laborer, had just started an analysis for bronchial asthma. The following dream was reported in the twelfth hour of his analysis, and was probably a reaction to the analyst's first interpretation of a dream in the tenth hour.

> I can't remember it. It was about father and mother. It seems mother was doing blacksmith work. She had hot iron and was hammering.

When the analyst reminds him that his father was a blacksmith, he adds a few details.

> Father was also in the dream but not so clear as mother. He was standing at the side of the shop—kind of dark. I plainly see my mother. She had hot iron and working at it, flattening it out and bending it, doing clean work, good job too.

In association he protests that his mother never did any blacksmith work, although she sometimes came to the door of the shop.

Corresponding to the patient's inarticulate character, he is quickly through with his associations, so the analyst tries to help him out. She suggests that perhaps she seems like a woman doing a man's job.

It seems quite certain that the analyst is right. Probably the patient was somewhat disappointed at being assigned to a woman analyst, but he has evidently been quite fascinated by the analyst's interpretation of his dream a few days before and is beginning to feel that she can do as good a job as if she were a man. He does not

* The Psychoanalytic Quarterly X: 561-572, 1941.

37

reply to the analyst's comment, but continues to dwell admiringly upon the details of the mother's work in his memory of the dream:

> Father was standing on one side. Mother took the iron out of the fire, performing the work on it—a long piece of heavy iron.

The iron resembled an iron used on locomotives to pull out clinkers. The mother was shaping it. There was a hook on the end of it.

If the mother's beating an iron bar on the anvil represents the patient's treatment, it would seem that the patient must be thinking of himself as the bar that is being beaten and bent. The analyst comes to this conclusion, and remarks that if she is bending the patient like iron, he must be afraid. He partially confirms this interpretation. He agrees that he really is afraid of the analysis. He does not know what it is all about, and feels helpless because he is in the dark.

My particular interest in presenting this material consists in its relation to the sequel. This dream, as we have seen, pictures vigorous muscular activity on the part of the mother and seems to represent the patient himself as being beaten upon an anvil. It seems like a sort of continuation of the dream, therefore, when we learn in the next hour that two days later he developed lumbago, and in the fourteenth hour, a week later, he complained of a stiff neck so painful that he could talk of little else during the entire analytic hour.

There are three possible ways to explain the onset of these muscular and arthritic pains which occurred within a few days after his dream of violent muscular activity.

1. It may have been merely a coincidence. The difficulty with this view is that 'coincidences' of this sort occur so frequently.

2. Freud (1925) has pointed out that an inflammatory or other pathological organic process may be unconsciously perceived some time before the symptoms to which it gives rise are sufficiently acute to attract conscious attention. This suggestion is supported by a number of observations in which dreams have seemed to predict organic lesions that developed later, but which at the time even careful medical examination was unable to discover.

3. As a third possibility we may perhaps surmise that the violent activity in the dream may be reflecting some intense excitation in the muscles, or in the associated nervous pathways, corresponding to the wish to beat or be beaten of which the dream is an expression. The subsequent muscular and arthritic pains would in this case be at least in part the result of this intense functional excitation.

In confirmation of this third possibility may be cited numerous dreams reported in the literature, in which the dreamer awakened to find that he was acting out the impulse of which he had just been dreaming. Thus one might dream of a little boy masturbating, and wake up to find that the dreamer was performing the act which his dream had attributed to the little boy; or he might dream that he was striking someone, and wake up to find that he was beating the pillow. Some years ago Dr. Leon Saul (1935) collected a number of instances to show that symptoms that seemed to be psychogenic in nature are often the result of activities during sleep of which the dreamer only later becomes conscious. Instances like these are sufficiently numerous, it seems, to warrant the assumption that activity represented in a dream is likely to indicate some sort of functional excitation or even activity of the organs that are involved in the dream activity, and that subsequent symptoms involving these same organs will most probably be also the result of these functional excitations or tensions.

We seem justified, therefore, in the conclusion that the manifest content of a dream may be a very valuable indicator of physiological excitations and tensions corresponding to the wishes and impulses of which the dream is an expression. Indeed, if we study the dream more carefully, I believe that we can go further than this. By careful study I believe it is often possible also to gain some indications of the shifts in the patterns of physiological tensions that have taken place during the dream work. Let us take again, as an example, the dream of the mother beating the iron bar.

We have not yet raised the question as to why Dr. McLean's patient should have come to his treatment with the expectation that it is the analyst's job to hammer him into shape, just as his father used to bend iron bars upon the anvil. This seems indeed to be an exceedingly masochistic concept of the analysis, and would seem to imply that the patient was suffering from a very great sense of guilt and need for punishment. We have not time in this short paper to give a very complete reconstruction of the latent content of this dream, but it will be of interest, at least, to make an attempt to trace the source of this sense of guilt.

We have not reported the content of the dream interpretation in the tenth hour for which this anvil dream of the twelfth hour expresses so much admiration. This patient's analysis had opened with a very considerable reluctance and embarrassment on the patient's part to bring into the discussion his discontent with his marital life and his great resentment of his wife, whom he criticized as fat and exceedingly sloppy in her dress and in her housekeeping, and very neglectful of their two children.

The dreams reported by the patient in the tenth hour dealt with this embarrassment at complaining about his wife to another woman. In one dream fragment which was particularly embarrassing to him, he was trying to avoid his wife in a railroad station and another lady was sympathizing with him and asking why he had married her. The analyst interpreted this dream as the fulfilment of a wish that she sympathize with him in his desire to separate from his wife. In the discussion which followed, the analyst had occasion to point out that the patient had really married his wife in the expectation that she would take care of him like a mother. Now in the analysis the patient was unconsciously hoping that the analyst would play the mother role which the patient so missed in his wife's attitude toward him.

The patient must unconsciously have sensed in this interpretation an implication of sexual interest in the analyst, inasmuch as the next day he stated that he never put any value in dreams and spent most of the hour protesting that he could not stand the idea of "wives and mothers" talking about sex. However his dream in the twelfth hour reveals that this was only one half of his reaction to the analyst's interpretation. Deeper down, he was much impressed.

It is now easier to understand why the patient felt the need to be beaten by the analyst.[1] Unconsciously he is intensely chagrined on account of the sexual interest which the analyst unconsciously awakens in him. The iron bar that is being beaten and bent is probably a symbol of his erect penis. Actually, in his young manhood, his choleric father had twice beaten him for his sexual activities, and in a dream, much later in the analysis, the patient himself is beating an iron bar which has the shape of a penis.

Let us now sum up the physiological implications of our reconstruction of the dream work. The dream seems to imply that the dream work started with sexual excitation, very probably an erection, associated with sexual wishes stirred up in the analytic situation. He reacts to this sexual excitation with intense guilt and develops an impulse to beat himself or be beaten. This, we suspect, finds ex-

---

[1] Analysts will recognize in this dream a still deeper source of the patient's need for punishment. Later in the analysis he recalled that his resentment toward his wife had begun during his wife's first pregnancy, and had become more intense during a second pregnancy, and that its deepest root lay in jealous resentment of the wife's relation to the two children. One of the central themes of the analysis was in fact the patient's intense resentment toward his mother's pregnancies (he was the eldest of six children), and his unconscious impulse to take the unborn child from the mother's body. It will be noticed that this wish is symbolized in the iron bar with a hook at the end to remove clinkers from a furnace. Physiologically interpreted, this dream suggests that the mother is beating down his erect penis into a grasping hand—an interpretation which corresponds with his mother's actual attitude towards him, her sharp inhibition of his developing genital sexuality and her urge to keep him a child, at least in the sexual sphere.

pression in some sort of tension or even activity in the muscles and in the associated nervous pathways. If we observe carefully, however, we note that this is not the final step in the dream work, for the manifest content of the dream does not represent the patient as beating or being beaten but rather as watching his mother beat an iron bar. If we follow literally the physiological implications of this fact, we must suspect that this projection involves a further displacement of excitation away from genital excitement, and from the impulse to muscular activity, to the visual apparatus. We might compare the significance of such a displacement to that of a man who inhibited his impulse to beat up someone and attempted to relieve the tension by going to see a movie that was characterized by a good deal of violence.

You will, perhaps, ask me how literally I am inclined to accept this physiological reconstruction. Do I believe that the dream work was actually accompanied by physiological excitations and tensions such as I have described? If you ask my impression, I shall say that on the basis of the analysis of the interrelations between a great many dreams I would be inclined to believe that the physiological reconstruction we have made would correspond roughly to the actual course of distribution and displacement of functional excitation during the dream work. I must admit, however, that without examination of a great deal more material than I can present in a short paper I would be unable to prove it. Nevertheless I believe that there is a great deal of value in attempting to reconstruct the apparent physiological implications of our interpretations of dreams and other psychoanalytic material. The method, as I have indicated by this example, is to trace step by step the pathway from the wishes that motivate the dream to their expression in the manifest content of the dream, and to pay careful attention to the organs or organ systems whose activity is implied in each of the steps of this process. We cannot, perhaps, be sure that what comes out will correspond in all details to the actual patterns of physiological excitation that accompanied the dream work, but I believe we have sufficient reason to suspect that it will have a fairly close relation to these physiological patterns and that it can form a good basis for further investigation (by comparison with other dream material of the same patient and by physiological experimentation, etc.) to test the rough hypotheses derived in this way.

Analysts will notice that what I am here proposing is merely an attempt to develop in very explicit form a procedure which analysts have long used in terms of Freud's original libido theory. We have long been accustomed to attempt to explain numerous psychological mechanisms by displacement of libido from one organ of the body to another. My only innovation in this procedure is to discard as unimportant the old and meaningless controversy as to whether the energy that is shoved about in these displacement processes is of a sexual nature or not. I think it is much more important to recognize that these displacements of energy are really of functional significance. As a matter of fact, every integrated activity involves the functional excitation now of one organ, now of another, according to the particular pattern of the activity. One moment we are looking, another we are thinking, and then there may be motor discharge. I believe it is introducing entirely unnecessary confusion to conceive of these "displacements of energy," when we encounter them in the dream work, as some sort of mysterious displacements of libido.

One of the most reliable ways of testing such hypotheses as those concerning the physiological excitations accompanying the dream work is by noting how far somatic symptoms that develop in the course of a psychoanalytic treatment correspond to what we might have expected from our physiological reconstructions. We have already discussed one example of such a correlation in noting that the forcible activity pictured in this anvil dream was followed within a few days by severe pains in all the muscles of the patient's body.

In fact, observations of this kind seem to suggest a very simple rule by which we may guess in many instances what organ will be chosen in a particular instance for the somatic discharge of an emotional tension. We are all familiar with Stockard's experiments (1921) in which he demonstrated that developing organisms exposed to some more or less indiscriminate toxic agent would be most damaged at precisely those points that were developing most actively at the moment of exposure to the poison. A similar principle would seem also to hold in our problem: symptoms resulting from the frustration of an activity are likely to involve especially the organs which are most active or most under tension at the moment of frustration. This principle is well illustrated in our reconstruction of the "anvil dream." Our hypothesis in this case was that the dreamer was activated by a strong impulse to violent muscular activity, but that the manifest content of the dream seems to represent an attempt of the dreamer to withdraw energy from these impulses to muscular activity and to content himself with a visual picture of the activities to which he is impelled. The attempted displacement to the visual apparatus already indicates an energetic effort to inhibit muscular discharge. In accordance with the principle just formulated, we should expect that symptoms developing at this time would involve the organs whose activity is being with difficulty inhibited—in this case the muscles and joints—and this proves in fact to be the case.

By contrast it will be of interest to describe a rather similar physiological pattern that seems to be followed regularly, not by muscle and joint pains but by severe frontal headache. The physiological pattern, in these cases also, involved the displacement of excitation away from energetic muscular impulse to visual and intellectual activity; but in the cases to be cited, the inhibition of muscular discharge is much more complete. In the dream that we have just cited, the patient seemed to be trying to satisfy his own need for violent activity by observing the violent activity of someone else. In the instances about to be reported, the inhibition of motility has gone much further. Instead of observing an active figure, the patient is fascinated by a motionless figure. The need for activity is not only projected; it is also denied. In accordance with our principle to expect the somatic symptom in the organ that is most under tension, we find that in these cases the patients develop a headache.

I am sorry that time permits me to report the examples of this pattern only in anecdotal form.

A young man reports a dream which consists merely in a picture of female genitals with a penis. While discussing this dream in the analysis the next morning, the patient develops an intense frontal headache which continues for several hours. Associations to this dream indicate, as usual, that the dream is a defense against the feminine wish to be attacked sexually, a wish which is associated with a fear of castration. It will be noted that the feminine wish and castration fear in this dream are both projected and energetically negated. The patient is merely observing a female genital which has a penis. Both the projection and the denial are achieved by the substitution of a visual image. Correlating with this intense fixation upon a visual image, the patient develops a headache.

A young professional woman was much disturbed by a conflict of loyalty between a male and female professional colleague, to both of whom she was much attached. The material at this time was obscure, but later material made it plain that she was disturbed both by sexual desires towards the man and by wishes to harm the woman. In the midst of this conflict she devoted herself intensely for a few hours to study in preparation for a lecture which she was giving that afternoon. During this time she developed a violent frontal headache which continued during the lecture, and which was not relieved until some time the next day. In this instance we see an energetic urge to distract interest from an intense emotional conflict. The method in this case is to become absorbed in intellectual activity. The result is a headache.

ig woman dreams of seeing a woman who is fascinated and
oy the sight of a huge Negro man. The Negro, though
i, seems about to attack her. While discussing this dream
ilysis the next day, she develops an intense frontal headache. It will be noted that in this instance there is again a projection
of the impulse to activity and an energetic denial of it.

It will be noted that the physiological mechanism implied in all
these instances is one of attempting to distract energy from some
conflict involving the need for energetic motor discharge by means
of an intense intellectual preoccupation or visual fascination. In each
of the two dreams cited we note that the implied activity has been
completely "frozen." An immobilized visual image replaces the urge
for violent activity. The emphasis upon visual excitation as contrasted with muscular activity is thus much greater than in the case
of the anvil dream in which the patient is observing a scene of violent
activity. In accordance with our principle, it seems consistent, therefore, that these patients should have developed severe headaches instead of muscular pains.

It is probable that in all of the instances cited so far we have
pathological exaggerations of the normal alternation between thinking and activity that must play a very important role in the physiology
of all kinds of behavior. By more careful and detailed study of such
instances we might hope to work out the quantitative dynamic principles that regulate this normal oscillation between thinking and
doing.

From our work at the Institute for Psychoanalysis we could cite
a number of instances that seem to indicate the association of particular psychosomatic symptoms with rather specific patterns of distribution of physiological excitation, insofar as these can be deduced
from a reconstruction of the dream work.

One of the first examples was Alexander's (1935) demonstration
of the frequency of dreams of unsatisfied desire for food in patients
suffering from duodenal ulcer. It will be recalled that Alexander
(1934) calls attention to the literature which cites physiological evidence of increased nocturnal gastric secretory activity in these cases,
as well as experimental production of ulcers by holding food just
outside of an animal's reach.

In our study of the psychogenesis of asthma attacks (1939) we
were struck by the reciprocal relations between asthma and crying.
It appeared that the asthma attack was very often a sort of substitute for a suppressed cry. Interestingly enough, the dreams of these
patients very frequently represented the patient as talking. The talk
usually had the meaning of an attempt to seek reconciliation by con-

fession to a mother figure from whom some forbidden impulse threatened to estrange the dreamer. If the danger of estrangement of the mother figure was too great to be quieted in this way, the patient usually awoke with an attack of asthma. We note here again an example of the principle that the psychosomatic symptom involves the organ active at the time of frustration, in this case the respiratory apparatus involved in talking and crying.

In conclusion I should like to bring these observations into relation with the wider field of psychosomatic research. At the present time an enormous amount of work is being done in the attempt to bridge the gap between the physiologist's detailed knowledge of the mechanisms of isolated reactions and the psychologist's attempts to work out the motivations that determine the larger patterns of behavior viewed as a whole. The two methods of research may be compared to two groups of workmen engaged in the building of a tunnel under a river but starting from opposite ends. The physiologists are doing valiant work trying to piece together a detailed physiological mechanism in order to build up a synthetic picture of integrated behavior as a whole. Those of us at the psychological end, as in the present study, must seek to extract from our psychological material as many hints as possible as to the physiological mechanisms and dynamic principles involved in the translation of motives into action. Sometime in the future we hope to meet somewhere under the river.

BIBLIOGRAPHY

1. ALEXANDER, FRANZ, BACON, AND CO-WORKERS. The influence of psychologic factors upon gastro intestinal disturbances: symposium. *Psychoanal. Quart.,* 1934, 3, 501-540. (In this volume, page 103.)
2. ALEXANDER, FRANZ, AND WILSON, G. W. Quantitative dream studies. *Psychoanal. Quart.,* 1935, 4, 371-407.
3. FRENCH, T. M. Psychogenic factors in asthma. *Am. J. Psychiat.,* 1939, 96, 87-98.
4. FREUD, SIGMUND. Metapsychological supplement to the theory of dreams (1916). In *Collected papers,* 4, 138. London: Hogarth Press, 1925.
5. SAUL, L. J. A note on the psychogenesis of organic symptoms. *Psychoanal. Quart.,* 1935, 4, 476-483.
6. STOCKARD, C. R. Developmental rate and structural expression: an experimental study of twins, "double monsters" and single deformities, and the interaction among embryonic organs during their origin and development. *Amer. J. Anat.,* 1921, 28, 115-275.

HYPOTHALAMIC FUNCTIONS IN PSYCHO-SOMATIC INTERRELATIONS *

By Roy R. Grinker, M.D.

Introduction

The hypothalamus developed from the basal portion of the dien-cephalon under the influence of the medial forebrain bundle in a position favorable for its role as a central integrator of several impor-tant functions. Receiving afferent fibers from the ascending sensory tracts by way of the thalamus and subthalamus, and sending efferent fibers which directly or indirectly affect the activity of the entire autonomic nervous system, the hypothalamus integrates individual activities of viscera, endocrine glands, and smooth muscles with ref-erence to the economical needs of the entire organism. Such regula-tion and integration of the body's internal milieu serves to maintain what Cannon (12) terms homeostasis.

The significance of its position in the sphere of the medial fore-brain bundle lies in the fact that the hypothalamus has developed in connection with primitive areas of the forebrain which were con-cerned in the function of olfaction (50). The sense organs concerned with smell were the first distance receptors evolved, and they influ-enced the development of the most primitive or olfactory cortex. Receiving its afferent impulses from primitive olfactory cortex and the great sensory systems, the hypothalamus, as the central organ affecting visceral regulation, was early concerned with olfactovisceral reflex integration. The functional significance of smell for the ac-quisition of food, avoidance or preparation against inimical agents, and the attainment of objects for sexual satisfaction indicates the importance that olfaction had in satisfying fundamental instincts. In humans smell has become of less importance, in its function as a distance receptor for stimuli which relieve primary instinctual ten-sions or hungers, but its anatomical mechanism, consisting of olfac-tory tracts and cortex, hypothalamus, and autonomic nervous system, are still concerned with the expression of the energies of instinctual life which, in their higher forms, we term emotions. Although this

* Psychosomatic Medicine I: 19-47, 1939.

fundamental function remains the same, its dependence upon specific sensations and actual stimuli has been superseded in gradual evolutionary development until, in man, even symbols suffice as stimuli for the gratification and release of instinctual tensions.

The hypothalamus is connected with the cortex indirectly through the thalamus and also by direct afferent and efferent fibers, with the peripheral autonomic system and its lower centers, and with the hypophysis. Thus it is concerned with several complicated functions, all of which are based on its primary capacity of maintaining the stability of the organism's internal milieu as the effector agent of the instincts. Related directly to the hypophysis and indirectly to other glands of internal secretion, the hypothalamus (a) regulates endocrine functions and their interrelations; (b) regulates and integrates conservating autonomic functions; (c) is concerned with teleologically defensive and protective reactions which we term emotional expressions; and (d) influences the activity of the cerebral cortex in the regulation of degree of wakefulness and excitation. Each of these functions will be considered individually, with special consideration to its normal and pathological performance in the human.

Anatomical Considerations

The hypothalamus is an extremely small structure weighing, as Le Gros Clark (55) points out, only 4 grams in an average human brain of 1200 grams. At the base of the brain it is visible only as a small diamond-shaped bulge, perforated in the center by the hypophyseal stalk and surrounded by the cerebral peduncles and optic tracts. The hypothalamus lies between the mid- and forebrains in the 'tween brain or diencephalon. It constitutes the floor of the third ventricle and extends from the lamina terminalis and anterior commissure cephalad, where it merges with the preoptic nuclei of the telencephalon, to the tegmentum of the midbrain, caudad, with which it also merges (52). It is separated from the thalamus above by the sulcus hypothalamicus, and merges laterally with the somatic motor elements of the diencephalic subthalamic nuclei.

Interest in the human hypothalamus decreases our concern with lower forms; in fact, to homologize the various hypothalamic nuclei is difficult, due to the positional changes accompanying foreshortening and deepening of the third ventricle to conform to the large growth of the primate telencephalon. The hypothalamus is relatively smaller than in lower animals except for the pars mammillaris which has increased in size. Added to these difficulties in homologizing are the reports of zealous subdividers who demarcate identical nuclei as new nuclear masses and apply new names to them. In the dog, from 12 to 21 discrete hypothalamic nuclei have been reported by various investigators.

Throughout the animal series hypothalamic nuclei, with the exception of a single posterior group of cells, are composed of small oval and fusiform cell bodies with scanty cytoplasm, vesicular nuclei, and several short processes, all characteristic of central structures belonging to the autonomic nervous system (4). Their position close to and beneath the sulcus hypothalamicus is homologous to the position of spinal vegetative structures within the lateral gray columns.

Grünthal (35) described a more complicated cell structure in the human embryonic than in the adult hypothalamus, and attempted to relate it with an observable progressive simplification of the cell grouping in evolution; the human hypothalamus has the least complicated structure. Le Gros Clark has shown that the lateral mammillary nucleus is smaller in man, but that the lateral hypothalamic area or the large-celled nucleus mammillo-infundibularis is more complicated and difficult to analyze. In man the medial mammillary nucleus reaches its largest size, and this growth is accompanied by an increased differentiation of the anteroventral nucleus of the thalamus and the connecting mammillothalamic tract.

The anterior hypothalamus is composed of several nuclei. Two preoptic nuclei, lateral and medial, lie below the anterior commissure. They send fibers posteriorly into the main body of the hypothalamus, thalamic peduncle, and thalamus. The paraventricular or filiform nucleus lies along the wall of the third ventricle and consists of large multinucleated colloid-filled cells which to the uninitiated give the appearance of being degenerated. Their normal appearance has been described in human cases as evidence of central pathology in diabetes mellitus, psychoses, etc., and their unusual structure has misled investigators searching for experimental retrograde degenerations (41). The colloid material has suggested to some that they elaborate hormones or even that they have engulfed colloid which ascends the infundibulum from the pars media of the hypophysis. The paraventricular cells give rise to fibers which terminate in the thalamus, tuber cinereum, and preoptic nuclei, and descend as low as into the medulla oblongata, although controversy exists as to their ultimate destination. It has been thought by some that the fibers descend as low as the thoracic cord (9), and by others that they exit by way of the vagus nerve. However it is probable from recent experiments that the descending hypothalamic fibers do not form a compact bundle but descend by short chains of crossed and uncrossed intercalated neurones. (41). The *supraoptic nucleus* lies above and straddles the optic chiasm. It also consists of large bipolar cells filled with colloid, and like the paraventricular nucleus has a rich vascular bed. Its fibers descend the stalk of the hypophysis to the posterior lobe as the supra-opticohypophyseal tract.

The middle hypothalamus, or *pars tuberalis,* contains the *ventro-median* and *dorsomedian* nuclei, which are only relatively circum-scribed portions of the diffuse small autonomic cells of the substantia grisea centralis. The *lateral hypothalamic,* or mammillo-infundibu-lar nucleus, is extremely complicated in man and extends throughout the middle and posterior hypothalamus imbedded in the medial fore-brain bundle. Its cells are larger than those of the median nuclei.

In the posterior portion of the hypothalamus is a large *posterior hypothalamic* nucleus lying above and in front of the mammillary bodies and composed of large motor cells. Its fibers descend through short neuronal chains to the lateral grey columns at various spinal levels and form a chief efferent system from the hypothalamus. The pars mammillarsis is composed of a large *lateral mammillary* nucleus, small *medial mammillary* nucleus, and two small aberrant premam-millary and supramammillary nuclei.

The *fiber systems* and connections of the hypothalamus are known only grossly (30). The fornix connects the hippocampus, which reaches its highest development in man, to the mammillary body, and this in turn communicates with the anterior nucleus of the thalamus by way of the mammillothalamic tract or bundle of Vicq d'Azyr. Thalamic fibers from the anterior nucleus reach the cortex of the cin-gulum. Thus there is a direct and indirect system of communication between the posterior hypothalamus and the olfactory cortex, which attains its most complicated development in man. Descending fiber-bundles arise from the mammillary body and from the entire hypo-thalamus, are collected in a periventricular bundle and distributed to the thalamus and brain-stem by way of the dorsal longitudinal bundle of Schütz. Fiber connections exist between hypothalamus and thalamus, subthalamus and globus pallidus. Frontal lobe rela-tions are effected indirectly through the medial thalamus, and a direct fiber pathway has also been described.

The significance of these anatomic connections of the hypothal-amus has recently been stressed by Papez (68). He calls attention to the fact that the hypothalamus receives an incoming stream of sensory impulses not only from the thalamus but from the subthal-amus also. Optic impulses enter from the nucleus pregeniculatus of the lateral geniculate body, auditory from the ventral part of the medial geniculate body, pain from the reticular nucleus of the spinothalamic and trigeminothalamic systems, and touch from medial lemiscus fibers ending in the mammillary peduncle. Thus the hypothalamus receives afferent impressions through all somatic and visceral sensory modalities. Its efferent systems to the hypophysis from the pars optica, and to lower autonomic centers from the pars tuberalis, have been described. Afferent connections from the cortex arise from the hippocampal system by way of the fornix so that hypothalamic activity may be stimulated or inhibited by the cortex. Efferent fibers from the hypothalamus arise, especially from the mammillary body, by way of the bundle of Vicq d'Azyr to the anterior thalamic nucleus from which radiations proceed to the gyrus cinguli. From this cortical structure hypothalamic impulses may radiate to other parts of the cortex. Thus the hypothalamus lies as a central organ, intermediate between the cortex and the peripheral autonomic system, connected directly and indirectly with both territories by a two-way neural system of fiber pathways.

The *blood supply* of the hypothalamus has been studied carefully because of its functional implications. The circle of Willis surrounds the hypothalamus and supplies numerous small branches which have a discrete area of distribution in zones, so that isolated thromboses may cause discrete lesions and result in a circumscribed symptomatology. Popa and Fielding (67) believe a portal circulation from the pituitary body brings secretory products to the hypothalamic nuclei, where their effects are exerted upon the autonomic cells. Wislocki and King (80), however, were unable to confirm this anatomical observation.

Endocrine Functions

An outpouching of the floor of the third ventricle gives rise to the posterior lobe, or neurohypophysis, which is a derivative of the primitive hypothalamus. In the adult, the posterior lobe of the hypophysis is connected to the hypothalamus by the infundibulum, through which passes the supra-opticohypophyseal nerve tract which conveys descending fibers from the supra-optic and paraventricular nuclei. Other evidence, to be discussed later, indicates that these nuclei subserve parasympathetic functions so that, according to Fulton (24), this fiber tract should be considered as an outflow of the cranial parasympathetic division of the autonomic system. A few descending fibers enter the pars media from the supra-chiasmic nucleus. The anterior lobe has no direct hypothalamic innervation, but receives orthosympathetic fibers from the superior cervical ganglia by way of the perivascular network along the intracranial blood vessels and is thereby indirectly under the influence of the hypothalamus.

The close proximity of hypothalamus and pituitary body has created great difficulty in determining the source of a particular symptom in clinical syndromes arising from lesions in this area (70). Functional investigations in man are so difficult that at one time the hypophyseal-hypothalamic syndromes were dismissed as arising from disturbances of both structures considered as a physiological unit. Adiposity and emaciation, genital distrophy, and pubertas praecox are even now disturbances observed in humans for which the basic lesion is not clearly either hypophyseal or hypothalamic, and until clear-cut animal experiments gave unequivocal results, diabetes insipidus was also imperfectly understood. The reason for these uncertainties lies in the fact that the pathological bases for syndromes originating in this region are most frequently pituitary tumors, craniopharyngiomas, or cysts which implicate both structures by pressure. Trauma associated with basal skull fractures, basal meningitis, are likewise unlocalized in their effects. However, vascular thromboses, lethargic encephalitis, chronic alcoholism, and multiple sclerosis involving the hypothalamus do not implicate the hypophysis, and in these conditions disturbances in fat and carbohydrate metabolism and in genital development are frequently observed, indicating a primary hypothalamic implication.

The hypophysis has been recognized as the master gland of the endocrine system, functioning as the elaborator of many hormones, most of which influence the action of other glands. It functions from its cephalic position as an integrator of general glandular activity very much as the hypothalamus regulates autonomic nervous structures. The close association of the two structures, their common embryonic derivation (at least part of the pituitary), and the nervous innervation of the gland from the hypothalamus further indicate the possibilities of a close functional cooperation.

According to modern endocrinologists, the endocrines fulfill a three-fold function of communication, correlation, and catalysis which contribute to the mechanisms concerned in the preservation of an adequate internal milieu of the body, but are relatively slow-acting and chronic in effect. Hypothalamic structures, through their natural neural connections with the autonomic nervous system, innervating all smooth muscles and glands, regulate and integrate the internal milieu with greater speed and less lasting but more violent effect. It has been found that denervation of most endocrine glands, which also means removal of the central influences from the hypothalamus, produces no profound insufficiency. This signifies that although the rapid, often emergency effect of their activities is lost, their constant activities are preserved as long as the pituitary is intact. Parasympathetic posterior lobe and probably adrenal cortex functions are, however, dependent on an intact nerve supply.

Cushing (14) has long maintained that secretory products of the intermediate lobe of the pituitary, consisting of colloidal material, obtain entrance into the general systemic circulation through the third ventricle. Lately he has considered that the hormone exerts its effect directly on the cells of the hypothalamus. The colloidal bearing cells of the supra-optic and paraventricular nuclei suggest to some that these cells pick up the hypothetical ambulatory secretion of the hypophysis. Others maintain that these cells are in themselves secretory. No decisive evidence is available at present.

Diabetes insipidus is a clinical entity characterized by an excessive thirst and polyuria, often accompanied by emaciation. Damaging lesions of the posterior lobe of the hypophysis, such as are caused by neoplasms, result in this syndrome (20). Extracts of the posterior lobe compensate for the deficiency of a posterior lobe hormone. However, diffuse lesions of the hypothalamus in multiple sclerosis or encephalitis often produce the same syndrome. Extensive experimental work has shown that the supra-optic nucleus, its tract, and the posterior lobe constitute a neuroglandular unit which affects production of an antidiuretic hormone controlling the function of diuresis residing in the anterior lobe as part of its general control over metabolism. Lesions anywhere in the system permit uncompensated anterior lobe function to become excessive and result in polydypsia and polyuria. It is thus not surprising that many pathological processes involving either pituitary or hypothalamus give rise to diabetes insipidus as a symptom. It has been confused with psychogenic polydypsia, sometimes seen in the purification ritual of schizophrenics, but the organically derived thirst is relieved by pitressin.

From the posterior lobe extracts can be prepared which have a pressor and oxytocic effect. It is not clear that these represent hormones rather than pharmacological substances. There is some evidence that retinal fibers entering the supra-chiasmic nucleus, relayed to the pars media, are concerned in the production of skin pigmentation.

Other functions of the hypothalamus concerned with internal secretions are far less clear and have not been definitely separated from anterior lobe functions. The paraventricular nucleus has been implicated in the cause of *diabetes mellitus* and, according to Morgan, (62) atrophies in the disease in man. However, lesions of the lateral portion of the tuber cinereum like hypophysectomy prevent pancreatectomized dogs from having diabetes. Posterior hypothalamic stimulation assists in the mobilization of carbohydrate reserve through excitation of the adrenals, and damage of the paraventricular nucleus increases sensitivity to insulin. Others consider the ventromedian tuber nucleus to be concerned in control of liver, pancreas and adrenal cortex. This has all yet to be confirmed, and only indicates that the posterior hypothalamus may be concerned in the function of these glands, not only in their rapid excitation in response to emergencies but perhaps also in their constant level of activity. Basal skull fractures with injury to the base of the brain are often followed by temporary glycosuria. Operations in this region are associated with a transient glycosuria and parasellar neoplasms also cause deviations in carbohydrate metabolism. However, none of these clinical disturbances are of localizing value.

Adipositogenital dystrophy is a clinical syndrome frequently associated with parasellar tumors that involve both hypophysis and the tuber portion of the hypothalamus. Retardation of sexual development in the young and loss of function in the adult are not uncommonly associated with deposition of fat. It is not clear which portion of this syndrome comes from the gland or the neural tissue, or even that either is necessarily hypophyseal in origin. There is suggestive evidence that adiposity, uninfluenced by hormone administration, arises from lesions of the hypothalamic region and genital dystrophy as a disturbance of the pituitary influence on growth and of its specific gonadotropic hormone. In the rabbit, ovulation can be stimulated by hypothalamic stimulation, according to Harris (37). In the human, purely hypothalamic lesions have been associated with genital dystrophy in the male and amenorrhoea in the female, not influenced by administration of pituitary or gonadal extracts. On the other hand, pubertas praecox, induced by tumors of the pineal body, has been observed in hypothalamic lesions, so that this supposedly pathognomonic sign of pineal tumors may be the result of pressure forward, on the hypothalamus. Similarly, adiposity without hypophyseal lesions and unresponsive to the administration of anterior lobe extracts is known clinically. Hypophyseal cachexia, or Simmond's disease, originally ascribed to atrophy of the hypophysis, has been observed in tumors involving only the hypothalamus, the hypophysis being normal. Nonneoplastic hypothalamic lesions may cause the same disturbance of fat metabolism.

It is now certain that diabetes insipidus, or abnormal water metabolism, may be related to a disturbance of the hypothalamus. Furthermore, diabetes mellitus, involving an abnormality in carbohydrate metabolism, obesity, or emaciation as evidence of disordered fat metabolism, and disturbances in ovulation, menstruation, and sexual maturation, may be due in part or whole to lesions of the hypothalamus. Whether they are due to loss of a direct and specific control, or an indirect influence of the hypothalamus on the hypophysis, pancreas, adrenal cortex, or gonads is not yet known.

Central Regulative Functions

Since Claude Bernard indicated the importance of the maintenance of a stabilized internal milieu of an organism for its normal existence, the importance of the autonomic nervous system in that function has been recognized (12). Although the sensory and motor systems are concerned with relations of the individual to its external environment, they operate under the influence of the autonomic nervous system, serving to free the internal conditions of living from tensions created by external events and to attain those stimuli which enable internal tensions to be discharged. It is too often implied that autonomic functions are only concerned in adjustments to external happenings by increasing or decreasing internal activities or by emergency massive integrated discharges. They are also effective in directing the external discharge of tensions which are basically internal and instinctual, the energy of which we term "emotion."

Between the somatic and autonomic nervous systems there is an interdependence and reciprocal action so well described by Hess (40). This intimate cooperation occurs at all levels of the nervous system, for both divisions are ubiquitously represented, often approximated so closely that anatomic separation is difficult. The more highly developed the organism and the more complicated and evolved its somatic functions, the more the autonomic components of adjustment have attained encephalization and control. Thus in the higher animals the hypothalamus attains more the role of a superior central regulating organ of visceral function subordinating brain-stem, medullary, spinal and peripheral centers. It attains this complicated function in conjunction with an equally complicated and developed thalamus and thalamocortical relationship that accompanies behavior which is less automatic and reflex but more purposeful.

Not only does the hypothalamus integrate all visceral and autonomic activity, but it functions as a balancing mechanism between parasympathetic and orthosympathetic divisions. The parasympathetic system is associated with anabolism, lessening the efficiency of the sensorimotor system and operating in the interest of individual organs. It furnishes the brake upon activities, conserves resources and reserves, and builds up tensions. The orthosympathetic system lies exterior to the visceral organs and enhances the functions of the sensorimotor apparatus, increasing its functional output. It is concerned with catabolic activity in massively discharging internal tensions. The fine cooperation of these two divisions results in the balancing of effects and the maintenance of an integrated regulated internal milieu, within certain limits of stress. This is done by no strict antagonism in function, for specifically opposite effects of the two divisions have been demonstrated only in respect to their influence on bladder, gastrointestinal, arteriolar, and sudomotor tone. A more general inhibitory control, however, is manifested by the anterior parasympathetic centers upon posterior orthosympathetic mass activity.

Since the discovery of the hypothalamus as a visceral center, a multitude of separate functions have been ascribed to it. Excitation of this structure effects rise in blood pressure, arteriolar contraction, dilatation of the pupils, elevation of the hairs, increase in blood sugar and circulating adrenaline, dilatation of the bronchioles, increase in heart rate, contraction of bladder, uterus, and gastrointestinal tract (65), secretion of tears and saliva, regulation of body temperature, and sleep regulation. All these are in addition to the metabolic functions concerned in water, carbohydrate, and protein metabolism and control of growth and sexuality (44).

As Beattie (55) points out, so many functions associated with an anatomical structure of such small size makes it improbable that there are multiple discrete centers except those controlling antidiuretic, diabetogenic, and pigmentary hormones of the hypophysis. Rather, the hypothalamus as a unit contributes to widespread activities which can be categorized into a few groups. As a matter of fact, those who have carefully stimulated hypothalamic fields of microscopic size with the Horsley-Clark stereotaxic machine have found each hypothalamic function represented over a rather wide extent of structure.

If the hypothalamus is an autonomic center concerned with maintaining a constant internal environment, it probably has two general systems, each with their own afferent and efferent connections and acting reciprocally to each other. There is considerable evidence that these dual centers exist. The posterior hypothalamus is an orthosympathetic and the anterior a parasympathetic center (18).

Change in temperature has been used by Beattie (55) to exemplify the integrating role of the dual hypothalamic centers. Exposure to cold is associated with attempts at conservation of body heat and increased heat production. There results a peripheral vasoconstriction, rise in blood pressure, increased heart rate, apneustic respiration, and increased oxidation of carbohydrates. To increase heat production, shivering finally ensues. Stimulation of the posterior hypothalamus evokes contraction of peripheral arterioles, increase in blood pressure and blood sugar, and apneustic respiration (56). Urine secretion is increased, and the bladder and stomach walls relax. Destruction of the posterior hypothalamus causes a fall in body temperature and absence of shivering response. Thus conservation of body heat is an orthosympathetic posterior hypothalamic function, accomplished through an integration of a widespread activity of the autonomic system, influencing the functions of many organs in the direction of increased activity.

Increase in external heat results in measures to increase the loss of internal heat. The peripheral vessels dilate, warm sweat secretion is increased, the blood pressure falls, and the heart slows. This same activity results from stimulation of the anterior hypothalamus in the region of the septal and preoptic areas. This area is probably parasympathetic in function. Experiments have shown that stimulation can also effect contraction of the bladder wall (49) and fall in blood pressure.

Experimental lesions of the anterior hypothalamus result in hyperthermia, and of the posterior hypothalamus in hypothermia (72). Alpers published several cases in humans in which this localization was confirmed by anatomical studies. Tumors of the hypothalamus produce marked disturbances of temperature regulation. Hypothalamic inflammatory lesions, traumatic lesions of the base of the brain, and other human diseases confirm the presence of heat regulating centers (18). The most convincing evidence for localization of the dual thermostatic mechanism in man comes from surgical operations. Operations on the parasellar region, especially for exploration of gliomas of the optic chiasm, frequently result in a fatal hyperpyrexia accompanied by flushed dry skin and panting respiration. Operations through a suboccipital decompression, during which the brainstem is manipulated, disturb the posterior hypothalamus and result often in hypersomnolence, subnormal temperature and cold, cyanotic body surfaces.

Cushing (14) showed that most patients with craniopharyngiomas and compression of the pituitary stalk have an unaccountably low blood pressure. He injected pituitary substance and pilocarpine into the lateral ventricles of patients and observed marked flushing of the entire skin, excessive sweating, fall in rectal temperature, blood pressure, and basal metabolic rate, and increase in gastrointestinal activity, all evidence of excitation of parasympathetic structures which we now know to be located anteriorly in the hypothalamus. The entire attack could be abolished by atropine. Cushing's results of parasympathetic excitation on gastric function, i.e., increased peristalsis, pylorospasm, hypersecretion, retching and vomiting he considers to be the basis of gastric erosions and ulcers found at postmortem examination in patients with tumors of the third ventricle.

Epileptic attacks of a specific type, arising from irritation of the posterior hypothalamus, have been recognized since the publication of an oft-quoted case of Penfield (69). His patient had a ball-valve tumor of the third ventricle which periodically gave rise to severe seizures. They were initiated by a sensation of fever during which the body surfaces became flushed, respiration slow, and perspiration copious. Saliva and tears flowed profusely; the pupils enlarged and exophthalmos appeared. Hiccoughing and shivering were violent; the pulse varied in strength and rapidity. Penfield attributed these disturbances to excitation of the thalamus, wherein he postulated that the superior autonomic centers lay, but animal experimentation clearly indicates that the disturbance can be correlated with irritative lesions of the posterior, lateral hypothalamus. The syndrome is predominantly an *orthosympathetic epilepsy*. Morgan (62, 63) produced similar epileptic attacks in animals, abolished by denervating the adrenals, thyroid, and parathyroid glands, through which he concluded that the peripheral effect was mediated. Furthermore, in a few cases of epilepsy in humans he described degenerative changes in the hypothalamic tuber nuclei, which were, however, not convincing. *Parasympathetic epilepsy* has been observed in its pure form only in the experiments of Cushing described above.

Human disorders of the hypothalamus give little in the way of localizing value to a particular symptom in the epileptic syndromes due to irritation. Tumors of this region cause a variety of attacks accompanied by syncope, cyanosis, flushing, slowed or increased respiration, lowered or raised blood pressure and temperature, etc. In these attacks, fragments of para- and orthosympathetic responses are mixed, as would be expected from a large pressing mass. Occasionally in epidemic encephalitis fragmentary manifestations may occur involving but one function. Panting dyspneic attacks are not uncommon, nor are attacks of localized flushing and perspiration in the chronic encephalitics.

Ransom (71) and his co-workers, using the Horsley-Clark apparatus, stimulated the lateral portion of the posterior hypothalamus and caused struggling, biting, and clawing, with dilatation of pupils, increased respiration, elevation of hair, salivation, and sweating, along with inhibition of gastrointestinal activity. These evidences of massive sympathetic discharge are identical with those observed in normal animals in fright. They constitute an expression of intense emotion. In the experimental animals an increase in adrenin and sympathin was demonstrable in the blood stream (57).

Such massive discharges are seen only rarely in humans, and then not in their entirety. Certain cases of tumors of the third ventricle give rise to some of these manifestations accompanied by a feeling of apprehension. In chronic encephalitis one occasionally observes spontaneous manifestations of rage without appropriate external cause, in which the patient feels angry and shows the corresponding signs of massive discharge of the orthosympathetic system. From experimental and clinical evidence there seems to be little doubt that the integration of the economically vital peripheral processes in emotional expressions of rage or fear occurs centrally in the hypothalamus.

Concerning the physiology of sleep, much has been conjectured in relation to its central mediator. During the first epidemic of lethargic encephalitis in 1890, known as Nona, Mauthner (58) correlated the pathological sleep with lesions in the floor of the third ventricle. The subsequent epidemic of this century has served to confirm the clinical impression that the hypothalamus has much to do with the function of sleep.

According to Hess (40), sleep is a positive adjustment as a protection against exhaustion. It indicates a rejection of stimuli and inhibition of sensorimotor functions through autonomic influences. Kuppers (53) considered that a connecting link between cortex and peripheral nervous system disengaged in sleep and resumed connections on awakening. The cortex seems to be dominated by a regulative action of the autonomic system in the form of a protective reflex. It is obvious that the phenomenon of sleep is not the sole evidence of autonomic influence, for changes in blood pressure, heart rate, distribution of circulation, respiration, temperature, and smooth muscle tonus are universally present in sleep. The change in psychic activity parallels these peripheral alterations. The hypothalamus, in which a balance between parasympathetic and orthosympathetic control over internal activities is found, acts in modifying the functional preparedness of the sensorimotor cortex.

The exact localization of a sleep center has not been possible on clinical evidence (Fulton and Bailey, 27). Rowe (74) believed, on the basis of human cases, that the lesion which produced hypersomnolence may be in the medial thalamic nucleus or in the thalamico-perventricular-hypothalamico-mesencephalic chain of neurones.

Demole (16) was able to produce sleep by injection of calcium into the floor of the third ventricle. Ranson (71) was able to produce somnolence in experimental animals by placing a lesion in the posterior hypothalamus in the region of the mammillary bodies, at the transition between hypothalamus and midbrain, blocking the passage of impulses from the hypothalamus to caudad structures. Somnolence could be produced without damaging any sensory pathways to the cerebral cortex. The lesions were in those same areas which, when stimulated, produced signs of excitement. Ranson's (45) animals showed, in addition to hypersomnolence, falling asleep when undisturbed, blank mask-like facies, and cataleptic attitudes of the extremities. There was loss of motor initiative, disinclination to walk or eat, acceptance of passively induced poses, vacuity of expression, and suppression of emotional reactions. Somnolence is associated with fall in body temperature and metabolic rate (26). Human encephalitics with disturbances in sleep rhythm show marked lack of evidence of emotional expression, blank masked facies, and general akinesia. Studies now in progress by Grinker, Reich, and Kobrin indicate that psychologically these people are rather passive, optimistic and hopeful when their reality has been years of slow progression of symptoms. This serenity is only occasionally broken into by a sudden unprovoked rage attack.

There is some doubt whether a sleep center exists in the hypothalamus or in any basal structure. Somnolence results from destruction of the area, stimulation of which causes emotional excitement. Stimulation experiments by Hess may have been accompanied by small electrolytic lesions (24). Yet in humans, sleepiness was evoked by stimulation of the exposed posterior hypothalamus at operation (28). Although the problem is far from solved, most of the evidence suggests that the hypothalamus functions in an excitatory role, increasing states of activity; that inactivity and sleep are negative phases which arise through inhibition of the hypothalamus, possibly from the cerebral cortex.

Natural experiments in humans produced by disease processes are of little localizing value for physiological conclusions except in rare, sharply localized tumors or softenings. Therefore in human cases in which the hypothalamus is involved, knowledge of exact experimentation must be drawn upon, which is methodically valid except when the higher qualities of emotion are considered. Trauma, operative manipulation, tumors, vascular lesions, and infections are etiological factors which produce an intricate combination of disturbances of hypothalamic functions. Fulton (24) considers that there are five main clinical syndromes in man, arising from the hypothalamus: (a) hyperthermia from anterior lesions; (b) diabetes insipidus and emaciation from anterior lesions; (c) adipositogenital dystrophy from lesions of the middle portion; (d) hypersomnia and hypothermia from the posterior portion; (e) epileptic autonomic discharges: parasympathetic from anterior irritation, orthosympathetic from posterior irritation. There are, however, miscellaneous combinations of these, isolated disturbances of sleep and tone as in narcolepsy, respiratory disturbances as in encephalitis, as well as disorders of sweat secretion. The great variety of syndromes due to organic lesions of the hypothalamus indicates the possibilities of bizarre and complicated functional or psychogenic disturbances utilizing the same anatomical mechanisms.

Cortical Influences on the Hypothalamus

Cannon's (11) studies on the homeostatic functions of the autonomic nervous system extended to its participation in emotional reactions or expressions. He concluded that emotion was not a central reverberation of peripheral autonomic changes, as the James-Lange (54) theory postulated, but that the visceral manifestations were secondary to a function of a central nucleus which effected purposeful peripheral changes (11). His analysis of the economic role of the autonomic nervous system in the body's reaction to anger or fear are summarized by Kempf (51) as follows:

Any form of potentially harmful stimulus, whether it stimulates the visual, auditory, olfactory, gustatory, cutaneous, or the entero- or prioprio-receptor fields, tends to cause a more or less vigorous fear or avertive reaction which is promptly followed by a compensatory reaction which either removes the painful stimulus from the receptor (fight) or the receptor from the painful stimulus (flight). In order that this vitally necessary procedure shall be quickly and safely accomplished, the autonomic apparatus has developed the capacity to compensate by increasing the amount of glycogen and adrenin in the blood, by increasing coagulability of the blood, by regulating the blood supply so that the organs necessary for the immediate struggle shall be given an increase of blood supply, by appropriately changing the blood pressure, by increasing the rate and amplitude of the heart beat, increasing the dilatation of the bronchioles and the working powers of the muscle cells.

Bard (7) was able to show conclusively that this central autonomic center resided in the hypothalamus. Removing the brain above the hypothalamus produced a struggling, lashing, clawing, snarling animal showing signs of massive orthosympathetic discharge. These were dilatation of the pupils, rise in blood pressure, increased heart rate, sweating, elevation of hairs, etc. These reactions constituted a "sham rage," since no consciousness of the emotion was possible. The intensity of the reactions decreased if the animals were not restrained, but then they were markedly restless. Removal of the hypothalamus abolished these responses. Furthermore Ranson (71) stimulated the lateral posterior hypothalamus in the intact animal and evoked identical sham-rage reactions. Thus there is little doubt that the hypothalamus is the essential central organ for integration of emotional expression.

Bard's experiments (6) also clearly indicate that the hypothalamus is normally inhibited by the cerebral cortex. The possible anatomical mechanisms for such inhibitory influences are (a) from the gyrus cinguli through the anterior medial thalamic nuclei to the hypothalamus, (b) from the hippocampus by way of the fornix to the mammillary bodies, and (c) from hypothecated direct fronto-hypothalamic tracts.

The hypothalamus is not the only center for autonomic activity, nor is it the most cephalad. At each level of the nervous system such centers exist, i.e., spinal, bulbar, pontine, etc. The hypothalamus re-represents visceral activity in more special, highly organized combinations. Its orthosympathetic areas control and integrate all visceral activity, its parasympathetic areas are more highly specialized and discrete.

However, autonomic representation exists in the cerebral cortex both of the parasympathetic and orthosympathetic type. Stimulation of the cerebral cortex evokes alterations in the cardiovascular system, body temperature, sweating, pilomotor system, intrinsic ocular muscles, gastrointestinal system, and bladder. These visceral reactions are elicited from the neighborhood of related somatic motor centers indicating an overlap of cortical autonomic and somatic representation. An overlap in the sensory field has also been postulated. As a result of such overlap, specific movements arising from the cortex are accompanied by simultaneous specific changes in blood supply, sweat secretion, etc., which apparently facilitate and increase the efficiency of the movement desired. These cortical functions are mediated partly through the hypothalamus, but also independent of it through extrapyramidal and possibly pyramidal motor fibers.

This overlap is lucidly described by Fulton (24) as follows:

The autonomic division of the nervous system can no longer be regarded as a purely peripheral system, but rather as an elaborately organized division of the central nervous system with representation at all levels. At each level, moreover, the somatic and autonomic systems dovetail with one another, and while the somatic may predominate in a given region—and thus obscure the autonomic component—it is generally impossible to evoke a somatic reflex that does not have an autonomic concomitant of central origin. . . . When, therefore, the intact picture is conjured up of two great interlacing systems —which share some receptors in common but which have others that are specific—and which discharge together in a synergenic manner that makes for unification of reaction in the organism as a whole.

Although hypothalamic activity integrates all autonomic functions, it includes but few somatic responses. Panting, shivering, running movements, and clawing are the extent of somatic responses from direct excitation of the hypothalamus. Cortical autonomic responses are all in association with a corresponding somatic innervation. It seems likely that the hypothalamus in its most vigorous activity utilizes the somatic system to facilitate its release of tensions in the service of instinctual reactions; the cortex utilizes specific autonomic functions in the economy of volitional or "least automatic" movements. In this cooperation of synergism, the close association of somatic and autonomic activity further indicates how their separation is impossible, for, as we shall see later, the cortex driven by the autonomic system in turn uses autonomic activities to further cortical responses, yet inhibiting their excessiveness.

The peripheral fine and coordinated movements arising from stimulation of the motor cortex are possible only if the cruder, more massive movements of the older motor system are inhibited and postural tonus is relaxed. Encephalization of function thus is accompanied by inhibition of lower, more massive reflex responses of the extrapyramidal systems. So, too, finely adaptive visceral changes accompanying cortical responses are possible only by inhibition of cruder hypothalamic massive visceral responses. We can compare the relation of the hypothalamus to cortical autonomic centers as the extrapyramidal motor system to cortical motor areas. Removal of the latter results in overactivity of the previously inhibited extrapyramidal system. Removal of the cortical autonomic centers results in overactivity of hypothalamic functions.

Thus we see that the cortex damps down hypothalamic responses and permits its activity upon appropriate occasions, and then in graded and modulated fashion. Were this not the case, stimuli of all sorts would evoke rage and flight reactions incapable of restriction. However, instead of such reflex behavior, the normal adult is able to develop a more adaptive response.

Clinical cases showing evidence of release of hypothalamic function from cortical control are rare. Tumors and infections have been observed, associated with wild, grotesquely violent behavior possibly due to interruption of the corticohypothalamic inhibitory fibers. Chronic encephalitis in children often produces rage-like states, and in some of the organic psychoses release of hypothalamic mechanisms is suggested. Yet in no case has it been demonstrated that the specific pathway was anatomically interrupted, so that our conclusions are all by analogy to animal experiments. Yet the significance of normal cortical inhibition of the hypothalamus in the intact human being is of great importance to our theoretical concepts concerning abnormal emotional expressions.

In the hypothalamus there are neural patterns responsible for emotional expressions and behavior which are normally inhibited by the cortex, and it is in the cortex that feelings of emotions are evoked. Both activities exist in the normal person in cooperation. The better conditioned a stimulus, the less direct emotional expression it elicits, whereas strange or sudden, unconditioned stimuli produce a more direct and violent reaction.

Hypothalamic Influences on the Central Cortex

Experiments concerned with hypothalamic release from cortical control furthered our knowledge of that structure as an organ for emotional expression. Animal experimentation has also served well to show the function of the hypothalamus in autonomic and endocrine regulation. However, its function in influencing the cortex, as expressed in direction of thought and conscious feelings, can be determined only in man. With this in mind, Grinker (32), experimenting on cats, was able to show that excitation of the hypothalamus could be produced by electrical shocks passed through the underlying bone in an intact animal. He was also able to show that typical action currents could be obtained from the hypothalamus through the bone, and since cortical action currents had already been well studied with the so-called electroencephalograph through the intact skull, a valuable method was at hand for studying corticohypothalamic relations in man.

The next step consisted in constructing an electrode which was suitable for experiments on man. This and the technique of its use have been reported by Grinker and Serota (33) and recently confirmed by Hoagland et al. (41a). It will be briefly described here, since it is hoped that others will use it to answer many important problems which require human experimentation.

The hypothalamic lead for the human consists of a sharply tipped steel drill rod about 3 mm. in diameter and 16 cm. long, with a slight upward concavity at its terminal third. It is insulated with celluloid and Duco-cement except at its tip, which for 2 mm. is heavily silver-plated. The other end is arranged for the attachment of fine wire to an electroencephalograph or stimulating inductorium. The details of the electrical connections will be dispensed with here as they are typical of any electroencephalographic arrangement.

The human hypothalamus lies above or just behind the sphenoidal air sinus which ends posteriorly at a point about the middle of the floor of the sella turcica. The hypothalamus is closest to the base of the skull, just back of the sinus and over the sella. Between it and the bone are dura, subarachnoid space, and hypophysis. The nasal mucous membranes of one nostril are cocainized with the patient in a sitting position. The lead is then slowly passed through the nasal passage, and on reaching the posterior pharyngeal wall it is tipped upward to engage the pharyngeal mucosa at the junction of the roof of the vault and the posterior wall. The needle tip is then firmly pushed through the mucous membrane, mucosa, and periosteum into the sphenoidal bone. As it engages, a crunching sound is heard, and the electrode becomes firmly embedded. A momentary pain is felt on insertion, but this passes off at once and patients are comfortable and able to speak, swallow, and walk about unhampered. Removal of the lead is simply accomplished by a sudden jerk and no antiseptic is necessary. No infections have been observed. The lead in position may be used for either stimulation, registration of action currents, or alternation of both purposes by means of a simple switching apparatus.

In both cat and man the typical cortical alpha wave appears 10 per second and about 50 to 70 microvolts in amplitude. Hypothalamic waves appeared in a much slower rhythm, only 4 to 5 per second, and were about 75 per cent of the amplitude of the cortical waves. Superimposed on these were minor, tiny, 13-per-second waves. Into the normal resting hypothalamus cortical rhythm often permeated resulting in an alpha type of wave which was less regular, lower in amplitude, and often receding and recurring. Destruction of the tissue to the point of extinction of the hypothalamic waves allowed the cortical alphas to become clear, frequent, and of usual amplitude in the hypothalamic lead. Cortical rhythm thus enters into the normal resting hypothalamus but dominates it only when the hypothalamus is injured. The resting human hypothalamic pattern seems to be more individual to a given person than his cortical pattern, and it may represent a valuable constitutional characteristic. On the other hand it may be a correlate of his psychological phenotype, and hence partially alterable. This is a problem worthy of study.

Stimulation through the hypothalamic lead in man produced the well-known general visceral effects on blood pressure, respiration, pupils, heart rate, sweating, vasomotor tone, bladder, and body temperature. Each of these functions may be studied further through this mode of stimulation with the use of appropriate measuring instruments, i.e., electrocardiograph, gastroscope, cystoscope, capillaroscope, etc. Additional evidences of excitatory effects were clinically observed in the emotional reactions of the patients. Frequently they showed profound anxiety. In one, protracted uncontrollable sobbing occurred, another felt his life pass before his eyes, another felt the end of the world approaching. These subjective reactions require further detailed study. In no patients were emotional expressions of anger noted; all responded with fear. Stronger currents elicited tonic and sometimes clonic movements of the extremities, comparable to the running or clawing movements of Ranson's cats.

The objective result of stimulation of the hypothalamus was excitation. The effect on the hypothalamus itself was a marked increase in fast waves and disappearance of the cortical alpha rhythm. The typical 4-per-second waves became irregular and often doubled in amplitude. A new type of wave, consisting of coarse undulations, 70 per minute, and of only 30 microvolts in amplitude, appeared. Giant waves interrupted the rhythm for several seconds at a time. After strong stimulation, the hypothalamic rhythm—this was true in the cat also—synchronized with that of the cortex. The late effects of stimulation on the hypothalamus itself were striking. The 70-per-second rhythm receded and reappeared. The giant waves often disappeared and were replaced by a modified 10-per-second alpha rhythm, interspersed by large round slow waves at 2 per second. These faded and returned; also large spikes and cusps appeared for one or two seconds to disappear again in a quiescent phase. An occasional train of fast waves also appeared. Thus after the initial excitation, short recurrent irregular waves of heightened hypothalamic activity reappeared.

The cortical objective responses to hypothalamic stimulation were equally striking. Large rounded waves, 100 to 150 microvolts in amplitude, appearing once in 2 or 3 seconds, were seen. These appeared sporadically for several minutes after cessation of the stimulation. Large wavy undulations appeared in the curve, gradually becoming lost after several minutes. Spikes of 100 or more microvolts, appearing 4 per second in the characteristic hypothalamic rate, often appeared in phase with large rounded waves in the hypothalamus in bursts lasting 4 to 5 minutes after stimulation. After stronger and longer stimulation, large series of giant round waves appeared in an identical form to hypothalamic waves of excitation, and in synchrony with bursts in that region. Alpha waves were slowed to 5 per second, and often intensified to as much as 400 per cent. Giant waves as high as 250 microvolts appeared in groups and isolated, often erupting as a late effect in the midst of a normal alpha rhythm.

Drugs which act upon the central autonomic nervous system were injected into animals and simultaneous action currents from the hypothalamus and cortex recorded. Their effects may be briefly described, only to show that a pharmacological effect on the hypothalamus secondarily influences the cortex similarly to electrical stimulation.

Adrenaline produced a strong excitatory effect on the hypothalamus, accompanied by a vigorous cortical response in the same direction, similar to strong electrical stimulation because synchrony with preponderance of the hypothalamic pattern was observed. Eserine produced a transient excitatory effect on the hypothalamus with a much more prolonged effect on the cortex, which is of interest in view of its capacity to inactivate choline esterase which destroys the parasympathetic hormone, acetylcholine. Metrazol evoked a rapidly passing excitation of the hypothalamus. Each of these drugs caused a hypothalamic excitation and influenced the cortex in the same direction. Thus the cortical effects from hypothalamic electrical stimulation are probably the result of excitation of the orthosympathetic centers in the hypothalamus.

Ergotamine resulted in a hypothalamic excitation, but inhibition of the cortical currents. This drug is an orthosympathetic paralysant, and thus its effects on hypothalamus probably liberated parasympathetic responses. Nembutal caused a slowing of both hypothalamic and cortical action currents, which is interesting in view of the now widely accepted idea that barbiturates exert their hypnotic effect by primarily quieting the orthosympathetic centers in the hypothalamus. Pilocarpine caused a marked paralysis of both hypothalamic and cortical responses, accompanied by signs of parasympathetic stimulation in pupillary constriction, sweating, and salivation. Its effects on the parasympathetic centers of the hypothalamus were opposite in direction to orthosympathetic excitation, slowing and decreasing cortical activity.

Parasympathetic excitants and orthosympathetic paralysants show a reversal of changes to those exhibited by electrical stimulation. Thus pharmacological experiments clearly indicate the antagonistic effect of the two divisions of the central autonomic centers in the hypothalamus on cortical activity.

Our next experiments were concerned with biological stimulations while hypothalamic and cortical currents were registered. Strongly emotionally-laden ideational stimuli were used. A patient with large amounts of free-floating anxiety loosely related to masturbation was told of the bad results which might accrue from the habit. The resulting hypothalamic and cortical excitation was similar to that described from electrical stimulation. The late recurring bursts of increased activity and the coarse disintegrated appearance of the curve were also noted, as well as irregularly appearing synchrony in the two leads.

Since these experiments are at present the only available objective evidences of the effect of hypothalamus on cortical activity, they may be discussed briefly. The combined results from electrical and pharmacological effects indicate that the hypothalamus excites cortical activity through its orthosympathetic centers. The apparent mass effect of electrical current through the bone eventuates in orthosympathetic predominance. This has been found true in animal experiments; orthosympathetic responses tend to overweigh those of the parasympathetic type. This excitatory effect on the cortex, in our experiments, is identical to the excitatory effect of emotionally-laden verbal stimuli. Finally, the effect of such electrical, pharmacological, and biological stimuli are homologous to the general excitatory effect that stimulation of the lateral hypothalamus has on peripheral organs of emotional expression, and orthosympathetic paralysants through the hypothalamus elicit cortical responses similar to destructive lesions of the posterior hypothalamus.

The resting hypothalamus has a typical pattern in which cortical elements enter weakly. After weaker currents, both hypothalamus and cortex are excited. Stronger currents elicit a synchronization of cortex and hypothalamus in which the pattern of the latter is dominant. When a certain excitation is reached, a mass activity of cortex probably results, homologous clinically probably to impulsive unconscious actions such as flight, impulsive suicide, or "blind" attacks of rage. Cortical dominance is lost, and hypothalamic "mania" dominates the picture. Certainly our results objectively indicate the assumption that emotions influence intellectual processes through the mechanism of hypothalamus driving the cortex.

The repeated long-prolonged bursts of excitation in hypothalamus and cortex indicate that the hypothalamus does not always discharge at once, but acts as a reservoir, exerting a chronic effect on periphery and centrum. Emotional stimuli given once caused the same prolonged discharges which gradually became feebler. Clinically, this phenomenon is homologous with the recurrent "popping up" of unpleasant ideas which the subject attempts to suppress.

There are many problems which can be attacked by this method. Is the functional hypothalamic pattern alterable by means of deep psychological analysis, or is it a fixed constitutional factor? The specific differences in the pattern in certain personality types, in various moods and in diverse mental and emotional disturbances should be determined. Furthermore, stimulation of the hypothalamus in the human has a therapeutic possibility in depressions, stupors, and perhaps in schizophrenia. Stimulation of the hypothalamus directly should influence the autonomic functions which are only indirectly influenced by metrazol and insulin. With the same idea in mind, Cerletti and Bini (13) treat schizophrenics by means of convulsions produced with electric shocks, which, however, are generalized and not in the form of specific induction shocks to the hypothalamus. They report results as good as those obtained from pharmacological shock.

Hypothalamus in Mental Disturbances

Clinical disturbances of the hypothalamus due to tumors of the parasellar region pressing on the base of the third ventricle have been reported in abundance (36). Bailey and Murray (5) studied a 15-year-old boy with a pinealoma who had symptoms of an obsessional neurosis for which he was treated. The patient had a compulsion for drinking water which, unlike diabetes insipidus, was not relieved by the administration of pituitary hormone but was improved by incarceration of his father in a reformatory. Psychological study of the case clearly indicated the dynamic mechanisms, and yet at necropsy the neoplasm had involved the hypothalamus. Schilder (75a) indicated that some compulsive neuroses have an organic foundation in chronic encephalitis which we know has a predilection for the diencephalon.

Gagel (28) pointed out that emotional changes were the most constant symptoms of hypothalamic disturbances due to tumors. These symptoms were either in the nature of euphoria or mania (75). Foerster and Gagel (21) reported one case, and since then Foerster has had several cases on whom electrical stimulation of the exposed human hypothalamus was performed at operation. The result of stimulation of the anterior hypothalamus was restlessness, excitement, euphoria, and mania which could be elicited from stimulation of no other locus. Stimulation of the mesencephalon and posterior hypothalamus produced sleepiness and unconsciousness. These authors believe that cortical functions are influenced by the hypothalamus, in that they are excited and stimulated from the oral part and inhibited from the posterior portion.

In the literature there are many cases of euphoria, mania, and mental excitation from supra-sellar neoplasms arising from epithelial cysts of Rathke's pouch (8, 78, 66). Fulton and Bailey, (27) in their reports of psychomotor excitation and mania from tumors of the third ventricle, go so far as to deny any psychogenic bases for these symptoms. The maniacal delirious state in Korsakoff's syndrome has also been correlated with lesions around the third ventricle (61). Cases of maniacal excitement in encephalitis of childhood are associated with hypothalamic lesions. Bender (10) made anatomical studies of alcoholics with disturbances of consciousness and felt that in the region of the third ventricle there were centers concerned with awareness. Neurosurgeons have come to the conclusion that the anterior part of the diencephalon is somewhat related to depth of consciousness. Manipulation of this region often results in loss of consciousness with hyperpyrexia. Grotjahn and French (34a) report seven patients with lesions of the hypothalamus who developed severe akinesia and showed evidences of dissociation between the cognitive and volitional aspects of the ego's synthetic activity.

Alpers (3) reported three cases of disorders of personality, one due to a verified tumor in the third ventricle. Megalomania, disorientation, irritability, facetiousness, and argumentativeness were characteristic. In another case, long-standing disorientation was described; in another, excitement, hallucinations, and combativeness were responsible for the erroneous diagnosis of manic-depressive psychosis. Horrax and Yaskis (42) report manic-depressive symptoms relieved by removal of an intradural cholesteatoma.

Gagel (28) summarized the hypothalamic syndrome as follows: The patients are coarse, and they show a loss of inhibitions and lack of niceness in behavior and of ordinary social courtesies. Many patients are irritable and hypersensitive and show loss of judgment. They have attacks of rage and swings of mood. Memory changes and quantitative reduction in intelligence appear late.

In the so-called endogenous, manic-depressive psychosis, an affective disturbance exists which is identical with variations of mood described as the result of hypothalamic lesions. Patients are slowed, retarded, depressed with difficulties in thought, attention, etc., or they are gay, euphoric, or maniacal with great psychomotor excitement. The primary disturbance involves the direction and extent of the mood, yet the effect on thinking is obvious, indicating, as the natural experiments of disease and the animal and human experiments previously described, the great effect of hypothalamic activity on cortical functioning. The absence of an organic disturbance demonstrable by our present technical means, and the complete reversibility of the effect, indicate a functional disturbance which, in producing the same symptoms as organic lesions or experimental excitation, probably utilizes the same anatomical mechanisms.

Morgan (62, 64) studied the diencephalic regions in certain cases of dementia and psychoses and found degenerative changes and reduction of volume in the substantia grisea of the third ventricle. There was no difference as to the site of the lesions in excited or deteriorated cases. This work requires rechecking. Fünfgeld, studying the neuropathology of schizophrenia, found changes of significance in the hypothalamus, and according to him and Kleist, personality is a function derived from activity of the diencephalon, truly a neurologizing of psychology.

Ingham (43) clearly summarizes the general impression of localization of consciousness in the hypothalamus:

The neurologic concept of consciousness is that it is a state of activity of the entire nervous system, and in particular of the brain, which varies quantitatively from the maximum degree of mental action to complete inactivity, as in coma or general surgical anesthesia. Although all parts of the brain may contribute to the mental processes during consciousness, mental activity of all kinds appears to depend on the normal functioning of groups of neurons in the primitive diencephalon. The normal cycles of sleeping and waking are evidences of the physiologic activity of this mechanism. As it would appear that energy liberated in the diencephalon is essential for the activation of all the rest of the nervous system so far as psychologic phenomena are concerned, it may be postulated that the "center" of consciousness is located in this region, and much clinical and experimental evidence supports this view. It is surely not accidental that other primitive functions of the nervous system related to the vegetative processes, instincts, and emotions have been found to be dependent on structures in the basal region of the brain in close proximity to those postulated as the center of consciousness. The application of this concept of consciousness to psychiatry seems obvious, since quantitative variations of consciousness are manifested in disturbances of behavior in terms of intelligence, emotions, and instinctive action.

Jelliffe (46, 48) stated that the disease epidemic encephalitis created a new orientation toward the mental and emotional life of man by indicating the close relationship between disturbances of the autonomic nervous system and behavior reactions, sleep disturbances, and rage attacks. Jelliffe (47) pointed out the similarity between epidemic encephalitis and schizophrenia. In a chronic encephalitis there are all gradations of affective reactions including placid optimistic states, trance-like phases, tetanoid, epileptoid, narcoleptic, cataleptic, catatonic, and stuporous states. In the chronic stage of encephalitis all combinations of disturbances of hypothalamic function are observed, including alterations in metabolism, autonomic regulation, degree of awareness or depth of consciousness and in emotional states. Unfortunately these effects are never pure, and the morphological alterations are not limited to the hypothalamus, so that anatomicophysiological correlations cannot be made. Yet these symptoms have indicated clearly how the hypothalamus in man is so vitally concerned in feeling attitudes and in what Head (38) has termed "vigilance."

Grinker (31), discussing the relation of cortex to hypothalamus in the production of human symptomatology, stated:

It is not impossible that either anatomical or functional (cytochemical, etc.) lesions of the hypothalamus or its connections with the cortex may cause complete or partial release of cortical (ideational) control of the emotional content of higher activities. The dominant external activity would then be, not a slow adaptive response produced by a process of long-circuiting, but a less deliberate (impulsive) response with accompanying visceromotor correlates of emotional reactions.

There is, however, equal evidence for the assumption that clinical symptoms referable to the hypothalamus are due to excitation rather than to release of its control by the cortex. The mechanisms involved in release must be more significant in the causation of hypothalamic overactivity of psychologic origin in the psychoneuroses.

A relationship of disturbances of the central autonomic nervous system to schizophrenia has for long been suggested by many observers. The central autonomic nervous system, regulating and integrating the quantitative output and direction of flow of energy and the forcefulness of a person's active adjustment, is probably concerned with the production of mental disturbances. True schizophrenia is to Singer (77) due to a structural lesion of the autonomic nervous system. His co-worker, Gellhorn (29), believes that the physiologic beneficial effects of hypoglycemia and metrazol are achieved by stimulation of the autonomic centers which function deficiently in these patients.

Many workers have carefully studied visceral functions in schizophrenia. The literature contains numerous reports indicating a relatively mild deficiency of basal metabolism, oxygen consumption, hypoplasia of smooth muscle, and many visceral activities suggesting a deficiency of the function of the autonomic nervous system in schizophrenia. However, there are many conflicting observations, as the negative studies of Freeman and Carmichael (22) indicate. Finkelman (19) most recently reported a low heat production in response to cold, and a poorly maintained heat production with no reactive hyperemia in schizophrenics, which he thought might be due to a hypothalamic disturbance. In schizophrenia, deficiencies in the autonomic nervous system are less under basal states, or conditions of ordinary maintenance, than under *stress,* during which normal reactive processes fail.

The biological data resulting from studies of schizophrenics suggest strongly a deficiency in some central autonomic coordinating process, mirrored clinically in defective homeostasis. There is also evidence from the psychological side that schizophrenics are incapable of adequately solving, with their psychosomatic constitution, the problems of frustration and separation that the bare act of living within a restricting society creates. Their visceral cravings or instinctual demands are of such strength that inhibitions are overridden, compromise rejected, and autonomic drives overwhelm the cortex, destroying ego functions. The strong urge to cling to the all-protective embracing mother, and the marked rage evoked at separation, are far beyond that seen in any normal person. The strong wish to return to the womb where existence requires no autonomic adjustments is dominant.

The difficulty that the schizophrenic has in relieving his tensions partially or symbolically in adaptation increases to a point where cortical inhibitions, conditioned by the adaptation-demanding reality fail, and hypothalamic activity forces itself into direct expression. The results are violent emotional outbreaks or, physiologically speaking, cortical activity under direct control by the hypothalamus. In this connection it is interesting to note that when emotional activity or hypothalamic excitation reached a certain height in our experiments, cortical activity, as indicated in the electrogram, became coarse, irregular, and of the hypothalamic pattern. In this phase the cortical curves resemble the disorganized curves found in clinical schizophrenia with excitement and overactivity.

Other types of schizophrenia show, during basal conditions, coldness of the extremities, slowed respiration, low blood pressure, and decreased metabolic rate indicating defective homeostasis at *rest*. We may postulate that in them the visceral tensions are decreased and the driving power of the hypothalamus is reduced to the point where cortical activity is not maintained. We may postulate that these patients range from the schizophrenic stupors to the dull, so-called deteriorated types, and in them the brain waves resemble those found in organic disease of the cortex. Regression has extended to a much lower level.

The above considerations concerning the role of the hypothalamus in mental disturbances are for the most part speculative. The positive facts are that stimulation of the hypothalamus produces excitement, restlessness and mania, and an increased activity of the cortex; destructive lesions produce the opposite effect. These variations of effect are probably homologous to excitation of what in the normal individual functions as a center of awareness, the inhibition of which results in sleep. Pathological variations in its activity result in mania, on the one hand, and stupor on the other. Functional or constitutional disturbances of such an anatomical hypothalamic-cortical mechanism are possible explanations of psychogenic variations in mood and alterations of cortical activity found in the so-called functional psychoses.

Psychosomatic Implications

In the early days of psychoanalysis, interest in conversion phenomena was mainly directed to hysterical paralyses, anesthesias, and pains. The "mysterious leap from psyche to soma" that attracted most attention were alterations of function in structures innervated by the voluntary nervous system. However, gradually interest veered to symptoms which were produced by disturbances in the autonomic nervous system, and it was then not long before psychiatrists turned full attention to what Freud, in the last decade, termed the "future of medicine." At the present date psychoanalysts are busy studying the psychogenesis of peptic ulcer, mucous colitis, spastic bowel, hypertension, bronchial asthma, diabetes mellitus, eczema, arthritis, migraine, and a host of other conditions hitherto segregated from psychiatric interest because of their supposedly organic causation.

It was Alkan (2) who first clearly stated that organic disease may be profitably studied by psychological methods. He indicated that psychogenic disturbances within the field of the autonomic nervous system may result finally in organic changes, the morphological mechanisms of which form only the last link of an intricate causal chain. He postulated that intrapsychic conflicts may be expressed by spasms of smooth muscle which secondarily lead to anemia of an organ, stasis, muscular hypertrophy, or infection. As a result of these secondary factors, organic changes result in the visceral tissues or somatic structures, which of themselves, as terminal events, are irreversible and constitute the so-called organic disease.

Independently, Alexander (1) was convinced of the psychogenesis of, at first, gastrointestinal disorders, later, respiratory and vasomotor disturbances, through his psychoanalytic researches. He believes that organic changes are the last link in a complicated function chain of events, the basic etiological factors of which are psychological conflicts. His analyses led to more detailed statements concerning the specific emotion on which the organ neuroses are based. This accomplishment depended upon a general methodological principle entirely different from the vague application of the never fully accepted Freudian death instinct. By the latter method, as applied by Menninger (59), who fully expressed his thesis in the title of his book, *Man Against Himself,* organic disease is but a manifestation of self, or internally directed aggression or death instinct, which results in focal or partial self-destruction. Thus, to Menninger, the organ disturbed, or the mechanism of its disturbance, represents symbolically the repressed emotionally-laden idea.

Alexander, however, states that no disturbance of innervation of an organ could symbolically express a specific fantasy or a repressed idea. On the other hand, an organ's specific function could be used to express a tendency or psychic direction which by a process of conflict could not normally be expressed through the voluntary nervous system and its organs of expression. Analyzing the psychological vectors it was possible to show that:

Physiologically, the process of life can well be described in terms of the three major functions of *in-taking* of substance and energy from the environment, partially *retaining* it during the process of growth, and *elimination* —elimination of the end-products of products of metabolism, elimination of substance for the purpose of propagation, and the constant production of thermic and mechanical energy. It would not be surprising at all if it should turn out that the most elementary psychologic tendencies of the individual correspond to these three biologic phases of life, and that psychologic dynamics . . . correspond to the biologic dynamics of life.

Why certain individuals choose a specific physiological solution for their conflicts is the unsolved field of the "choice of the neurosis," and Alexander assumes the answer probably lies in some unknown organic factors which, in cooperation with psychic factors, leads to the organ neurosis. The organ neurosis is then, primarily, the abnormal use or innervation of an organ in an expression of a repressed tendency, thus disturbing its function. The disease is the end-result of the abnormal function.

Dunbar (17) collected a wealth of data regarding psychosomatic interrelations, and clearly indicated the extent of the field and the possibilities of further study. Her analysis showed the importance of a more complete understanding of the position of the autonomic nervous system and its regulative centers in the effector role of emotional expression in normal and conflictual situations. According to Grinker (34), in order to understand the role of the autonomic system in the so-called functional disturbances in which regressive infantile modes of emotional expression are utilized, the processes of evolution and so-called normal development must first be understood.

Hughlings Jackson (79) considered that the nervous system was developed gradually into an hierarchy in which several definite levels could be discovered. His main interest was with the anatomico-physiological scheme of the somatic nervous system which, however, is equally valid for the autonomic nervous system. Jackson's centers or levels of evolution consist of (a) the lower motor centers in spinal cord, medulla, and pons; (b) the middle level or motor and sensory cortical regions, and (c) the highest motor (prefrontal) and sensory (occipito-parieto-temporal areas of Wernicke's zone) centers of the cortex. The higher the level, the more indirectly it represented the body and the more complex and numerous it could effect combination of the parts which it represented.

This evolutionary principle of gradually developing levels is concomitant with the principles of encephalization, according to which functions wander toward the head end or higher levels of the organism, newer functions are attributes of newer more cephalic developed structures, and older more primitive functions of lower centers are inhibited by dominance of cephalic segments over caudal centers. In this way most functions are represented at all levels, some are specific to certain levels, but all are dovetailed by higher dominance to effect smooth-working function. When higher centers are damaged or disturbed, lower centers act alone and uninhibited, and their excessiveness furnishes the positive aspects of disturbed function, while the negative aspect is only the loss of function exclusively resident in the disturbed tissue.

According to Fulton (25) :

Newer disclosures concerning the relation of the cerebral cortex to the autonomic system give an adequate physiological basis for the relationship long recognized between mental states and visceral processes. To be a little more specific, it is clear that one now has adequate reason for believing that the load which is placed upon the heart and circulation may be determined in large measure by the mental status of the individual, and be thus quite independent of the more obvious factors of overexercise and exertion. The heart and circulation may be worked just as hard, and just as much as a detriment to the body as a whole, from the swivel chair as from a rower's seat. Many disturbances of gastrointestinal functions undoubtedly have a similar basis, and one might add that instead of referring to them as "psychogenic disturbances" one may more appropriately designate them as purely physiological aberration and explicable in terms of recognized physiological mechanisms. The more precise analysis of these psychosomatic relationships will come from the study of man, and hence can only come through active collaboration between clinician and physiologist.

Fulton's thesis postulates that positive mental and emotional states, concomitant with activity of cerebral cortex, are accompanied by visceral changes also arising from cortical excitation. According to this theory the visceral changes are secondary to the mental state or neurosis, but most of our psychological data suggest that the visceral activity indicates a concomitant psychological vector and that the neurosis is both the mental and visceral change. They cannot be separated and neither is cause nor effect; at least such is our concept in psychosomatic medicine.

It is difficult to homologize levels of the autonomic system to the Jacksonian somatic levels because of its peripheral ganglionic system, central representation, and its dual divisions of para- and orthosympathetic divisions which are mutually antagonistic. However it is suggested that the visceral ganglionic system, spinal medullary, and pontine centers comprise the lowest level; the hypothalamus and cortical areas, which are adjacent to the cortical motor centers, and premotor areas, the middle level; and the hippocampal formation and gyrus cinguli (perhaps others), the highest level. As in the somatic nervous system, the highest levels not only add new functions and take over in more complex form older functions from lower centers, but they also inhibit and damp down the functions of these lowest centers (34). In disease states, the functions of the lower centers are released and, in their then excessive action, comprise the major portion of the symptomatology. For example, cortical ablation in its production of "sham rage" has released from cortical control hypothalamic orthosympathetic functions which then are excessive and represent a caricature of normal activity.

Higher activity means, of course, inhibition of lower, more rapid, intrasegmental and simpler reflex functions; there occurs a long-circuiting of impulses to higher segments. What are these simpler autonomic functions and their psychic concomitants? They are based upon simple visceral functions of intaking, retaining, and eliminative functions innervated by the autonomic nervous system, and are the only means by which the immature infantile nervous system expresses its feelings. The concomitants of these functions represent its emotional life. As development occurs, the instinctual drives and tendencies are long-circuited to higher cortical centers where they are normally symbolically formulated and discharged as, at the same time, the simple visceral expressions of emotion are inhibited.

Hence the highest level has added the new functions of (a) synthesis of perceptions and (b) discharge in symbolic expression, but also (c) damped down lower orders of responses and reactions to stimuli as individual excitations. These new functions are cortical and correspond to the psychological ego which synthesizes and discharges.

In excessive psychological excitation, passing beyond the capacity of the ego for symbolic discharge, in which the pressure of instinctual drives meets resistances, ego functions become fatigued or paralyzed.

There result two aspects as of any lesion. The negative aspect is evidenced by the fact that the instinctual drives are not expressed through the highest level in highest symbolic expression. There is a hole in cortical activity which, however, is not a gaping wound through which psychic material readily flows. It is a nonconducting gap. The positive aspect, or so-called "return of the repressed," is a symptom which bears evidence of regression, for the push toward activity must find its expression through lower levels now permitted to act by release due to the absence of higher inhibiting functions.

Psychoanalytic theory of symptom-formation implies that the repressed or undischarged energy must escape elsewhere than through the motor activity of the ego—that it returns modified as a symptom. The same phenomenon has been described by Pavlov, for when reflexes are inhibited from one skin area they are increased elsewhere. In neurological terms, Jackson stated that diminished action in one part of the nervous system results in exalted action in another part, but this so-called new action takes place on a lower level. Neurologically, release of lower levels results in a greater preponderance of visceral participation in reflex activity and, psychologically, alloplastic reactions are replaced by autoplastic innervations. Innervations engage organs whose functions represent the level of psychological activity to which the psychic life has regressed, thus producing sucking, biting, soiling and retaining psychologically, as Alexander has shown in his vector analyses. Thus functional innervations of various appropriate organs, released from inhibition, set into effect the first link in the causal chain of events that end in visceral disease. Regression in the psychoneuroses and organ neuroses probably does not extend lower than the hypothalamus. Evidence of preservation of its integrating function in the visceral systems and personality indicates its intactness.

The problem of choice of regressive symptoms remains, however, as obscure in a physiological analysis as in a study of the emotions. Isolated hypertension, decreased peristalsis, etc., are difficult to explain psychologically, since the orthosympathetic centers in the hypothalamus act in unison to evoke mass reactions. From the work of Schou (76) with the minor emotions it seems possible that more than an isolated visceral function is disturbed, and it is suggested that the entire autonomic nervous system be investigated in these cases. Parasympathetic disturbances and endocrine symptoms of the parasympathetic group, such as diabetes, adiposity, genital disturbances, vasomotor changes, gastrointestinal hyperfunction, and ulceration are, as we have seen, much easier to understand as isolated physiological responses.

Differing from the schizophrenics, in whom the tension of the autonomic nervous mechanisms cannot be diminished, expressed symbolically, or only partially, the organ neurosis probably represents a graded release of inhibition from the cortex. In the schizophrenic, visceral tensions become too powerful; in the organ neuroses, our hypothesis considers that the obstacles and difficulties of reality, conditioned by specific frustrating experiences, become too strong, and the resulting fatigue of a focal area of the cortex releases its control over the lower centers. The result is a shunting of expression through direct visceral activity in a regressive manner instead of in a long-circuited symbolic expression.

General Considerations

Before attempting the following dynamic speculations, it must be repeated that the hypothalamus was primarily a precipitate within the olfactory system in a region from which central autonomic structures developed. It became a primitive center for olfactovisceral correlation. In 1934 Grinker (31) wrote:

Just as in the diencephalon, with its numerous olfactory interconnections, the great bulk of apparent olfactory and gustatory fibers in the hippocampal structures seem all out of proportion to the insignificance of these functions in man. Perhaps evolutionary processes have not yet atrophied this previously important structure. I should surmise, however, that much of the olfactory system is no longer subserving its original function, but may be concerned in more evolved, perhaps higher, autonomic functions. Herrick (39) suggests, for example, that the olfactory cortex may maintain a tonic influence on the neopallium, perhaps important in the function of learning.

Papez (68) recently wrote in the same strain. He states that the great sensory station within the thalamus gives rise to three great pathways. These converge (a) to the striatum which constitutes the stream of movement, (b) to the cortex or the stream of thought, and (c) to the hypothalamus-gyrus-cinguli unit as the stream of feeling. He believes the latter gyrus receives impulses from the hypothalamus which evoke emotional feelings, then influencing other cortical areas. According to Papez (68), the gyrus cinguli constitutes the cortical center for dynamic vigilance, for tumors in its neighborhood are associated with apathy and drowsiness. This agrees with Herrick's (39) concept of olfactory cortex exerting a tonic influence on the cerebrum. The hippocampal portion of olfactory cortex in man is also probably largely concerned with emotional feeling, for therein are found the negri bodies in rabies, a disease in which insomnia, irritability, restlessness, and fright are so striking. In this connection Klüver's recent extirpation of both temporal lobes in monkeys is important, for the experimental animals exhibited no normal expressions of fright or anger.

Since any discussion of the hypothalamic mechanism includes consideration of emotion, it is well to turn to its definition. All concepts of emotion are concerned with energy either in action or symbolism. McKinney (60), in paraphrasing Spinoza, formulated the following definition: "By emotions I understand the modifications of energy by which the power in action of the body is increased or diminished, aided or restrained, and at the same time the ideas of these modifications."

Concerning the argument regarding the peripheral or central origin of emotions we need concern ourselves little (73). *Emotional expression* is always peripheral, and one cannot deny that it may reverberate and amplify the central feelings. To express the idea that *emotion* is of peripheral origin is to forget the evolutionary significances of central structure and the processes of encephalization. The developed human may express his feelings symbolically with a minimum of visceral accompaniment, yet in certain conflictual situations regression may release peripheral expressions and re-evoke old patterns. The amount of such regression is probably one quantitative factor in the neuroses.

As a cephalic representative of the autonomic nervous system, the hypothalamus has to do with energies of visceral origin which are the forces of the instincts. It controls activities of the periphery in metabolism, balancing the constructive and destructive tendencies, and it forces activities of the cerebral cortex. It represents tensions or "cravings" within the autonomic system (instinctual) which are precipitated and coordinated in the hypothalamus rather than expressed individually and incoordinatedly. Its transmitted tension stimulates activity within the somatic nervous system, including the cerebral cortex, into a search for adequate stimuli (food or sexual), which stimuli release tensions and end in visceral quiescence.

Evolutionary development took away from the hypothalamus its dominant role in emotional expression during the processes of encephalization. Instinctual cravings become synthesized and formulated in a slower-acting more adaptive structure in which the processes of conditioning, or learning by experience, dominate rapid reflex action. To achieve these slower adaptive responses, the hypothalamus became subordinated to higher newer cortical centers by inhibitory processes emanating therefrom. The hippocampal-cinguli formation, subserving the conscious sensation of emotion revalued in relation to other cortical functions, also damps down hypothalamic excessive responses and allows only mild peripheral activities to be carried on in economically graded form, avoiding excessiveness.

However, in turn the hypothalamus influences activity within the cortex or ego. Its drives are synonymous with id demands or necessities of the instincts. This is represented clearly in the hypothalamic influences on the cortex in sleep, wakefulness, and consciousness, which represent modulations of drives called emotional. There is postulated, then, a mutually antagonistic system with cortical inhibitory influences predominating in most spheres. A phasic release of such inhibition results in appropriate centrally directed visceral responses and graded emotional expressions. Cortical inhibitions are, however, directed by learning or conditioning involving ego functions. Psychologically we are justified in assuming that such inhibitions or releases are directed upon the ego by environmental or social forces or their intrapsychic incrustations. Freud (23) spoke of all this when he stated that the ego served three masters: reality, the super-ego, and the id.

The emotion of anger is teleological in that it results in the stimulus being removed from the receptor. Fear removes the receptor from the stimulus and flight occurs from a real danger. In anxiety, however, the danger is not real, it is unknown, internal, and results from an increase in instinctual tension demanding expression. As Freud (23) points out, it is a conditioned signal within the ego, conscious within the personality as a warning of impending danger. There are specific unpleasurable feelings, efferent discharges and their perception. The result may not be fight or flight, as to a real danger, but a paralysis of certain higher ego functions. Anxiety is then the first sign of an autonomic influence on the cortex or ego, which has been learned by previous testing to indicate danger for the organism. It is a feeling which accompanies autonomic forces sufficiently strong to overcome cortical inhibition and force the cortex into activity, movement resulting in an attempt at solving the situation which has evoked the internal tension. Psychological fight or flight or compromises are attempted. Often successful solutions are not possible, and the cortex or ego "gives up," allowing regressive and infantile modes of exteriorization of emotional expression for the sake of avoiding more prolonged or greater emotional feelings. The result is visceral expression or organ dysfunctions, which we term organ neuroses, that constitute the first step toward organic disease.

BIBLIOGRAPHY

1. ALEXANDER, FRANZ, AND CO-WORKERS. The influence of psychologic factors upon gastrointestinal disturbances: a symposium. *Psychoanal. Quart.,* 1934, **3**, 501. (In this volume, page 103.)

2. ALKAN, L. *Anatomische Organkrankheiten aus seelischer Ursache.* Stuttgart: Hippokrates Verlag, 1930.

3. ALPERS, B. J. Relations of hypothalamus to disorders of personality. *Arch. Neurol. Psychiat.,* 1937, **38**, 291.

4. BAILEY, P. *Intracranial tumors.* Springfield: Thomas, 1933.

5. BAILEY, P., AND MURRAY H. A case of pinealoma with symptoms suggestive of compulsion neurosis, *Arch. Neurol. Psychiat.,* 1928, **19**, 932.

6. BARD, P. The central representation of the sympathetic system. *Arch. Neurol. Psychiat.,* 1929, **22**, 230.

7. BARD, P. The neuro-humoral basis of emotional reactions. In *Handbook of general experimental psychology.* Worcester: Clark University Press, 1934.

8. BARUK, H., AND GEVANDON, Y. Periodic psychoses in children associated with infundibular-hypothalamic syndromes. *Ann. méd.-psychol.,* 1937, **95**, 296.

9. BEATTIE, J., BROW, F. R., AND LONG, C. N. H. Physiological and anatomical evidence of nerve tracts connecting the hypothalamus with spinal sympathetic centers. *Proc. roy. Soc.,* London, 1930, (s.B.) **106**, 253.

10. BENDER, L. Anatomical pathological data on personality function. *Am. J. Psychol.,* 1925, **92**, 325.

11. CANNON, W. B. James-Lange and thalamic theories of emotion. *Psychol. Rev.,* 1931, **38**, 281 and *Am. J. Psychol.,* 1927, **39**, 106.

12. CANNON, W. B. *Bodily changes in pain, hunger, fear and rage.* New York: D. Appleton Co., 1929; *The wisdom of the body.* New York: W. W. Norton & Co., 1933.

13. CERLETTI, V., AND BINI, L. Electric shock in the treatment of mental diseases. *Policlinico,* 1938, **45**, 1261.

14. CUSHING, HARVEY. *Pituitary body and hypothalamus.* Springfield: Thomas, 1932.

15. DAVISON, C., AND SELBY, N. C. Hypothermia in cases of hypothalamic lesions. *Arch. Neurol. Psychiat.,* 1935, **33**, 570.

16. DEMOLE, V. Pharmakologisch-anatomische Untersuchungen zum Problem des Schlafes. *Arch. f. exper. Path. u. Pharmakol.,* 1927, **120**, 229.

17. DUNBAR, H. F. *Emotions and bodily changes.* New York: Columbia University Press, 1935.

18. ECTORS, L., BROOKENS, N. L., AND GERARD, R. W. Anatomic and motor localization in the hypothalamus. *Arch. Neurol. Psychiat.,* 1938, **39**, 789.

19. FINKELMAN, I., AND STEPHENS, W. M. Heat regulation in dementia praecox. Reactions of patients with dementia praecox to cold, *J. Neurol. & Psychopath.,* 1936, **16**, 321.

20. FISHER, C., INGRAM, W. R., AND RANSON, S. W. *Diabetes insipidus and the neuro-hormonal control of water balance: a contribution to the structure and function of the hypothalamico-hypophyseal system.* Ann Arbor: Edwards Bros., 1938.

21. FOERSTER, O., AND GAGEL, O. A case of ependymal cyst of third ventricle (Contribution to the question of relation of mental disturbances to the brain stem). *Ztschr. f. d. ges. Neurol. u. Psychiat.,* 1933, **149**, 312.

22. FREEMAN, H., AND CARMICHAEL, H. T. A pharmacodynamic investigation of the autonomic nervous system on schizophrenia. *Arch. Neurol. Psychiat.,* 1935, **33**, 342.

23. FREUD, SIGMUND. *The problem of anxiety.* New York: W. W. Norton & Co., 1936.

24. FULTON, J. F. *Physiology of the nervous system.* London: Oxford Medical Publications, 1938.

25. FULTON, J. F. New horizons in physiology and medicine: the hypothalamus and visceral mechanism. *New England J. Med.,* 1932, **207**, 60-94.

26. FULTON, J. F., AND INGRAHAM, F. D. Emotional disturbances following experimental lesions of the base of the brain. *J. Physiol.,* 1929, **67**, 27.

27. FULTON, J. F., AND BAILEY, P. Contribution to the study of tumors in the region of the third ventricle: their diagnosis and relation to pathological sleep. *J. nerv. ment. Dis.,* 1929, **69**, 1, 145, 261.

28. GAGEL, O. Symptomatology of diseases of the hypothalamus. In Bumke-Foerster *Handbuch der Neurologie.* Berlin: Julius Springer, 1936.

29. GELLHORN, E. Effects of hypoglycemia and anoxia on the central nervous system. *Arch. Neurol. Psychiat.,* 1938, **40**, 125.

30. GREVING, R. Zur Anatomie, Physiologie und Pathologie des vegetativen Zentrums im Zwischenhirn. *Ztschr. f. d. ges. Anat.,* 1922, **24**, 348.

31. GRINKER, R. R. *Neurology.* Springfield: Thomas, (1st Ed.) 1934; (2nd Ed.) 1937.

32. GRINKER, R. R. A method for studying and influencing cortico-hypothalamic relations. *Science,* 1938, **87**, 73.

33. GRINKER, R. R., AND SEROTA, H. Studies on cortico-hypothalamic relations in the cat and man. *J. Neurophysiol.,* 1938, **1**, 573.

34. GRINKER, R. R. A comparison of psychological "repression" and neurological "inhibition." *J. nerv. ment. Dis.,* 1939, **39**, 765.

34a. GROTJAHN, M., AND FRENCH, T. Akinesia after ventriculography. *Psychoanal. Quart.,* 1938, **7**, 319. (In this volume, page 514.)

35. GRÜNTHAL, E. Cell structure in the hypothalamus of rabbits and Macacus Rhesus. *J. f. Psychol. u. Neurol.,* 1931, **42**, 425.

36. GUTTMAN, E., AND HERMANN, K. Über psychische störungen bei Hirnstammerkrankungen. *Ztschr. f. d. ges. Neurol. u. Psychiat.,* 1932, **140**, 439.

37. HARRIS, G. W. The induction of ovulation in the rabbit by electrical stimulation of the hypothalamo-hypophyseal mechanism. *Proc. roy. Soc.,* London, 1937, (s.B.) **122**, 374.

38. HEAD, H. Vigilance. *Brit. J. Psychol.,* 1926, **14**, 126.

39. HERRICK, C. J. *Brains of rats and men.* Chicago: University of Chicago Press, 1926.

40. HESS, W. R. On the interrelations between psychic and vegetative functions. (Translated by S. E. Jelliffe and L. Brink.) *J. nerv. ment. Dis.,* 1931, **74**, 301, 511, 645, 726.

41. HILLER, F., AND GRINKER, R. R. The nervous regulation of sugar metabolism. *Arch. Neurol. Psychiat.* 1929, **22**, 919.

41a. HOAGLAND, H., CAMERON, D., AND RUBIN, M. Emotion in man as tested by the delta index of E. E. G. *J. gen. Psychol.,* 1938, **19**, 227, 247.

42. HORRAX, G., AND YASKIS, M. Calcified intradural cholesteatoma of unusual size in a patient showing manic depressive symptoms. *Arch. Neurol. Psychiat,.* 1935, **33**, 1058.

43. INGHAM, S. Some neurologic aspects of psychiatry. J. Amer. med. Assn., 1938, **111**, 665.

44. INGRAM, W. R. The hypothalamus: a review of the experimental data. *Psychom. Med.,* 1939, **1**, 48.

45. INGRAM, W. R., BARRIS, R. W., AND RANSON, S. W. Catalepsy: an experimental study. *Arch. Neurol. Psychiat.,* 1936, **35**, 1175.

46. JELLIFFE, S. E. *Postencephalitic respiratory disorders.* New York: Nervous & Mental Disease Publishing Co., 1927.

47. JELLIFFE, S. E. Schizophrenia and epidemic encephalitis: their alliances, differences, and a point of view. *Am. J. Psychiat.,* 1927, **6**, 413.

48. JELIFFE, S. E. *Psychopathology of forced movements in oculogyric crises.* New York: Nervous & Mental Disease Publishing Co., 1932.

49. KABAT, H., MAGOUN, H. W., AND RANSON, S. W. Reaction of the bladder to stimulation of points in the forebrain and midbrain. *J. comp. Neurol.,* 1936, **63,** 211.

50. KAPPER, C. ARIENS, HUBER, W., AND CROSBY, E. *The comparative anatomy of the nervous system of vertebrates, including man.* New York: The Macmillan Co., 1936.

51. KEMPF, E. J. *The autonomic functions and the personality.* New York: Nervous & Mental Disease Publishing Co., 1918.

52. KUNTZ, A. *The autonomic nervous system.* Philadelphia: Lea & Febiger, 1929.

53. KUPPERS, H. Der Grundplan des Nervensystems und die Lokalization der Psychosen. *Ztschr. f. d. ges. Neurol. u. Psychiat.,* 1923, **75,** 1 and 1923, **83,** 247.

54. LANGE, C. G., AND JAMES, W. *The emotions.* Baltimore: Williams & Wilkins, 1922.

55. LE GROS CLARK, W. E., BEATTIE, J., RIDDOCH, G., AND DOTT, N. M. *The hypothalamus.* Edinburgh: Oliver & Boyd, 1938.

56. LEITER, L., AND GRINKER, R. R. Role of the hypothalamus in regulation of blood pressure. Experimental studies with observations on respiration. *Arch. Neurol. Psychiat.,* 1934, **31,** 54.

57. MAGOUN, H. W., RANSON, S. W., AND HETHERINGTON, A. The liberation of adrenin and sympathin induced by stimulation of the hypothalamus. *Amer. J. Physiol.,* 1937, **119,** 615.

58. MAUTHNER, L. Zur Pathologie und Physiologie des Schlafes, nebst Bemerkungen über die "Nona." *Wien. med. Wchnschr.,* 1890 (June 7), **40,** 961; (June 14), **40,** 1001; (June 21), **40,** 1049; (June 28), **40,** 1092; (July 5), **40,** 1144; (July 12), **40,** 1186.

59. MENNINGER, K. A. *Man against himself.* New York: Harcourt, Brace & Co., 1938.

60. McKINNEY, J. M. What shall we choose to call emotion? *J. nerv. ment. Dis.,* 1930, **72,** 46.

61. MILLER, M. L. Psychoses associated with probable injury to the hypothalamus and adjacent structures. *Arch. Neurol. Psychiat.,* 1934, **31,** 809.

62. MORGAN, L. O. Further observations on the mammillo-infundibular region of the diencephalon: Relation to epilepsy, dementia, and the psychoses. *Proc. exp. Soc. Biol. Med.,* 1928, **25,** 617.

63. MORGAN, L. O. The nuclei of the region of the tuber cinerium. Degenerative changes in cases of epilepsy, with a description of their significance, *Arch. Neurol. Psychiat.,* 1930, **24,** 267.

64. MORGAN, L. O., AND GREGORY, H. S. Pathological changes in the tuber cinerium in a group of psychoses. *J. nerv. ment. Dis.,* 1935, **82,** 286.

65. MASSERMAN, J. E., AND HAERTIG, E. W. The influence of hypothalamic stimulation on intestinal activity. *J. Neurophysiol.,* 1938, **1,** 350.

66. MÜLLER, L. R. Die Lebensnerven und Lebenstriebe. (3rd Ed.) Berlin: Julius Springer, 1931.

67. POPA, G. T., AND FIELDING, V. A portal circulation from the pituitary to the hypothalamic region. *J. Anat.,* 1930, **65,** 88.

68. PAPEZ, J. W. A proposed mechanism of emotion. *Arch. Neurol. Psychiat.,* 1937, **38,** 725.

69. PENFIELD, W. Diencephalic autonomic epilepsy. *Arch. Neurol. Psychiat.,* 1929, **22,** 358.

70. RAAB, W. Diencephalic-hypothalamic system and its disorders. *Ergebn. d. inn. Med. u. Kinderh.,* 1936, **51,** 125.

71. RANSON, S. W. Some functions of the hypothalamus. Harvey Lectures, 1936-1937.

72. RANSON, S. W., FISCHER, C., AND INGRAM, W. R. Hypothalamic regulation of temperature in the monkey. *Arch. Neurol. Psychiat.*, 1937, **38**, 445.

73. REYMERT, M. L. Feelings and emotions (The Wittenberg Symposium). Worcester: Clark University Press, 1928.

74. ROWE, S. N. Localization of the sleep mechanism. Brain, 1935, **58**, 21.

75. SCHILDER, P., AND WEISSMANN, M. Amente Psychose bei Hypophysengangtumor. *Ztschr. f. d. ges. Neurol. u. Psychiat.* 1927, **110**, 767.

75a. SCHILDER, P. The organic background of obsessions and compulsions. *Am. J. Psychiat.*, 1938, **94**, 1397.

76. SCHOU, H. I. Some investigations into the physiology of emotions. *Acta psychiat. et neurol.* Sup. XIV, 1937.

77. SINGER, H. D. Psychoses and the central nervous system. *J. Amer. med. Assn.* 1938, **110**, 2048.

78. SPECHT, G. Vegetatives Nervensystem und Geistesstörung. *Ztschr. f. d. ges. Neurol. u. Psychiat.*, 1923, **81**, 560.

79. TAYLOR, J. *Selected writings of John Hughlings Jackson.* London: Hodder & Stoughton, 1932.

80. WISLOCKI, C. B., AND KING, L. S. The permeability of the hypothalamus and hypophysis to vital dyes with a study of the hypothalamic vascular supply, *Am. J. Anat.*, 1936, **58**, 421.

A NOTE ON THE PSYCHOGENESIS OF ORGANIC SYMPTOMS *

By Leon J. Saul, M.D.

Some psychogenic organic symptoms, such as tremor or blushing, are the *direct* expressions of emotions or conflicts, while others are only their *indirect* results. Examples of the latter are (a) the effects of acting out, such as catching cold from throwing off the bedclothes during sleep, (b) the incidental soreness of an arm due to an hysterical tremor. This indirect type was described by Deutsch in 1922.[1] He stated that psychogenic organic symptoms were not necessarily "conversions," but often represented a result of an organic process initiated by emotional disturbances. This distinction was stressed and clarified by Alexander in his theory of the etiology of peptic ulcer.[2] His evidence indicates that the ulcer may be the more or less incidental result of years of gastric dysfunction arising largely from emotional tension of a specific kind. The clinical notes here presented illustrate this mechanism (emotion—appropriate physical expression—organic pathology) with special reference to activities during sleep.

They are taken from the analysis of a very intelligent married man of forty. The patient's surface attitude was a show of great superiority and independence. This was a compensation for hurt masculine pride—hurt by the fact that actually he was very dependent, always got people to make decisions for him and to give him things—the "get something for nothing" type. These desires, as expected, were expressed in his dreams in the infantile language of eating, being fed, aggressive biting, etc., i.e., getting via the mouth—typical "oral-receptive" and "oral-aggressive" trends (Alexander).

During the end phase of his analysis this man developed a mild sore throat. It was always worse upon awakening in the morning, and usually practically disappeared after eating breakfast or during the following few hours. The patient's wakeful wife noticed that at

* *The Psychoanalytic Quarterly* IV : 476-483, 1935.
[1] Deutsch, Felix. Biologie und Psychologie der Krankheitsgenese. *Int. Ztschr. f. Psa.*, 1922, **8**, 290. Studies in pathogenesis: biological and psychological aspects. *Psychoanal. Quart.*, 1933, 2.
[2] Alexander, Franz. The influence of psychologic factors upon gastro-intestinal disturbances: a symposium. *Psychoanal. Quart.*, 1934, 3.

this time the patient slept on his back and breathed through his mouth, although he had always previously lain on his side and had never been a mouth breather. Hoping to prevent the formation of a habit of mouth breathing, she awakened him on one of these occasions and thus allowed him to make two observations, the relationship between which he did not then realize: the first was that he had been dreaming of being fed, and the second was that his throat felt very sore, due obviously to its dryness caused by the mouth breathing. Although not adequately proven and substantiated until later, this simple mechanism is best described immediately: the analysis had reached a phase of dawning insight into oral trends, which, particularly strong in this patient, began to express themselves quite frankly in his dreams. During a dream of being fed the patient acted out this passive infantile desire in his sleep to the extent of lying on his back with his mouth open and breathing through his mouth. This resulted in dryness of the throat for a sufficient number of hours to cause soreness. Upon awakening in the morning, the soreness alone was apparent. This soreness was then secondarily utilized by the patient's masochistic trends, chiefly to ease oral guilt by suffering and to justify desires to be passive, which he had indulged by stopping work.

Further evidence for the part played by such a direct process in producing the so-called "conversion symptom" of sore throat was obtained easily and amply. For the ten days, approximately, during which this oral material appeared intensively in the analysis, the patient presented many symptoms in the mouth region. This period was marked by oral-aggressive dreams, such as getting a salad out of the body of a woman. The sore throat, appearing in the morning and disappearing by evening, became constant and worse at this time, and new symptoms developed: bleeding gums, two stomatous ulcers, sore left jaw joint, and mild laryngitis. A clue to all this again came from the patient's wife who observed that the patient had suddenly begun to grind his teeth at night, so loudly as to awaken her. She awakened him on several occasions to stop this, and thus made some further observations. Once, grinding his teeth while awakening, he found that he was using such great force that it was impossible to exert it voluntarily when entirely awake. The occurrence of this symptom in the setting of intense oral-aggressive impulses was made clear by the analysis; and so far as it could be correlated with the dreams of these nights, especially dreams during which it occurred and from which the patient was awakened by his wife, it appeared to be a direct expression of rage at oral thwarting, at having to cut loose from mother's apron strings and relinquish to some degree the pleasure of dependence and receiving. This unusually powerful oral attachment the patient unconsciously struggled to retain, while his masculine narcissism was forcing him to relinquish it; grinding of the teeth was frequently associated with tensing of the throat muscles, as the patient noticed on awakening; these activities resulted in the morning in soreness of the throat, mild laryngitis, easily bleeding sore gums, and sore left temporo-mandibular joint.

A dramatic climax illumined the process still further. With increasing insight and resistance, these symptoms were exacerbated, and one day all appeared in rather severe form. The patient came to the analytic hour with all the signs of coming down with a severe infectious sore throat and laryngitis, including slight nausea, malaise, and loss of energy. During the hour there occurred a burst of insight into the oral desires and destructive aggressions. The nausea and asthenia disappeared within an hour or two. (The nausea was evidently a reaction against these oral impulses.) What appeared to be a febrile reaction was a typical mild depression. (The patient's temperature was not elevated.) That night the patient slept better than any night of the preceding few weeks, felt markedly relaxed, and on awakening during the night felt by striking contrast how relaxed his jaws and pharynx were. In the morning his throat was not worse, as usual, but very much better, and by that evening not a single symptom of the incipient cold or grippe was in evidence.

Before proceeding it may be well to make a few remarks by the way. The first is the obvious one that infections usually improve over night, and that it is therefore very suspicious of unconscious nocturnal activities to find such a condition worse in the morning rather than better.

Secondly, to avoid any possible misunderstanding, the fact must be borne in mind that biological phenomena are rarely comprehensible in terms of single simple cause and effect, although this may be the most useful approach for the scientific study of isolated problems. In biology we are dealing with an extremely complicated dynamic mechanism, in sensitive internal and external equilibrium, the intrinsic detailed workings of which are functionally related. We must therefore usually be content to succeed in establishing the relative importance of certain factors in producing a condition which obviously has many interrelated determinants. Thus the clinical observations made above indicate only one of the causal sequences at work. Under other individual and environmental conditions (immunity. etc., climate, etc.), our patient might not have developed a sore throat at all. Or, such determinants might serve only to exacerbate an already present infection. This mechanism (emotional state—

appropriate activities during sleep—organic consequences) is only one of the determinants, and may be either of subsidiary or of critical importance in different cases.

A third remark concerns the relationship between oral material and upper respiratory symptoms. This relationship is not surprising when one considers their intimate physiological association in the adult (swallowing, vomiting, "down the wrong pipe," air-swallowing, etc.). Also, recent work [3] indicates that in infants, sucking, swallowing, and breathing form a single reflex mechanism.

We now return to the patient, for he afforded clues to three more symptoms. One of these appeared along with the other oral symptoms described, and was omitted merely to facilitate simplicity of presentation. This was a small ulcer of the tongue ("stomach sore") near the right margin, opposite the second molar tooth. That it, too, was probably of traumatic nocturnal origin, the result of biting his tongue during sleep, was strongly suggested by the following incidents: about ten days after the analysis of the oral material referred to above, when the patient had rather good insight into it, he twice bit his tongue at this same point. On both these occasions he was at dinner with his wife and was in the middle of a sentence suggesting a new and delectable dessert. This resulted in a small "stomach sore," just like the first one which persisted for two days. Thus it is probable that the first ulcer was also caused by biting, but by biting during sleep in response to oral aggressive dreams. Its greater severity and persistence was doubtless due to repeated traumata during that period and consequent lowered resistance of the mucosa, for it disappeared on the day that followed the burst of insight and "relaxed" night's sleep.

Further evidence was obtained when the patient developed a soreness of the right cheek at the ampulla of the parotid duct, and the following night was awakened by his wife because of grinding his teeth. He found that he was chewing, and because he was lying on his right side, that he was severely biting and rubbing this region.

Thus closer observations of the same patient yielded further examples and confirmation of the validity of this simple process of (a) emotion, (b) direct, appropriate, and readily comprehensible expression of it (although unconsciously and usually during sleep), and (c) a consequent organic condition. Further verification is readily obtained from other cases, and other symptoms become more intelligible. A few examples may be mentioned briefly:

A young male patient with strong oral trends complained bitterly

---

[3] Peiper, A. Die Atmung des Neugeborenen. *Jahreskurse f. ärtzl. Fortbildung,* 1933, 24.

that his teeth and the left side of his jaw pained him, although his dentist found no oral pathology. At this time the patient dreamed of battling a rapidly growing snake, to which he associated his fear of snakes and antagonism to them, his belief in the strength-giving qualities of the snake's flesh, his having eaten a snake as a child, the penis, and his envy of his father's strength and possessions. In response to the interpretation of his oral aggression he said that he had just come from the dentist, who had told him that the teeth were worn down more than could be accounted for by eating, and that nocturnal teeth grinding must be frequent with him. The dentist remarked that teeth grinding in sleep is very common, as he sees it through his practice, "and is caused by nervous tension." A few weeks later this patient was thwarted by a woman and reacted with intense rage and with conscious wishes to kill her. That night he had an overtly cannibalistic dream of eating a woman. He awoke from this dream, grinding his teeth with great force. His dentist, whom he saw at this time, told him that his teeth showed twenty-five more years of wear than they should, due undoubtedly to nocturnal grinding. To prevent further soreness, aches, and damage from nocturnal grinding, the dentist prescribed a rubber guard for the patient to wear during sleep over the teeth of his lower jaw.

After nearly two months of this the patient's teeth and jaw, especially on the left side of the maxilla, were constantly sore, and his whole head felt congested. He found himself grinding or clamping his teeth together even when working during the day. The annoyance became so great that ideas of suicide occurred (chiefly, of course, because of the unconscious aggression due to oral thwarting). He got no relief from his dentist, who found no organic etiology. One analytic hour the patient reported a dream of holding his little sister up in the air at arms length while a big woman stood by him. Associating, he reluctantly admitted what for two months he had struggled so hard to deny: that his unbounded show of strength and superiority was a denial to himself and the world of a feeling of inner weakness due to strong oral claims. As in the dream, part of his life technique was to be supported by strong substitute mothers while demonstrating his strength in relation to the weak (young boys and girls). This insight touched the patient deeply, particularly the realization of his hostility when orally thwarted. At the next visit the patient reported spontaneously and with great astonishment that almost immediately after the preceding analytic hour he had experienced a noticeable relief of the pain in his teeth and jaw. That evening, about six hours later, he could eat comfortably, and he realized to his amazement that the ache was almost gone. It disappeared completely that evening and since then (five months) he has felt relaxed and able to work effectively with no trace of pain.[4]

The following material illustrates the same mechanism operating through the involuntary nervous system. A male patient developed a pain in his right testicle for which the urologist whom he consulted found no organic source. A simple explanation came to light following the analysis of a rather frank Oedipus dream, in which the patient got into bed with an older woman. He related that he awoke from this dream on the verge of an orgasm, and this occurred although he had had intercourse only a few hours before. Moreover, he just then realized that for the past week or so, despite regular intercourse, every time he awakened at night his penis was in rigid erection and probably was so all during his sleep. With changing dreams and disappearance or diminution of nocturnal sexual excitement, erections, and emissions, the ache also disappeared and has not returned. The ache had been merely the usual result of prolonged erection, but this erection had occurred in response to sexual fantasies during sleep so that only the ache was noticed.[5]

The material here presented merely stresses the point observed by others, namely, that psychogenic organic symptoms, although related to emotional conflicts, need not be primarily symbolizations of these, but only incidental results of appropriate and readily comprehensible emotional expressions. Recognition of this mechanism robs the "jump from the psychic to the physical" of some of its mystery.

[4] Cases of teeth grinding have been observed and symptomatically cured by non-Freudian methods. See Frohman, B. S., Occlusal neuroses. *Psychoanal. Rev.*, 1935, **19**.

[5] A detailed discussion of urological cases was presented by Dr. Karl Menninger (Psychogenic factors in urological disorders) at the American Psychoanalytic Society at Chicago in 1934. In this connection see also Menninger, Karl, Some unconscious psychological factors associated with the common cold. *Psychoanal. Rev.*, 1934, **21**.

THE PHYSIOLOGICAL EFFECTS OF PSYCHO-
ANALYTIC THERAPY *

By Leon J. Saul, M.D.

I

That emotions produce physiological effects has long been common knowledge—blushing in embarrassment, tachycardia and incontinence in fear, fainting from emotional shock, weeping in sorrow,
and so on. A variety of such effects have been vividly depicted in
belles lettres by many authors, for example, Balzac. Cannon (1)
and his followers demonstrated in detail the physiological effects of
acute emotional states, primarily in relation to the sympatheticoadrenal system. Pavlov (2) and his school initiated studies of
chronic emotional states, particularly in relation to the higher levels
of the central nervous system. Psychoanalysis developed from the
demands of hysterics for relief from their organic symptoms (3).
These symptoms turned out to be the physiological end results of
emotional tensions. The requirements of therapy necessitated a
study of the environmental stresses and strains upon the patient, and
of the patient's emotional responses to these. Since in most cases,
cure could not be effected by altering the environmental difficulties,
the only hope was to deal with the patient's pathological emotional
reactions to these. Thus the clinician, working with neurotic patients, has naturally developed a different approach to the problem
than the experimental physiologist working with normal animals.
The clinician can tamper but little with the patient's life situation or
physiology. He cannot experimentally set up stresses and strains
upon the organism, and so must wait for considerable periods for
nature and chance to send him adequate series of parallel cases. Then
he must be content to concentrate his study upon the reactions of the
individuals to the experimental situation which life provides. He
must leave to the physiologist and laboratory psychologist the reproduction of emotional reactions by experimental situations, and also
the study of the underlying physiological mechanisms.

---

* *The Research Publications of the Association for Research in Nervous and Mental Disease* XIX : 305-317, 1939.

II

The chronic mental state of a neurotic human is far more complex than the mental state of an experimental animal in an acute and patent state of rage or fear. To study the mental state, therefore, the psychoanalyst employs a special technique. This technique depends upon the fact that functional symptoms result, basically, from powerful impersonal biological impulses which are inadequately dealt with by the organized, socialized part of the personality. In other words, part of man's "lower" or "animal" nature, although controlled by his "higher self" so far as his behavior toward other persons is concerned, is still a powerful enough inner physiological force to cause mental and physical symptoms. Insight into this process, as it is reflected in the mind, is obtained by a laboratory technique: The subject is seen regularly under standard conditions, and, because of his need for relief of suffering, he communicates his thoughts and feelings.[1] The analyst observes the changes in these communications in the behavior, and in the symptoms, as the patient's emotions develop toward him, and as the patient reacts to interpretations and becomes acquainted with hitherto unknown or unappreciated elements in his mental life. The mental life, as it manifests the powerful and often conflicting biological instinctual impulses, and the forces of control, can be observed with considerable depth and precision by this technique. The raw data with which psychoanalysis works are predominantly verbal—the spoken communications of the patient. They are no less valid, therefore, as the subject of scientific study than are visual data. The material can be examined by independent workers who can check their findings on the same material and on other cases. Psychoanalysis is basically a descriptive science, like anatomy or astronomy, but it is also experimental insofar as it establishes a situation in which the patient's emotional reactions to another individual—the analyst—can be watched as they develop, and insofar as they are affected by the analyst's interpretations. Most of the findings can be studied experimentally, and there is need for more work, such as Lewin's frustration experiments with humans or the experimental neuroses of animals.[2]

III

The human mind being what it is, the psychoanalytic technique of investigation is also one of therapy. The physiological effects of

---

[1] Probably the need for relief of suffering is the only motive regularly adequate to bring people to reveal their deeper feelings and motives.

[2] See, for example, Lewin, Kurt, *A dynamic theory of personality.* New York: McGraw-Hill Book Co., Inc., 1935. Liddell, H. S., and Anderson, O. D. Observations on experimental neurosis in sheep. *Arch. Neurol. Psychiat.,* 1935, **34,** 330-354.

this therapy have been studied in two main ways—by observing changes in clinical signs and symptoms and by direct physiological measurements either during the analytic sessions or at frequent intervals. These measurements have been made by a number of workers and include records of respiration, pulse, blood pressure, psychogalvanic reflexes, temperature changes, and electroencephalograms. Most of these studies are only now in progress and important results have not yet been reported. Their value will depend upon the ability of psychoanalysis to describe the mental states with an exactness comparable to that of the physiological measurements.

Knowledge of the physiological effects of the psychoanalytic therapy has come chiefly from the observation of specific clinical signs and symptoms, as they change concomitantly with exacerbation or relief of specific emotional tensions. I shall present very briefly two examples of such observations. In this short paper only one aspect of the problem can be considered, namely, the effects of insight and working through, and not, for example, of transference or of reopening the process of development.

A man of 30, near the end of his analysis, which lasted nineteen months, came to his hour with a severe headache. He was subject to headaches about twice a month. This one had begun the previous day. Speaking of events preceding the onset, the patient told that a close friend, a man somewhat older than himself, had requested the patient to take a rather burdensome responsibility for a short period —but for a period which the patient had planned to utilize as a very self-indulgent, comfortable vacation. However, the patient generously assented and thought no more about it. During the analytic hour his associations dealt chiefly with resentment and guilt. When the analyst asked if he might not be reacting to the friend's request, his response was an immediate sense of conviction and relief. He then recounted a dream of the night before in which a man attacked him and put him out of a house. The patient, who had been excessively indulged in childhood, was in reality furious at the friend for putting him in a position of having to forego his vacation and undertake fresh efforts. He showed no outward sign of rage, however. He remained the perfect gentleman and did not himself realize that he was angry. But he got a headache. This headache diminished dramatically when he achieved a clear insight into this reaction, and disappeared a few hours later.

A young woman, in the fourteenth month of the analysis, came to the hour complaining of a severe diarrhea which had begun suddenly the preceding evening. She was subject to similar attacks about a dozen times a year. Since she had eaten all her meals for 3 days with her sister and mother, neither of whom showed any symptoms, a toxic or infectious etiology was unlikely. She soon revealed that the mother had given her the use of the family automobile during the mother's absence, and this car meant a great deal to the patient. Now the mother was going to give it to the patient's recently married sister who lived some distance away. The patient raised no objections. She considered it entirely fair that the sister should have it for an equal period. But from the spiteful, depreciatory content of her associations it soon became clear that, without realizing it, the patient was furious at her mother and sister and wanted to tell them spitefully to take back their old car, she didn't want it anyway. With this insight the diarrhea ceased abruptly.

Similar observations can be made in cases of essential hypertension [3] in which the blood pressure is recorded before and after every psychoanalytic session. Here, too, a role is played by anger and resentment, of intensities which the individual does not at all appreciate and which he may not even realize he has. During periods when such resentment, unperceived by the patient, is stimulated, the blood pressure fluctuates at levels 30 to 40 points higher than when it is not stimulated or than when the patient becomes conscious of these feelings within himself as a result of the psychoanalytic work. Becoming conscious of the hitherto unconscious anger results in a lower level of the blood pressure. This can be observed not only in the changes of level over long periods but in the falls during individual sessions in which important insight is achieved. (Needless to say, it is not concluded that unconscious anger is the sole cause of essential hypertension. It may be that the fluctuations it produces are superimposed upon an elevation from other sources.)

Studies of cases of gastrointestinal disturbances (4), for example, psychogenic constipation, colitis, and even duodenal ulcer show the involvement of impulses other than anger, although again it is not concluded that these impulses are the only factors in the etiology of these conditions. The approach is merely to isolate, so far as possible, the psychological factors in order to describe them and to observe the effects of changes in them upon the organic symptoms. Alvarez, Draper, and others have long described the typical "ulcer personality" as the overly ambitious, driving, aggressive business man. The cases which have been psychoanalyzed have shown that beneath this hard-driving surface are opposite tendencies—cravings to be dependent, loved, protected, supported, fed, as in early childhood. These impulses, like the anger in the first two examples, are

[3] Symposium on hypertension. *Psychosom. Med.,* 1939, 1.

not perceived by the individual himself because they are at variance with his ideal of himself. In this case, moreover, they conflict with his normal adult masculine drives. He cannot admit them, even to himself, and even goes to extremes of activity and independence to deny them. Such persistent infantile cravings can usually be traced back to excessive spoiling or deprivation, or to an alternation of the two, in early childhood. If the analysis succeeds in getting the individual to see these repudiated desires in himself, i.e., makes him conscious of them, his need for the excessive drive as a denial diminishes, and so do his organic symptoms. The therapeutic results are much better with colitis than with ulcer, but the latter is given as an example because the psychological structure is simpler and the theoretical value is the same.

Examples of dramatic relief of hysterical symptoms are common in psychoanalytic practice, as shown by a survey of the experiences of the analysts at the Chicago Institute for Psychoanalysis.[4] They are only incidents, however. Insight alone is not everything, as it was thought to be in the early days of analysis. It is effective only when the emotions are of optimum intensity, and when the individual is prepared for the insight. Then, as the examples illustrate, insight into the previously unconscious emotion produces a marked effect upon the physiology—the organic symptom diminishes or disappears. But lasting effects, such as relief from repeated attacks of headache or diarrhea, are achieved only by daily patient "working through" of the conflictual emotional tensions, from the first intellectual glimpse of them to a full emotional realization and integration of them into the rest of the personality. It is for this "working through" that the emotional relationship to the physician must be taken into account, for the conflicting emotions are regularly "transferred" to him. Working through these feelings toward the physician is the most effective psychotherapeutic procedure. For with insight alone the patient is not cured.[5] He loses his organic symptom only to have in its place a conscious emotional problem. The man with the headaches went through a period of several months during his analysis in which he was in a state of anxiety due to dawning realization of the extent of his hostilities to those very persons who were nearest to him. His physical symptom, the headache, had been replaced by a mental symptom, anxiety, and by a conscious emotional problem. For a few weeks he was so disturbed by the insight that he wished he had his headaches back. But he worked it through with good

---

[4] Twelve analysts reported that they observed such dramatic relief of headaches by insight.

[5] Other factors which influence the mental state and symptoms, such as the feeling of permission, cannot be discussed here.

therapeutic effect as regards his headaches, his frame of mind, and his human relations.

The girl with the diarrhea did not develop anxiety but became mildly depressed when she began to realize her hostility to her mother and sister. The attacks of diarrhea became extremely infrequent, but she had a conscious emotional problem to wrestle with. As in most diarrhea cases,[6] she worked through the emotional problem satisfactorily. It is clear that from the analytic point of view a therapeutic result means not only relief from the physical symptom but solution of the emotional tensions which caused the symptom and which have been made conscious to the patient.

The converse situation is seen, for example, in a suicidal patient who developed a psychogenic diarrhea. This was a good sign because it showed that some of the unbearable emotional tension which was driving her toward suicide could be discharged as an organic symptom. This is true for probably all patients who struggle with more emotional energy than they can master.

The analyst, then, sees the patient's behavior, organic symptoms, and mental life as these are affected by powerful emotional forces such as hate and anger or demands for love and care. These forces, their intensity, sources, and objects may not be recognized at all by the patient or may be inadequately appreciated. Few of us "see ourselves as others see us." The individual does not see these impulses and tendencies in himself because they would disturb his opinion and ideal of himself. He represses and is not conscious of that within himself which not only psychoanalysis reveals but which is often perceptible to any observer of human nature.

IV

These emotional energies manifest themselves in various directions, as though the nervous system were a hydrodynamic one. The man with the headaches developed tachycardia and extrasystoles for two months before his anxiety was worked through, and the girl with the diarrhea developed low back pains. It is well known that one hysterical symptom will give place to another. It would seem that emotional energies which are not discharged via the voluntary nervous system persist somehow, somewhere, probably at what Cannon calls the "emotional level," and act as chronic stimuli to parts of the voluntary, sympathetic, or parasympathetic systems. In civilized communities man's hostile and sexual impulses must be con-

---

6 Survey of 226 individual cases accepted for psychoanalysis: 1932-1937. *Supplement to the Five-Year Report of the Institute for Psychoanalysis.*

trolled to a large degree. This control becomes to a certain extent automatic and unconscious. But the drives persist and can affect the physiology. When the girl's anger at her mother and sister became intense enough, she developed diarrhea.

The physiological effects of the psychoanalytic therapy depend first upon making conscious to the patient those emotional energies (loves, hates, fears, and so on) which act as stimuli to parts of the nervous system and result in symptoms. The symptoms may be referable to the voluntary, as hysterical tremors, to the sympathetic, as tachycardia, or to the parasympathetic, as diarrhea. Secondly, it is necessary to help the patient master the emotions which, if I may use the expression, are no longer "drained" by the symptoms, and which must now be dealt with psychologically by the patient, i.e., by the higher levels of his nervous system. Consciousness evidently has a special buffer effect. Through it these emotional problems, which otherwise usually persist for life, can be resolved. As Macfie Campbell has put it: "Conscious emotion is not perpetual emotion." Or, as Freud said: ". . . we have conceived the principle which governs all mental processes as a special case of Fechner's *tendency to stability,* and consequently have ascribed to the mental apparatus the aim of extinguishing, or at least of maintaining at as low a level as possible, the quantities of excitation flowing into it." Why this is, if it is, what neurological mechanisms are involved, what are the sources of emotional energies, and similar vital questions, the analyst must leave to the biologist and physiologist.[7]

The above described relationship between emotional tension and symptom is seen quite clearly in patients who are studied psychoanalytically. It can also frequently be observed without analysis. The question arises whether it is not possible to treat the symptoms by some other form of therapy, either directly physical in approach

---

[7] For provisional theories see, for example, Freud, Sigmund, *Beyond the pleasure principle.* London: The International Psychoanalytical Press, 1922. Alexander, Franz, *The medical value of psychoanalysis.* New York: W. W. Norton & Co., 1936.
The following are just a few examples of some of the important problems in this field, and of some of the recent work upon them: What are the sources of these impulses that have the power to so affect the physiology of the organism? This is a question the answer to which must probably come from the biological study of instinctual impulses and perhaps from endocrinology. In what way is the physiology affected by the different emotions? Cannon's studies of bodily changes have pioneered the way to this approach. How are these impulses affected by the early environment? An example of an experimental approach to this question is: David Levy overgratified the sucking of half the puppies of a litter and frustrated the sucking of the other half, with very marked effects upon their later sucking activities and temperaments.
Can the conflict and repression which are observed psychologically be described physiologically? An example of the experimental approach is the work of Liddell in which conflicts are produced in animals by the technique of conditioned reflexes; and for localization, the work of Bard. Whatever the eventual sources in the tissues, do these impulses set up detectable excitations in the central nervous system? If so, where? What is the nature of the excitation? How is repression effected? How is the region of the brain which is concerned with consciousness able to handle these excitations so that they do not stimulate other pathways and disturb function? Such questions are in the realm of neurophysiology.

or by other forms of psychotherapy. In many cases this is, of course, both possible and advisable. Analysis is like major surgery and is not advisable if good results can be obtained by more superficial methods. Sometimes the symptoms are relieved simply by the patient's establishing rapport with the physician, that is, the so-called transference cures. In other cases, insight without working it through can produce marked results. But the reflections in the mental and emotional life of an individual's often conflicting biological drives are usually complex. Since they reflect themselves in his mental life, the best approach to them is usually through his mental life, that is, by psychotherapy. But since these mental manifestations are usually deep-seated and complex, any radical cure must involve very thorough study of them. Hence, to influence through psychotherapy the underlying conflicting biological urges requires a thorough study of the mental and emotional representatives of these urges, namely, of the patient's psychology. No matter how clearly worked out are the relationships between the symptoms, the drives, and the mental life, no causal therapy by this approach is possible without an understanding of the individual's psychology. One of the main points which distinguish psychoanalysis from other forms of psychotherapy is that by encouraging the patient to free association the analyst encourages the development toward himself of the conflicting emotions which the patient has toward human beings. The analyst thus has a laboratory sample, so to speak, of the patient's emotional life as it develops toward himself, and he can subject its development to careful study. In learning to handle this concrete sample of his emotional reactions toward another individual, the patient becomes conscious of his conflicting drives and learns to handle them consciously in life, that is, to deal with them through the higher levels of the central nervous system. The chronic effects of these drives on the viscera are thus relieved, and the patient need no longer use large amounts of energy in unconsciously controlling them.

Only a few remarks can be made upon the question of the choice of symptom or the choice of neurosis. Probably the stresses of life produce particular physiological or psychological (i.e., neurophysiological) effects in individual cases because of the differences in the stresses experienced, in individual constitution, in relative weaknesses of certain organs which then give way rather than others, and in the conditioning experiences of early childhood. For example, one child may be allowed to express his rages quite freely as compared to another. Later in life he will allow himself to become angry while the other gets a headache. Again, a person who has been overprotected in childhood will more readily feel the stress of a highly competitive society which demands extreme aggressiveness and independence and will more readily develop symptoms. Another factor, as shown by recent work, is that certain emotions tend to affect predominantly certain organs or symptoms. Repressed longings for a retreat to love, care, and protection in overtly driving, aggressive business men is the picture regularly found in cases of gastric ulcer. Chronic rage hidden beneath the surface of gentle, considerate individuals has been found regularly in a small series of cases of essential hypertension. Such studies point the way to the problems of why some individuals act out their drives through the voluntary nervous system and become men of action or neurotic character, while others manifest certain symptoms chiefly referable to the sympathetic nervous system, such as elevations in blood pressure or palpitations, and others show chiefly parasympathetic symptoms such as gastrointestinal disturbances or asthma. In still other cases the somatic symptoms are in the background and the main disturbance is in the sphere of mental functioning, i.e., in the higher levels of the central nervous system. It is obvious that to understand these problems, even from the physiological aspect alone, one must take into account the history of the organism, its early conditioning experiences, and its reactions to life situations.

Summary

In every person there are powerful biological impulses of which he is unaware. Sometimes these impulses, with their accompanying ideation and effect, are so blocked and unsatisfied that they are the source of constant inner stimulation which disturbs the normal functioning of the organism. Physiology studies the effects of these excitations on organs, psychology observes them through the behavior and mental life. The basic problem is biological in terms of the organism as a unit. Psychoanalysis produces marked physiological effects, in the direction of the relief of physical and mental symptoms usually after temporary exacerbation, by making conscious these unconscious impulses with their ideation and affect and then helping the patient deal with this affect and with the emotional problem. The energy hitherto used in repressing the impulses is put at the disposal of the voluntary system, i.e., is freed for use in living. What the mechanism of these processes is is a central problem in the rapidly developing domain of psychophysiology. This problem is already susceptible of experimental investigation, and certain phases

are fast coming within the scope of endocrinology and neurophysiology.

BIBLIOGRAPHY

1. CANNON, W. B. *Bodily changes in pain, hunger, fear, and rage.* New York:
   D. Appleton-Century Co. 1934.
2. PAVLOV, I. P. *Conditioned reflexes.* London: Oxford University Press, 1927.
3. FREUD, SIGMUND. On the history of the psychoanalytic movement. In *Collected
   papers,* Vol. 1. London: Hogarth Press, 1924.
4. FREUD, SIGMUND, AND BREUER, JOSEF. *Studies in hysteria.* Washington, D. C.:
   Nervous & Mental Disease Publishing Company, 1938.
5. ALEXANDER, FRANZ, AND CO-WORKERS. The influence of psychologic factors
   upon gastro-intestinal disturbances: a symposium. *Psychoanal. Quart.,* 1934,
   3, 501, 588. (In this volume, page 103.)

PART II

DISTURBANCES OF THE GASTROINTESTINAL TRACT

PSYCHOLOGIC FACTORS IN GASTROINTESTINAL DISTURBANCES *

GENERAL PRINCIPLES, OBJECTIVES, AND PRELIMINARY RESULTS

By Franz Alexander, M.D.

The research upon the influence of psychic factors on gastrointestinal disturbances, a collective work by the Chicago Institute for Psychoanalysis, is part of a more comprehensive study, namely the systematic investigation of the influence of psychic factors upon the different vegetative systems: the circulatory, respiratory, and the endocrine systems. The principal reasons for beginning with the investigation of parallel cases of gastrointestinal disturbance are three:

1. In former years I made certain observations in cases of gastric neuroses which seemed to me not only typical of such cases but also important in respect to the etiology of peptic ulcer, one of the great riddles of internal medicine. In a patient with a chronic gastric neurosis of fifteen years duration, who at one time developed a peptic ulcer, I could trace with great clarity the relation to gastric symptoms of certain emotional conflicts and situations, and with wider experience the wish to study a number of similar cases for further confirmation of these connections became more urgent. In private practice the choice of suitable cases is not always possible, but the organization of the Chicago Institute for Psychoanalysis, the primary aim of which is to further research, has given me the opportunity I desired, with a freer choice of parallel cases suitable for such investigations.

2. The second reason for beginning with the study of the gastrointestinal tract was the well-established fact, recognized both by organicists and psychoanalysts, that the alimentary tract is a system which the psychic apparatus uses with great predilection to relieve different emotional tensions. The connection between psychic stimuli and physiologic expression is here direct and relatively uncomplicated. Oral-receptive and aggressive-taking tendencies as well as

* The Psychoanalytic Quarterly III : 501-588, 1934.

anal-sadistic and retentive impulses have long and well-established relationships to such phenomena as nausea, vomiting, constipation, and diarrhea.[1] In this field our investigation could therefore start from well-established premises, and we were on more solid ground than we should have been, for example, in the field of the respiratory tract or of the internal secretions.

3. Finally we could profit from previous studies by internists who for a long time, and in increasing measure, have recognized the importance of psychologic phenomena as causative factors in a great many disorders of the gastrointestinal tract.

Though we took our departure from valuable psychoanalytic and medical observations, we found almost all the statements, both from organic and from psychoanalytic circles, incomplete. In medicine the usual attitude toward etiology is that when the organic origin of the symptom has been carefully eliminated, and when, at the same time, the patient's manifest behavior exhibits what is commonly called "nervousness," then one is justified in assuming psychic factors. After such a diagnosis has been made and expressed in vague terms taken from everyday language, such as "nervous exhaustion," "unstable personality," or "fatigue from overwork," or by the eclectic use of old and new technical terms such as "neurasthenia," "psychasthenia," "psychopathy," and other more or less indefinite expressions, the physician feels himself prepared to give therapeutic advice. The general notion is that the patient's nervous system is somehow overtaxed by the emotional strain of worries, fears, manifest discontent with life as it is, or by simply too much responsibility or overwork. There is little inclination to go more deeply into the nature of the patient's psychologic situation.

Without wishing to minimize the importance of such excellent

---

1 Here only a few references are made to the original observations of various analytic authors:

Regarding the fundamental connection between nutritive and erotic tendencies, see Freud, Sigmund, *Three contributions to the theory of sex*, Washington, D. C.: Nervous & Mental Disease Publishing Co., 1930. P. 43.

Regarding vomiting as defense or rejection tendency, see Ferenczi, Sándor, The phenomena of hysterical materialization in *Further contributions to the theory and technique of psycho-analysis*, London: Hogarth Press and the Institute of Psycho-Analysis, 1926. P. 95. Also see Disgust for breakfast, *ibid.*, 326.

Regarding the influence of complexes on the large bowel, see The phenomena of hysterical materialization, *ibid.*, 94.

Regarding psychic factors in constipation and diarrhea, see Freud, Sigmund. From the history of an infantile neurosis, in *Collected papers*, London: Hogarth Press and the Institute of Psycho-Analysis, 1926. Vol. 3.

Abraham, K. The narcissistic evaluation of excretory processes in dreams and neurosis, in *Selected papers*, London: Hogarth Press and the Institute of Psycho-Analysis, 1927. P. 321; Contributions to the theory of the anal character, *ibid.*, 387; A short history of the development of the libido, *ibid.*, 426.

Jones, E. *Papers on psychoanalysis*, New York: Wm. Wood & Co., 1923. P. 681.

Alexander, F. *The medical value of psychoanalysis*, New York: W. W. Norton & Co., 1932. P. 197.

work as Walter C. Alvarez's *Nervous Indigestion*,[2] we must state that the author's general attitude toward psychologic factors is exactly the one we have just described. Nevertheless, studies such as his [3] and those of Russel H. Oppenheimer,[4] George M. Underwood,[5] Albert J. Sullivan,[6] and W. B. Cannon [7]—to mention only a few recent publications—indicate definite progress in this field. They show a clear recognition of the fact that psychologic factors may play a causative role in organic disturbances, and moreover they attempt to establish, through careful clinical observation or experiment, the kind of disturbances which may result from emotional factors. They do not, however, attempt to describe precisely the psychologic situation or to find deeper relationships between certain types of emotional factors and certain types of physiologic process. This defect is common to all similar studies undertaken by internists and physiologists, with the exception of George Draper and Grace Touraine,[8] to whose work I shall return later.

I do not at this time propose a detailed and critical evaluation of the analytic literature in this field. The pioneer work of Georg Groddeck, Felix Deutsch, and Ernst Simmel has the merit of extending the view of hysterical conversion mechanisms from the field of the voluntary and sensory systems to organic diseases. In general, in the analytic approach to organic processes, there is a great readiness to interpret somatic phenomena as direct expressions of definite psychologic content. The fact that the organic symptoms are usually the final result of a chain of intermediary organic processes is hardly ever fully taken into account in analytic literature. Deutsch, who proceeds with more methodological care than other psychoanalytic authors in this field, in an early paper clearly distinguished between initial disturbances of innervation and those morphological changes which may result following such a functional disturbance of long duration.[9] As will be seen, this concept serves as a basis for our theory of the formation of peptic ulcers. But even Deutsch is not always consistent in the interpretation of organic con-

2 Alvarez, Walter C. *Nervous indigestion.* New York: Paul B. Hoeber, Inc., 1931.
3 *Ibid.*, and Light from the laboratory and the clinic on the causes of peptic ulcers. *Amer. J. Surg.,* 1932, **18**, 207-231.
4 Oppenheimer, Russel H. Gastrointestinal manifestations of the psychoneurotic state. *J. med. Assn. of Georgia,* 1932, **21**, 431-433.
5 Underwood, George M. Emotional and psychic factors in the production of gastro-intestinal diseases. *Texas J. Med.,* 1932, **27**, 798-800.
6 Sullivan, Albert J., and Chandler, C. A. Ulcerative colitis of psychogenic origin. *Yale J. Biol. Med.,* **4**, 1932, 779-796.
7 Cannon, W. B. *Bodily changes in pain, hunger, fear and rage.* New York: D. Appleton-Century Co., 1934.
8 Draper, George, and Touraine, Grace Allen. The man-environment unit and peptic ulcer. *Arch. intern. Med.,* 1932, **49**, 615-662.
9 Deutsch, F. Biologie und Psychologie der Krankheitsgenese. *Int. Z. Psychoanal.,* 1922, **8**, 290.

ditions. For example, in one case he interprets pulmonary hemorrhage as the direct expression of birth fantasies.[10] This impresses us as even more inconsistent because in the same place he considers the possibility that psychologic stimuli may lead to increased adrenalin production and in turn to changes in the blood pressure. The bleeding is then not the direct expression of a fantasy but the result of a change in blood pressure, even if the whole process was initiated by a very specific psychologic stimulus (specific fantasies or wishes). To state that in such a case the end result, the hemorrhage, has a simple and direct relation to a specific fantasy is not very convincing. It seems unquestionable that conversion in the vegetative nervous system does not always follow exactly the same rules as in the voluntary and sensory systems in which the original concepts of hysterical conversion have been formulated. Whereas in conversion hysteria the unconscious tendency finds a direct expression in the physical disturbances, in organic processes controlled by the vegetative nervous system often a longer chain of intermediary physiological processes is interpolated between psychological stimulus and organic end result. It is a methodological error to attempt to interpret psychologically an organic symptom which is the end result of an intermediary chain of organic processes, instead of trying to understand those vegetative nervous impulses in their relation to psychologic factors which introduce a chain of organic events resulting in an organic disturbance. Thus an ulcer of the stomach or duodenum is the direct result of a disturbance in the motor and secretory functions, which disturbance, however, may be caused by emotional factors. Yet the end result, the ulcer, cannot be interpreted psychologically because, in itself, it has no psychologic significance whatsoever. What *can* be interpreted as a direct effect of psychologic factors is the hyper- or hyposecretion and the change in the motor activity and blood supply of the stomach. Similarly, even psychogenic vomiting itself may not always express anything psychologic, for example, disgust, although the conditions in the stomach which led to vomiting may have been called forth by psychologic factors.[11]

Therefore psychophysiologic investigations must pay equal attention to psychologic and physiologic causal chains and carefully avoid confusion between the two series.

Pursuant to these considerations, we have made in the past two

---

10 Deutsch, F. Der gesunde und der kranke Körper in psychoanalytischer Betrachtung. *Int. Z. Psychoanal.*, 1926, **12**, 498.

11 I do not question, naturally, that often a specific psychological content can find direct expression also in the vegetative system, for example, blushing, psychogenic sweating, emotionally increased peristalsis, etc.

years at the Chicago Institute for Psychoanalysis a systematic study of psychic factors in gastrointestinal cases, and we are now extending the investigation to other vegetative systems—the respiratory and the circulatory. The guiding principles of these studies can be summarized under three headings:

1. Our first assumption or working hypothesis is that the psychic factors causative of the somatic disturbance are of a specific nature. They can be defined as certain emotional attitudes adopted by the patient toward his environment or directed toward his own person. Adequate knowledge of these causative factors can be obtained during the analytic treatment of the patients, and no other method—not even a careful psychiatric anamnesis—can be fully substituted for the analytic approach.

2. The patient's conscious psychologic processes play a subordinate role in the causation of somatic symptoms, since such conscious emotions and tendencies can be freely expressed and relieved through the voluntary system. Somatic changes, the influence of manifest anger, fear, and similar violent and outwardly apparent emotions, are of an acute nature and have only a precipitating influence. Repressed tendencies, however, lead to chronic innervations causing chronic dysfunction of the internal organs.

3. The patient's actual life situation has usually only a precipitating influence on the disturbance. The understanding of the causative psychologic factors must be based on a knowledge of the development of the patient's personality, which alone can explain the reactions to acute traumatic situations.

The object of our research is to establish the affinity of specific emotional factors or conflict situations, first, to specific vegetative systems, and second, to certain specific organic expressions within the same system. In addition to these theoretic objectives, we also expect to establish more definitely the therapeutic efficiency of the psychoanalytic approach to such cases, and to establish criteria for determining which cases need psychoanalysis and which can be handled by specific practical readjustments of the patient's life.

I shall proceed now to a few general formulations regarding our preliminary results. We have found that it is useful to make a rough preliminary classification of our cases into three groups. We distinguish with reference both to the somatic symptoms and to the typical psychologic conflict situation involved: *First,* a group of gastric cases including a wide range of patients with minor subjective gastric symptoms such as epigastric distress, nausea, heartburn, belching, etc., but also severe cases of peptic ulcer. The *second* group consists of cases with the predominant symptom of diarrhea, cases which are usually diagnosed as mucous or spastic colitis, exhibiting the symptoms of painful cramps and evacuations and often alternation of diarrhea and constipation. The *third* and last group comprises cases with the predominant symptom of chronic constipation. We shall refer to these three groups as the *gastric* type, the *colitis* type, and the *constipation* type.

We turned our attention at first to the patient's manifest emotional relations to the environment, and tried to decide whether certain *manifest* (overt) emotional attitudes, together with their immediate dynamic background, could be established as typical for the different groups of organic cases. For this purpose we could use analytic material obtained in cases whose analysis had not all been completed, or who were accepted only for anamnestic exploration. Of course a series of cases was accepted for complete analytic investigation and therapy, but in a number of cases we contented ourselves with the establishing of surface attitudes and their immediate unconscious background. These unconscious conflict-situations, which are the dynamic sources of the surface attitudes, can usually be adequately described before a full analytic reconstruction of their genesis has been accomplished.

Our second objective was to try, in selected cases, to obtain as complete a picture as possible regarding the analytic history of the patients. It should be emphasized that this second problem is at the present stage of our investigation of only secondary importance. One can hardly expect any great conformity regarding genesis, since we know that similar conflict-situations may develop from very different individual backgrounds. At first we wished to establish whether there is any constant parallelism of psychologic features in cases with the same organic syndromes. The next step will be the more precise comparison of the details of the developmental history of the patients.

Regarding the first problem, even in this early phase of our research we have been much impressed by a certain constancy of definite types of conflict-solution which seem to be characteristic for the different organic groups. This constancy of conflict-solutions becomes very striking if we describe the patient's emotional trends in terms of the three elemental tendencies of (a) the wish to receive or take, (b) the wish to give, or eliminate, (c) the wish to retain. It should be emphasized, however, that this kind of analysis of the emotional attitudes was not arbitrary, but was forced upon us during the course of our case studies. Furthermore we do not claim originality in differentiating these three fundamental tendencies : *in-taking, eliminating,* and *retaining,* for the recognition of these elementary tendencies is fundamental to the original concepts of the pregenital tendencies of oral, anal, and urethral erotism. Jones' and Abraham's analysis of the anal trends, in differentiating between anal-retaining and anal-eliminating tendencies, and Ferenczi's ideas regarding the amphimixis of anal retentive and urethral eliminating tendencies in genital sexuality, have paved the way for our consistent application of this point of view to cases of gastrointestinal disturbance.[12]

Apart from identical conflict-solutions, a remarkable similarity has been found with respect to certain surface attitudes, conspicuously in the gastric cases and almost equally in the colitis cases. The small number of investigated cases with chronic psychogenic constipation does not yet justify any final statement about typical surface attitudes and conflict-solutions in these patients.

Regarding the genesis of these conflict-solutions we have not yet been able to find any predominantly constant features.

It may be added that, in speaking of typical surface attitudes (emotional attitude toward the environment) and conflict-solutions, we do not refer to trends which we find as one among many other equally obvious features but refer to the predominant central dynamic trends. The predominant *surface* attitude, which the patient usually expresses in the very first interviews and in the first typical transference manifestations, and also the underlying dynamic conflict-situations, can, as a rule, be reconstructed soon and clearly.

In this report we restrict ourselves to the presentation of the most typical surface attitudes and underlying dynamic situations, and only in a few cases we refer in condensed case histories to the genetic material. The problem which we set ourselves here is to describe the different types of gastrointestinal cases with reference to the relation of their overt behavior, their emotional attitudes, and their psychosexual manifestations to the determining unconscious tendencies.

The material for our study is preserved in the form of semiverbatim reports of every analytic interview of every case. These reports contain full material of the patient's free-associations and the physician's interpretations without omissions.

The Gastric Type

This group included nine cases: six duodenal ulcers, (three of which were still active at the time of the analysis), and three gastric neuroses. The investigation of these cases has fully corroborated my

---

[12] Jones, E. *Papers on psycho-analysis*, pp. 696-704.

Abraham, K. A short study of the development of the libido viewed in the light of mental disorders, in *Selected papers*, pp. 425-433.

Ferenczi, Sándor, **Versuch einer Genitaltheorie**, pp. 7-27.

earlier observation that gastric symptoms often appear in connection with intense oral-receptive tendencies, the wish to be taken care of and loved, which usually are more or less repressed. In most cases the typical conflict-situation can be described as the rejection of strong oral-receptive tendencies on account of their incompatibility with the aspiration of the ego for independence and activity. In these patients the conscious attitude could be best verbalized as follows: "I am efficient, active, productive; or I give to everybody, help people, assume responsibilities, like to have people depend on me, like to be the effective leader and the self-sufficient, active, or even aggressive personality." At the same time we find in the unconscious exactly the opposite attitude: an extreme and violent craving for love and the need for dependence and help. These tendencies we find in most of our cases repressed and denied by the patient and associated with violent conflicts.

The next question now is, why does the wish to be loved and to receive become in these patients so full of conflicts that it must be strongly repressed and overcompensated? It is highly characteristic of these patients that in their actual life relations they avoid dependence and assume the exact opposite of the infantile oral-receptive attitude: instead of receiving we see in them often the tendency to give; instead of leaning on others, leadership; instead of dependence, the assuming of responsibility. It is evident that these overcompensations must reactively increase in their unconscious the longing for passive dependence because these individuals live beyond their psychic means in so strongly refusing and denying their need for external help. That their extreme, overemphasized independence and efforts in life increase the opposite unconscious longing for help does not need further explanation. The question, however, is, what is the basis of the phobic rejection and avoidance of the receptive dependent role, an avoidance which sometimes leads to an almost grotesquely exaggerated refusal to accept any help from the outside. In all of our cases we see in the unconscious a deep oral regression to the parasitic situation of the infant which in most cases is incompatible with the attitude and ideals of the adult ego and therefore must necessarily be rejected. The analysis of our cases shows among the specific reasons for the ego's rejection of these parasitic infantile claims two predominant motives: (1) a narcissistic injury caused by the infantile claims and manifested on the surface in a sense of inferiority on the one hand, and (2) guilt and fear on the other.

1. Let us consider the first conflict-motive, the *sense of inferiority*. The extreme infantile receptive cravings create a strong feeling of inferiority, they hurt the aspirations of the ego toward an independ-

ent, superior, active, and generous attitude.[13]   This leads to the typical mechanism of overcompensation.   In most of our cases we found that this overcompensation is not only expresed by fantasies of efficient activity, but usually has led to a really active and responsible attitude in life, to real efficiency and success, or at least to real efforts in this direction.   The tendency to an extreme and concentrated exerting of effort is most characteristic of these patients.   However, we also see that this compensatory overactive and often "giving" (generous) attitude again increases in turn the repressed receptive wishes for dependence and love.   These patients do not seem willing to allow themselves in practice any gratification of a receptive nature, and for this very reason the thirst for rest and receptiveness increases in them as a reaction to their actual overexertions in life.

One solution of the same conflict between the receptive cravings and their rejection I have described in a former paper.[14]   This was an alternating gratification of the two conflicting tendencies; active and receptive gratifications alternate or find simultaneous expression in different life relations.   I refer to the case of the active leader of a great industrial concern who at the same time assumed, like a little boy, an attitude of extreme infantile dependence on his wife.   Although this patient has some neurotic gastric symptoms, patients of the gastric type seldom adopt this solution.   As a rule they live for long periods a one-sided life of extreme activity and responsibility, and the dynamic equilibrium between the indulgence of passive-receptive and active-giving tendencies is emphatically dominated by the latter.   This general dynamic situation we have found both in male and in female patients.

2. In addition to the motive of the sense of inferiority caused by the unconscious receptive tendencies, another constant motive for the repression of the receptive tendencies is a *guilt reaction*.   The extreme receptivity (I shall call it now parasitic receptiveness) in addition to the feeling of inferiority or shame, leads also to the feeling of guilt and the tendency to compensate for this in-taking attitude with actual giving of real values such as love, help, efforts for the sake of others, and productive activities of every kind.   The guilt reactions, however, are especially pronounced in cases in which the oral-receptive tendency under the influence of early thwartings in life assume an oral-sadistic connotation.   The wish to receive often changes both

---

[13] Abraham observed the connection between oral character trends and generosity which he considers an oral character trait.   He observed the fact but explained it through identification with the bounteous mother and did not yet see the over-compensative nature of this connection.   The same is true of his explanation that the tendency to sucking changes into the need to give. Abraham, K. The influence of oral eroticism on character formation, in *Selected papers*, pp. 401-403.

[14] Alexander, F. The neurotic character. *Int. J. Psycho-Anal.*, 1930, 2, 300-302.

in women and in men under the influence of early thwarting into the wish to take aggressively: "If it is not given to me, I must take it by force." Usually, however, the passive-receptive and the oral-aggressive tendencies, the wish to receive and to take, are intermingled. It is evident that such strong oral-aggressive grabbing tendencies necessarily must lead not only to an inhibition of these aggressions but make it difficult for the individual to indulge in his receptive wishes, make it impossible for him to accept support or affection from those whom unconsciously he wants to rob.

Our studies have not yet been able to establish any constant background regarding the origin of the strong regression to the parasitic oral-receptive attitude other than the usual conflicts in the field of genital sexuality, conflicts based on guilt feelings, in men centering around castration fear.

In the great majority of our cases we found an inner rejection of passive-receptive and oral-aggressive tendencies. In one case, however, the tendency towards oral-dependence was thwarted chiefly through external circumstances and to a less degree through inner rejection. In another case we have seen a mixture of both external and internal thwartings of receptive dependent tendencies. In two recently observed cases of severe recurrent peptic ulcer, the extremely strong oral-receptive cravings were not successfully repressed or overcompensated, but appeared more openly in consciousness. The history of both of these cases showed early and extreme oral deprivation in childhood. It seems that their real sufferings in childhood and in later life made it possible for these patients to cling more openly to their receptive claims.

However, the predominance of an inner conflict over the longing for dependence in our gastric cases might encourage the expectation that we shall find a personality typical of the larger group of oral characters with overcompensated oral-receptiveness and oral-sadism which is especially inclined to gastric disturbances. One might even find that this is the peptic ulcer personality which many internists are eagerly seeking to define. Indeed in recent years various clinicians, such as Von Bergmann,[15] Westphal,[16] Alvarez,[17] Hartman,[18] Draper,[19] and others, have come to suspect that factors in the per-

15 Bergmann, G. von. Ulcus duodeni und vegetatives Nervensystem. *Ber. klin. Wchschr.,* 1913, 50.

16 Westphal, K. Untersuchungen zur Frage der nervösen Entstehung peptischer Ulcera. *Deut. Arch. klin. Med.,* 1914, 114.

Westphal, K., and Katsch, G. Das neurotische Ulcus duodeni. *Mitt. a. d. Med. u. Chir.,* 1913, 26.

17 Alvarez, Walter C., *op. cit.*

18 Hartman, Howard R. Neurogenic factors in peptic ulcer. *Med. Clin. N. A.,* 16, No. 6, p. 1366.

19 Draper, George, and Touraine, Grace Allen, *loc. cit.*

sonality are active in the causation of peptic ulcer. They find that certain types of personality are more inclined to peptic ulcer than others. Westphal emphasizes the liability of the vegetative nervous system as characteristic of ulcer patients. His master, Bergmann, attributes the same importance to the influence of the vegetative nervous system upon peptic ulcer formation, and is inclined even to consider psychologic factors. Some American authors pay even greater attention to personality factors. Alvarez speaks of the type of efficient, active Jewish business man, the "go-getter" type, as being particularly disposed to recurrent peptic ulcers.[20] Hartman characterizes the peptic ulcer type as a man who is "encountering obstacles which prove to him trial and handicap which he must, because of his nature, endeavor to overcome." [21] He claims that the Indians of Latin America and the Chinese coolies never have ulcers, and explains this as a result of the stoic, almost apathetic attitude, the lack of strain and ambition, characteristic of these races. According to him, ulcer is a disease of the civilized world and afflicts chiefly the striving and ambitious men of Western civilization.

George Draper and Grace Touraine have arrived at a similar assumption.[22] Their investigation of the patient's personality trends was based on a better psychologic background than most clinicians have; they did not rely entirely on the general impression which a good clinician receives from the type of personality he deals with. In their article they quote a series of case histories which they refer to as "analyzed" cases, and other cases which are based on nonanalytic but careful anamnestic studies. Due to their finer psychologic method they were able to penetrate beyond the surface and to discover in addition to certain manifest personality factors a typical conflict-situation. They come close to the picture which I have just described. They found typical of their patients a masculine protest, a rejection of unconscious female tendencies, the same tendencies which, according to our psychoanalytic study, we prefer to describe as oral-receptive or oral-sadistic impulses which, as we know, are closely related to strivings commonly regarded as female. Draper also complemented his studies with anthropologic measurements and tried to describe the peptic ulcer type as characterized psychologically by the presence of a masculine protest and anatomically as the asthenic or longitudinal type.

On the basis of our studies we would also be inclined to assume that in a certain personality type gastric symptoms, or even peptic

---

[20] Alvarez, Walter C. Light from the laboratory and the clinic on the causes of peptic ulcers. *Amer. J. Surg.*, 1932, **18**, 225.
[21] Hartman, Howard R., *loc. cit.*
[22] Draper, George, and Touraine, Grace Allen, *loc. cit.*

ulcers, may more frequently develop than in other types, but the exceptions which we have encountered at a very early stage of our research do not encourage us to expect such a simple and generally valid result. What we find characteristic is not so much a certain personality type as a typical conflict-situation which may develop in very different personalities. Though certain types will be more inclined to become involved in the conflict between receptive and active-giving tendencies and to solve it by overcompensation-mechanisms, yet we see that under *right external conditions* other types of character may develop the same conflict.

For example, in one of our peptic ulcer cases (a 46-year-old man who was subjected to an anamnestic analysis of three weeks), it was much more the external life situation than a deeply located internal rejection of his passive wishes that had deprived the patient of the satisfaction of his oral-receptive tendencies. During his childhood and adolescence he had indulged profusely in receptive gratification, was not at all the leader type, but, on the contrary, his attitude entirely lacked the usual ambition so frequent in peptic ulcer cases. He married an extremely able, intelligent, intellectually superior, active woman of the leader type; his marriage, however, soon disappointed all his expectations of finding in his wife a superior person who would serve as a substitute for a generously giving mother. Not that she changed after their marriage, but from the beginning she devoted her life entirely to the promotion of her career, to learning, working, and producing. Moreover their sexual life was most unsatisfactory. The wife was frigid and the patient suffered from premature ejaculation. The husband received nothing from his wife, and being thwarted in his receptive tendencies he soon was driven into a competitive attitude toward his wife who even financially was the chief support of the household. Instead of being mothered by his wife, he had been driven by her superiority to an ambition and effort which he deeply detested. This was quite a contrast to the majority of our gastric cases who generally enjoy their responsible and active role. I may add that he never succeeded in any active efforts and remained always mediocre in his profession. At the peak of this conflict-situation, after 20 years of marriage, he developed a severe hemorrhage as a result of a peptic ulcer. But during all those years he suffered from gastric symptoms, chiefly from pain a few hours after eating, which was relieved by food, and from chronic hyperacidity. The ulcer appeared after this gastric disorder of 18 years duration.

Shortly after this hemorrhage he started a sexual relationship with another woman of a motherly type, the exact opposite of his wife. His wife, he complained, never would cook for him, but this woman did. She was a nice, soft, everyday type of woman who did not drive him into unattainable ambitions. He could live with her the modest life of the petty bourgeois, which, as he openly admitted, was his only ideal. Since establishing sexual relations with this woman, all the symptoms have disappeared. Life supplied a cure in allowing him the gratification of his receptive tendencies.

This one example alone shows that it is the thwarting of receptive cravings, and not a certain personality type, that is of primary importance. Here the specific external situation in which the patient lived created a conflict through external deprivation similar to the one which, in the majority of cases, is produced by internal deprivation as a result of an inner conflict.

The typical conflict between the repressed receptive infantile wish and the claims of a masculine ego may explain the following interesting observation. One of my former patient's stomach symptoms appeared with great regularity when he saw scenes in the movies or theater in which the hero was accomplishing strenuous and daring feats and had to concentrate all his forces in a great effort. Our accumulated observations regarding the connection between passive-receptive tendencies and stomach symptoms indicate the following explanation: The patient's identification with such an extremely heroic and masculine character provoked in him a reaction of the infantile receptive part of his personality which found expression in stomach innervations leading to severe heartburn and epigastric distress. Having thus identified himself with a degree of aggressiveness and boldness which exceeded his own capacity, the child in him claimed its own rights as a flight from all these dangers to the securest situation at the mother's breast. This regression to infantile attitudes as a reaction to danger can clearly be seen in traumatic neuroses, in cases of traumatic mutism and abasia, in which very often, as a reaction to the trauma, the patient's ego abandons all faculties which are acquired during development, loses the faculty of walking and speaking, and returns to the entirely helpless situation of the infant.

Having described the typical psychologic situation which we find in our gastric cases, I should like to suggest briefly a tentative explanation as to how repressed oral-receptive and oral-aggressive impulses may lead to gastric symptoms and even to peptic ulcer of the stomach or duodenum. This explanation which I am about to advance is an attempt to account for the constancy and predominance of intensive oral-receptive and oral-aggressive tendencies, both of which I should like to summarize under the heading *in-taking tendencies,* which become so intensive as a result of *internal* rejection or, probably much less frequently, *external* deprivation of these cravings.

Most clinicians agree that peptic ulcers are due to certain physiologic changes in the secretory and motor functions of the stomach and possibly also to changes in the blood supply. A great many cases of peptic ulcer develop after a long period of subjective symptoms of epigastric distress and chronic heartburn. It is a logical assumption that the peptic ulcer itself is the end-result of certain dysfunctions of the stomach which in due time lead to morphologic changes, i.e., to the ulceration of the tissue. It is probable that either the decreased resistance of the stomach wall against the gastric juice or, in other cases, a chronic hypersecretion is the causative factor. The etiologic problem is to establish the causes of these chronic changes of the stomach function which lead to the final result, the ulcer.

The assumption that the ulcers are the end-result of a previous chronic state of functional disturbance of the stomach justifies our procedure of comparing pronounced cases of ulcers with gastric neuroses. This hypothesis is also confirmed by the fact that we find the identical conflict-situation in both functional and organic cases. Also Westphal found an identical picture in cases of gastric neurosis and peptic ulcers regarding their general constitution.[23] He assumes a causal connection between gastric neurosis and peptic ulcers, and is even inclined to consider ulcer as an aggravating complication of the neurosis.

In the light of psychoanalytic theory it is not difficult to understand why the functions of nutrition are especially adapted to express the repressed or externally thwarted receptive tendencies which we find predominant in all of our cases. The infantile wish to receive, to be taken care of, to be loved, to depend upon someone else is most ideally gratified in the parasitic situation of the suckling infant. Thus these emotional qualities of receptivity, the wish to be loved and taken care of, become closely associated in an early period of life with the physiologic functions of nutrition. Being fed thus becomes the primordial symbol (*Ursymbol*) of being loved.

If the intense wish to receive, to be loved, to depend upon others, is rejected by the adult ego and consequently cannot find gratification in normal life relations, then only the regressive pathway remains open; the wish to be loved becomes converted into the wish to be fed. The repressed longing to receive love and help mobilizes the innervations of the stomach which are, since the beginning of the extra-uterine life, closely associated with the most primordial form of receiving something, namely, with the process of receiving food. These innervations serve as a chronic stimulus of the stomach func-

---

23 Westphal, K. Untersuchungen zur Frage der nervösen Entstehung peptischer Ulcera. *Deut. Arch. klin. Med.*, 1914, **114.**

tions and lead to its dysfunction, since this stimulus of the stomach is independent of the normal organically conditioned stimulus, namely, the need of food; this stimulus has its origin in emotional conflicts entirely independent of the physiologic state of hunger. Those individuals who, on account of the described conflict-situation, have to repress and abnegate their overstrong receptive cravings, express them in the tacit physiologic language of the stomach functions. Such a stomach behaves all the time as if it were taking or were about to take in food. The greater the rejection of every receptive gratification in life, the greater will be this unconscious wish (we may now call it justifiably *hunger*) for receiving love and help. They want food, not because of organic hunger, but as a symbol of love and help.

My present notion is that the stomach under this permanent chronic stimulation behaves constantly as it does during digestion. A chronic hypermotility and hypersecretion may be the consequence. The empty stomach is thus constantly exposed to the same physiologic stimuli to which, under normal conditions, it is exposed only periodically when it contains or is about to receive food. The symptoms of nervous stomach, epigastric distress, heartburn, and belching probably are the manifestations of this chronic stimulation which sometimes may even lead to ulcer formation.

The question as to whether a constitutional or an acquired weakness of the stomach is responsible for the fact that only certain cases of gastric neurosis develop real ulcers must be left unanswered at present.

There is much experimental and clinical evidence for the correctness of these assumptions. Alvarez, in one of his studies, considers such chronic stimulation of the empty stomach as one of the etiologic factors in peptic ulcer.[24] Most interesting in this respect are the experiments of Silbermann, who produced ulcers in the stomachs of dogs by sham feeding through an artificial esophageal fistula.[25] The food which the dog swallows falls on the floor and the dogs snaps it up again and goes on eating greedily for perhaps even as long as three quarters of an hour. The result is a powerful stimulation of gastric secretion in the empty stomach which leads regularly to ulcer formation. The process at work in the patients which we

---

[24] Alvarez, Walter C. Light from the laboratory and the clinic on the causes of peptic ulcers. *Amer. J. Surg.*, 1932, 18.

"Perhaps the greatest difficulty with the patients with intractable ulcer or with a tendency to the formation of ulcers is that the gastric cells go on secreting acid at times when there is no food in the stomach to sop it up." . . . p. 222.

"It might be helpful to study also the reactions of the ulcer-bearing patient to sham feeding, and more might be learned about the mechanisms which cause juice to flow when the stomach is empty." . . . p. 226.

[25] Silbermann, I. S. Experimentelle Magenduodenalulcuserzeugung durch Scheinfüttern nach Pavlov. *Zbl. f. Chir.*, 1927, 54, 2385-2392.

have investigated can best be compared with this sham feeding of dogs. They are in a state of chronic stimulation of the stomach, not as a result of the process of nutrition, but in reaction to the psychologic stimulus of longing to be loved and to receive, or to take in aggressively what they do not get freely. Since these tendencies are repressed because of a sense of inferiority in being so receptive, and because of guilt for the aggressive, "taking" wishes, they cannot find a normal outlet through the voluntary system. In seeking discharge they are converted into the wish to be fed or to eat, and this is the basis of the dysfunctions of the stomach. Of course, in addition to further psychologic investigation of similar cases, further physiologic corroboration of these ideas is also necessary to prove their final validity.

A very interesting corroboration of the assumption that one of the causative factors in peptic ulcer formation is due to continuous secretion under the influence of chronic psychological stimuli (oral fantasies and oral tendencies) is contained in the experimental studies of Henning and Norpoth,[26] in Germany, and Palmer and Winkelstein,[27] in America. Henning and Norpoth found a maximal permanent secretion (*maximale Dauersekretion*) of the stomach glands during the night in cases of stomach disease. The greatest number of these cases had ulcus duodeni. They also found high nocturnal secretion in cases of chronic gastritis, and also in cases of "vegetative neurosis" with healthy stomach. Similarly, Winkelstein observed high acid curves in ulcer patients produced with sham ("psychic") feeding. Furthermore, contrasted with controls, the patients with gastric or duodenal ulcer showed a high nocturnal curve of acidity. These observations are in full correspondence with our views. They show the sensitiveness of the stomach secretion of the ulcer patients to nervous stimuli, and they also show that the assumed continuous secretion is present in them. It seems that not the absolute grade of hyperacidity is important, but the chronic state of excitement of the stomach, the chronic secretion of gastric juice. Our studies add to these observations the actual predominance and frequency of oral tendencies and oral fantasies which we consider as those psychologic stimuli which lead to the continuous secretion of gastric juice.

Finally, I should like to repeat again that our whole concept regarding the psychogenic factors in peptic ulcer is based on the ana-

26 Henning, N., and Norpoth, L. Untersuchungen über die sekretorische Funktion des Magens während des nächtlichen Schlafes. *Arch. f. Verdauungskrankheiten, Stoffwechselpathologie, und Diätetik,* 1933, 53, 64.

27 Winkelstein, Asher. A new therapy of peptic ulcer. *Amer. J. med. Sci.,* 1933, 185, 695.

Palmer, Walter L. Fundamental difficulties in the treatment of peptic ulcer. *J. Amer. med. Assn.,* 1933, 1604-1607.

lytically well-established fact that the wish to be taken care of and to be helped, which we have so constantly found in the investigated cases, is emotionally connected in the unconscious with the wish to be fed. We do not claim originality in establishing this connection, and we refer to the abundant psychoanalytic literature in which this connection has been described by various authors.[28]

Furthermore this explanation cannot be considered as an attempt to formulate a generally valid etiological theory of peptic ulcer. It refers to a series of observed cases, and we have no evidence whatsoever that other cases of peptic ulcer may not develop on a different and perhaps nonpsychogenic basis. Moreover, our material unfortunately consists only of cases of duodenal ulcer, and consequently all our conclusions are restricted to this localization of ulcers.

Finally a last question must be answered. We found in our cases of peptic ulcer and gastric neurosis a strong regression to the infantile attitude of oral receptiveness and aggressiveness. Furthermore we saw that these infantile cravings become thwarted externally by circumstances, but more frequently internally by the conflict connected with the oral-receptive and oral-sadistic impulses which lead to overcompensations, to an overemphasized independence that again in turn eliminates all legitimate normal satisfaction of the so-human claims in the direction of leaning on others and being helped by others. We understood that this increases even more the unconscious craving for the infantile dependent role, which longing again mobilizes the emotionally associated wish for being fed, and that this latter wish serves as a permanent stimulus of the empty stomach and causes its dysfunction. This all seems clear and is in harmony with our psychologic and physiologic knowledge and explains the observed facts. However, the same intensive conflicts about oral-receptive and oral-aggressive tendencies connected with the feeling of guilt and inferiority and with the typical overcompensations are common in many forms of neurosis. The psychological situation which we have described in our peptic ulcer cases and gastric neuroses is by no means specific and restricted to these cases. Consequently the conversion of the wish to be loved and to receive into the innervations of the stomach can be considered as only one of the many possible dynamic outcomes of the same unconscious conflict-situation. Why certain individuals choose just this physiological solution remains an unanswered question which belongs to the dark, hitherto unsolved, field of the "choice of neurosis." The most probable assumption is that if

---

28 Regarding the connection of oral gratifications in the sucking period with the pleasure in taking and in being given something, I refer to the original observations of Freud and Abraham: Freud, Sigmund. *Three contributions to the theory of sex,* p. 43. Abraham, K. The influence of oral eroticism on character formation, in *Selected papers,* p. 399.

certain unknown organic factors coincide with the above described psychodynamic configurations, they, together with these psychic factors, will lead to ulcer formation. The constancy of the oral regression and the frequency of the overcompensation and repression of oral-receptive and oral-aggressive trends entitles us, however, to suspect this psychodynamic situation to be the outstanding *psychic* factor in the etiology of duodenal ulcer. The contribution of psychoanalysis to this problem ends with the description of the typical psychodynamic conditions characteristic of ulcer cases.

The Colitis Type

A different solution of the same conflict was found typical of the second group of cases which I call the colitis type. This includes cases usually called mucous or spastic colitis, characterized by constipation alternating with painful diarrhea with cramps and often mucous evacuations. We have chosen five cases in which the diarrhea is the most conspicuous symptom.

One of our patients has had six to twenty evacuations daily for three years. In order to eliminate the possibility of organic factors, we have so far avoided cases of ulcerative colitis.

On the surface these cases present a very different appearance from the gastric class. Whereas most of our gastric cases emphatically deny all their receptive tendencies, their need for help—their wish for dependence—these colitis patients emphasize, in the first place, that they do not receive from others what they should in spite of their own great willingness to help and give, and in spite of their generosity and interest in others. Whereas the gastric types in reality are efficient, frequently also helpful and generous, or at least make real efforts to be so, the colitis cases do only lip service in this respect. It is true that before their illness they had often been efficient and active, but afterward they easily accepted a dependent position, which is not the situation in the gastric cases. They readily give up their work, or, if they have worked, they have usually done so as a result of external necessity and have lacked the genuine effort and ambition characteristic of the gastric patients.

The difference between the colitis and the gastric type is similar to that between a phobia and a compulsion neurosis. In the phobia we see only fear and inhibition of activities that have an objectionable unconscious symbolic significance, such as walking on the street, which is avoided because it is symbolic of prostitute fantasies, or such as writing as a symbol of incest, or touching people as a symbol of murderous wishes; but we do not see any neurotic devices that permit the acceptance of these forbidden tendencies.

If a phobia, however, develops into a compulsion neurosis, we find that by submitting to certain conditions the patients are able to achieve all of these symbolic gratifications by certain compensatory symptoms: They can eliminate the fear and guilt reactions to the rejected unconscious tendencies—they may walk on the street, provided they carry out certain ceremonies; if they perform a washing ceremony, they may touch people; the rejected tendencies may be gratified, provided that other symptoms make atonement for their symbolic fantasied crimes and give restitution for fantasied damages.

Like the phobias, many of our gastric cases are not able under any conditions consciously to permit the indulgence of their receptive or oral-aggressive tendencies, or at least have to fight continuously against them, whereas our colitis patients, like the compulsion neurotics, are able to receive, to make demands on others and be supported by them, provided they pay for it in the form of painful evacuations. In their unconscious, often even in consciousness, we find the same oral-receptive and acquisitive aggressive tendencies which are so strong in the gastric cases, but both the fear and sense of inferiority are eliminated, probably because of the symbolic meaning of the physiologic symptom, diarrhea. This has the meaning of restitution for what they wish to take from others, and also that of activity and aggression in contrast to passive in-taking.

In these cases the lower end of the intestinal tract, the function of which consists mainly in elimination, is mobilized and excited to increased activity. They give anal, or rather, intestinal values as a compensation for oral receptivity and aggressiveness in order to keep up the balance between the receiving and the eliminating tendencies. In two of our cases—both office girls—the envy of the younger sister who replaced them in the receptive role of the baby played an important role. In one case the presence of this younger sister was a stimulating factor in precipitating the diarrhea. "I do not want to take anything away from her, and, even if I do, I pay for it," is the dynamic formula of this symptom.

In the case of an extremely successful business man suffering from a severe case of colitis, we found that even as a young boy he successfully competed with his father in the support of the family. Very early in adolescence he became their chief support. The leading motive of his life is a fantasy of rescuing the parents. "I took my mother from my weak father, but only in order to help her. Apart from supporting her, I also helped him." He indeed became very successful in his life, and his leading motive everywhere was, "I give real values and therefore I deserve my success." This emotional balance prevails until he is 44 years old. Then at the peak of his success, he loses all his money. To give and pay with money had been his means of keeping up his inner equilibrium. Struggling to reestablish his business, he develops a most severe form of colitis with six to twenty daily evacuations, and these now serve the same inner purpose as did formerly his financial gifts.

Apart from relieving guilt for oral aggressions, these patients have also another inner conflict to solve—the sense of inferiority caused by their oral-receptive tendencies. Especially in one of our female cases we saw very clearly that the diarrhea, apart from the meaning of restitution, had also the narcissistic significance of masculine activity, and expressed the masculine strivings of the patient.[29] In all of our female cases of the colitis type we found a rejection of the genital female attitude for two reasons. First, it is considered the inferior role, emotionally closely connected with parasitic oral-receptive tendencies, but besides that the female role is also rejected on account of its aggressive-sadistic, castrative significance. The aggressive-castrative feature of the female wishes is regularly a reaction to the thwarting of the passive-receptive tendencies, and our impression is that the female receptive tendencies are rejected often when thwarting has given them an aggressive-castrative significance. In all of our female cases the diarrhea both means restitution for castrative wishes and also represents masculine activity in contrast to female receptivity. In one case the wish for restitution by diarrhea seems on a deep level to be the equivalent of giving birth to a child. That the diarrheas have both the meaning of restitution and masculine activity, and sometimes also the meaning of an aggressive attack, we could establish by repeated observation of those psychologic conditions which introduced attacks of diarrhea; especially dreams from which the patients awoke with an attack of diarrhea have been very instructive. The most constant, outstanding feature which determines the specific character of these cases is the wish for restitution as a reaction to guilt for receptive and aggressive taking tendencies (castration wish).

As yet we are unable to advance a detailed physiologic theory to explain how the wish for restitution and giving (productivity) and aggressive tendencies are converted into those physiologic changes that are responsible for the symptoms of colitis. It is not difficult, however, to understand why the lower end of the intestinal tract, the main function of which is elimination, is specifically suited to express activity, aggression, and the wish to give. By a mechanism similar to those in the gastric cases, we assume that the peristaltic function of the intestines, under the permanent psychic stimulus of the wish to eject and to give, becomes independent of the normal physiologic regulations. Normally the peristaltic functions are periodically regulated by the intestinal content, but in these neurotic cases a psychologic tendency, independent of the nutritional process, stimulates the peristaltic functions. This explanation is based on well-established findings of psychoanalysis, namely on the unconscious symbolic significance of the intestinal content as a valuable possession and gift on the one hand, and as a means of aggression on the other. The unconscious attitude which considers the intestinal content as a valuable possession and excretions as a present given to others, corresponds to the earlier coprophilic attitude of the child before it develops the negative disgust attitude toward the excreta. On the other hand, the use of the excremental functions for the expression of sadistic or aggressive tendencies corresponds to the attitude which is developed after the child learns to assume a deprecatory negative attitude toward his excremental function. We find that both tendencies in all cases are intermingled; the emphasis, however, lies in the colitis cases more on the restitution-significance of the diarrheas. Regarding these psychologic connections, we refer to the abundant psychoanalytic publications, especially to Jones', Brill's, and Abraham's work on anal-eroticism.[30]

Although these formulations should not be regarded as an attempt to advance a generally valid etiological theory of spastic colitis, in all of the investigated cases we were able to reconstruct a connection between the diarrheas and repressed unconscious tendencies of restitu-

---

[30] Regarding the gift significance of the intestinal content see Freud, Sigmund, On the transformation of instincts, with special reference to anal-erotism, in *Collected papers*, Vol. 2. Also Jones, E., Anal-erotic character traits, in *Papers on psychoanalysis*, p. 691.

Regarding the relation between extravagance and neurotic diarrhea, see especially Abraham, K. Contributions to the theory of the anal character, in *Selected papers*, p. 387.

Regarding restitution significance of the excretory act, see Dr. Géza Róheim's Heiliges Geld in Melanesien, *Int. Z. Psychoanal.* 1923, 9, 384. In this article Róheim shows that in burial ceremonies of the Tonga Islanders the most valuable possessions of the clan are put into the grave of the dead chief, but parallel with this ceremony the men evacuate their excrement on the grave.

Regarding the sadistic significance of the excretory act see Abraham, K. The narcissistic evaluation of excretory processes in dreams and neurosis, in *Selected papers*.

"Returning to the sadistic significance of defecation, I may mention that the patient who killed her family in her dream by means of her excretions was severely troubled with nervous diarrhea. Besides the usual causes, psychoanalysis discovered a sadistic element at the bottom of this symptom. Her diarrhea proved to be an equivalent of suppressed outbursts of rage. Other analysed cases have confirmed this connection. For instance, I know a neurotic woman who reacts with diarrhea to any event which excites anger or rage." P. 321.

See also Brill, A. A. *Psychoanalysis*, pp. 274-275.

tion or aggression. We cannot claim that all cases necessarily develop on a psychogenic basis.

In connection with our findings, an interesting question arises regarding the well-known effect of fear upon the control of the sphincters and on peristalsis. In general one can say that fear mobilizes all kinds of active-aggressive mechanisms of the individual. Cannon has shown, for example, that fear mobilizes the adrenalin production in dogs and emphasizes the teleological nature of this phenomenon in referring to the stimulating effect of adrenalin on the muscle activity and carbohydrate metabolism which the animal needs in defending itself against an external danger. He also points out other effects of the mobilized adrenalin, for example, a certain change in the distribution of blood, which is favorable in conditions of increased muscle activity.[31] It is not so easy to understand, from the teleological point of view, how the excremental function could ever serve for defense or attack. Psychoanalytic experience shows, however, that the excremental functions are deeply linked with aggressive tendencies in the emotional life, which leads to the analytic concept of anal sadism. Fear mobilizes aggression, and excremental elimination is psychologically linked up with aggression. Those who have no "guts" move their bowels under the influence of fear instead of attacking the enemy. In this perspective, the reflex mechanism of moving the bowels under the influence of fear is an example of those pathological, even if common, phenomena in which a nervous impulse is transferred from the voluntary system to the vegetative system. Instead of a muscular attack, a symbolic infantile expression of aggression occurs, evacuation having the symbolic meaning of attack.

Undoubtedly this interesting connection could easily lead to further speculations. The well-established but peculiar connection between excremental elimination and hostile aggressiveness may be not only an infantile but an archaic mechanism. Possibly there is a fundamental psychogenetic connection between active-aggressive impulses and eliminating innervations. They may belong to the same category. We see many examples in animals in which secretory and eliminating functions, squirting out offensive substances, are used for defense and aggression. The sadistic significance of the excretory act possibly follows the same psychophysiologic pattern.

The Constipation Type

I come now to the third group, the constipation type. In only one of our cases is constipation the central symptom, and therefore in the

---

31 Cannon, W. B. *Bodily changes in pain, hunger, fear and rage.* (2nd Ed.)

other four cases both those surface attitudes and conflict-solutions which might be characteristic for the constipation types are necessarily mixed with other, more predominant features. Yet there are some trends which seem to be characteristic. A pessimistic attitude toward receiving help from others or depending upon them seems to prevail. These patients seemingly do not expect anything from anybody, in contrast to the optimistic attitude of Abraham's oral types. At the same time, however, there is a more or less conscious, very extreme sense of obligation to give, of which the patient tries to rid himself by renouncing all conscious receptive tendencies. "I cannot expect anything from anybody, and therefore I do not need to give anything. I hold on to what I have."

One of my constipated patients keeps constantly arguing with himself about emotional or financial obligations toward other people. This patient always has to prove to himself that he does not need to support his brother or send money to a woman, because sending money would really only do harm. In emotional relations he has the same attitude. He has strong guilt feelings for letting down women who have certain hopes regarding him, and he tries to escape this feeling of obligation by a deep renunciation of any acceptance or even expectation of receiving anything from others. He does not want to be bothered with any problems in which giving is involved. He has an older sister and a younger brother. He arranged his obligations toward them in a very characteristic way. His income automatically is divided into certain portions, and a considerable part of it goes into a life insurance policy for his brother, another into life insurance for his sister, and a third part into his own life insurance. The rest he spends in a tolerably rational and not overly thrifty way. He explains that he does not want to have any worries about whom he should support. He wants this problem to be eliminated from his life and to be taken care of automatically.

A patient of Wilson's presents a strikingly similar picture. This 26-year-old architect suffers both from an obsessional neurosis and also from obstinate constipation which he relieves by the continued use of cathartics. His father has had severe financial reverses during the past three or four years and is dependent to some slight degree on the patient and his brother for support. The patient has an open conflict about supporting his father. He says he would like to live away from home, but that is impossible because they need his money. His rationalizations continue somewhat as follows: "I feel guilty for not contributing more, but, if I did, my father would only use it for useless purposes, so the only way I can do is to save money so that when he has a complete financial breakdown, I shall be able to come to his rescue." His emotional attitude toward his family is similar. He says that they do not deserve his love or respect, as they are themselves the cause of his neurosis, and that people like them should not be permitted to have children. In the unconscious there is an extreme guilt feeling toward his father and brother for this hostile attitude. This guilt feeling is the main obstacle to his becoming successful. He always emphasized that he does not expect anything from anybody, and he himself must get everything he needs. But also there is a great uncertainty regarding his ability to do so, and therefore he has to stick to what he has.

This case offers the well-known mechanism of anal retentiveness as a reaction to oral inhibitions.[32]

In a deeper layer we find that the aversion to all kinds of obligation to give is based on intense castration fears which the patient tries to get rid of by renouncing and denying his oral tendencies.

I wish here also to recall a case of chronic constipation which I have described on another occasion.[33] I refer to the egocentric, neglectful artist's wife who during her marriage of two years suffered from an obstinate form of constipation. This was spontaneously relieved on the day on which her husband brought her a bouquet of flowers, the first gift since their marriage. To this gift she reacted with the first spontaneous evacuation in two years. This present from the husband destroyed her dynamic formula, "Inasmuch as I do not receive, therefore I do not have to give."

In addition to the positive evaluation of the intestinal content as a valuable possession, we found in these cases also an anal-sadistic attitude, the inhibition of which contributes to the anal retention.[34] The psychologic connection between the two different attitudes, between the withholding of something valuable and the inhibition of elimination on account of its aggressive soiling significance, could be reconstructed as follows: The spiteful rejection of the obligation to give leads to the attitude, "Well, if I have to give, by all means you may have it, but nothing better than excrement." The ambivalent attitude toward the excrement makes this change of emphasis possible. The conflictual rejection of this anal-sadistic attitude is the basis of the constipation.

Constipation, as rejection of the obligation to give, corresponds

---

32 Abraham explains neurotic parsimony in people who are inhibited from properly earning a livelihood: "The pleasure in acquiring desired objects seems in this case to have been repressed in favor of pleasure in holding fast to existing possessions." *Loc. cit.,* p. 399.

33 Alexander, F. *The medical value of psychoanalysis,* p. 197.

34 A connection of constipation on the deep layers with the fear of castration has been known since Freud's study, The history of an infantile neurosis. However, constipation resulting from the inhibition of anal-sadistic impulses which we find in three of our cases very clearly, according to my knowledge, is not so generally familiar.

to the positive evaluation of the excreta as a valuable possession; whereas constipation as a result of inhibited aggressions corresponds to the negative attitude toward the intestinal content. Thus, like the diarrhea, constipation also can result either from the positive or from the negative cathexis of the excremental act: from the refusal either to give up a value or to use the excrement for aggression.

A 42-year-old patient who suffered from a chronic constipation of long duration had an extreme inhibition of the sexual instinct. He suffered from a severe headache whenever there was an opportunity for intercourse with a sexually attractive girl. The analysis revealed that the sexual act in his unconscious was equivalent to anal soiling. After this connection became conscious, the patient's sexual inhibitions and constipation disappeared and he started at this late date his first sexual affair.

A similar depreciative attitude toward sexuality is also very characteristic of two of Wilson's cases of chronic constipation. Both patients have the tendency always to choose depreciated sexual objects, and at the same time show an overcompensated aggression toward women. This manifests itself in impotence and ejaculatio praecox as a result of denying every aggression toward women.

We submit these few observations without claiming that they describe typical attitudes and conflict-solutions of the same validity as those characteristic mechanisms which we find in the gastric and colitis cases. Justification for including these observations lies in the fact that the mechanisms now described corroborate the well-established emotional reaction, namely, that the tendency to withhold the excrement often expresses the spiteful rejection of the obligation to give, typical for cases with oral deprivation and inhibition of the acquisitive tendencies.[35]

Summary and Conclusions

In comparing the predominant conflict-situations and their solutions in each group, (gastric type, diarrhea type, and constipation type), I could express the differences by the following schematic formulae:

The most conspicuous feature of the gastric cases (gastric neuroses and duodenal ulcers) is intense receptive and acquisitive wishes (in-taking or incorporating tendencies) against which the patient fights internally because they are connected with extreme conflict in the form of guilt and sense of inferiority which usually lead to their

---

[35] Regarding holding back excrements in relation to stubbornness and spite, see Abraham, K.: *loc. cit.*, p. 373.

denial. "I do not want to take or to receive. I am active and efficient and have no such wishes." Our assumption is that the stomach symptoms are conditioned by the repressed and pent-up receptive and aggressive taking tendencies which serve as chronic psychic stimuli of the stomach function. In some cases the receptive and acquisitive wishes are not *internally* inhibited by conflicts but *externally* by circumstances.

The dynamic formula of the colitis cases is: "I have the right to take and demand, for I always give sufficiently. I do not need to feel inferior or guilty for my desire to receive and take, because I am giving something in exchange for it." Our assumption is that the diarrhea, apart from expressing aggressions, serves as a substitute for the giving of real values.

Finally, in the constipation cases the dynamic background of the symptom may be verbalized as follows: "I do not take or receive and therefore I do not need to give." Our assumption is that the constipation is a reaction against the obligation to give. This intense sense of obligation to give, on deeper levels, is linked with the fear of castration.

On account of the impressive parallelisms regarding the dynamic structure of the gastric cases, there seems to be very little doubt that the content of the chronic psychologic stimulus responsible for the secretory and motor dysfunctions of the stomach are intensive intaking tendencies both of passive-receptive and of aggressive-taking nature. These tendencies have become intense, usually on account of inner rejection, and probably much less frequently because of external deprivation of the wish to be loved, taken care of, and dependent. These impulses, if eliminated from the voluntary system, cannot find adequate gratification in the normal life relations of the patients, and consequently find expression in vegetative innervations (dysfunction of the stomach).

Thus our studies can explain why the impression of a number of authors has been that personalities who are overactive in life, like to take responsibilities and make concentrated efforts, are so often found among the peptic ulcer cases. Our analyses show that these tendencies toward overactivity, efficiency, and ambitious effort are compensations to cover up the underlying strong dependent-receptive tendencies which in turn are increased because of the fact that they are not allowed even normal expression. A vicious circle is at work here. The high claims which these individuals have regarding efficiency, activity, productivity, and success lead them to make overexertions which then stimulate the opposite, receptive side of their nature, which in turn necessitates stronger and stronger overcompensations. The gastric symptoms are in direct causal connection with the repudiated in-taking tendencies, and not with the overt picture of overexertion and activity.

It seems to us equally well established that the content of the chronic psychologic stimulus responsible for the increased peristalsis in colitis is (a) either a narcissistic wish to produce and chiefly the urge to make restitution (excrement=gift) or (b) an anal-sadistic impulse in which the excrements are used as weapons of aggression. In these cases the psychologic impulses to make restitution, to produce, or to attack are expressed through the vegetative system instead of the voluntary system. The excretory functions, because of their symbolic significance of giving and attacking, are substituted for either giving real values to others (restitution, production) or attacking others.

It should be emphasized that different types of surface attitudes are sometimes intermingled, as different organic symptoms may be present in the same cases. One of our gastric cases shows, besides the predominant gastric symptoms, also a periodic tendency to diarrhea. The diarrhea cases almost always show intermittent or periodic constipation, the psychologic significance of which we have not yet established. Possibly they are due merely to physiologic mechanisms. The following diagram should therefore be considered as a simplified scheme. It expresses the overt and unconscious psychologic features present in the most extreme or typical cases, and does not do justice to the mixed types. The third column, in which the attitudes and mechanisms of constipation are listed, is added with great reservation. It should serve rather as a tentative suggestion to stimulate further research and we shall not hesitate to change it as the evidence carries us further. (See diagram on page 131.)

Our investigation leads to the conclusion that the gastrointestinal tract, according to its three major functions of in-taking, retaining, and eliminating, is especially suitable for the expression of these three elementary tendencies if their normal expression through the voluntary motor system or through the sexual apparatus is inhibited through inner conflicts.

The upper end of the gastrointestinal tract, corresponding to its normal function, is well fitted to express the receptive or taking tendencies, whereas the lower end of the tract is more suitable for the expression of giving and retentive tendencies. Both the in-taking and the giving-eliminating tendency may assume either a more constructive (erotic) or a more destructive connotation:

In-taking $\Big\langle$ passive receiving
aggressive taking

Eliminating $\Big\langle$ giving of positive value (restitution, birth)
aggressive and sadistic elimination (attack, soiling)

I am convinced that the analysis of the individual's emotional attitude to his environment in the terms of these three major tendencies, (a) to receive and take, (b) to retain, and (c) to give, will not only prove useful for the understanding of gastrointestinal disorders but will also be found to have more general significance. These three groups of emotional tendencies seem to be of the most elementary nature, and their recognition makes possible the further analysis of the emotional reactions of the individual to the environment, including the sexual relations.[36]

It seems to me that the analysis of the content of male and female sexuality into these three elementary tendencies can give a more specific meaning to less definite terms such as "active" and "passive," "male" and "female." In pregenital sexuality these three elementary tendencies appear unmixed. In the later organizations of sexual life, active and passive, male and female strivings may be thought of as mixtures in varying proportions of these three more elementary tendencies. It seems to me that such an analysis promises a much more accurate description of the sexual organization than is possible in terms of the more general concepts now current.

It must be left for future research to determine whether or not the dynamic relation of the individual to his environment can be exhaustively reduced to these three groups of elementary tendencies.

Physiologically, the process of life can well be described in terms of the three major functions of *in-taking* of substance and energy from the environment, partially *retaining* it during the process of growth, and *elimination*—elimination of the end-products of metabolism, elimination of substances for the purpose of propagation, and the constant production of thermic and mechanical energy. It would not be surprising at all if it should turn out that the most elementary psychologic tendencies of the individual correspond to these three biologic phases of life, and that psychologic dynamics—as Ferenczi has assumed in his *Genitaltheorie*—correspond to the biologic dynamics of life.

---

36 Ernest Jones in an earlier writing (1918) suggested the understanding of love relations on this basis: Anal-erotic character traits, in *Papers on psychoanalysis*. "It is true that, from both the psychological and physiological basis of love, the greater part of all love-life is modelled on the prototype of giving and receiving." . . . p. 700.

	Gastric Type	Colitis Type	Constipation Type
Typical conscious attitudes toward environment schematically verbalized.	"I do not want to receive or to take. I have no such wishes. I am independent, active, and efficient."	"I have the right to take and demand because I give sufficiently. I do not need to feel inferior or guilty on account of my receptive and grasping wishes because I am giving something in exchange for it."	"I do not take or receive, and therefore I do not need to give."
The deeper dynamic background of the symptoms.	The denied and repressed oral-receptive and oral-aggressive tendencies are converted into the original pattern: into the wish to be fed or to eat. These tendencies serve as chronic psychic stimuli of the stomach independent of the process of nutrition.	1. The permanent wish to give restitution for oral-aggressive tendencies, and 2. the wish to be active and aggressive in the ejective (and not oral-receptive) way serves as permanent irritation of the peristalsis, independent of the digestive functions. The diarrhea substitutes for giving of real values, for making real efforts and being actually active, and for being aggressive.	1. The rejection of the obligation to give on account of fear of loss (castration-fear) and 2. the inhibition of anal-sadistic impulses (to give spitefully in a destructive way) are the chronic inhibitory stimuli leading to constipation.
The content of the psychic stimuli which cause the dysfunction.	1. Receiving 2. Taking	1. Giving (restitution for receiving or taking). 2. Aggressive elimination.	Retaining because of 1. fear of loss 2. fear of doing damage.

BIBLIOGRAPHY

1. ABRAHAM, KARL. *Selected papers.* London: Hogarth Press and Institute of Psycho-Analysis, 1927.
2. ALEXANDER, FRANZ. *The medical value of psychoanalysis.* New York: W. W. Norton & Co., 1932.
3. ALEXANDER, FRANZ. The neurotic character. *Int. J. Psycho-Anal.,* 1930, 11.
4. ALVAREZ, W. C. *Nervous indigestion.* New York: Paul B. Hoeber, Inc., 1931.
5. ALVAREZ, W. C. Light from the laboratory and the clinic on the causes of peptic ulcers. *Amer. J. Surg.,* 1932, 18.
6. BERGMANN, G. VON. Ulcus duodeni und vegetatives Nervensystem. *Ber. klin. Wchschr.,* 1913, 50.
7. BRILL, A. A. *Psychoanalysis.* Philadelphia: W. B. Saunders Co., 1913.
8. CANNON, W. B. *Bodily changes in pain, hunger, fear and rage.* (2nd Ed.) New York: D. Appleton & Co., 1929.
9. DEUTSCH, FELIX. Biologie und Psychologie der Krankheitsgenese. *Int. Z. Psychoanal.,* 1932, 8.
10. DEUTSCH, FELIX. Der gesunde und der kranke Körper in psychoanalytischer Betrachtung. *Int. Z. Psychoanal.,* 1926, 12.
11. DRAPER, GEORGE, AND TOURAINE, GRACE ALLEN. The man-environment unit and peptic ulcer. *Arch. intern. Med.,* 1932, 49.
12. FERENCZI, SÁNDOR. *Further contributions to the theory and technique of psycho-analysis.* London: Hogarth Press and the Institute of Psycho-Analysis, 1926.
13. FERENCZI, SÁNDOR. *Versuch einer Genitaltheorie.* Leipzig: Internationaler Psychoanalytischer Verlag, 1924. Trans. Thalassa, a theory of genitality. *Psychoanal. Quart.,* 1933, 2.
14. FREUD, SIGMUND. *Collected papers.* London: Hogarth Press and the Institute of Psycho-Analysis, 1925.
15. FREUD, SIGMUND. *Three contributions to the theory of sex.* Washington, D. C.: Nervous & Mental Disease Publishing Co., 1930.
16. GRODDECK, GEORG. Über die Psychoanalyse des Organischen im Menschen. *Int. Z. Psychoanal.* 1921, 7.
17. GRODDECK, GEORG. *The book of the it.* Washington, D. C.: Nervous & Mental Disease Publishing Co., 1928.
18. HARTMANN, H. R. Neurogenic factors in peptic ulcer. *Med. Clin. N. A.,* 18, No. 6.
19. HENNING, H., AND NORPOTH, L. Untersuchungen über die sekretorische Funktion des Magens während des nächtlichen Schlafes. *Arch. f. Verdauungskrankheiten, Stoffwechselpathologie u. Diätetik,* 1933, 53.
20. JONES, ERNEST. *Papers on psycho-analysis.* New York: Wm. Wood & Co., 1923.
21. OPPENHEIMER, R. H. Gastro-intestinal manifestations of the psychoneurotic state. *J. med. Assn. Georgia,* 1932, 21.
22. PALMER, W. L. Fundamental difficulties in the treatment of peptic ulcer. *Amer. J. med. Sci.,* 1933, 101.
23. RÓHEIM, GÉZA. Heiliges Geld in Melanesien. *Int. Z. Psychoanal.,* 1923, 9.
24. SILBERMANN, I. S. Experimentelle Magenduodenalulcuserzeugung durch Scheinfüttern nach Pavlov. *Zbl. f. Chir.* 1927, 54.
25. SULLIVAN, A. J., AND CHANDLER, C. A. Ulcerative colitis of psychogenic origin. *Yale J. Biol. Med.,* 1932, 4.
26. SIMMEL, ERNST. Über die Psychogenese von Organstörungen und ihre psychoanalytische Behandlung. Allgemeiner ärztlicher Kongress f. Psychotherapie in Dresden XIV-XVII, 1931. Abstract in *Psychoanal. Quart.,* 1932, 1, 166.
27. UNDERWOOD, G. M. Emotional and psychic factors in the production of gastrointestinal Diseases. *Texas J. Med.,* 1932, 27.

28. WESTPHAL, K. Untersuchungen zur Frage der nervösen Entstehung peptischer Ulcera. *Deut. Arch. klin. Med.,* 1914, **114**.
29. WESTPHAL, K., AND KATSCH, G. Das neurotische ulcus duodeni. *Mitt. a.d. Grenzgeb. d. Med. u. Chir.,* 1913, **26**.
30. WINKELSTEIN, ASHER. A new therapy of peptic ulcer. *Amer. J. med. Sci.,* 1933, **185**.

TYPICAL PERSONALITY TRENDS AND CONFLICTS IN CASES OF GASTRIC DISTURBANCE

By CATHERINE L. BACON, M.D.

I am reporting three cases of gastric disturbance which I had under my observation, and one case which was under the care of Wilson. In all of these cases the typical conflict-solution which Alexander has already described is seen.

Mr. K was referred to us because of epigastric distress, flatulence, and belching, for which no physical explanation could be found. He had had this distress for several years. He also had a nervous cough and vague nervous disturbances such as mild attacks of dizziness on standing up.

He is a successful Jewish business man of about 40, externally very masculine, active, and sure of himself, giving the impression of being likable and trustworthy. He is the second of four children, all of whom were brought up very strictly. As a child he had to work hard and rarely had time to play. Every afternoon after school he had to go to Hebrew school even as a small child, and he never got home for his dinner until eight or eight thirty and rarely got to bed before ten. He did brilliantly in his school work, skipping several grades, but at 14 had to leave school to work because of his family's financial circumstances. He was devoted to his mother, but complained that she had never had time to give him affection and knew nothing about diet, probably an unconscious reproach against her for her orally depriving him. His father he loved and feared more than God, even though he was a strict disciplinarian and beat the patient for minor infractions of disciplinary rules, especially for even a slight show of disrespect at Hebrew school. He said his father could not help him much because he was foreign-born and ignorant of American customs. The patient was docile and was almost never disobedient. When he started earning his own living at 14 he was successful from the beginning, and his relationship to the family changed almost over night. At 16 he was earning a hundred dollars a month as the head of his department in the firm in which he worked. His mother and father looked to him for advice, and he became "a pillar of society." He is now the head of a successful business.

He has never married and still lives at home with his father. His mother is dead. He has had few sexual relationships and these always with prostitutes. Although he says he is conscious of sexual interest in women of his own class, he never yields to it in any form. For ten months preceding his analysis he had no sexual relations at all. He has no memory of ever having masturbated.

In his first interview he emphasized his prowess, referring to himself as a "self-made man," a "lone wolf" who always does for others but who neither needs nor wants help. This is not only his concept of himself but the desired ideal according to which he wishes to live. This emphasis on self-reliance and independence is a most conspicuous trait, which even a casual observer would recognize as striking. The denial of any need for help was pronounced at the beginning of the analysis, but dependent wishes soon appeared and later developed into a marked passive receptive attitude to the analyst, against which he struggled continually.

He is the type of active, efficient Jewish business man described by Alvarez as being particularly disposed to recurrent peptic ulcers. This case was once diagnosed as ulcer and treated for it, although this was not confirmed by later more thorough studies. The psychoanalytic investigation showed that the superficial picture of a strong man by no means corresponds to his total personality. Carefully hidden or denied, there are many signs of passive receptive trends. He accepted the passive analytical situation readily and enjoyed asking questions, trying to secure advice about diet, asking that his temperature should be taken when the objective reason was very slight, although at the same time he protested energetically against the passive role he was playing and tried to analyze the analyst and to play a dominant role. In the world at large, although he was very active, he would get his business acquaintances to do things for him, and was emotionally dependent on their good will and on the favors they did him. He once said that he realized that he was the type of man that other men liked to do things for, and that this helped him greatly in business. Because of the help he received from other men, he felt he had to repay them excessively with favors and had to lead a very ethical life. This attitude probably was related with the fact that he denied himself almost all sexual pleasure.

In this case the conflict between the active, conscious, aggressive masculinity and the denied receptive trends is clear. The surface attitude of independence was obviously a protection and reaction against the rejected dependent wishes which caused him so much conflict. The emotional connection between the overt and emphasized independence, and the greatly repressed dependence, was clearly observed in the transference behavior.

In the course of the analysis there were repeated opportunities to observe the relation of his symptoms to this conflict, for whenever he tried to repress his receptive wishes symptoms would result. The following episode is characteristic: He was sitting in the waiting-room, thinking with pleasure of his analysis, at a time when his passive receptive tendencies had become more conscious through the analysis. Suddenly he came into conflict over whether or not he should continue the analysis. Then he felt he should not indulge in such useless thoughts, as though something within him said, "The general is here!" He pulled himself up and changed his train of thoughts to active, aggressive thoughts about his business, and immediately felt the typical discomfort in his epigastrium. Or again he reported that when, after having listened to a lecture with pleasure, he stood up to comment on it (thereby changing from the receptive role of listening to the active role of contributing), he felt his epigastric distress. This was a frequent type of experience for him.

His cough was interesting, also, in that it came on at times when he was in conflict over his receptive desires or desires to take something away from someone. It seemed to symbolize a rejection of these wishes. For instance he played bridge for money one evening, and was winning by a technique of such passive-aggressive plays as finessing, squeezing, and tenace. Then he felt guilty because his competitors could afford to lose less than he, so he bid recklessly and lost. During the time he was winning he coughed continually, but stopped as soon as he lost.[1]

Another time he spent the evening with a woman to whom he was attracted because he felt she was intellectually and socially superior to him, and in reference to whom he had unconscious receptive expectations and also, of course, castration fears. During the whole time he was with her he coughed. He also coughed the first time he was asked to lie down on the couch. Another time, when lunching with some business acquaintances, he had a feeling of weakness in his throat which made him feel inferior. He said he immediately overcompensated for this by being overaggressive.

---

[1] The psychodynamic tendency to eject, to give back, is well established in vomiting. It also can create nervous coughing since the respiratory tract is also often used for the expression of intake and ejection.

In Freud's case of Dora (Collected papers, Vol. 3), Fragment of an analysis of a case of hysteria, her nervous coughing was associated with fellatio fantasies. These fantasies were strongly rejected. Although Freud does not directly state that the cough symbolized a rejection of these fantasies, it is implicit in the material.

David Forsythe in an article, The rudiments of character (Psychoanal. Rev., 1921, 8), discusses the respiratory zone as a "nutri-excretal zone" of the first rank of importance. Although he emphasizes the emotional aspects of the inspiratory phase, he mentions in passing that the expiratory phase is also significant and gives the example of a six year old boy making a "gift" of a handful of his breath to a friend who was panting after a race.

Karl Menninger (Psychoanal. Rev., 1934, 21) reports a case of a woman with a cough from a chest cold. The patient identified her cough with labor pains and giving birth to a child and then said, "Perhaps the cough is a rejection of masculinity and perhaps . . . femininity also, because I seem to be both a man and a woman. I make myself pregnant by getting my own cold down in my own chest."

His dizziness also seemed to have to do with this conflict between receptive trends and the compensatory urge for independence and activity; for he frequently felt dizzy when he stood up after having indulged in some receptive pleasure, as reading, dizziness apparently being an expression of his infantile desire to return to the dependent state of the infant who cannot maintain his balance without the help of others.[2]

In relation to women of his own social circle he had enormous fears of being the receptive and therefore the inferior party. For instance, once when asked if he was married, he was tempted to reply that he had not had his tonsils out yet. Although attracted to women whom he considers "superior," he avoids all close association with them and takes pleasure in thwarting them sexually by not reacting to their advances.

Two motives were noted for the conflict about his desire to receive. This seemed, first, to be due to a sense of inferiority which resulted from his strong receptive wishes and probably stimulated in deeper layers by castration fears as a guilt reaction to aggressive taking tendencies. He once declared that he was afraid a socially superior woman to whom he was attracted would puncture his pride. The second motive is guilt at receiving, insofar as this assumes the character of a taking away from others, as is seen in his reaction to winning at bridge and to taking business away from competitors.

The connection between his gastric symptoms, nervous coughing, and dizziness as expressions of his repressed receptive and aggressive taking tendencies thus became clear. The origin of his strong receptive trends can only be concluded from the history of early oral deprivation, and the concept that this fixation and regression are due to early and permanent oral deprivations seems to be justified.

The second case, Mrs. G, is 35. She was referred by her physician because of an illness of seven years duration in which he felt that the psychogenic factors were large. Her symptoms, which had persisted intermittently throughout this time, consisted of epigastric distress which at times was so agonizing that she had to have opiates, severe attacks of belching, flatus, congestion of the throat which she thought was due to her belching, and occasional attacks of diarrhea or constipation. She also had attacks of bulimia lasting from

---

[2] Sándor Ferenczi (*Further contributions to the theory and technique of psychoanalysis,* Ch. 23, "Sensations of Giddiness at the End of the Psychoanalytic Session") relates the dizziness to the unwillingness of the patient to give up the gratification of feeling himself loved by the analyst.

Thomas M. French (Psychogenic material related to the function of the semicircular canals, *Int. J. Psycho-Anal.,* 1929, 10) confirms Ferenczi's ideas of dizziness in a patient he observed, and relates this further to the desire of his patient to be carried around in his mother's arms, as well as to the patient's feminine identification. Interestingly enough, this patient became dizzy only when he began actively to reject his passive tendencies.

ten days to two weeks, during which she would put on ten to twenty pounds.

She was a pleasant out-going woman, pretty, very attractive to men and flirtatious. She was feminine in appearance and always nicely dressed, although her financial condition was straitened. She was always the first to make approaches to people, made friends easily and quickly, but in general the friendships were of short duration, usually broken up because of disillusionment and thwarting.

She was the youngest of three girls. Her father was 70 when she was born. He died about six or eight years later. He was well educated, whereas her mother was ignorant. During his lifetime they were wealthy, but they became very poor later. She was born in Europe and came to this country when she was eight or nine, after her father's death. She was her mother's favorite; she slept with her mother. Her earliest memories are of her father getting into bed with her mother for sexual relations, and of her mother's berating him because he could not give her satisfaction. She has few memories of her father except that he was looked up to by his own fellow townsmen. Her mother was brutal to the patient. A typical example is that when at the age of six, an older man tried to attack her and she screamed for help, her mother came out and beat her without trying to find out why the child had cried out. As a small child she had great fears of the feminine sexual role which she attributes to the fact that in her town there was a gang of very rough boys who used to take girls to an abandoned fort in the neighborhood where they would attack them. Although the townspeople heard the girls' screams, they were so afraid of the boys that they never did anything about it. Throughout her childhood she had to take care of her own clothes and help her mother after school. She always worked very hard. She was very jealous of the next older sister who she felt got everything and was always demanding and selfish. When she was about twenty, she married a man more than 15 years her senior, and for the first time in her life she had a great deal of care and attention. Her husband was successful in his business and intellectually superior. At first he represented to the patient her intellectually superior and wealthy father who was so respected by the townspeople. Later, however, he became the impotent father who was unable to satisfy her mother. She traveled with him a great deal. He sent her to boarding school for a couple years after their marriage. Although she was frigid with him, she was quite happy. This situation of happy dependence was broken up, first, by the birth of their child, seven years after the marriage. Then she had to stay home and take care of the baby for whom she showed a great deal of anxious overprotection, while her husband traveled on business and was away from home much of the time. When the baby was two, she found out that her husband had been married before and that he was supporting his first wife and child. She showed great rage and jealousy of the first wife and resented the money he gave her. It was at this time that her gastrointestinal symptoms began, and from then on they continued for the next seven years until the beginning of her analysis. After the birth of her child her husband became neglectful about sending her money. Although he had a large income, he also had many debts, so that she frequently suffered from lack of money. He had always had ejaculatio praecox, but this had become worse in recent years and irritated her greatly. She worked hard to keep up her home, worked hard to take care of the child, and always made a point of serving elaborate well-cooked meals, even when she was so sick that she could not eat them herself. She took care of her mother for long periods of time when her mother was ill. Her husband lost his job and had to stay home. Their financial situation becoming worse, she reacted with enormous hostility to his failure to support her, and her symptoms became aggravated.

Her conscious attitude about herself is that she is always doing things for other people, that she is only happy in giving and in fact likes to "stuff her kindness down other people's throats." She feels superior to her associates. Underneath this attitude are seen strong oral-receptive and oral-aggressive trends, apparently directed chiefly toward men, but also evident in her relations to women. She complains bitterly about her husband's lack of support, but it can be seen that she herself tends to thwart her receptive tendencies not only by choosing a husband older than herself, who gets great unconscious satisfaction from "holding out on her," but also in the choice of lovers, one of whom had ejaculatio praecox and another one of whom, she complained, had a small penis and took great delight in thwarting her, breaking dates with her, giving her nothing, but maintaining a very oral-dependent attitude toward her.

In this case a strong oral fixation was reinforced by regression. As long as she was satisfied on the oral level she was well. When her oral desires were thwarted by external frustration, she went into a rage, the content of which was a desire to attack the penis of the thwarting object and incorporate it. To this she reacted with guilt and a rejection of her oral desires and her rage, whereupon her gastric symptoms appeared.

Her sexual dreams, for instance, were closely connected with eating, and when she spoke of being sexually aroused she always made remarks like, "Gee, I'm hungry!" She declared she was like a baby wanting food from her husband, but that he only gave her water.

Her attacks of bulimia appeared at periods when she was conscious of unfulfilled sexual desire, as, for instance, once during the analysis, when a lover of hers began to drop her. On the other hand, when she was in the midst of a happy love affair in which she was frigid, but from which she derived great satisfaction, she lost interest in food and reduced her weight by about 10 pounds in a month.

Her attitude to the mother is a similar one of strong oral dependence. She dreams of her mother as a poor woman who gives her a basket of food containing meat. She has a thinly disguised dream of the analyst as a woman with a penis who has sexual relations with her, in which she plays the feminine role, and then they eat oysters and fish. In this attitude we can discover behind the oral-aggressive attitude toward the penis, in a deeper layer, the original oral aggressions against her mother.

As was pointed out above, whenever her oral desires were thwarted, she went into a rage, the unconscious content of which was an oral attack against the penis. For instance during a period of bitter complaints against her husband for his failure to support her, she dreamed she found a bottle of wine that tasted like gin, but a ragged man said to her that she could not keep it for he would find the owner. On the basis of her associations, this dream was interpreted to mean that the bottle was her husband's penis and the ragged man the husband toward whom she felt guilty. During this period she experienced epigastric distress after eating rare meat which reminded her of "something that once had life in it." She declared that going back to her husband whom she had left "would be like eating something you have thrown up." This way of expressing emotional relationships in terms of eating was very characteristic.

Because of the guilt at her oral aggressions she thwarted herself. For instance, once she saw a beggar on the street who represented to her unconscious her castrated husband. She gave him a dime, and felt guilty because she had food and he did not. She went home and worked hard, sewing and cooking for her husband (another guilt reaction); she ate little, but had epigastric distress and thought of licking salt and of salt on wounds as being painful. This was an oral punishment for her oral aggressions. By her hostile behavior to her husband, she also discouraged his doing things for her.

Her belching was a reaction of rage against the external thwarting object, usually her husband, and seemed to have the content, "I do not want anything from you." Her sore throat was directly connected with her guilt reaction to her oral castrative tendencies. For instance, she said once that she thought her sore throat came from eating oranges and grapes, and her first association was "testicles."

The reasons for her regression to the oral level became clear after a year and a half of analysis. She rejected the feminine role because of her masochistic conception of it and because of her great unconscious fear of men who seemed masculine to her, that is, who were sadistic. She had a feeling of guilt toward men because of her strong oral-castrative tendencies toward them, and feared their retaliation. She had to reject genital sexuality to prove to herself she had taken nothing from men. She feared her mother if she indulged in sexual relationships, as seen in the memory of being beaten by her mother after a man had tried to attack her. She had a reactive fear of her mother because of her death wishes toward her, which came up in numerous dreams of killing or dismembering her mother, in association with sexual relations with men. And then there was her oral dependence on her mother, the woman with a penis, which she feared she would lose if she succumbed to her feminine wishes. In this case, also, as in the other case, we see early oral deprivation both from her neglectful mother and her feeble father as the basis for her strong oral fixation.

The third patient, Miss A, is a contrast to the first two, in that she was a severe case of recurrent duodenal ulcer which had resisted dietetic and medical treatment and a gastro-enterostomy. Her symptoms were classical ulcer symptoms with the pain worse at night. They were of about nine years duration, the last four of them while under medical care. Her personality was a classical example of the type which Alexander found frequent in cases of peptic ulcer.

She was a small, rather feminine but old-maidish girl of 30 who weighed only 90 pounds. She would undoubtedly belong to Draper's longitudinal or Kretschmer's asthenic type. She was outwardly very active, always talking about what she wanted to do for others. She emphasized how hard and how efficiently she worked when she was well. She denied any need for help, especially of a psychological nature. The only receptive claims which she admitted were desires for help from her father, which, however, she never received, partly because of her father's drunkenness and lack of interest in the family, and partly because she thwarted herself by her hostile behavior to him, thereby actually receiving less from him than her sisters.

She was the oldest of five children. As a child she had been a tomboy, competing successfully with boys, disobedient and carefree, repudiating every feminine attitude. Her worst punishment was being put to bed by her mother, being forced to be inactive. The other children were whipped, but her mother knew that being put to bed hurt her worse. She was always submitting to her next sister, Marie, and the early analytic hours were filled with tales of the latter's selfishness. Her favorite was James, the only brother, who like herself was always giving to others but toward whom nonetheless she assumed a maternal attitude. Her trend for independence and masculinity showed themselves at a very early period of her life. She recalled how, at the age of 2, she ran away from home and told the police who found her that her mother was sick. When she was 4 her mother once dressed her in a pretty new dress and told her not to go near the river where she might get dirty, whereupon she ran straight for the river. Her father saw her and said if she went down to the river bank he would throw her into the water; she promptly disobeyed and he threw her in. She laughed and asked him to do it again. When she was six or seven she balanced herself on a porch rail four stories above the ground and threw kisses at her father who was standing at a near-by elevated station. Her father came home in a rage and whipped her. It is significant that these memories of boyish independence came out on the first day of analysis, apparently as a protest against her feelings of inferiority and against the passive nature of her transference feelings.

Her father drank and the mother had to assume the responsibility of supporting the family very early in the patient's life. When she was eleven, her father, in a fit of drunken rage, struck her mother for the first time and the mother drove him out of the house to which he never returned. She partly blames her mother for her father's leaving, saying that if her mother had not been so willing to support the family, perhaps her father would have done better by them. For nearly 15 years the family hardly saw the father at all, but in the last four or five years the girls have been going to see him. She had to leave school at an early age to go to work. At first in her jobs she was tomboyish and disobedient, as she was at home. She lost one job after another until finally her mother told her she had no time to go around and look for jobs with her. This was when she was about 20. She suddenly changed her personality to that of a hardworking and responsible business woman. Shortly after this her gastric symptoms began, which led four years ago to her undergoing medical treatment.

In spite of this external picture of boyishness, desire for independence, rejection of help and denial of any need for it, which is very much accentuated and pushed into the foreground, the analytical procedure soon discovered the dynamically much more powerful receptiveness which was strongly denied. For instance after denying to the analyst that she wanted to talk about herself, even in the first consultation, she poured out a long story about herself. She projected her receptive desires on to her sisters, and spent much time complaining about their selfishness and how she had to give to them. She complained that her father did not give to her. However after relieving her conscience by expressing desires to give to others, she sometimes developed long fantasies about being cared for and having luxuries. An interesting feature of these fantasies was that she always had money and could satisfy her own needs and pay people to do things for her.

During her analysis, which was broken off after six weeks, probably almost entirely because she could not assume a dependent relationship to the analyst, she always resented violently assuming a passive receptive role. Almost every hour she objected to lying on the couch, which represented the passive role to her and reminded her of being sent to bed by her mother for punishment. Because of her denial of her passive receptive tendencies and the great danger of her breaking off the analysis every day, there was an unusually difficult problem in trying to win her to accept analytic help. Any suggestion that an analysis might help her to get well or to get married, which she consciously desired, was responded to with hostile statements to the effect that she did not need help or did not think the analyst could help her. She declared that her only reason for coming to analysis was one of loyalty to the physician who sent her and who kept encouraging her to return. She broke at least a third of her appointments, usually with the excuse she had to help at home. The only way it was possible to get any attachment to the analysis or any manifestation of positive transference was by some casual praise of her accomplishments. This almost fanatic denial of every wish for dependence made necessary this atypical device of activity. The analytic situation was undoubtedly more difficult because the analyst was a woman, and receiving from a woman meant to her being inferior to her mother and therefore surrendering the father to her. Reality was lent to this situation by the fact that in order to be analyzed she had to give up her gastro-enterologist, who was a father image, and had to come to a woman. That the gastro-enterologist spoke highly of the analyst probably increased her resentment and jealousy. She did accept more consciously her receptive desires toward men.

Her strong drive toward masculinity came out clearly in an early hour. Because of the material, she was asked if she did not feel inferior because she was a girl. She replied, "Sure, I would lots rather be a man. They are a lot stronger and have so much more they can tinker with. They can get around and see things and see how the wheels go round. They are so handy with their hands. I don't blame Jim (her brother-in-law with whom she had very violent arguments) for my inferiority complex." I then asked her if she did not want to show Jim she was as good as a man. She answered, "Well, no. I want to tell him my points are just as good as his." A little later, in the same hour, she expressed her feelings of inadequacy as a woman by saying regretfully, "My mother and Margaret can do beautiful sewing. I can't. Margaret played with dolls and did not like rough games like I did."

Two examples of the precipitating causes of the ulcer pains may be noted. She wrote to her father asking him to give her money for a coat, for she had no winter coat but had to share her mother's. He replied that he could not afford to buy her a coat now because he was very hard up. A few days later she heard he was ill and went to see him and found that he had gone on a spree during which he had probably spent much more money on drink than the coat would have cost. She went into a rage and scolded him bitterly for his drunkenness, and complained in analysis later that he never gave her anything. On leaving him she felt her typical ulcer pains much worse than they had been for a long time. After three weeks of analysis, in the midst of the conflict about continuing it, she went to see a woman friend who told her that of course her stomach trouble was nervous, that she should fight her nervousness herself instead of being a baby and looking to us for help. Although this corresponded closely to what the patient had been maintaining in the analysis, she responded with rage toward the woman, and the typical ulcer pains followed shortly after she left her. That this was a reaction to a threatened internal frustration, the fear that she would have to leave the analysis, is quite obvious, and shows that although she protested against analysis she was probably getting some receptive satisfaction from it.

She had a typical conflict in her relationship to men. Although her attraction to them was apparently quite normal and she expressed receptive desires toward them, she always felt in competition with some other woman for them, though frequently this other woman was very remote. This conflict eventually caused her to give them up, just as she gave up her father to her mother and to her younger sisters. Underneath her outwardly feminine attitude to men, of course, are seen the strong oral-castrative wishes which she unconsciously exhibited to her father.

In this case we see both an inner and an external thwarting of receptive tendencies. The thwarting from the father and from men in general seems external, although one can observe an internal element there too. In relation to her mother, sisters, and the analyst, only the inner thwarting is seen.

As to the motives for the rejection of the receptive role, we note the fear of receiving. Receiving means that she has to give up her father to her mother, for to be receptive means to be inferior to her independent, self-supporting mother. There is also some evidence, however, for guilt connected with the receptive feminine attitude; for example, in giving up everything to her sisters, the guilt resulting evidently from a competitive and envious (oral envy) attitude toward her sisters and mother. The active, boyish tendencies have the significance of masculine superiority to the mother and the siblings, and undoubtedly have the significance of winning her father's love and approval (competition with a capable mother and a selfish sister), as well as rejection of the female role. In this case, also, we see the very early oral thwarting which seems to be inner because of guilt at her jealousy of her younger sister and mother; but there must also have been external thwarting at the hands of her father, who is a chronic drinker.

Mrs. M, a patient of Wilson's, was referred to us because of severe anxiety attacks and fainting spells, in which she injured herself, and inability to continue her highly intellectual work. The gastrointestinal symptoms of two years' duration were severe epigastric pain coming on about two hours after eating, relieved by soda. She was diagnosed as a case of duodenal ulcer, which was confirmed by X rays.

She was 40 years old, an extremely intellectual woman, very succesful in her life, ambitious, entirely absorbed in her career and work. She had great envy of men and was in constant conflict with them. She had one child of 8, and was separated from her husband. She was the second of four girls. It is necessary to refer only to the chief points of the character development and the main conflict-situation. Her father, a storekeeper in a small town, wanted a boy and did everything to make a boy out of her, expecting from her masculine accomplishments. By 10 she was managing a department in her father's store, as well as attending school. She always worked hard, and as a child never had any chance to indulge in receptive gratifications. She was always doing things for her sister and father, who said he could get anything he wanted from her if he gave her a little praise. During the period of puberty there was a manifestation of a definite discontent with her inability to assume the feminine attitude, regarding which at the same time there was a strong conflict on account of masturbation, associated with a fear of damaging herself. There were typical fears of insanity.

She married an intellectually inferior, passive, inefficient man with no ambition, with whom she was always frigid. Her married life was characterized by her superiority over her husband in every respect. She was the chief financial supporter of the family and the leader in every situation, having no conscious dependent attitude upon him. She devoted her life to professional activities and paid very little attention to the household, which her husband very much resented. Their sexual life had the typical picture of frigidity on her part and a reactive increasing lack of interest on the part of her husband, which later amounted to full impotence. Although during the marriage there was little sign of a great dependence upon or attachment to her husband, now that they were separated and the danger of a divorce was imminent she became more and more conscious of her longing for her husband—for men. This patient also started out the analysis with the same picture of denying every help. Characteristic was also her lying on her abdomen rather than on her back, which revealed itself as the masculine attitude. During the course of the analysis, however, the repressed oral-receptive and passive-feminine tendencies became entirely obvious and conscious. In this stage she described her mental situation as a strong desire for feminine gratification, and at the same time an utter inability to yield to it. Once she had passive gratification by accepting the analytic situation, her symptoms entirely disappeared. With the gradual admitting of her feminine desires, the rather neglected and unappealing exterior of this woman changed and she became very pleasant and began to pay much attention to her appearance. The analyst had some difficulty in dissuading her from having a plastic operation.

When she felt thwarted in the feminine role she reacted with strong castrative tendencies, as may be seen by two dreams which occurred on two successive days during which her receptive demands on the analyst were very strong. When he did not respond she accused him of being indifferent to her. The first dream was that her husband's hemorrhoids were bothering him again and that his underwear was a mass of blood. In the second dream her little boy was lying in a crib. They were standing over him trying to see if he was a prodigy, and it seemed that his head or body had to be severed. Her associations were mainly attacks on the analyst's ability and masculinity, and fears that she had hurt his feelings. She confessed the desire, during intercourse with her husband, to draw his penis in deeper and retain it.

In another dream she was sitting with a colored man, eating onion soup which was half water. Then she saw Anne, a friend of hers, in a tugboat. Anne was enjoying herself. Her associations showed that she felt that the analyst rejected her oral-receptive demands; that she depreciated him, calling him a Negro and an impotent person. She became Tug Boat Annie, the woman who belittles men and makes them inferior by playing the masculine role herself, but who nevertheless thereby wins their love.

She had quite intense gastric distress when she began to have some conscious negative transference reactions, which were protections against the feminine attitude connected with the fear of being thwarted in her receptive feminine role in the analytic situation. In spite of the increasing acceptance of the feminine role, the battle between the masculine aggressive tendencies and feminine receptive ones continued in her persistent attempts to take the lead of the analysis from the analyst's hands and conduct it herself, both in reality and in her dreams.

This patient rejected the feminine role very early in life because of rejection on the part of her father, who wanted a boy, and her mother's very repressive attitude regarding sex which gave her deep guilt feelings. The oral-dependent attitude was also untenable to her because of real oral deprivation by her mother, to whom she was an unwanted child; by her father, who always demanded masculine accomplishments from her; and by her older sister, who was outspoken in her hatred of her. This led to a masculine identification and strong castrative trends, particularly of an oral nature, which were inhibited through strong feelings of guilt and fear of the loss of love. The patient then denied all her receptive and oral-aggressive desires, became more and more masculine and active, and then developed her gastric symptoms.

TYPICAL PERSONALITY TRENDS AND CONFLICTS IN CASES OF SPASTIC COLITIS

By GEORGE W. WILSON, M.D.

It is not the intention in this paper to give complete case histories, but only to indicate in a series of cases a general type of conflict-situation and solution which seems to be constant and prevalent in cases of spastic colitis.

The first patient was a 40-year-old man who was referred to the Institute by his physician with a diagnosis of spastic colitis. He had had careful gastrointestinal studies which confirmed the diagnosis. His symptoms had been severe for a period of three years during which time his diarrhea varied from a minimum of six mucous bowel movements daily to a maximum of twenty. He had tried every recommended form of medicinal and dietary treatment, with only slight modification of his symptoms. These had begun three years before, approximately six months after his having lost in stock speculations a large fortune which he had accumulated entirely through his own efforts. Prior to this time he had never had gastrointestinal disturbances.

In appearance he was a small man of the pycnic type, with clear-cut features, expressionless face, and a distinctly phlegmatic manner; he gave the impression of being quite ill, i.e., he walked slowly with the aid of a cane and appeared confused and unsure of himself. Like all the other cases in this series, he consented to an analysis only as a last resort. He was the oldest of three children, the next being a sister, three years younger, and the last a brother, five years his junior. He was uncertain as to the date of his father's death, but thought it was either four or five years ago, and that his death was due to paralysis following an accident.

At the beginning he showed a childish and dependent attitude, and was accompanied by his wife who did most of the talking. He said that he was willing to undergo an analysis or any other type of treatment which was recommended to him by his family physician, in whom he placed great confidence. He said he was almost penniless, and he objected to accepting treatment which he could not finance. He was quite willing immediately to accept certain responsibilities, providing he had an arranged obligation. He had a great urge to do something for us, providing he received an adequate return. He exhibited readiness to pay and difficulty in accepting help without recompense, but at the same time expressed a frank wish to be helped.

Early in the analysis he spoke of his father's death and said that for a year preceding his death the father's bladder and bowel incontinence was a source of considerable anxiety to him. This he told with considerable difficulty because he felt very badly about it. He went on, however, to state that his father was a ne'er-do-well. He had been a professor abroad, and, after coming to this country, attempted several times to establish himself in business but was always unsuccessful.

As a result of several failures on the part of the father, the patient had at a very early age felt it necessary to provide funds for the family, and already at the age of 9 was helping in their support. He felt that his family did not have the position in the world to which they—and especially his mother—were entitled. From the beginning he fantasied himself as the rescuer of his mother. Before he entered college he had purchased a home which he presented to his parents. This characteristic he retained throughout his life to the time of his financial losses.

His symptoms began six months after the financial breakdown which reduced him from the status of wealthy man to one of dependence. He had supported his family very substantially, even maintaining a separate savings account for his mother. This same attitude was also shown toward his brother and sister, whom he constantly helped. He assumed a condescending and apologetic attitude toward the father, whose kindly weakness he emphasized. He always spoke about his father with manifest distress.

His attitude in school followed the same pattern. He assumed responsibility in his class affairs, deprived himself of athletics and other recreation in order to do things for the good of the whole; became attendant in the school cafeteria and student manager of the football team, and assumed other less important responsibilities. All of this he did effectively. His manifestly altruistic social attitude and activity were dictated chiefly by this wish to give substantial values and *not* to gain prestige. It gave him satisfaction to be efficient, and he emphasized this. The same attitude was characteristic of his whole life.

Before graduation from high school he became the production manager of one of the largest city theaters. Later he became production manager of a national theater agency. This was followed by appointment as production manager of a larger theatrical agency; and then he established a very successful business of his own which he conducted up until his illness. It is a very interesting repetition in his life that he succeeded where others had failed in rescuing under-takings which were near failure.

This success was based on absolute honesty, insistence on paying in full, refusal to accept any advantages for which he did not give corresponding values, and the expectation of receiving full value for what he gave. For example, when a certain client in the theatrical business proposed to give him $2,500 cash in settlement of an account of $3,000, he refused to accept it. He gave the account to an attorney, and only after several months of persuasion would he consent to any compromise whatsoever, although the attorney advised him that, unless he accepted this, he would probably receive nothing. The purposeful nature of his giving attitude is well illustrated by this example; i.e., he gave so that he might feel free to receive.

What was characteristic of him was the uncanny consistency of his financial success. He left a position which paid a hundred and fifty dollars a week to take a job at sixteen dollars because he could see a future in it. Similar incidents were common throughout his life. Until his financial breakdown he had never had a failure of any description. The beginning of the failure dates back four years, at which time he had done many favors and had made considerable money. His friends took advantage of him, another characteristic of his fate. In spite of a first and then a second loss, he continued to gamble, each time berating himself for having trusted someone else; but he was drawn to repeat the procedure until finally he had nothing left.

We are inclined to see the intentionally arranged losses caused by the infidelity of his friends as another manifestation of his guilt following success. The active giving of values expresses the same psychological dynamics. He has to pay for success and can have it only if he gives full recompense. It seems that all these devices of giving values or being cheated by his friends were not sufficient to placate his feelings of guilt, because finally he managed to lose his money and, when he no longer possessed the power to give money and other values, he responded with the symptom, namely diarrhea. Following the loss of all his reserve, he resumed his business, but in a short time this illness necessitated his retirement.

Typical of this patient's psychological attitude and development is the extreme tendency to produce values and give to relatives and friends. This explains his uninhibited earning capacity, for only through giving real value is he able to eliminate his strong guilt feelings at receiving, which he could do only in exchange. An example of this was his reaction when the secretary of the Institute explained to him that he need not pay each day the two dollars which he had wished to pay for his analytic hour. He told this incident to the analyst with tears in his eyes, and associated to it the dislike of receiving sympathy or being placed in a dependent position—this with particular reference to the family situation and his inability to provide for them as he had done in the past. Without being able to give full proof of the correctness of the assumption, we have the impression that the intestinal symptoms served the same emotional purpose of giving money and other values. This conflict-situation began in his childhood, when he successfully competed with his father as a contributor to the family finances, and his illness began when he ceased to be an adequate provider.

He reported a dream early in the analysis, after he had brought out considerable material regarding the father's financial failures and his humiliation when he compared his home to that of his school associates. In these associations he placed particular stress upon the desire to protect his mother. "I was operated upon. The operation was upon my abdomen. I thought I was dead or would die." He awoke with abdominal pain, went to the bathroom, and had a severe diarrhea. He associated to this dream by telling of an intended operation upon his wife, which was advised by a local surgeon, and then to an operation upon a child who died in the hospital while he was a patient there, and to the fact that her death was due to an internal hemorrhage.

This patient interrupted his analysis in the third month and therefore the deeper unconscious basis of the guilt feelings cannot as yet be fully reconstructed. However, the dream I have quoted may throw some light on the deepest layers of his conflict. In this dream he was afraid of an abdominal operation which he connected, in his associations, with the intended operation upon his wife and with bleeding to death. Because of this female identification, and the unconscious significance of operations in general, we assume that the fear expressed in this night terror was castration-fear. It was castration-fear which he tried to overcome by giving money, by conscientious determined efforts, and by distinctly philanthropic behavior, and similarly, in illness, by diarrhea. The castration-fear became accentuated in his childhood when he succeeded in replacing the father as a supporter of the family. That may also explain why his financial success, which was the basis of his Oedipus victory, was connected with a deep sense of guilt, and also why he has to placate his conscience by anal sacrifices, that is, by diarrhea, when he can no longer do so by money sacrifices.[1]

---

[1] In this connection Abraham (in the article on The spending of money in anxiety states [1917] in *Selected papers*, p. 299) states : "From the few cases that I have been able

This patient interrupted his analysis apparently for the reason that his illness served his purpose so well that to renounce it was for him almost impossible. Specifically it permitted him to regress to the level of indulgence in the infantile role, particularly with reference to his wife, who now mothers and cares for him. He could at the same time successfully justify his inability to carry out active efforts, provide for his family, produce values, for the very obvious reason that he is too ill to do so. Furthermore he carried heavy sickness indemnity in an insurance company, and the cessation of his symptoms would automatically cancel this monthly income. The main obstacle seems to be the secondary gain obtained through the patient's neurosis. This case could probably be classified among those termed *Rentenneurosen* (compensation neuroses). In the analysis when dependence upon the analyst aroused his sense of guilt, he took flight into an exaggeration of his symptoms and it became necessary for him to renounce either the passive dependent attitude, which he was living out in reality, or to terminate the analysis. He chose the latter.

The second patient was a single woman, 28 years of age. She was referred to the Institute following complete gastrointestinal studies. A diagnosis of chronic spastic colitis was made. Careful treatment along the lines of dietary and medicinal therapy had produced little therapeutic result.

In appearance she was of the asthenic type, of medium height, and exceedingly thin. She had clear-cut features, a distinctly Semitic facial contour, and she wore a forced quizzical smile, giving the impression of knowing what she wanted and a certain determination to obtain it.

She was the fifth of six siblings, having two older brothers and sisters and one younger sister. Both brothers seemed to be well adjusted. Three of the sisters were single and appeared to be definitely neurotic; one of them complained of gastrointestinal symptoms. The father died when she was 11 months old. The mother was living and had chronic diarrhea. The patient and the three neurotic sisters lived with the mother. The present illness began five years before, immediately after an operation for an ovarian cyst. She complained of alternating attacks of diarrhea and constipation, which became

---

to observe during my psychoanalytic work, it seems to me that this condition is found in a definite group of neurotics—in persons who are in a state of permanent infantile dependence on the parental home and who are attacked with depression or anxiety as soon as they are away from it. The patients themselves say that the spending of money relieves their depression or anxiety; and they produce rational explanations for this, such as that spending money increases their self-confidence, or that it distracts them from their condition. Psychoanalysis takes the unconscious into consideration and adds a deeper explanation to this purely superficial one."

progressively worse until dietary and medicinal therapy produced some symptomatic relief but without permanent cure. At the time of this operation her youngest brother married and left the city, and her older brother failed to come to see her in the hospital. She remembered this with conscious resentment, which, however, she was quite willing to overlook. Three years later she became attracted to a young painter, a married man to whom her younger sister had introduced her. She felt tricked by this man, even though he divorced his wife and asked her to marry him. She believed his offer was not sincere.

The first difficulties which she remembered occurred when she was thirteen, coincident with her first menstrual period, and necessitated her remaining away from school for a period of six months because of her inability to concentrate on her studies. She reported that during this period she had had many fears, particularly in relation to her teachers and classmates. Prior to this time she had been an excellent student, but now she found her work very difficult and required considerable help to finish her course. She felt irritable toward people, but had a strong desire to be with her mother and to sleep with her, which she did from that time up to the second month of analysis. The patient attributed all her present difficulties to this period of her life. Later she took up a course in business accounting which led to an excellent position as cashier with a large concern. She was so successful that, when this firm moved to another city, her employer advanced her two months' future salary. She immediately secured another position doing the same type of work with a larger concern, and has been giving complete satisfaction up to the present time. In spite of this external success she constantly complained of her dislike of responsibility, of figures, checks, and money.

At the beginning of the analysis her most outstanding manifestations were a complete lack of conscious emotional reaction to her family, and an amnesia regarding her early childhood reactions toward her family. Characteristic also is the way in which she spoke about this, declaring, "I must have had some feelings for them, because, if my brothers or sisters were ill, I noticed them then and became disturbed." In recalling her interest in her brothers, she remembered that she had wanted very much at an early age to sleep in her oldest brother's bed, and that she had envied the younger brother's apparent enjoyment in going about with girls. During most of the analysis she avoided associations regarding her emotional feelings toward her brothers, but she gradually became more and more conscious of her attitude toward her oldest sister. She had a distinctive way of refusing to take notice of this sister by being unable to remember her external appearance. At one period of the analysis she transferred the same reactions to the analyst and stated that she often confused the analyst with this sister. It is significant that she carried out this transference attitude through the greater part of the analysis, in that she denied any feelings whatever during the analytic session, but found it possible to feel some hostility toward the analyst after she left the Institute. Even this hostility she confessed only after several months. Later in the analysis she also confessed this same hostile rejection of her mother, as well as of almost everybody with whom she came in contact. She had made a habit, during the last three or four years, of calling her mother by telephone several times daily. This the patient herself analyzed as a denial of her hostility and proof of her friendly feelings.

It is obvious that the leading feature of the emotional reactions to her family was repressed and denied hostility. Regarding the deeper motives of this hostility toward the different members of the family, her attitude toward her younger sister appeared most clearly. In one of her first dreams this sister stole milk from her. In the patient's associations she remembered that, at the age of 3, she had on several occasions stolen her youngest sister's milk and had been punished for it. From the projection in this dream it is clear that she considers her sister the one who stole from her the infantile role in the family and robbed her of receptive gratification.

Her intense oral aggressive wishes are best demonstrated by reference to some of her other dreams.

"I go to the kitchen to get a drink of milk. I drink part of a glass and have the feeling that I have taken more than my share, so I pour back what remains in the glass and notice then that there is more milk than there was originally."

Her associations to this dream dealt with attempt at oral gratification and oral aggression, with severe guilt reactions. Following an interpretation along these lines, in which it was pointed out that the pouring back represented the diarrhea, there was a complete cessation of her symptoms. We assume that the symptom has the same significance as the pouring back of the milk; i.e., she gives back what she has taken and thus eliminates the sense of obligation and guilt toward her younger sister, and is even able to assume the martyr attitude. She gives back more than she receives. There is more milk in the bottle than there was at first.

In the family situation she refused to take any responsibility whatsoever, permitting and expecting the older sister to care for and entertain her, and her mother to provide for her physical requirements.

Similarly, as in the former case and in contrast to the gastric types, we see here that the patient, in spite of the conflict connected with oral receptive and aggressive tendencies, can permit herself to indulge these tendencies, though only under *certain* conditions. Our assumption is that the symptom of diarrhea relieves the guilt and serves as a recompense for oral aggressive tendencies. This symptom, as Alexander has pointed out in his introduction, has a significance similar to symptoms with moral content in compulsion neurosis; and it serves as a symbolic restitution or self-punishment which allows the patient the gratification of hostilities and other rejected tendencies.

As to the deeper significance of the oral aggressive tendencies, the analysis revealed the following facts. She remained single and virginal because of her distrust of men. She considered this entirely a man's world, and complained that men have many privileges that are denied the female sex. This attitude is particularly well expressed in her business activities in which she enjoyed playing the role of a superior to the men who held a position inferior to hers. Her whole attitude toward heterosexuality is demonstrated in the fact that she considered a man merely as a means of entertainment in the way of providing money and transportation, and never exhibited any affectionate interest in men whatsoever.

The oral aggressiveness expresses castration tendencies which in turn leads to the distrust of men and the fear of the feminine role. The reactive desire for the masculine role is well substantiated in the material just given, and especially in her dreams, of which I quote an example.

> "I'm dancing with you. We stumble and fall upon the couch. I
> fall on top." Also a second fragment of the dream: "I am eating the
> leg of a chicken. I think there is not enough to go around."

In her associations she declared that she awoke with diarrhea. In associating directly to the dream, she spoke of her pleasure in dancing with girls, and also referred to having witnessed, when a very young child, a rabbi killing chickens and having enjoyed the procedure. The sense of guilt is clearly expressed in, "There is not enough to go around." She returns what she took in the form of diarrhea.

In summary we may say that the typical conflict consists in: (a) guilt on account of her receptive tendencies derived from oral envy toward the younger sister; (b) rejection of the female role, which she considered as inferior and humiliating; (c) guilt feelings resulting from the castration tendencies toward the male. The symptoms relieved all this conflict by serving as restitution for oral aggression (toward both male and female) and also by expressing the active (ejecting in contrast to receiving) and supposedly superior masculine role.

The third case in this series is that of a 26-year-old unmarried Jewish girl who was referred to the Institute by her family physician. For the past five years she had been trying every known form of medical treatment for a condition which had been diagnosed as spastic colitis. Various types of treatment, including a long hospitalization, dietary measures, glandular therapy, chemotherapy, and some superficial attempts along the line of mental hygiene, had been tried without any permanent improvement in her symptoms.

In appearance she was a rather slight, good-looking girl of the asthenic type, with a childlike aspect. She had a pleasant smile but never laughed. She walked with a decided stoop of the shoulders, but gave the general impression of self-satisfaction, determination, and self-assurance. At the beginning of her analysis she was about eight pounds under her best average weight.

She was the third of four siblings, having one older brother and sister and one younger sister, all of whom seemed to be fairly well adjusted. The father had died six years before as the result of an accident. The mother had died thirteen years before from gastric carcinoma. The patient's illness began about one year after her father's death, and coincided with the pregnancy of her oldest sister and with her brother's financial failure. Prior to this time she had been supported by her father, but had made considerable progress in the business world as a saleswoman. She was ambitious at an early age, became the manager of several jewelry stores owned by her brother, and later was sales manager of a large organization, a position she held until the time of her illness.

She remembered having some diarrhea as a very young child, together with alternating attacks of constipation. At the age of fourteen she had an appendectomy. She did not menstruate until she was eighteen. At the time of her father's death it became necessary for her to go to live with her oldest married sister and to become more or less dependent upon her, although at the beginning she believed herself quite independent financially. This sister's husband lost all her money in stock speculation, and she was faced with the necessity of providing for herself. However, she continued to accept money and clothes from her brother, and to live in the house of her sister without paying for her board, although it is true that she supervised the kitchen to a large extent and did much of the housework. At the beginning of the analysis she did not exhibit any hostility toward her brother-in-law or sister for the loss of her money, and she stated that her love and respect for them was "the most perfect thing" in her life.

During the pregnancy of her sister the patient had a sudden severe attack of diarrhea. She was taken to the hospital, where the similarity of her attack to labor pains was so evident that it was remarked upon by the internes.

During analysis she became aware of an intense hostility for the youngest sister as the one who had threatened her role as the baby of the family. However, it became clear that she had always clung to this role quite successfully, not only toward the parents but toward the older sister and brother as well.

Soon after the beginning of her illness she became engaged to a prominent and successful business man. Prior to this she had been engaged to a man much older than herself, whom she had thoroughly disliked; but, as she stated quite frankly, she had accepted his marriage proposal merely with the idea of attaining financial security, since he was very wealthy. The consummation of this second engagement she continually postponed for one reason or another.

As in the case of the two former patients, she was unusually successful in her business activities, and this success was based on her thorough honesty and the giving of value in every instance. She was conscientious and philanthropic. She gave many and expensive gifts to her friends and relatives, but felt extreme humiliation whenever anyone gave her a present. It was thus she appeased her sense of guilt until the death of her father, her brother's financial failure, and her sister's pregnancy, which, as her analysis showed, intensified her feelings of guilt. These were due to her castration tendencies regarding men, and her extreme envy of her younger sister which became greatly accentuated with the expected arrival of another competitor for her older sister's affection.

Her attitude to the analysis formed an instructive contrast to the masculine identification which she maintained in her social and business relationships. At the beginning she wanted the analyst to do all the talking, complained of her inability to think of free associations, and in every way exhibited an almost infantile wish for help. She complained that she was always giving to others and received little in return. For example, she gave her youngest sister spending money, clothes, and took all the care of the room which they shared; shopped for her oldest sister, taught her to cook, planned delicacies, etc., for her guests and did other innumerable favors for the family, but received nothing in return, not even gratitude for her efforts.

Late in the analysis the conflict between passive dependent and aggressive competitive desires in relation to the older sister became predominant. She denied all infantile dependent wishes toward her, although she continued to live them out; that is, she permitted this sister to choose her clothes and to dictate all the plans for her proposed wedding, even though she complained about the unfairness of her sister's attitude. She recalled with intense hostility her inability to compete with this sister for the mother-role, and at the same time complained of never having been treated affectionately by her. With considerable emotion she told that she was thwarted in every direction; that is, she could not be the baby because the youngest sister was that. She was not treated as an equal by the oldest sister, and was ignored by the brother, whose attitude toward her was extremely sadistic. (He often slapped and spanked her, told her she was brainless, and considered her useless and generally a nuisance.) We may assume that she solved the conflict through identification with the brother in her masculine activities and in her relations to society, while maintaining her dependent position without guilt in the family situation by giving presents, expressions of affection, and valuable aid to the sisters. This procedure seems to have been successful until her father's death, her brother's financial failure, and her sister's pregnancy.

To these events she reacted with her symptom which, like that of the other two cases cited, served several purposes. First it meant restitution for aggressive taking tendencies which were precipitated by the birth of the younger sister and stimulated again by the pregnancy of the older one; secondly, it meant restitution for castrative tendencies which are most clearly expressed toward the fiancé and the brother; finally it meant a substitute for masculine wishes and activities which she satisfied before her illness by active behavior.

Out of a wealth of material regarding the connection of the symptom with her aggressive castrative tendencies toward men, I wish to give only two examples. The first is a dream to which she reacted with a severe attack of diarrhea.

"My brother-in-law's business became bankrupt. I was calling on the telephone to tell my fiancé about it and to find out if he too had lost all of his money. My sister was standing there and I did not want her to hear the conversation."

Her associations to this dream were about her wishes to own and operate a business of her own, her now conscious hostility to the brother-in-law, and her resentment at having to play what she considered an inferior and humiliating role in life, namely, that of a woman.

A second dream, also reacted to with a diarrhea, is the following:

"I came to the Institute to see you. My father was there. He was having a severe hemorrhage. I thought you could stop the blood, but I could not find you."

That the excretory act has also an anal-sadistic significance for her unconscious is clear in the following dream:

"I was bathing a child. A robber, a colored man, enters my room. He wants to steal my ring. I throw pins at him and he leaves."

Her associations to this dream had to do with maintaining her virginity, her resentment of the "double standard," her fear of aggressive men, and the fact that men have much greater social liberty. We may assume that the depreciated analyst (robber) is being driven away, punished by the throwing of pins, which the patient associated with her diarrhea.[2] She uses the well-known symbolic representation: throwing as an anal aggressive gesture.[3] In the dream this attack on the robber is obviously a reaction to the masochistic evaluation of the female role (to be robbed of virginity).

In spite of these aggressive and masculine competitive attitudes, it appears typical in all the colitis cases we have analyzed that there is willingness to renounce the independent attitude and to become almost completely passive after the onset of the illness. It seems that the diarrhea, through its unconscious emotional significance, satisfied all aggressive and masculine aspirations.

A further unconscious significance of the symptoms which I have not referred to in the other two cases, that of anal birth (gastro-intestinal reproduction), as originally formulated by Freud[4] and elaborated by many other writers, is clearly present as an overdetermining factor in this case. Reference was made to the similarity between abdominal symptom and labor pains earlier in this paper. I quote in substance from the patient's own associations, in the third month of her analysis: "My first severe attack began just before my sister's baby was born. She was preparing to enter the hospital but I beat her to it. The cramps were exactly like those of a woman who is giving birth to a child. The pains came and disappeared at regular intervals. I kept a chart showing the exact length of time consumed by the attack, as well as the intervening painless period. My sister only had one baby while I had several." A dream which occurred in

2 In this connection see Brill, A. A. *Psychoanalysis*, pp. 274, 275.
3 Róheim, Géza. *Australian totemism*, pp. 298, 299.
4 Freud, Sigmund. On the transformation of instincts with special reference to anal-erotism. *Collected papers*, Vol. 2.

the fourth month, and which was reacted to with a diarrhea attack, is the following:

"I was walking down the street with some members of my family. They seemed to be large women. I was carrying a baby. I saw a large balloon shaped like a banana."

Her associations to carrying the baby revolved about her envy of her sister's healthy male child and the fact that she had always fantasied giving birth to many boys. She identified the balloon first with a banana, then associated to German sausages, and laughingly told me that it was probably a large penis. She then spoke of her early beliefs regarding oral impregnation and anal birth, stating that she had believed until she was sixteen that impregnation could take place merely through kissing a man.

The unconscious material which became conscious during the analysis of this case furnishes a classical corroboration of the unconscious equation, child = gift = feces = penis, as described by Freud in the above reference. We need only add that the excretory function has also the meaning of an aggressive action, as is so clearly demonstrated in the "pin" dream to which I referred.

ORAL TRENDS AND ORAL CONFLICTS IN A CASE OF DUODENAL ULCER

By Harry B. Levey, M.D.

The following observations were made during the first ten weeks of the psychoanalytic treatment of a student of technology, 22 years of age, who suffered from a marked difficulty in concentrating his attention on his studies, complained of sexual inadequacy, and was accepted by the Institute of Psychoanalysis as a research case because, apart from these complaints, he had a duodenal ulcer.

From the beginning of the analysis the material centered around certain oral trends and conflicts which, in keeping with the schizoid coloring of his personality, have been close enough to consciousness to find unusually clear expression. Because of the interesting nature of the verbalizations by which the patient has given expression to his weakly repressed material, many verbatim quotations are included from the free-associations. Genetic explanations and reconstructions, which are not warranted in this early phase of the analysis, are avoided, and the description will be confined to the surface attitudes and the immediate dynamic background which the patient has revealed since the beginning of his treatment.

The patient is the middle brother of three, three years apart. He is "the cleverest but a slacker," and expresses envy and jealousy of his older brother who, according to him, is less intelligent but a harder worker. The youngest is poor in scholastic achievement, but has more social grace. The father, an uneducated but ambitious and successful business man, has ruled the family with a violent temper which has mellowed somewhat in recent years. The patient fears him and resents his authority. The father, since an ulcer operation several years ago, disregards gastric symptoms and dietary restriction. The mother is considered intellectually inferior to the father, and occupies herself chiefly with worrying about her children, whom she treats with every indulgence.

The patient finds it difficult to study; yet, "I am never able to get away from work and do something else without feeling I am wasting time and neglecting work. Even if I walk along the street, I feel this is wrong. *I must always work and think.*" He delays to the last moment the preparation of required assignments. When he receives high grades, he lies to those who compliment him, telling them that he did not study and that it was his good luck. Although he secured hospitalization ostensibly for his gastric symptoms, he did so really in order to escape from examinations for which he was unprepared because of his difficulties in studying. He purposefully neglected his soda in order to aggravate his pain, and so to justify his hospitalization with suffering. In his initial interview, both his ambitious drive to study and his simultaneous effort to force himself to work were conspicuous.

He has suffered from guilt and fear about masturbation as long as he can remember, and has dealt with these by attempting to prove to himself that he is still a man. He discovered his sexual inadequacy when, at the time of his initial attempt at coitus, he found himself impotent. Since then he has suffered from ejaculatio praecox. This ushered in the obsession that his testes were too small. Three months of suggestive treatment by a psychiatrist produced no amelioration of his symptoms. As a reaction to his sexual inadequacy, he wishes to be extremely potent, and in one of his dreams, prior to analysis, his intercourse killed numerous women in succession. The patient expresses admiration for feminine buttocks of "amazing size." He often depreciates an interpretation with "Nuts," which he explained once as follows: "Nuts! That is a slang word for testes and breasts, but I am not sure."

One year prior to his analysis, the patient was hospitalized for observation of his gastric symptoms. He gave a typical history of ulcer distress of two years duration, and it had been diagnosed as due to ulcer in the previous year. Repeated examinations of his stomach by X-ray revealed a definite deformity of the duodenal bulb, which was interpreted as an ulcer with considerable stenosis. Although the symptoms were well controlled by regular ulcer management, the prognosis made was that while gastro-enterostomy would ultimately be indicated, it should be postponed as long as possible. For many months the patient had been aware of a moderate tachycardia.

In the first weeks of the analysis the patient described his resemblances to his father and his attitude of dependence on his father, stating that for him sexuality meant suckling, and that he had observed strong feminine traits in himself. Yet at the same time he showed a rejection of feminine tendencies, for which he attempts to compensate by great ambitions to be clever and potent. He had, he said, entered the analysis not to receive therapy, but to test the validity of psychonanalytic theory. He could only accept interpretations made by himself "in the mental set of the (positive) Oedipus complex." During the analysis of these defense reactions against his passive feminine trends, the transference oscillated between passive feminine wishes and the desire to castrate. "I like you because you are a big man. . . . I don't believe you are competent. . . . No one is competent to take care of me. . . . As sometimes I mentally do with a pretty woman, I am taking the clothes off of you. . . . Perhaps after I undress you I will castrate you. . . . If I cut off your penis, I will be even superior to you." Then followed content revealing his guilt over this aggression and his methods of dealing with it: symbolic self-castration, the denial of a dependent attitude and the assertion of an overcompensatory attitude of superiority. He also related fantasies of taking a gun from a policeman's holster and shooting him without provocation; of cutting off women's breasts with a butcher knife; and of cutting down all the telegraph poles from the window of a moving train——"these are penises, cutting off your penis." His aggressive and possessive tendencies toward the penis and breast run parallel.

I would note that although the patient revealed, in his associations, some acquaintance with psychoanalytic terms, this did not lessen the spontaneity of the material. The ideas quoted are the patient's and not referable to any interpretations made by the analyst.

His pronounced oral trends are illustrated by the following: The patient was nursed 18 months, and was said to have had no feeding difficulties. "Mother said that as an infant I used to sit happily for hours with just a crust of bread." For him, sex is suckling; he does not want intercourse with a woman, but to be a baby, "to touch a woman's breasts and suckle it. . . . Breasts to me mean milk—full of milk. . . . When I think of my mother's breasts, maybe I think I would like to give up responsibilities. . . . Any girl I like, I like because she is a mother substitute. . . . When I fondle Mary's breasts, I have a temptation to bite them because I am angry. They are the wrong breasts, because they are not my mother's. This means I want to go back to an early stage minus any responsibility." He fantasies the earth, the air, and the universe as composed of breasts, himself floating in a sea of breasts, and the Capitol at Washington as having a breast pinned on it. The inferiority conflict on account of his dependent (suckling) attitude, described as characteristic in ulcer cases by Alexander, was spontaneously verbalized by the patient in the eighth week of his analysis, no interpretation of this conflict having been made before by the analyst. *"If I could let go,* I would like to have people take care of me, but it would make me feel too inferior." He gets a kind of thrill from taking care of others, i.e., in protecting petite girls, "as I would like to have my mother protect me." He will marry a girl who will have a lover and will mother him. He eats hastily—"it must have some connection with suckling,"—eats small meals so he can eat more frequently, and often, when he experiences gastric pain, he purposely avoids soda so as to experience a suffering satisfaction from his pain.

He relates a dream in which he has called his father home to make the bed and experiences a feeling of "malicious triumph" over his father's annoyance. He associates to this dream as follows: "If father makes the bed, I can help mother dress." And further along: "I could eat. I would not be sick any more. To eat will be to defy father. Father told me not to eat. Eating is suckling."

The following material, which reveals the guilt-conflict connected with oral-aggressive tendencies, is quoted from the notes of the seventh week of the analysis: "Once I saw a circumcision. A very interesting process. Not horrified, but why do I say I was not? I guess I am afraid of castration. Food. That I don't want to eat. Do you know what came to my mind? Why should I have connected up not eating and castration? If my father threatened castration, he did it to warn me to keep my hands off his wife. The way I put my hands on her was to suckle her. The way I must escape castration fear is not to eat. I feel bad now because I don't feel bad. If I were trembling in every limb, I would feel happy now, but I am not. I do feel my pulse has gotten faster."

He expresses his strong oral envy of his brothers on the basis of the diminished quantity of milk left in the mother's breast after nursing each child, ergo, the youngest is weaker and the oldest brother is stronger. He exhibits in daily life the typical conflict of a middle child, i.e., competition with his older brother in the direction of activity and masculinity, and oral competition with the younger brother for the privileges of his dependent role. Whether the guilt aroused by oral envy of his brothers, and of his father, has led to the denial of competition by a passive homosexual relation to his rivals can only be determined later by the material yielded in the remainder of the analysis.

The patient's oral envy toward his brother and his castrative tendencies in the form of cannibalistic impulses against his father, as well as his solution of the guilt engendered, were revealed in the events of a visit home. In the sixth week of the analysis, prior to a vacation period, the transference changed to a passively colored positive attitude, and he preferred to remain in the analysis during most of the vacation, leaving, however, a week end in which to visit his family. "The whole time I was home I was sick with gastric pain." While at home the following significant episode occurred: One evening he usurped the right to lead the family in prayer, which his father had assigned to the older brother. That night he slept fitfully for only two hours, awakening with severe gastric pain. He took soda, returned to bed, and, unable to sleep, recalled that in the third grade at school, while he was standing in a line of pupils waiting to march into the school, his mother appeared, was very angry with him, scolded him as he stood in line, and pulled his ear. He now occupied himself with a fantasy of soldiers in grey, dressed in clerical garb, with cowls over their heads, marching solemnly and slowly, which brought tears to his eyes and associations about the funeral of his grandfather's sister. "I could not sleep, so I read. I remembered it was Easter morning. I had the fantasy that I was Jesus, and that this was the morning I was to rise, so I took off my pajamas and shaved and thought how incongruous that Jesus should be shaving. I put on my new suit and thought to myself, 'Jesus is discarding his old garments and will now appear before his God.' Then I went to six o'clock mass in a Catholic church. . . . I saw Communion, the blessing of the wafers. I do know that miraculously somehow the wafers are changed into the body of Christ. The priest put one into the mouth of each one. It struck me as the most horrible thing I ever saw, that if this was Christ how could they eat him, detestable canni- bals. Then I remembered I was Jesus and felt for a moment that I would stand up and yell that I am Jesus and that they were eating my body, but I did not. Then I went home when the service was over. When I got home I decided this scene had made me so dirty I had to take a shower, which I did." That morning he intentionally angered his father by refusing the latter's request to sing at a large family reunion later in the day. The patient reacted with guilt over having taken away the brother's role, which was for him the equiva- lent of receiving the father's regard and appreciation. He reacts to his guilt with vivid fantasies and emotions during the Communion service, in which at first he attacks people for eating Christ, then puts himself in Christ's role. It is obvious that he reacts here to the guilt for oral-aggressive tendencies by identifying himself with Christ, who is being devoured by the people.

The patient's surface attitude is the overambitious one described by Alexander, and by Bacon, as typical for gastric disturbances. He wishes for sexual potency, but at the same time has the desire, associ- ated with strong guilt, to be cared for and mothered. It is character- istic of this analysis, thus far, that there appear parallel frank ex- pressions of oral-receptive and passive-feminine wishes. Although the feminine and parasitic-oral wishes became conscious quite early, yet he cannot accept them, and the conflict thus aroused is impressive. The oral trends are overcompensated by the wishes for masculine potency, intellectual qualities, ability to concentrate, to sustain effort, and to be independent. Inferiority feelings connected with the parasitic suckling wishes are further solved by fantasies of unusual potency, and by a depreciative castrative attitude toward persons in authority whom he wishes to reduce to his own level. Guilt for oral aggression is relieved in him by self-castrative tendencies which furnish also the basis of his belief that his testes are too small.

His conflict over oral receptivity is so great that he can fantasy himself in his desired role of being mothered and cared for only after he fantasies having lost both legs; his wishes are to be parasitic but to avoid guilt and inferiority feelings. "I wish to have ears that hear not and eyes that see not. That is the fetus." In order to justify to himself his hospitalization and psychoanalytic treatment, he received each of these only after he had wilfully increased his gastric suffering by neglecting his medication. "I have the fantasy that I have my legs cut off and that Mary is taking care of me." His wish for infantile dependence with a minimum of conflict about it is seen in his fantasy: "Again I want to lose my legs above the knees, and resting, so (illustrates resting on a chair), Mary would come and weep and I would say to her that instead she should be comforting." In one form of the fantasy the conflict is diminished by the declaration that he gives as well as receives: "If defecation was something pleasurable to me, it is because feces were a gift to my mother in return for suckling." The same exchange of goods, but on a sublimated level, is expressed in the following fantasy: "I fantasy that Mary and I are married and living in her house. She sits and reads (to me) while I lie. I say to her, 'Excuse me, dear!' Then either I read something to her or tell her a new word." Here not milk and feces but intellectual products are exchanged. Occasionally when he refers to Mary, from whom he wishes lifelong mothering, he will call attention to a feeling of flushing of both legs.

The conflict between his passive-receptive tendencies and his reaction against them is also clearly shown in the transference. He comes for help, yet he comes only to test the validity of psychoanalytic concepts; he objects to lying down, tries to analyze himself, keeps his eyes shut, and rejects all interpretation; later, when he does accept interpretation, his comment is a classical example of oral guilt, that the analyst's interpretations "leave me with a bone in my throat." To him, being analyzed means being fed by the analyst, whom at the same time he wishes to castrate, and therefore he must avoid deep guilt feelings by this self-castration, else by rejection of the food. He often expressed his castrative wishes toward the analyst early in the analysis, in the delusion that he had seen the analyst having his hair cut in a near-by barber shop. He tells, also, that he instructed his barber to give his brother a "good haircut," explaining that the brother had an oddly shaped head. The loss of hair, as is shown by the patient's associations, means diminished potency. After the analysis of this transference attitude (the interpretations of this attitude were never made in sexual terminology), the patient's nearly conscious castrative wishes found direct verbal expression.

Actually his chief overcompensation is emphasis on his cleverness "to be clever will cover anything"—in being an excellent student, and in the wish to improve his effectiveness by making himself capable of better mental concentration and sustained effort. Another interesting overcompensation is his passage of large quantities of urine after the analytic hour, a proof of his masculinity, as was described by Alexander [1] in one of his cases. The patient stated that the passage of large amounts of urine affords him the feeling of being masculine. Once, after a dangerous fall in childhood, his mother, following an old superstition, took him to the roof to urinate as a reassurance. "I drink more water than I used to, so I will urinate a lot and feel more potent."

It is especially noteworthy that his overcompensation for inferiority feeling is dealt with more constructively than for guilt. His need to resolve guilt is relieved masochistically through his belief that his testes are too small, through fantasies that his legs have been amputated, and through his satisfaction in suffering gastric pain. This masochistic solution of the guilt conflict may help to explain the fact that he does not have much urge to be generous to others. He receives without restraint if in fantasy he can inwardly justify his dependent attitude by helplessness and suffering. From his inferiority feelings, however, he tries to free himself by cleverness, study, and concentrated efforts in his work.

---

[1] Alexander, Franz. The relation of structural and instinctual conflicts. *Psychoanal. Quart.*, 1933, 2.

PREGENITAL TRENDS IN A CASE OF CHRONIC DIARRHEA AND VOMITING

By MAURICE LEVINE, M.D.

This case is of special interest for two reasons. It belongs to the diarrhea group as well as to the gastric group, and at the same time manifests a compulsive type of character and compulsive symptoms. Secondly, it demonstrates a variety of "giving" reactions in response to strong receptive urges which have dominated the picture from the beginning of the analysis.

The patient was a 27-year-old man of Scotch-Irish descent, a teacher of mathematics, who came for analysis because of recurrent exacerbations of a chronic diarrhea, nausea, and vomiting. He had had three or four bowel movements a day for the previous ten years, and an almost daily mild nausea and vomiting. In addition, he had various compulsions; such as, for example, that of spelling out words while reading. Repeated medical examinations had revealed a low basal metabolic rate and an intestinal hypermotility, shown fluoroscopically. Thyroid, ephedrine, and whole adrenal gland therapy raised the metabolic rate, but left the patient's condition essentially unchanged. Medicinal, mechanical, and dietetic therapy for the gastrointestinal complaints were of little value.

Superficially, the man's outstanding trait was his impulse to give of himself to others. He seemed not to want to spend money on himself, preferring to spend freely on others, being especially openhanded with his mother and a brother who was three years older than himself. He had the reputation of being an excellent teacher of mathematics, a reputation based on his enjoyment of the giving of explanations. He was regarded as being "nice," gentle, and kind in his superficial everyday relationships. He emphasized the fact that he had little "property sense," i.e., that he had apparently little regard for exclusive ownership and shared his belongings without hesitation. The organic symptoms, his chronic diarrhea, vomiting, retching, and nausea, and frequent periods of belching, can also be described in terms of "giving," and more obviously in terms of eliminative trends. His phrase, "a lack of property sense," might correctly be applied to his attitude toward the contents of his gastrointestinal tract.

In contrast to his generosity, the analysis revealed strong receptive trends; for example, his heterosexual love objects were almost without exception women much older than himself, toward whom his attitude was that of giving small attentions and manifestations of affection; more fundamentally, however, there was a strong need for their undivided interest, affection, and attention. His openhanded attitude toward his mother was a reaction against strong urges to receive from her and from the older women to whom he was compulsively attached. He was jealous of any attention shown by the mother-substitutes to other men, and had a possessive attitude even to the point of not permitting them to dance with other men. His receptive urges were so strong that he was unhappy if the woman kept any of her thoughts from him. His openhanded attitude to his brother was a reaction, in part, to a passive female attitude to this brother, and also a reaction to the envy that he had toward the brother, who was a rival for the dependence on the mother. His excellence as a teacher had obvious narcissistic and exhibitionistic components, but was to a conspicuous degree a reaction to his own desires to be the eternal student. He was excellent at giving explanations to students, but these explanations were based on statements he could receive from others or from books; self-dependent or original explanations were almost impossible for him to achieve, in spite of his unusual intelligence. Although he gave money so freely, beneath it he felt a desire to receive, at times associated with a fantasy that it would be pleasant to be in a sanitarium suffering from an incurable disease, to force others to support him. The happiest memory of his life was of a period in hospital for a fractured femur; he gave a lyrical description of the attention he received from nurses and doctors, the delight of being cared for in all ways, the excellent food and intermediate nourishment. His apparent lack of property sense was a reaction against a strong desire to own exclusively and to have what others had. After giving some money to his brother, he had a dream in which his mother is criticizing the brother for not giving something to the patient. Later, when he was trying consciously to persuade himself and the analyst that his attitude to the mother-substitute was adult and masculine, he had a dream in which the mother-substitute is preparing food for his teacher, a man of 60; the patient, in the dream, asks for some of the food; she refuses, but on leaving, leaves some of the food for him. In this dream he tries to prove that even a 60-year-old man, his teacher, wishes to be fed from a mother, and after having thus eliminated the conflict about his dependent attitude, he can, in the dream, indulge in oral gratification.

The transference situation was marked by his compliments, his offers to do things for the analyst, and his bringing magazine articles and cartoons that might interest the analyst; underneath, however, there was a powerful urge to depend on the analyst, with an intolerance of the loss of any minutes from the hour and a willingness to have the analysis continue pleasantly for many years. His resistance took the form of giving—an avalanche of words during the hour and as many as eight long dreams in one session—an impressive picture of psychic diarrhea.

In general, his giving attitude was a repayment for what he had received, or wanted to receive, and as a means of permitting further receptiveness. In part, also, the giving attitude to his brother and to other rivals was a reaction motivated by his guilt connected with the oral envy. His childhood attitude of envy toward his sister was expressed in overt hostility to her; he hit her so frequently that, as a child, she would run when she saw him; against this he later developed the reaction-formation of thinking constantly of how to help her; her education, her marriage, and the support of her child were matters of great interest on his part, with the expenditure of time, money, and energy. His early envy of his older brother led to a constant urge to depreciate the brother and to shame him by public demonstrations of his own intellectual superiority. Against this hostility he later developed the reaction-formation of unremitting helpfulness to the brother, paying his doctor bills, giving him an automobile, and financing a venture in business.

With his equilibrium of giving and receiving, he had made a fairly comfortable adjustment, even to the point of erotizing the diarrhea and nausea so that they were consciously enjoyable and not regarded as symptoms needing amelioration. But when he was thwarted in his craving for dependence, his attitude became distinctly demanding and hostile, and, in reaction to this hostility, there was a marked exacerbation of his symptoms. When the mother-image wanted to lessen the frequency of their social contacts to avoid external dangers, he reacted immediately with attempts to force her to continue on the old basis by an aggressive playing on her own uncertain emotional reactions and by frightening her with the possibility of upsetting him. This aggressive demanding attitude was associated with enough guilt feeling to produce a marked increase in his somatic methods of giving, i.e., an exacerbation of the nausea, vomiting, diarrhea, and belching. In addition, to some degree, his diarrhea expressed a direct hostility on the basis of the negative evaluation of the intestinal content. In any case not all of the guilt was alleviated by the giving; in part it led to the turning of the hostility on himself with feelings of depression and with suicidal fantasies. At the same time the compulsive trends were accentuated. As soon as the mother-substitute was no longer able to withstand the onslaught of his aggressive demands and compromised with his wishes, the exacerbation of his symptoms subsided.

The most characteristic feature of this personality is the predominance of pregenital trends in their quite transparent dynamic relation to each other. His relation to the sexual objects is pronouncedly of the oral-receptive type, which he compensates by giving money, gifts, and words. The same attitude is manifest in the transference situation. He overtly enjoys the situation of receptive dependence, but balances it with a diarrhea of words and material and slight signs of chivalrous attentiveness. In the transference the anal nature of this generosity becomes obvious. Oral-receptive and anal-restitutive tendencies keep the balance from the beginning of the analysis and appear in consciousness.

His organic symptoms are in conformity with this dynamic picture and express in physiological terms the need to give back what he receives, or to give something in return for all he received and wants to receive. It is noteworthy, in this case, that the physiological form of elimination (anal giving) runs parallel with the sublimated form of giving (generosity and helpfulness). The presence of both types of response may be explained by the intensity and uninhibited manifestations of his oral-receptive tendencies. His desire to receive and to take is so strong that he must give back in every possible way, physiologically as well as in personal relations. This dependent infantile attitude comes to an extreme expression in his relationship to much older women; a relationship which is an almost undisguised picture of a mother-son relationship.

This patient shows one of the characteristics described in the previous papers as frequent in the gastric group: the urge to help. At the same time, in a more pronounced fashion, he shows also the characteristics of the colitis type, the lack of rejection of receptive tendencies, probably because of the fact that this is balanced by extreme forms of elimination and giving. This mixture of psychological characteristics corresponds to his mixture of physiological symptoms, which are partially those of a gastric neurosis and partially those of a chronic diarrhea.

In this patient there was little need for a denial of his oral-receptive trends because they were so well balanced by anal-eliminative trends. This dynamic picture was apparent very early in the analysis; the receptive trends were close to the surface and could be expressed quite openly, for the most part, because of the equilibrium provided by the many varieties of anal restitution. Such a technique of permitting the gratification of certain trends by subsequent or simultaneous balancing by other reactions is characteristic of the compulsion neurosis, and it is noteworthy that this patient, in addition to his organneurosis, had a compulsive character structure and compulsive symptoms. Such a finding offers evidence in support of Alexander's suggestion that the colitis cases are similar in dynamic structure to the compulsion neurosis.

The understanding of the historical background of this dynamic picture is still incomplete. I wish to mention, as one factor, the guilt reaction resulting from his oral envy to his siblings which was one of the factors contributing to his great need to compensate for the oral gratification. Furthermore, the exacerbations of the diarrhea were part of an accentuated need to give resulting from guilt feelings which were based on aggressive demands to be given attention and care by the mother-substitute when this was withheld.

As the analysis progressed, it became clear that the emphasis on oral and anal reactions in his life were the result of his fear of castration. Masculine heterosexual urges aroused strong fear of the loss of the penis and resulted in a regression to pregenital attempts at adjustment. When the analysis aroused in him urges to give up the infantile dependence on the mother-substitute and to consider an emotional relationship with a younger woman, he reacted with an undisguised castration dream, a nightmare, in which a younger girl destroys his penis. In his development, fixation at pregenital levels during infancy undoubtedly was of importance. Of still greater importance, however, was the regression to pregenital levels as the result of castration fear.

A CASE OF PEPTIC ULCER AND PERSONALITY DISORDER *

By Franz Alexander, M.D.

The purpose of this presentation is to demonstrate the nature of the psychoanalytic material, of the therapeutic process, and results obtained by a treatment procedure which in certain aspects deviates from the customary psychoanalytic technique. The material and results here presented were obtained in thirty-six sessions during ten months of treatment of a 23-year-old university student suffering from duodenal ulcer and disturbed by a deep-seated personality problem. This presentation will show that during these thirty-six interviews the same type of unconscious material was obtained and the same kind of therapeutic results were achieved, as in the customary prolonged psychoanalytic treatments in daily interviews. Of course no complete evidence can be offered for the validity of this statement because the same patient cannot be treated by both methods. The comparison must be based on extensive experience with similar cases treated by the usual technique. In the last 15 years I have had the opportunity to treat, and to supervise the treatment of, several patients suffering from peptic ulcer, and my statement is based on this experience. Naturally the generalization cannot be drawn that every case can be successfully treated in such a relatively small number of interviews. On the other hand it appears to me and to some of my co-workers that this more active type of treatment with less frequent interviews is more suitable in a large number of cases which in the past were treated with the customary technique. Moreover, in many cases the customary technique is not necessary; indeed it may be unsuitable, since it may prolong recovery and even counteract it. To try to decide this crucial problem of technique is not the purpose of this study. I do not propose to formulate precise indications for therapy conducted in less frequent but more active interviews, although to arrive at such formulations is the ultimate aim of case studies of this nature.

---

* From The Proceedings of the Third Psychotherapy Council, 1946. Chicago, Institute for Psychoanalysis, pp. 18-40. Also in Psychosomatic Medicine IX: 320-330, 1947.

The patient was a 23-year-old university student, who, during the treatment, was working on a thesis for his Master's degree. He had had a hemorrhage from ulcer 5 years before treatment, when he was 18 years old. The hemorrhage was preceded by only a short period of stomach complaints. From that time the patient was on a strict ulcer diet and medication (atropin and alkalis); he suffered continuous but mild discomfort which was relieved by eating. The repeated X-ray examinations showed a fleck and scarring in the duodenum. Stomach fluoroscopy on October 30, 1945, showed a slight deformity of the duodenal bulb with a tiny central fleck which was interpreted either as a small crater or central scar. From this, radiating folds were seen.

The patient came to me on the recommendation of his best friend whose father had had peptic ulcer and whom I had treated successfully in psychoanalysis some years before. In the first consultation the patient lucidly described his major problem: his difficulty in expressing any form of emotion. This manifested itself outwardly by a studied casualness which pervaded his total behavior. He dressed with a pronounced sloppiness, exceeding even the usual college style; his shirt was unbuttoned, his tie conspicuously loose, his shoes worn out and unpolished, and his trousers wrinkled. He was, however, quite clean in both body and attire. His facial expression was that of boredom mixed with a condescending superior attitude manifested by a sophisticated noncommittal smile. His speech was somewhat monotonous, and he used the technique of understatement to an excess. While all these mannerisms—obvious character defenses in Reich's terminology —were not conscious, he was painfully aware of his inhibitions in expressing feelings toward other people. He could never sustain a love relationship because he did not allow himself to become involved. After the first or second intimate contact the whole affair became a "bother" for him and he soon terminated it. In fact he had never had more frequent sexual contact with a girl than once or twice. After this he had a great desire to extricate himself from the affair, and became irritated toward the girl. He suffered invariably from premature ejaculation. Apart from these disturbances he was scholastically successful and quite interested in his field. He was ambitious and had the ability to sustain concentration over a long period of time.

The patient was the son of a professional man of high reputation in an Eastern city. While the patient was quiet and amenable to parental guidance, his brother, three years older, the only sibling, was independent and rebellious and not well controlled by the parents. The brother was frequently punished, on which occasions the patient felt guilty because he escaped punishment and was held up to the brother as an example; yet secretly he approved of his brother's independent actions and admired his bravado.

The patient had attended public school and was an excellent student, but could not attain a sense of security as a member of any group of contemporaries. Instead of spending his time with persons of his own age, he became the junior and protected member of the group with whom his brother habitually spent his time. As a consequence he could satisfactorily avoid, for a time, the necessity of assuming any social responsibility and of participating as an equal in the activities of his associates. Thus he became quite dependent upon his brother. When he was 13 years old, his brother went to college and the patient no longer had a group with whom he could feel at home and secure. As a reaction he turned to his parents completely for affection and approval, and even as companions for his extra-school hours. For exercise he took private gymnastic lessons, and in the evenings he frequently played cards with his parents. When he was 14 years old his brother died suddenly, leaving him even more dependent upon his parents. His parents, in turn, spent more and more time with him, making him feel that he had become increasingly important to them. Instead of going to camp he spent the summers with his parents.

During the initial consultation the patient was quite confused concerning his reaction to his brother's death. He felt it as a great loss— he had lost his protector—but he thought that he might have had some hidden satisfaction in becoming the only interest of his parents. He did not know whether or not he had guilt feelings about this.

Two years later, after the brother's death, his father died. The patient was then 16 years old. When his mother broke down under her grief, the patient was aware of her desire to treat him as a little man, as an adult. She began to consult him in her business affairs; he responded as she wished and acted as a mature person. At that time, however, and also when he consulted me, he was not aware of his affectation, playing the role of the superior man; neither did he realize the extreme insecurity underneath his sham maturity. Outwardly he acted the part of the secure, imperturbable, casual strong man so well that he succeeded in convincing himself of the reality of this role. This statement is based on the fact that he completely repudiated my first interpretations concerning his dependent feelings toward his mother. He emphasized that he was not dependent on her, but that she was dependent on him. So far as external appearance went, this statement was certainly valid.

Shortly after his father's death the patient left home to go to school. Later he dated the beginnings of his mannerisms of casualness from this period, but at the beginning of his treatment he believed that no person or thing was of great emotional significance to him. Nevertheless he strove for academic and athletic success. He achieved academic success, but that did not give him the kind of esteem which he secretly cherished, although he was not ready to admit this to himself. His defense, that he did not care for anything, was not quite successful. He was also aware of the fact that he was actually more dependent upon the good opinion of others than he wanted to believe. He dreaded anyone's perceiving any form of insecurity in him; he loathed pity and sympathy from his friends. His character defenses were weakest in his relationship to women. Here he was quite aware that everything was not all right. He was puzzled by the fact that once he succeeded in making a conquest he lost interest, was incapable of returning affection which he aroused in his sexual partner, refused any responsibilities which such a relationship involves, became unstable, and terminated the relationship at once. He was, of course, much concerned about his premature ejaculation and the sham of his pose as a successful lover. His inadequacy, sexual and emotional, was the chief motive for his desire to be analyzed. He had some general knowledge that this emotional problem might have something to do with his ulcer.

The first therapeutic session, following two preliminary interviews, was spent in talking of his inability to express emotions, to commit himself to anything because of fear of failure, his feelings that to show emotion is a sign of weakness. He remarked that his father, who also had suffered from peptic ulcer, had had the same attitude; he had been undemonstrative and casual. He mentioned his ambition in grade school to be on the ball team. He admitted that he was afraid that he would give the analyst the impression of being young and immature. He spoke of his embarrassment in having pimples; he dwelt upon his fear of rejection, his concern about premature ejaculation. In response to my interpretation of his studied casualness he became aware that this was a defense against showing concern for the opinion of others. He related a recurring dream in which he could not make a train because of some kind of obstacle; he dropped the ticket and found a taxi. This dream was interpreted as an attempt to attach his basic insecurity to some trivial thing such as fear of missing a train. Whereupon the patient began to speak of the time when his brother died, and when his mother explicitly told him that he must now take the place of two sons. He mentioned his mixed feelings at his brother's death. The emotional content of the first interview can be summarized as follows: the patient had verbalized his extreme ambition to live up to expectations, particularly those of his mother, his fear of failure and his defensive measures, covering up his inferiority feelings with his manneristic casualness.

As often occurs in psychoanalytic treatment, the patient's first dream, related in the second interview, brought his central conflict clearly to the fore. In this dream the patient was riding on a bicycle with his mother. He was at the handle bars and lost control; the brakes did not work, and the two fell over a precipice. The patient fell first and then saw his mother fall. She was obviously hurt; probably she died. The patient remained unhurt. His associations centered around his mother's unselfishness, and yet he would not consider her death at present a tragedy. This dream was not interpreted in all its overdeterminations at that time. In the course of the treatment, however, we returned to it repeatedly. In this interview I called his attention only to his denial of his dependent attachment to his mother. I also suggested that the dream might show some insecurity about assuming the leadership his mother had expected of him, that he should be a substitute for the two deceased members of the family, and that the dream might indicate that because of her strong excessive demands upon the patient the mother was an emotional liability. The patient immediately accepted the latter statement but denied any dependence.

In the third interview, a week later, the patient brought memories of his father, and then of a professor who was very kind to him. Although the memories of the father were ambivalent, the tender feelings prevailed. He recalled his father's giving him an extra dollar in an amusement park. This made him feel tender and he felt ashamed while telling it. He also mentioned his difficulty in accepting any gift, adding that he could never allow anybody to pay for him in restaurants. The patient appeared much less tense in this interview, and his whole behavior revealed the beginnings of a positive dependent transference towards the analyst. The patient also reported that during this last week he had felt much better and that his stomach symptoms had remarkably improved.

A guiding principle which we have found of great therapeutic value in the Institute is not to allow the patient more regressive gratification in a dependent transference relationship than is necessary for the treatment. For this reason, one should not give more interviews than are needed. However, in order to give further relief to this patient from his symptoms, I saw him again three days later. In this interview he talked about his early sexual curiosity, about childhood masturbation and his father's attempts to impress him with its evil effects. He then spoke about his first ejaculation, his first sexual contact with a girl, and his ejaculatio praecox which he could never control. He described his feeling that after ejaculation he wanted to get rid of the girl, "to kick her out of the bed"; he spoke of his complete lack of tenderness. At this time the patient was going with three girls; with one he had had intercourse. He was brutal with her afterwards, and did not even walk home with her. He was quite aware of his fear of appearing weak by showing emotion. The shame about tender feelings was the outstanding emotional content of this interview.

In the fifth interview the patient's aggressive feelings were expressed and discussed for the first time. He reported a dream in which he tried to hurt someone but was prevented from doing so. The association material centered around his relationship to men. It became obvious that although the patient would like to have friends upon whom he could lean, he could not allow himself to do so. We discussed his competitive tendencies, fed by his feelings of inferiority, which in themselves were the result of his dependent leanings. The association material made it possible to trace his competitiveness back to his attitude toward his aggressive and independent brother and father. We also discussed how his inferiority feelings were responsible for his exhibitionistic trends, his desire to become the center of the party, and why he was interested in girls only for the sake of conquest, for the prestige which he derived from the conquest. In this interview, three weeks after beginning treatment, the patient reported that he continued to feel much better, although he did not keep his diet strictly any longer.

A week later, in the sixth interview, the patient's material continued to revolve around his exhibitionism. Now the tendency to blush and to become embarrassed came to the fore. This could be explained as reaction to his exhibitionistic tendencies; it was caused by his guilt feelings. In a dream he was walking down a grandstand with a girl. She was following him. He was afraid she would fall through the benches. She actually fell but was not hurt. We see that the patient in the dream is willing to make the girl a fallen woman only in order to gratify his vanity. This dream was one of a dream pair; the second was a punishment dream for the narcissistic inconsiderate gratification expressed in the first dream. In the second dream he was with the same girl in a room and felt much shame when she saw his soiled underwear.

In the next interview, three days later, the patient continued to produce material concerning his exhibitionism. He reported a dream in which he was in a room, probably in a hospital, about to undress. His mother was in the room and the patient wanted her to leave. His mother said, "Don't be silly, you will be undressed for the operation anyhow." His associations led directly to memories of her seductive ways. His mother often walked around the house completely naked in his presence. When the patient had to undress in a doctor's office, his mother was always present. When he was twelve his mother told him that she purposely exposed herself to him in order to acquaint him with female anatomy. He remarked that this was inconsistent with her disinclination to discuss sexual matters in his earlier years.

At this time his mother was just about to come to Chicago for a visit and wanted to stay in her son's apartment, but he reserved a room in a hotel for her. He said that he felt uncomfortable when his mother touched his leg or had any physical contact with him. He remembered that, even when he was 6 or 7 years old, he felt uncomfortable when his mother bathed him. Further memories were about mutual masturbation with a neighbor boy when he was five or six. About this his mother had suspicions and had questioned him. The patient mentioned in this interview that he had never had wet dreams in which he ejaculated after introduction of the penis; ejaculation always occurred before. In this interview the patient's inferiority feelings were retraced to the mother's contradictory attitude toward sex. Without being aware of it she had a seductive influence upon him, and at the same time intimidated his sexual manifestations. This created in the patient the feeling that he could not live up to his mother's wish that he be a full-grown man. On this occasion his character defense of studied casualness was again discussed and explained as the patient's desire to assume the external earmarks of a strong mature man since in this way he could allay his feelings of inadequacy. In the same interview the discrepancy between his actual immaturity and his histrionic display of maturity was impressed upon the patient. He was at this time symptom free, and felt that he had reached greater capacity to control his embarrassment in the company of men.

For external reasons the next interview, the eighth, was held two weeks later. In the meantime, the patient's mother had visited him for six days. During this time he had a relapse; he felt more inhibited towards his girl friend; he became angry at her because of her seductive behavior; he had a homosexual dream and his fear of premature ejaculation increased. He felt that he wanted to get rid of his mother. He hated to show any feeling toward his mother in the presence of others, but even when he was alone he showed no real affection toward her. He recalled that when he was fifteen the headmaster wanted to promote him to another grade but his mother did not believe that he could make it. This had hurt him profoundly.

During this interview the patient showed marked signs of a dependent transference relationship. The psychodynamic situation of this session could be reconstructed as a retreat from heterosexuality because of the old insecurity pattern in relation to his mother. At the same time his dependent attitude toward the analyst was coming to the fore as a substitute for dependence on his mother. From the point of view of therapeutic progress, however, it is important to note that the patient became more tolerant towards his dependent wishes. He observed this and remarked that he was able for the first time to ask and receive something from another person.

A week later, in the ninth interview, he invited to dinner a girl who appealed to him very much. This girl, however, was in love with someone else and he felt rebuffed. His interest in this girl was motivated mainly by his need for prestige. Sexual conquest was his means of overcoming his shame, which had become more intense because of the mobilization of his dependent leanings towards the analyst. During the same interview, the patient reported a dream about his mother which preceded the dinner with the girl. Two of her sons were killed in the war. The patient was the third and only surviving child. He told his mother to go to bed. There were three pillows on the bed but none under her head. The patient put one pillow under her head, and while he was doing it he became panicky, realizing that she was now depending solely on him. In associations the patient mentioned that after his brother died his mother had called him her two little boys. The following night the patient had a dream in which he received a special delivery letter from the analyst, which he was very happy to get. This sequence of dreams corresponds to his basic psychodynamic pattern: the patient retreats from the difficulties of adulthood, into which his mother wants to push him, to dependent relationships toward men—at the moment, towards the analyst. This retreat in turn creates an intense injury to his pride and drives him to an immature exhibitionistic type of relationship with girls, with sexual conquest as the only goal. Failure in his sexual relationships then throws him back again to his dependent role, which he tries desperately to deny in his external behavior. This vicious circle, typical of many neuroses, can be reproduced graphically. (See page 181.)

At this phase of the treatment there was a definite sign that the original pattern was beginning to be modified: the patient became more tolerant toward accepting some dependence upon the analyst, as evidenced in the dream in which he is openly happy to receive the analyst's special delivery letter. This was further evident in his less defensive attitude during the interviews, which showed the earmarks of a positive dependent relationship to the analyst. This new be-

PSYCHODYNAMICS OF A NEUROTIC VICIOUS CIRCLE

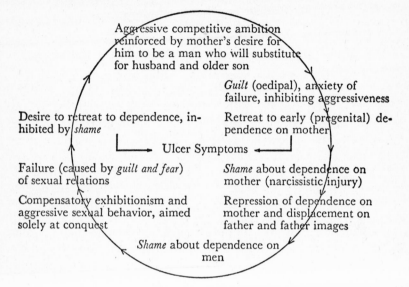

Aggressive competitive ambition reinforced by mother's desire for him to be a man who will substitute for husband and older son

Guilt (oedipal), anxiety of failure, inhibiting aggressiveness

Desire to retreat to dependence, inhibited by *shame*

Retreat to early (pregenital) dependence on mother

Ulcer Symptoms

Failure (caused by *guilt and fear*) of sexual relations

Shame about dependence on mother (narcissistic injury)

Compensatory exhibitionism and aggressive sexual behavior, aimed solely at conquest

Repression of dependence on mother and displacement on father and father images

Shame about dependence on men

havior pattern in the patient was once present in the past, namely, between his sixth and thirteenth years, when he could still allow himself tender dependent feelings towards his father and the protection of his brother. After his brother's death this attitude became repressed because of the mother's emotional demands. When his father died he became his mother's only emotional support.

The question is, what made the ego at this time of treatment more tolerant of accepting help without shame? This hitherto unconscious desire was now becoming conscious because it had been interpreted consistently and dealt with by the analyst as a natural wish. This attitude of the analyst was the main factor in helping the patient to make the shift. The unconscious dependent feelings towards the analyst had not been allowed to become too strong, and their earliest manifestations had been interpreted without criticism or condemnation. The analyst avoided speaking of his dependent needs with any condemnatory connotation, such as, "You are showing infantile dependence upon your analyst," "This is your latent homosexuality," etc. Instead, it was always emphasized, as quite natural, that one should lean on one's doctor; that this relationship gives opportunity to satisfy repressed dependent longings. The technique of seeing the patient in infrequent interviews was adopted for the same reasons. Previous experience with ulcer patients has shown that they are likely to get involved during analysis in a severe conflict between overly strong dependent desires and the need to reject them because

of shame and the wish to deny this dependence. The technical problem was to help the patient to tolerate a certain amount of dependent tendencies and to gratify them in an acceptable manner com-
patible with his age and total personality. It was anticipated that
when the patient's dependent needs were drained through acceptable channels, his needs for overcompensation would diminish. This,
in turn, would diminish the patient's feeling of inferiority and embarrassment, and also the guilt feelings aroused through his aggressive, competitive exhibitionistic behavior. The therapeutic plan was
then to help the patient have life experiences which would increase
his security: namely, to achieve a successful relationship with women
and a greater ease in the company of men. This aim could be
achieved by making conscious his guilt feelings, a result of his aggressive tendencies, and allowing him to recognize the main source of his
insecurity: the premature demands of the mother to have her son substitute for the deceased husband and older son. Improvement in the
peptic ulcer symptoms could then be expected as a natural consequence
of this changed personality pattern. By allowing the patient to drain
his dependent needs in the treatment situation without arousing
shame, thus modifying his need for overcompensatory competition
and aggression, his chances were increased for achieving more successful interpersonal relations—sexual and social.

In the next two interviews, three days apart, the patient expressed,
in a dream, his desire to be loved by "a good mother." In this dream
the mother image was split. The housekeeper of a snobbish, ambitious lady friend of the mother's appeared as the good mother; the
snobbish lady corresponded to the bad mother. This housekeeper
helped the patient with a task his mother had demanded he perform.
In the past this housekeeper had actually showed her liking for the
patient, and when he and his mother were invited to this home, she
always prepared the patient's favorite food. In the same interview
the patient for the first time openly expressed a demand for more
attention from the analyst and showed irritation because these demands were not fulfilled. This may be considered as a definite shift
from a dependent father transference to a more deeply repressed
dependent mother transference.

During the Christmas holidays the patient left town for four weeks.
When he returned for the twelfth interview he reported that he had
no stomach symptoms; the only dietary direction he still kept was to
eat frequently. In a dream before this interview, the day after he
returned to resume his analysis, he missed the train to Chicago, one
train after another. His cousin, "B," and mother tried to get him on

the train but were unsuccessful. "B" was a substitute for his brother: he was the brother's friend, a big bully, who often frightened the patient in the past. This dream expresses his feelings that both his mother and his brother had had the same influence upon him, namely, they stimulated his desire to grow up. Abundant memory material came up during association to the dream of his envy of the brother's strength and independence. He recalled that when he was eleven he noticed that his brother had pubic hair. Many similar memories were related during this session. The content can be summarized as the patient's unsuccessful attempts to emancipate himself from his mother. His brother's example stimulated this desire, but he was not yet ready, and he shrank back into the dependent role toward both parents.

In the next interview, a week later, the same topic was continued. It is interesting to note that the interval did not interrupt the unconscious process. The night before the interview the patient dreamt again of his mother and cousin, "B." There was a party for "B's" wedding; "B" had no car, and the patient and mother offered to give him a lift. "B" phoned that he would be a little late. The mother answered, "You cannot expect us to wait. You must find your own way." In his associations the patient spoke of his mother's dislike for "B." It is obvious that the patient in this dream clearly expresses his wish that his mother would leave the brother out in the cold and concentrate entirely on the patient. He gives up the struggle expressed in the previous dream to become like his brother, and accepts the simple resolution of becoming the mother's only beloved son. In this session, for the first time, he began to realize that his inability to accept his mother's love was caused by his guilt toward his brother who was always scolded and punished by the parents.

In the fourteenth interview competitive oedipal material toward his father appeared for the first time in the form of memories concerning his father's interest in other women, and in a dream in which his father appears with another woman and conspires against the patient and his mother. The week end before this interview, when he visited his mother at home, he felt more relaxed than usual.

In the fifteenth interview competition with his brother came out, mixed with a hostile deprecatory attitude towards his brother and male competitors in general. This appeared in the form of a dream about baseball, in which he saw another fellow who played very well and whom he then depreciated. The patient was never a good player, while his brother was excellent. In the same interview, however, the patient reported another dream which expressed the opposite tendency, a retreat from competitiveness into a passive attitude.

In the sixteenth interview the patient reported a dream in which his mother and father had a quarrel and patched it up. The patient felt great elation over this. The associations led back to several episodes in the patient's life in which the parents quarreled with each other. He usually took the mother's side, but never completely; his feelings were always somewhat mixed. In this connection another motive for the patient's inability to identify himself with his brother and father began to become apparent. The mother's pushing him to become an adult intensified his oedipal tendencies and at the same time increased his guilt, thus throwing him back to the more passive and dependent attitude. In this dream the patient made an effort to solve this problem by the principle of live and let live. He allowed the parents to be happy with each other. About a week before this dream the patient had invited a girl to dinner, someone who appealed to him a great deal and with whom he later had a very satisfactory sexual relationship. This relationship was already fairly well established when the patient dreamed about the parents patching up their quarrel. The patient's habitual premature ejaculation completely disappeared. He felt a great deal of self-confidence because this was the first time he had had a continued relationship with a girl. He liked the girl very much. She cooked for him and the whole relationship assumed a steady character. It became clear that the patient's dream, allowing his parents happiness, was prompted by his being successful and happy with his girl.

While the patient's actual behavior showed definite improvement in the direction of sexual maturation, in his dreams unsuccessful competition with the brother and brother images continued. These dreams were characterized, however, by persistence in making an effort towards success. At that time the patient had no stomach symptoms and ate everything without restriction. His apparently good adjustment, however, was still not on a solid foundation, as is evidenced by such immature acts as calling his mother by long distance while his girl friend was preparing to have intercourse with him. In the next few interviews this tendency to brag and to emphasize his successful adult behavior became more and more conspicuous. It appeared also that this girl did not completely satisfy his thirst for prestige. Every little fault which he discovered in her made him embarrassed in the company of other people.

In the nineteenth interview he reported that he had had for the first time in his life a sexual dream in which he completed the sex act.

In the twentieth interview short aggressive dreams appeared. In one he murdered two small children, and in the second he stole a bicycle and was caught. The associations showed that murdering the children referred to his desire to get rid of his own childish tendencies. The bicycle again showed the same progressive desire. Bicycling was the only activity in which he was superior to his brother. He liked to do stunts and ride fast. It is therefore understandable that in this bragging period he dreamed of bicycling. It will be remembered that his first dream was of bicycling with his mother. The fact that he stole the bicycle and was caught showed that he regarded his present masculine attitude as stolen from his brother and he therefore felt guilty about it.

In the next few sessions the seesawing conflict between aggressive, almost megalomanic, identification with persons of authority and retreat caused by self-punishing attitudes continued. He was working through his competition with his father and the consequent guilt. In one dream he took the place of General Eisenhower and wore his uniform. He had to go somewhere by aeroplane and had to change his clothes. He could not find them, could not fix the medals, and could not fasten the buttons; he could not make the plane. In another dream he was sick, went home, and was glad to be taken care of. In that interview, the twenty-second, he reported a slight relapse: his stomach bothered him for the first time after a long period. In the dream of being sick both a self-punishing tendency and a retreat to dependence are clearly expressed.

In this phase of the analysis I began to discuss with the patient a long interruption of treatment. It was obvious that he had made a forward step in his personality development, as manifested particularly in his relationship to his girl friend. He was somewhat ahead of himself, however, because his guilt feelings toward his brother and father had not yet been resolved. I felt it was necessary to curtail the unconscious hope in the patient to have a prolonged treatment, since this would have become an undesirable gratification for all his regressive tendencies. While I did not tell him we would terminate treatment on a definite date, I said that the problem was now to consolidate our results, that this would not require a very long period. His reaction to this impending termination was slightly more than I expected. It manifested itself in a desire to go home, enjoy home cooking, and, as he said, "to be a parasite again for a while," a feeling he had never had before. He had always had a distaste for going home. At the same time he was struggling against giving in to his regressive tendencies. This was a crucial change. The conflict was now raised to the conscious level, and he struggled against giving in to his now completely conscious regressive tendencies. The enemy was in the open and the patient could fight against it with his conscious ego.

The psychodynamics of what took place after mention of the interruption is self-evident. He reacted to the suggestion of termination by transferring his dependent tendencies to the original object, to the mother. Once these wishes became conscious in his relationship to the physician, he could no longer repress them; displacing them to his mother was the only possible solution. At the same time he showed a definite tendency to put his girl friend in the mother role and to assume toward her a dependent role. This was evident even in their sexual relationship; he wanted to make the girl the aggressor. During this time, however, dreams appeared in which he openly expressed his competitive attitude towards his father. Fear of his competition and guilt were the most powerful factors in the past which drove him into dependence on his mother. In one dream he tried to change a dressing gown with his father. His mother said it was not necessary. In reality, however, the mother gave him his father's robes to wear. Even now he feels uncomfortable in these robes. It is instructive to note that the patient in this dream corrects reality : he attributes to his mother an attitude which could have saved him his neurotic development. The analyst's attitude, however, was exactly that which the patient attributed to the mother in the dream. Most of these oedipal dreams appeared in pairs : the first dream expressing his competitive wishes, the second having a passive homosexual connotation. A typical dream of the second type was one in which his teacher in the university treats him by putting tweezers in his nose. Actually, he had been a patient of his uncle, a dentist. The meaning and dynamics of these dreams, the oscillation between aggressive competition and passive submission, were freely discussed during these interviews.

This oscillation manifested itself also in his relationship to his girl friend. Now he asumed the role of the leader, then again he became afraid and tried to discourage the girl's ideas about marriage. At that time the patient made a decision regarding his future career and contemplated marriage. During these weeks his sexual relations became more and more satisfactory.

In the thirtieth and thirty-first interviews the patient related dreams which clearly dealt with his early castration fear. At first it was expressed in anal symbolism—a long rigid blackhead was squeezed out of his head. In the second a doctor grabbed his testicles. In another dream of the same night the patient was in the analyst's office and had an argument with the secretary about appointments; his mother helped him. He had a vivid memory in which his father yelled at him to shut up, and he felt terrified.

In the thirty-second interview the patient reported a dream of hostile content directed towards the analyst. The motivation, however, was not competition, but frustration because of the pending interruption. The patient expressed the feeling that the analyst owed him something. This was interpreted, and the patient laughingly admitted that he had felt this way in the last few days. He apparently felt that he was forced prematurely to stand on his own feet.

In the next interview, the thirty-third, which was scheduled for three weeks later, the patient reported that he felt surprisingly well. His girl friend was away and he felt lonely. He recounted a recent dream in which an encyclopedia fell upon his mother and blinded her. She was sorry only because she could no longer see her son. The association material dealt with his visit to his mother the week before, when she told him she saw a tremendous change in him. She naturally became curious about how this happened, and asked about the details of the analysis. He did not want to tell her because he wished to appear strong to her. The dream expressed his desire that his mother should not be able to see his weakness—she is blinded. The encyclopedia was associated with the analysis. Unconsciously he hoped that the analysis would help him to live up to his mother's expectations which, in fact, were the main cause of his neurosis. Because deep down he did not yet trust himself, he hoped that the analysis would teach him how to act maturely and to deceive his mother about his still existing insecurity. Another dream of the same night had the same unconscious content: the patient had a secret illness and told his father not to tell his mother. He urinated blood. He told his father it was gastric hemorrhage. Then his grandmother died, and the patient cried. To urinating blood, the patient associated that his girl friend had just had her period. That feminine identification was his secret weakness was clearly expressed in this dream.

In the thirty-fourth interview, the last before a long interruption, the patient reported premature ejaculation and some irritation with his girl friend. He had been bragging also of his academic achievements. The patient suspected that this relapse was a reaction to the impending interruption. The analyst dismissed the patient saying that this relapse, no matter how insignificant, showed that his recovery was not yet complete and that further interviews might be indicated. We agreed that, in any case, after some weeks he should have one or more interviews.

The thirty-fifth interview took place ten weeks later. The patient had felt well with very slight occasional gastric discomfort. All dietary measures and drugs had been abandoned. His relationship with his girl friend remained very satisfactory. During the ten weeks there were only three days in which he had had premature ejaculation. These were the first days of his mother's visit to Chicago. The patient, his mother, and his girl friend were frequently together, and his mother expressed openly her jealousy of the girl. He was tense the first three days, but then had an open talk with his mother and frankly told her she was jealous of his girl. From then on his mother behaved graciously towards the girl and the patient had no further disturbance. It was only during these few days that he felt the need of analytic treatment.

In the thirty-sixth interview, a week later, the patient told a series of recent dreams with regressive connotation. In one, girls with whom he grew up appeared and took the sexual initiative. In another, he had a western hat. Someone remarked that his aunt gave it to him, and he was embarrassed because it sounded childish. In reality he had such a hat. On the inside there was an inscription, which he disliked, saying it was made especially for him. In actuality, however, he remarked he did not have any such regressive symptoms; both his sexual and social contacts were more satisfactory than ever. The clue for this discrepancy was offered by another dream. He was on a submarine and could not get off. It was quite near to the pier but not close enough for him to dare to jump. The patient himself understood the dream: the submarine symbolized the analysis which he did not yet dare to give up, although he really could. The regressive dreams could then be explained as the patient's attempt to convince the analyst that he needed further treatment. This interpretation was confirmed by the patient, who asked whether it would be of interest to mention a few recent occasions in which he felt slightly embarrassed. It turned out that all these occasions would have embarrassed anyone. It became obvious that the patient was looking for excuses to continue the consultations. He readily admitted that he no longer felt that he needed the interviews, although they gave him an added feeling of security. Such an emotional situation I consider as the most classical indication for a tentative termination. It was agreed that the patient should have one more interview and then a long interruption, after which he could return to check the stability of the therapeutic gains.

A brief evaluation of the nature of the therapeutic results and the psychoanalytic material will now be attempted. The patient's ulcer symptoms have practically disappeared, although the ulcer regime in diet and medication have been abandoned for more than a half year. It will be remembered that from his hemorrhage, five years before, up to the third week of treatment, he had had constant distress, relieved only by eating, in spite of careful diet and steady medication. There is good evidence that the improvement was achieved to a large extent by changing the patient's emotional reactions. The symptomatic improvement took place parallel to the development of an openly dependent transference relationship; with this came profound changes in the dynamic structure of his personality. These changes consisted outwardly in the disappearance of his studied and affected casualness and his sloppy way of dressing. He looked now like a college student and not the caricature of a college student. His facial expression was no longer that of superior boredom but showed animation and interest. His tone of conversation became natural, and there was a give and take of emotional responses. The patient's tendency to feel uneasy and embarrassed in the company of men disappeared. His ejaculatio praecox ceased, and he was for the first time capable of a continued affectionate relation with a woman.

These external changes were based on an internal shift in the psychodynamic structure of the patient. Most important was the achievement of tolerance toward accepting without shame a certain amount of dependence upon others. The defense reaction against his intensive dependent longings were consequently no longer needed. These had consisted earlier in the denial of dependence through his studied casualness, his fear of involvement with women, and his inability to show and even feel emotion. Furthermore, his defensive competitive ambitiousness and aggressive exhibitionistic trends became superfluous. His fear of failure, a direct result of both his guilt and overambition, also disappeared. This gave him a greater security with people in general, and with his girl friend in their sexual relations.

The last question is how the therapy consisting of thirty-six interviews brought these changes about. This has been answered in part by the presentation. Only a brief recapitulation is needed.

The patient developed a transference neurosis of low intensity. He transferred to the analyst, first his dependent attitude towards the father, then his dependence on the mother, and later to a less degree some of his competitiveness towards his father. The dependent tendency was made conscious consistently as it appeared, and was interpreted in an objective way, with careful avoidance of even a veiled critical connotation. It was treated primarily as the natural dependence of a patient upon a physician, a fully acceptable reaction adequate to the actual situation. The regressive significance of the transference was gradually impressed upon the patient. The transference neurosis was kept from becoming intensive partially by making it conscious from the beginning, and partially by interrupting the treatment whenever there was a danger signal. The regular interval between sessions was one week, during which the patient had to live without leaning on the analyst. The position was always face to face. Only in the very beginning of treatment was the patient given two weekly interviews in order to relieve his symptoms, and thus to gain his confidence and allow the development of a mild transference neurosis. After the patient's ego became more tolerant towards these repressed dependent tendencies, the treatment became a gradual working through, step by step, of the different defense mechanisms— such as exhibitionism and aggressive ambition and sexuality for the sake of conquest. The tertiary derivatives of these defenses, such as fear of failure, embarrassment, and ejaculatio praecox were automatically resolved as soon as the patient's behavior became less motivated by exhibitionistic aggression. Then his more mature tendencies emerged, such as genuine interest in other people and enjoyment of activity for its own sake and not for the prestige involved.

As to the psychoanalytic material itself, it is of the same nature as that usually obtained by the customary technique. In every session but six the patient related one or more dreams containing pregenital and phallic material and early castration fears. The sequence of the dreams, as in every analysis, showed a continuity, the type of problem-solving activity of the unconscious as described by French. The patient produced some forgotten memories; some existing memories became filled with emotional content. He became conscious of his envy toward his brother, his admiration and fear of his father, and, above all, of his completely repressed dependence upon his mother. He became conscious of the meaning of his character defenses: his studied casualness and affected sloppiness.

So far as prognosis is concerned, it can be expected that the patient will from now on continue his emotional maturation. Depending upon external circumstances, there is a good chance that he will have no serious recurrences of his ulcer symptoms. In this regard it is important to know that he has selected a career in which he will be in partnership with a somewhat more experienced person. At the termination of the treatment the patient was fully reconciled to give his partner, although equal in financial responsibility, a slight preponderance in leadership. Four months after the interruption of the treatment the patient had one follow-up interview. He felt well both physically and emotionally. Very rarely he had slight distress at night which yielded to drinking a glass of milk. He had had no medication and had not restricted his diet in any unusual way. What is even more important, his personality change appeared well established. His relationship to his girl friend remained stable; they had set a date for their marriage.

It is my conviction, based on extensive experience with similar cases, that the customary procedure would have delayed recovery and would possibly have resulted in an insoluble transference neurosis. I am also convinced that there is a large number of patients in which this type of treatment is preferable, not only because it is more economical but also because, in suitable cases, it is more penetrating and avoids the danger of becoming interminable.

The technique of less frequent interviews with frequent interruptions and tentative termination is preferable in all those cases in which the patient can stand greater pressure towards solving his basic conflict. In this type of treatment the patient has less opportunity for regressive evasion which, as we know, often cannot be counteracted with our customary procedure. With all this, however, we are not advocating an essentially different kind of technique. We do not believe in a dichotomy: here standard psychoanalysis—there brief psychotherapy. Frequency of interviews, the duration of treatment, the position of the patient, etc. are not the essential criteria of adequate technique. These details depend upon the psychodynamic requirements of the case. Psychoanalytic therapy represents a continuum comprising shorter and longer treatments, frequent and less frequent interviews with more or less activity on the part of the therapist; the details of the technique, the external aspects of the treatment, may vary, but the essential dynamic principles remain the same.

THE RELATION OF PERSECUTORY DELUSIONS TO THE FUNCTIONING OF THE GASTRO-INTESTINAL TRACT *

By Franz Alexander, M.D.,
AND
William C. Menninger, M.D.

Parallelism Between the Psychodynamic Background of Psychogenic Chronic Constipation and Persecutory Delusions

An attitude characterized by pessimism, the belief that one is not loved, that one receives nothing from others, the fear of not being able to earn a living, has been described by Alexander (1) as characteristic of many cases suffering from psychogenic chronic constipation. These character trends coincide with features described earlier by Abraham as belonging to the "anal character." The same pessimistic defeatist attitude in an exaggerated form is common in melancholias and becomes most pronounced in the delusions of poverty. In constipation cases, together with this mistrustful attitude, there is also the tendency to deny all obligations toward the environment, to refuse, for example, to make efforts for other people's sake, or to give help or money. These two features, first the mistrustful pessimistic attitude, which is characteristic both of melancholias and of cases suffering from chronic constipation, and second, the tendency to repudiate obligations, corresponds schematically to the following emotional syllogism: "I do not receive anything from others, and therefore I do not need to give; indeed I have to cling to what I possess." (2) This emotional attitude seems to be in causal connection with the tendency to retain the intestinal content and explains the frequency of constipation in depressive states. The connection lies in the unconscious evaluation of the intestinal content as a valuable possession, in the coprophilic tendency of the child before and during the period of training to cleanliness.

During the study of psychogenic factors involved in gastrointestinal disturbances in the Chicago Institute for Psychoanalysis, it was noted by several members of the staff that in some cases suffering

* The Journal of Nervous and Mental Disease 84 : 541-554, 1936.

from chronic constipation marked paranoid tendencies were frequent. These patients go further in their misinterpretation of the environment's attitude than do the depressed cases; whereas these latter are content to believe that nobody loves them, that nobody gives them anything of value, these paranoid cases maintain not only that what people give them is of no value, but that on the contrary it is harmful —an attitude that is most clearly expressed in the delusion that their food is poisoned. According to these clinical findings, we began to distinguish between two types of constipation cases, those exhibiting more the features of melancholia, and those who show more paranoid trends. The above described causal connection of the constipation with the emotional trends typical for melancholia was rather obvious: the fear of not receiving increases the possessive-retentive tendencies of these patients, which they also extend toward the intestinal content. The question arose, whether the frequent paranoid tendencies in certain types of constipation may have also a causal psychodynamic relationship to intestinal retention. This seemed probable because of certain psychological findings obtained during the analysis of cases suffering from chronic constipation. In the dreams of these patients, and in their fantasy life, the idea of soiling or attacking people with filthy epithets or even with excrements is frequently quite frankly expressed, and their dream symbolism also quite regularly refers to all kinds of attacking and soiling others by means of excrements. These frequent coincidences of intense unconscious and even conscious and sadistic impulses with chronic constipation led us to assume that these three tendencies, (a) the tendency to retain the intestinal contents, (b) the anal sadistic impulses, and (c) the paranoid tendencies are all somehow psychodynamically connected with each other. The obvious explanation was that the excremental act in these cases is connected unconsciously with hostile attacking tendencies which cause fear of retaliation, denial of, and finally projection of, the hostile tendencies, and at the same time an inhibition of the excremental functions.

The psychologic background of this inhibition differs from the syllogism just mentioned as characteristic of the depressed constipated cases; it is based on a negative depreciating attitude toward the excrements and on an anal sadistic concept of the excremental act. The above described tendency to retain the excrements on the basis of their positive evaluation as a precious possession corresponds to the earlier coprophilic phase of childhood development; the inhibition of the excretory function, caused by the negative sadistic evaluation of the excremental act as a means of attacking others, corresponds to the latter phase in which the child already has developed a disgust reaction as a result of his training. However, both sources of intestinal retention, one based on the coprophilic tendency, the other on the inhibition of anal sadistic impulses, are found together in the unconscious in all cases. Sometimes the one, sometimes the other motivation is more prevalent; the depressed cases retain their intestinal content more out of possessive tendency, the paranoid cases more out of inhibition of the sadistically evaluated excretory act.

These considerations explain the coincidence of inhibited anal sadistic impulses with constipation, and it remains now to understand the connection between paranoid delusions and constipation and anal sadistic impulses.

That the denial and projection of anal sadistic impulses play an important role in the psychogenesis of persecutory delusions is well established through psychoanalytic experience. Ophuijsen (3) and Stärcke (4) have pointed out that in persecutory ideas, the unconscious identifies the intestinal content as the attacker. In paranoid psychoses there are frequent ideas of being poisoned by gas, or of food being poisoned or mixed with disgusting things. These fantasies are obviously based on the projection of the patient's own anal soiling tendencies. The projection of the anal sadistic impulses allows the patient to put the blame on the environment, to assume a negativistic, even aggressive attitude, and at the same time to deny his own original destructive tendencies. He can interpret these as reactions to the hostility of the environment against himself. It is also obvious that if in their unconscious they consider the excremental act as an attack, and if at the same time they wish to deny their own aggressions, this probably will have an inhibitory influence on the excretory process itself. Therefore we expected that the tendency to constipation would probably, as a rule, be frequent among patients suffering from persecutory delusions. Even though our few analyzed cases of chronic constipation did not have real persecutory delusions, their general attitude toward their environment was somewhat paranoid. They had a tendency to blame the environment and deny their own aggressions, but at the same time, in their dreams, they expressed their anal sadistic soiling tendencies with great clarity. Of course, in their conscious life, only traces of the paranoid trends were present, and these were corrected by the patient's unimpaired judgment, just as the depressed types of chronic constipation cases exhibit the emotional attitude of melancholias only in a diminished form.

These psychodynamic observations have induced us to subject their general validity to a statistical study of the excremental habits of a larger number of frankly paranoid cases. This study was especially challenging, since it meant a conclusive test of the correctness of our psychodynamic conclusions based upon the analysis of a relatively small number of cases. We approached the problem of selecting a hundred psychotic patients suffering from persecutory delusions, investigating their gastrointestinal habits, and then comparing them with cases of schizophrenics in which the described type of delusions were not present. A typical comparative statistical study of forty cases of manic depressive patients was also made because the detardation of intestinal elimination is well established in this type of psychosis.

Statistical Findings

Two hundred forty cases have been investigated and classified symptomatically into three groups, one hundred showing active persecutory trends or delusions at the time of the examination, forty cases showing depression without showing paranoid coloring, and one hundred cases showing neither ideas of persecution nor depression—the latter group being used as controls for the first two. We are indebted to Dr. Charles F. Read, Managing Officer of the Elgin State Hospital, for the privilege of studying these cases at this institution. We recognize that certain dietetic factors common to all large institutions are operative in these cases, but these factors are uniform in all the groups. It is to be expected that a certain number of persons would complain against institutional food, and that mental hospital residency in many instances necessitates considerable confinement as compared with the previous habits of the individual.

Material. We wish to emphasize that we are not classifying our cases according to diagnostic categories, but on the basis of the psychological content of their symptoms. The great majority of the hundred cases showing persecutory trends were diagnosed by the hospital staff as paranoid schizophrenia. There are, however, a few cases in this group suffering from paranoid delusions who were diagnosed differently, and on the other hand many of the cases diagnosed as paranoid schizophrenia on admission, but who did not show paranoid trends at the time of the examination, were consequently not included in this group but in the control group. The great advantage of this classification is that our results are conclusive regarding the question of how frequently persecutory delusions and constipation coincide, independently of other diagnostic criteria. Our control group consists of a heterogeneous group of schizophrenic patients without persecutory delusions. Our statistical study on depressed cases included, for the most part, typical manic depressive psychoses in the depressed phase, although a few of the cases had been diagnosed differently, the depression being in all cases, however, the predominant symptom. None of these patients have been in the hospital more than five years.

The depressed cases have been included in our investigation mainly for comparative reasons because their tendency to be constipated is a well-established fact.

Method. An abstract was made in each case from the original case record as given on admission. Each patient was interviewed for the purpose of making a short mental examination, and specific inquiry was made regarding the eating habits, their opinion regarding the food, indigestion, bowel habits, the use of laxatives, and the occurrence of diarrhea. Patients were excluded when, in the opinion of the examiner, the statements were unreliable, except in those instances where the facts could be verified by the physician in charge of the ward, or, more frequently, by the attendant.

Results. The following tables indicate the tabulation of three groups into three classes, divided on the basis of the severity of the constipation. A more detailed study of each group is presented below, also criteria for the classification of the degree of the intestinal stasis.

PERSECUTORY DELUSIONS

	Female	Male	Total	Per Cent
No constipation	13	15	28	28
Mild constipation	12	2	14	14 }
Severe constipation	18	40	58	58 } 72%
			100	100

DEPRESSED

	Female	Male	Total	Per Cent
No constipation	7	2	9	22.5
Mild constipation	3	1	4	10 }
Severe constipation	20	7	27	67.5 } 77.5%
			40	100

CONTROLS
(Not Paranoid—Not Depressed)

	Female	Male	Total	Per Cent
No constipation	22	52	74	74
Mild constipation	5	9	14	14 }
Severe constipation	5	7	12	12 } 26%
			100	100

It is conspicuous in these tables that the paranoid group shows 72 per cent of the individuals with either mild or severe constipation, the depressed group shows 77.5 per cent, in contrast to the control group which shows only 26 per cent with constipation. The findings are even more conclusive if we include only those cases showing severe constipation. The paranoid group shows 58 per cent, the depressed group 67.5 per cent, and the control group only 12 per cent.

Closer analysis of the groups specifying the degree of constipation is made in the following three tables. It will be noted that the degree of constipation is for convenience classified into twelve groups, the first three of which we are listing as "no constipation," the second three as "mild constipation" and the other six as "severe constipation." We recognize fully that "constipation" is a vague term, in view of the fact that certain individuals can hardly be said to be constipated if their normal evacuations occur every two or three days, whereas a similar state of affairs for another individual is evidence of marked constipation. Similarly, we recognize that an individual may have several bowel movements a day, and yet his actual peristaltic activity may be so slow that the intestinal content requires five or six days for complete passage through the tract. The frequency of evacuation is not an ideal criterion for judging peristaltic activity; for this purpose a barium meal and X-ray examination is the only suitable method. This method has been employed in the work by Kaiser and Henry, which we shall discuss later. Our interest, however, was not so much in the relation of persecutory ideas to the peristaltic activity in general, as in their relation to the excremental functions in particular, which latter are dependent both upon the peristaltic and sphincter activity.

PARANOID DELUSIONS OF PERSECUTION

	Number of Cases	Per Cent
No constipation		
1. Two or more movements daily	5	
2. One movement daily	17	
3. Daily movement with special aids (much water, no meats, etc.)	6	28
Mild constipation		
4. Daily movement with periodic constipation (periodic laxatives)	6	
5. Movement once every one or two days	4	
6. Movement once every one or two days with periodic constipation	4	14
Severe constipation		
7. Once in two days	7	
8. Once in two or three days	13	
9. Once in three days	4	
10. Once in three or four days	7	
11. Once every four days or more	13	
12. Only with laxative or enema	14	58
	100	100

DEPRESSIONS

	Number of Cases	Per Cent
No constipation		
1. Two or more movements daily...........................	1	
2. One movement daily......................................	8	
3. Daily movement with special aids (much water, no meats, etc.)	0	
	9	22.5
Mild constipation		
4. Daily movement with periodic constipation (periodic laxatives)	1	
5. Movement once every one or two days....................	3	
6. Movement once every one or two days with periodic constipation...	0	
	4	10
Severe constipation		
7. Movement once in two days.............................	5	
8. Movement once in two or three days.....................	10	
9. Movement once in three days...........................	2	
10. Movement once in three or four days....................	6	
11. Movement every four days or more......................	4	
12. Movement only with laxative or enema..................	0	
	27	67.5
	40	100

CONTROLS

	Number of Cases	Per Cent
No constipation		
1. Two or more movements daily...........................	18	
2. One movement daily......................................	52	
3. Daily movement with special aids (much water, no meats, etc.)	4	74
Mild constipation		
4. Daily movement with periodic constipation...............	5	
5. One movement every one or two days....................	6	
6. One movement every one or two days with periodic constipation	3	14
Severe constipation		
7. Movement once in two days.............................	0	
8. Movement once in two or three days.....................	1	
9. Movement once in three days...........................	1	
10. Movement once in three or four days....................	2	
11. Movement every four days or more......................	4	
12. Movement only with laxative or enema..................	4	12
	100	100

Previous Studies on Intestinal Stasis in Psychosis

The association of intestinal stasis with various types of psychoses, and particularly with depressions, has long been recognized, and in fact is the basis for the very extensive usage of colonic irrigation in the treatment of these illnesses.

Believing that the constipation was due to a local infectious process, Cotton (5) originally recommended in many cases the removal of the colon, but along with many other therapists used high hot colonic irrigations extensively. These therapeutic experiments have been based on the obviously erroneous concept that the psychosis was caused by the dysfunction of the intestinal tract, in contrast to our assumptions that the intestinal stasis is conditioned psychodynamically through some psychological process such as the psychosis. The relationship between depression and constipation was suggested by Abraham (6), namely, that the retardation of visceral functions is a physiological expression of the tendency to retain within the self the orally incorporated love objects.

Although there are many reports of colonic therapy in mental disease, we have found only two recorded studies of the actual peristaltic activity as shown by roentgen-ray examination after a barium meal. Kaiser (7) examined the actual peristaltic activity by roentgen ray after a barium meal in 37 cases of schizophrenia, 21 cases of manic-depressive psychosis, and 12 cases of psychoneuroses. He found that the normal evacuation time of the colon was from 36 to 48 hours, in contrast to the 37 cases of schizophrenia which showed an average of 113 hours, and to the manic-depressive group which averaged 154 hours. Henry (8), of Bloomingdale Hospital, New York, three years previously had reported his roentgen-ray observations of 51 cases of schizophrenia. In this group he found a normal function in chronic deteriorated cases, but 70 per cent of the acute, actively hallucinating cases showed a retention of the barium in the colon for a period longer than five days. Sixty-seven per cent of 12 paranoid schizophrenics showing hallucinations, confusion, and ideas of reference had a retention longer than five days.

In a subsequent study Henry (9) reports 40 cases of manic states and 56 cases of depression with 18 recovered cases used as controls. In this group he found that 25 per cent of the manic patients and 68 per cent of the depressed retained barium for a period longer than five days. He contrasted this with a group of 14 acute schizophrenics, of whom 72 per cent retained the barium longer than five days. He found that there was no change in the gastrointestinal function so long as there was no change in the emotional state.

Henry feels that his observations might be regarded as corroborative of the psychoanalytic formulations, namely, that the retardation of visceral functions is a physiological result of the incorporative and retentive tendencies of the patients toward their love objects. Henry also observed intestinal stasis in cases of schizophrenia, but did not raise the question of a possible psychodynamic relationship between intestinal stasis and schizophrenic delusions.

Stärcke in 1919 and Ophuijsen in 1920 pointed out the association of paranoid ideas in neurotic patients with anal tendencies, suggesting that the persecutory ideas originate from the projection of anal aggressive tendencies (4 and 3). In the first chapter of this study we refer to the psychological findings of the Institute for Psychoanalysis of Chicago, in cases of constipation which led us to suspect that persecutory ideas and constipation have a close relationship to each other (1).

General Evaluation of the Statistical Findings

A definite correlation has been found between the frequency of mild and severe constipation and the occurrence of persecutory ideas. Schizophrenics without persecutory ideas show much less frequency of constipation. These findings confirmed our expectation that the tendency to retain intestinal content is psychodynamically connected with the persecutory ideas. Both are results of the patient's conflict about his anal sadistic tendencies. The persecutory delusions are projections of the patient's own anal sadistic tendencies which he denies and attributes to others. The constipation can be explained as the result of the inhibition of the patient's anal-sadistically evaluated excremental functions.

Although these conclusions seem convincing, yet it could be questioned whether one is justified in explaining the frequent constipation as due specifically to persecutory mechanisms. The fact that cases with persecutory delusions show constipation in a higher percentage could be explained on a different basis: Persecutory fantasies are common at the beginning of all types of schizophrenia, which later may develop into a hebephrenic, catatonic, or paranoid direction. This fact and other reasons suggest that paranoid symptoms are signs of an acute process, of an undecided conflict, paranoid symptoms being of all psychotic symptoms those which are nearest to neurotic mechanisms. They show the defense reactions of the ego against objectionable unconscious impulses. They are signs of the presence of a definite guilt conflict (super-ego reaction) because, through the paranoid psychosis, the patient tries to push the blame onto others and thus eliminate his guilt for his own destructive tendencies. In the light of these considerations one might argue that the frequent coincidence of persecutory phantasies with constipation is not due to a certain specific psychological content, but to the fact that

these cases are the more acute ones in contradistinction to deteriorated hebephrenics. According to this concept, constipation would
belong to the syndrome of an acute schizophrenic process. This possibility can hardly be eliminated on a merely statistical basis. We
have to recur to detailed psychological material regarding the psychotic's attitude toward his nutritional, and particularly toward his
excremental, functions. A few examples of such attitudes in individual cases included in our statistical material are presented in the
following section, and will supply further evidence for the correctness of assuming a specific psychodynamic relationship between persecutory ideas and chronic constipation.

Examples of Paranoid Schizophrenics' Attitudes to the Excremental Act and Food

As we have already emphazised, the sadistic evaluation of the excremental function is always mixed with its positive (coprophilic)
evaluation. The two unconscious different motives for retaining the
intestinal content are always intermixed: (a) because it is considered a valuable possession; (b) because it is considered a destructive weapon.

Some of the remarks of the paranoid patients made about their
excremental habits, although not allowing a specific interpretation of
their motives, nevertheless show clearly that there is a psychological
tendency to retain the excrements:

> "I feel better when I don't have a movement, and I won't take a
> laxative."
> "My bowels never move. I am glad they don't move. I feel stronger
> when they don't."

This latter remark indicates a narcissistic evaluation of the excrements, well known from the analysis of psychoneurotics as a residue
of the infantile emotional life, attributing to the excrements the
significance of potency.

In this connection it should be mentioned that the positive (coprophilic) attitude toward the excrements often serves as a basis for
megalomanic fantasies. The megalomanic delusions are frequently
transparent elaborations of the infantile way of connecting the excremental function with a feeling of power and potency. In a case of a
young schizophrenic patient of Thomas A. Ratliff the patient's delusions were centered around ideas of his ability to destroy and control the environment through his excremental functions. In the majority of cases, however, the anal-erotic source of megalomania is not

so frankly expressed. It is to be expected that in cases suffering from such megalomanic delusions there will be less tendency for constipation. Patients who have no conflicts about their anal sadistic tendencies, but who accept them and derive from them a feeling of potency, naturally should not show any inhibition regarding their excremental functions. The number of megalomanic cases in our material is not sufficiently high to draw any conclusions. The few cases with megalomanic delusions included in our control group seem, however, to indicate that in fact the incidence of constipation in such cases is very small. A special statistical study is required to prove the correctness of this assumption. If this prediction should prove to be correct, it would be a further corroboration of these psychodynamic concepts about the influence of specific emotional factors upon the function of the gastrointestinal tract.

Most conclusive are those remarks of patients which show that they do not want to assume the responsibility for their bowel movements, probably because of their destructive significance :

> "The radio does it—there are wires in it."
> "I can't take laxatives because they don't do any good."
> "It is all controlled by an urge from some general system."
> "My bowels are directed by forces outside myself."
> "I have only scientific movements."
> "Your soul and mind can control your movements."
> "I am irregular, but I believe it is due to my bathing."

The formerly described emotional syllogism which is more characteristic for the depressive type of constipation, "I do not give because I do not get," is clearly expressed in the following remark of one of the paranoid cases :

> "I only go once a week because we don't get enough to eat."

As has been mentioned before, a great number of these patients suffering from persecutory delusions are apt to express some objection about their food, that it was poisoned, that it had been tampered with, that the juice had been extracted, that there was no nourishment in it, that there was saltpeter or spanish fly in it, that its consistency was such that they could not swallow it. In these complaints the projection of anal sadistic tendencies are clearly expressed. They depreciate the food which they receive, often in such a way as to leave no doubt that they compare it with excrements, as if they wanted to say :

> "It is not that I want to attack or soil or poison other people with my excrements—it is they who do it with me."

The food is either disgusting, or the nourishment has been extracted from it, or it smells, etc. Of this group of 39 delusional cases who expressed this type of objection against food, 8 (20.4 per cent) showed no constipation, 4 (10.3 per cent) mild constipation, and 27 (69.3 per cent) severe constipation.

The Homosexual Component in Persecutory Delusions in Relation to Chronic Constipation

In our discussion we restricted ourselves to explaining the correlation of anal sadistic tendencies, persecutory delusions, and intestinal retention. It is now time to consider the role of passive homosexual tendencies, because since Freud's early studies their close relationship to persecutory ideas is well established. In his *Psychoanalytic Notes Upon an Autobiographical Account of a Case of Paranoia (Dementia Paranoides)* (1911), Freud (10) pointed out that the aggressive hostile tendencies which the schizophrenic projects onto others are defense reactions against the patient's passive feminine longings. The emotional syllogism which Freud expounds in this paper is: "I do not love him—I hate him." And the next step: "I do not love him—I hate him because HE PERSECUTES ME."

According to this theory the aggressive tendencies do not constitute the deepest layer. They are only secondary defense reactions against the patient's denied and rejected passive homosexual longings. The validity of this concept for male paranoias has been corroborated repeatedly by a number of psychoanalytic authors. Also in our statistical material we found a series of cases whose remarks obviously pointed to this deeper homosexual component. In many cases it was quite obvious that the delusions did not refer so much to being persecuted or tortured, but were of a pleasanter nature. The patients spoke only of being the center of attention, said that people were talking about them, and they obviously derived much satisfaction from this special interest which people paid to them. Other patients expressed their passive homosexual interests more directly— they believed they were being accused of homosexuality but denied it, or by their obvious mannerisms they assumed a coquettish female behavior toward the interviewer. In other cases the specific content of the paranoid delusions referred to the homosexual component. One of the patients believed, for example, that he received magnetic influences through a nail in his anus. The more the patient's ego is able to accept the female passive tendencies, the less are denial and defense reactions against them necessary. The first part of the emotional syllogism "I do not love him but I hate him" is not necessary if the patient has little conflict about admitting his feminine love toward another man. In these cases the delusions originate less from a guilty attitude, can express more directly the passive homosexual longings, and do not take such a sadomasochistic character as in the persecutory cases. Psychoanalytic experience with neurotics with unconscious passive homosexual tendencies has shown that constipation can serve as an autoerotic satisfaction of the passive desires, the anus assuming the role of the female receptive organ, the excrement that of the male organ. Thus the patient is able to satisfy autoerotically the desire for anal intercourse. We have little doubt that in a number of paranoid cases this autoerotic use of the excrements plays an important role in the causation of chronic constipation. These are the cases in which the inhibition of anal sadistic impulses is probably of lesser importance; the original passive feminine drive can express itself directly in the constipation. In the majority of the cases, however, according to the Freudian emotional formula, the original passive feminine tendency is denied and is strongly repressed and overshadowed by reactive hostile tendencies. Our study shows now that these hostile tendencies are of anal sadistic nature, which the psychotic denies and projects onto others, thus producing the persecution fantasies and at the same time the inhibition of the sadistically evaluated excremental act.

Summary

In a number of psychoanalytically treated cases of chronic constipation, two different psychodynamic mechanisms, one typical in melancholia and another typical in paranoid disturbances, have been observed. Patients either manifested a pessimistic defeatist attitude, to be rejected and not to receive anything from others, or they showed paranoid trends of being attacked and unjustly treated by others. A causal psychodynamic relationship between these emotional attitudes and the tendency to constipation had been assumed on the basis of the psychoanalytic material. In order to test the general validity of this causal connection, a group of 100 cases showing persecutory delusions, and 100 control cases, have been investigated with reference to their excremental habits and to their attitudes toward the excremental functions and toward food. It is conclusively shown that in the control group there is an incidence of 26 per cent of constipation, in contrast to 72 per cent of individuals suffering both from constipation and persecutory delusions. These figures in connection with the psychological attitude toward the excremental function and food expressed by these paranoid individuals confirm our conclusion that the psychodynamic basis of constipation is the same in psychotics suffering from persecutory delusions as in chronic constipation cases which show only traces of a paranoid attitude. The frequent constipation of patients suffering from persecutory delusions is mainly conditioned by their conflict about anal sadistic tendencies which they deny and project. Their frequent deprecatory attitude and delusions about their food is another manifestation of the projection of their anal sadistic impulses.

A statistical study of 40 patients suffering from depression corroborated the clinical observation regarding the frequent coincidence of depression and constipation (76.5 per cent). The specific causal relationship between the emotional attitudes in melancholia and constipation has been described on the basis of analytic observations made on cases suffering from chronic constipation who at the same time exhibited attitudes typical for depressions.

BIBLIOGRAPHY

1. ALEXANDER, FRANZ. The medical value of psychoanalysis, pp. 197-201. New York: W. W. Norton & Co., 1932.
2. OPHUIJSEN, J. H. W. VAN. Über die Quelle der Empfindung des Verfolgtwerdens. Z. Psychoanal., 1920, 6, 68-72.
3. STÄRCKE, AUGUST. Die Umkehrung des Libidovorzeichens beim Verfolgungswahn. Z. Psychoanal., 1919, 5, 285-287.
4. COTTON, H. A. Etiology and treatment of so-called functional psychoses. Amer. J. Psychiat., 1922, 2, 157-210.
5. ABRAHAM, KARL. Contributions to the theory of anal character. Selected papers, pp. 370-392. London: Hogarth Press, 1917.
6. KAISER, N. W. Colonic therapy in mental disease. Ohio med. J., 1930, 26, 510-515.
7. HENRY, G. W. Gastrointestinal motor functions in schizophrenia: roentgenologic observations. Amer. J. Psychiat., 1927, 7, 135-152.
8. HENRY, G. W. Gastrointestinal motor functions in manic depressive psychoses. Amer. J. Psychiat., 1931, 11, 19-28.
9. FREUD, SIGMUND. Collected papers, Vol. 3, pp. 387-470. London: Hogarth Press, 1925.

A STUDY OF MECHANISMS IN TWO CASES OF PEPTIC ULCER *

By CAREL VAN DER HEIDE, M.D.

Present Concepts of the Etiological Significance of Emotional Factors in Peptic Ulcers

A psychoanalytic approach to the understanding of the relation between emotional disturbances and the occurrence of gastric disorders, in particular of peptic ulcer, was first made by Franz Alexander in 1931 (1). He inaugurated further research at the Chicago Institute for Psychoanalysis on a group of patients "with obvious personality problems" and gastric symptoms (six cases of duodenal ulcer and three of gastric neurosis). The preliminary results, together with illustrative case histories by Catherine Bacon and Harry B. Levey, were published in 1934 (2). The "psychosomatic" concept developed in those studies [see also Alexander (3)] may briefly be reviewed as follows.

Under the influence of certain unhappy experiences, interfering too much with a natural development, a child can be forced to fall back in its emotional maturation. This may sometimes increase such wishes as to be cared for, to be loved, to depend on others, to receive, and—if thwarted—to take aggressively (regression to oral receptiveness and oral sadism). Whereas the ego reacts to such tendencies with feelings of inferiority and guilt, these are repressed from consciousness, sometimes under seal of a strong overcompensation, manifest as in independent, efficient, later responsible and giving attitude in life. This type of "conflict-solution" was regularly found in the gastric patients whose unconscious longing for care, love, and dependence could not be concealed from the analytic observation. Next to the described internal reaction, sometimes external factors were found to be capable of maintaining a fatal frustration of these infantile cravings. The latter, obviously, once in life are perfectly gratified, namely at the time of being nursed, when almost indistinguishably love and food are abundantly offered. Alexander states: the wish to be loved becomes emotionally associated with the

* Psychosomatic Medicine II: 398-410, 1940.

wish to be fed. If wishes for care and dependence are now strongly repressed, we may assume that these easily activate, or rather are "converted into" the desire to be nourished, which, as a continuous unconscious psychic stimulus, influences the secretory, muscular, and vascular condition of the stomach by means of the vegetative nervous system until it behaves "as if it were taking or were about to take food." Such chronic functional gastric disturbances, besides being likely to cause neurotic stomach complaints, appear to be of essential importance for the development of gastric and duodenal ulcers.

This theory about psychogenic factors in gastric disorders and peptic ulcers did not spring simply from some isolated psychoanalytic observations and understanding, but is equally based upon important data from physiology and pathology, e.g., the "psychic" gastric secretion (Pavlov's experiments), the role of hyperacidity and hypermotility in the pathogenesis of peptic ulcers [the mechanical-functional theory to which von Bergmann (7) added the factor of local ischemia and "neural" influences], and the observations of peptic ulcers after parasympathetic stimulation by operative irritation of the midbrain [Harvey Cushing (14)] or by pilocarpine injection in the ventricles [Light (26)]. On the other hand the psychoanalytic findings threw a new light on the valuable observations of Draper and Touraine (18) who described "femaleness and masculine protest" in their male ulcer patients [later reemphasized by Daniels (16)]. Moreover a pattern of a psychogenesis of an organic disorder was suggested: emotional conflict, related to the function of a certain organ → specific stimulation of subcortical centra → alteration in the vegetative innervation of the involved organ → dysfunction of the organ which, if chronic, finally results in an organic, morphological change (4).

Thus Alexander described a "central" origin for gastric neuroses and peptic ulcers, though admittedly dealing with only *one* factor which may coincide with others, partially still unknown. He also stated: "There is no evidence whatsoever that other cases of peptic ulcer may not develop on a different and perhaps nonpsychogenic basis" (2). Finally, in contrast to some other authors, Alexander pointed at the described specific type of the emotional conflict rather than at a certain type of personality, although of course in some individuals the typical conflict may have become predominant and chronic.

That functional disturbances of the stomach, considered as a *conditio sine qua non* for the development of gastric ulcers, can be caused by other than local factors (in which most pathologists were chiefly interested) revived once again the theory of Rossle; i.e., "gastric ulcer is only secondary to a distant primary disease process." Thus increasing attention was paid to psychic factors as well as to neurological processes. In the American literature since 1934 there have been numerous papers dealing with gastric neuroses, nervous indigestion, and the "nervous etiology of peptic ulcers." Most of them show clearly a discontent which the clinician feels concerning the treatment of his stomach patients. In general they express as much conviction that the trouble may be emotional in origin as embarrassment and inability to cope therapeutically with this psychological factor. Others [Rivers (29), Crohn (12, 13)] simply stress the noxious tension of hasty, modern life. Authors like Walter G. Alvarez (5, 6), David C. Wilson (36), and Emery and Monroe (20), although deserving particularly the merit of teaching the anamnestic recognition of the neurotic background in stomach disorders, furnish little information so far as the specificity of the neurotic process is concerned. Remarkably, in the American Gastrointestinal Association the subject was presented twice by psychiatrists, William C. Menninger (27) and Earl Danford Bond (8).

Meanwhile, at the London Tavistock Clinic, Daniel T. Davies and Macbeth Wilson (17) took the life histories of 205 unselected ulcer patients, paying special attention to the external events preceding the ulcer symptoms in new cases as well as in relapses. They found that in 84 per cent the symptoms began soon after some incident affecting the patient's work or finances or the health of his family (only 22 per cent of a control series of patients with hernia gave history of such events). In most of their patients the anxiety preceding the dyspepsia (which the authors consider as the onset of the peptic ulcer) was related to "insecurity, money difficulties, increased responsibility at work, the possibility of dismissal, and so on." From some of their brief case histories, however, one gets the impression that the so-called "external events preceding the ulcer symptoms" were rather critical threats to the balance of that particular conflict situation which Alexander described as typical for ulcer patients. Alvarez, Rivers, and Eustermann (21) of the Mayo Clinic have stated: "In peptic ulcer the causative factor, operative in the vast majority of the cases, is the psyche, mediated through the autonomic nervous system."

Steigmann (33), a supporter of the last view, could prove that, regarding the Negro population of Chicago, peptic ulcer does not have such a racial selectivity as formerly was believed [Robinson (30)]. Negroes living for more than five years in the city, under the same stress and strain of responsibility as the whites, have ulcers just as well; the author claims that in particular their "environmental conditioned psychic factors," effecting an automatic disbalance, make them different from the ulcus-free colored population elsewhere. Similarly Kouwenaar (25) threw some light on the frequent occurrence of ulcers among Chinese in the tropics, contrasting to the Javanese who rarely have them. Both the Chinese and Europeans, on coming to live in the Dutch Indies, are susceptible to several disorders depending on a vegetative autonomic disbalance—diseases which seldom or never are observed among the native population. Kouwenaar, who is well acquainted with the ways of living of different races, assumes that the Javanese, who generally show so little emotional expression, also have a much more stable vegetative autonomic system, less sensitive to different stimuli.

Significant, although not dealing directly with the pathogenesis, is an "experiment" of Chappell and coworkers (11) who treated ulcer patients with group psychotherapy—teaching them to control their worries as well as the discussion of their complaints and "to limit their efforts to master themselves." Although 15 patients from their group of 32 dropped out, the authors claim remarkably good results, checked after three years and compared with a control group of 20 patients who did not have this kind of treatment.

Case Histories

In this paper the history of two patients, whose psychoanalyses enabled a fairly precise reconstruction of the psychological setting of previous attacks of peptic ulcer, will be briefly reported. Since both analyses were undertaken for other complaints and ran over a long period of time, no claim will be laid on completeness, and psychoanalytic details will be given only so far as needed for the understanding of the typical personality conflicts.

CASE 1. An American-born salesman, thirty years of age, came to the Institute on his own initiative, complaining of lack of success in business which he attributed to a "defeatist" attitude. In spite of his intelligence and pleasant personality—in school and games as well as in different jobs—he has never done very well and has continuously worried about becoming a failure. He has been married for two years.

In the introductory interview the patient emphasized continued quarrels with his apparently eccentric and paranoid mother; he also referred to the good relationship with his father, from whom, however, he would never be able to ask financial aid. In spite of the overt preference which, according to the patient, the mother always displayed for the brother, 6 years younger, he did not feel resentment against the latter. Instead, he rather admired this brother for his more successful development. The medical history revealed gastric complaints more then one year ago and a roentgenogram, made at that time, showed "an ulcer of the first portion of the duodenum which extended into the pylorus of the stomach." Because the patient refused to remain in the hospital, a gastric analysis could not be made, but under a mild diet the complaints of pain disappeared. He continued, however, to have occasional distress and heartburn until he came for analysis, when a careful examination gave no longer evidence of organic changes. X ray disclosed normal visualization of the gall bladder without stone, normal esophagus, stomach, and duodenal bulbs. The Ewald free acidity was normal, 62, and the stools were negative for occult blood.

Accepted for analysis as a research case, the patient displayed an initial resistant attitude which, as in so many cases, was rather in contradiction to his good insight but quite characteristic of the neurosis. Long talks about big business and outlooks for getting a mighty bonus, attempts to impress the analyst with stories stressing masculine efficiency, and expressions of contempt for the "sentimental" treatment filled many hours. This lasted until it could be shown that this behavior served only the purpose of hiding an extreme sensitivity, an attachment to the analytic procedure which the patient considered as weakness and a sign of femininity. Yet gradually he became freer in speaking about his fear of becoming a hypochondriac like the quarrelsome and unhappily married mother, about sharing his father's marital misfortune, and his originally repressed jealousy of his brother. Later he confessed an intense strain of forcing himself to fulfill his business duties, displaying a great discontent at not succeeding as perfectly as he wished (quite similar to puberty worries about defeats), and finally his dissatisfaction with the marriage, newly complicated by the first pregnancy of his frigid wife.

His neurotic marriage and its background are of significance. The patient had married, secretly and without love, a girl who was the daughter of a very wealthy man. The reason for the secrecy was definitely a fear of not being accepted by his father-in-law, who rightly could have been suspicious of some money interest. Another motive for a hurried marriage was that the patient wanted to escape further involvement in a homosexual experience into which, against his conscious wish, he had been dragged shortly before. Marital sex relations were very unsatisfactory; however, the premature ejaculation and anxiety which the patient used to have in former adventures with rather uninhibited girls disappeared.

Once married, the patient began to realize the hopelessness of the situation in which he found himself. He resolved to make the best of it and decided that he would not take advantage of his wife's money; but in spite of his efforts to live up to this intention, he lost his position. Meanwhile both the parents of his wife had died. At that time the patient was fighting for his existence, and he accepted an exhausting job in a factory under unfavorable conditions. Shortly after, it became known that by some testamentary disposition his wife could not touch the inheritance for many years, the estate having been put into a trust fund and the guardianship given to a relative. It was at that time that the stomach complaints developed, whereupon the ulcer was diagnosed.

In the analysis, the crisis which preceded the occurrence of the ulcer could be recognized as the real acme of the patient's conflict situation. Pressed by guilt feelings because of his marriage for money, he tried to deny to himself his dependent wishes and leaned over backwards in his desperate fight for an independent existence. The more he struggled to repress those wishes, the stronger the wish for protection grew in his unconscious. As the expected inheritance meant a source of security, the will came as a sudden blow to the patient. Money meant being cared for; it was unconsciously linked with nourishment. The functional disturbance of the stomach was the logical somatic reaction to the acute emotional conflict which centered around "getting and taking" tendencies. This typical, deep-seated conflict, which was activated by the frustration he experienced in the will of his father-in-law, however, had a deeper foundation leading back to his childhood.

Until his sixth year the patient was an only child and, as his father used to be away on business trips most of the time, he lived quite closely to his mother who let the child sleep with her. She was a woman of poor self-control, and had both a seducing and a frightening influence upon the little boy. With the second pregnancy, however, much in her behavior changed; she began to be impatient with her older son, used to spank him, and, in an irresponsible and conspicuous way, turned all her love and care to the younger child towards whom the patient developed an intense envy. Shocked and frustrated, he directed his need for affection to the father. At that time he had frequent nightmares, and his father often had to stay at his bed in order to calm him down. He began to suffer from enuresis (which disappeared only in puberty when wet dreams occurred) and renounced his boyish masculine strivings. The analysis revealed that in this way he competed with his mother for his father's affection. Meanwhile he assumed an affectionate and protective, almost mother-like attitude towards his younger brother. Thus he overcame his envy and intense hostility against the baby, the first reaction against the little newcomer; the earliest recollection was how he hated to give the bottle to his brother. This method of overcoming hostility against the brother by assuming the role of a mother formed the basis for latent passive homosexual tendencies and also intensified the wish to receive. He was generous towards his brother, but in exchange he demanded love and care from the adults. The intense receptive claims, however, were not only frustrated, but also became incompatible with his further development, and thus a strong reaction in the direction of independence took place. The patient tried not to lean any longer on either of his parents, and went on his own way. Successfully, but with much inner fear, he beat up one of his schoolmates, secured a job of selling newspapers when he was 7, and accepted work many times too hard for him in spite of the fact that he feared a physical breakdown and longed intensely to stay at home. Without any real need for it he became extremely eager to make money, which he always handed over in full to his parents, but inwardly he resented the fact that he did not get any pocket money in return. Thus he worked his way through high school and college, living a life which was exactly the opposite of indulging in those receptive wishes which in his childhood were intense but which he had to give up so abruptly upon the arrival of his baby brother.

In his marriage the patient relived the same sequence of emotional changes. Before his marriage he gratified his passive wishes in a relationship with a male friend, which ended up in an incidental homosexual experience. He exchanged this form of passive gratification for dependence on a wealthy girl. This, however, he could do only in a disguised fashion. As in his childhood, he had to over-compensate for his secret parasitic tendencies by an overt and exaggerated sense of responsibility and a desperate effort to earn money in order to become independent of his wife's wealth. He kept his promise of not taking advantage of his wife's money, and struggled hard. However, his marriage to a woman whom he did not love became nothing but a source of suffering. She was on such bad terms with the patient's parents that finally, against his will, he ceased to see them. He questioned his wife's feelings and interpreted her frigidity (quite correctly) as the expression of an unconscious rejection. When, in this situation, his wife became pregnant, this meant to the patient only a new responsibility, a new and unwelcome tie to his wife. When, during the course of the analysis, a son was born, the patient was overwhelmed with contradictory feelings: sincere parental affection and, less consciously, envy of the love and care which was given to the newborn. That the old death wishes and oral envy towards his baby brother, with all its conflicts and compensatory reactions, were revived in this relation seems clear in the following dream: The patient's wife bore twins, but one was born five months later, after it had already died. However, when the patient looked at it, as it lay wrapped up, it started to breathe; he saw that its legs were all right, was happy to see it alive, and ordered that it be fed immediately.

The intimate, unconscious relation between the different manifestations of receptivity, getting affection, care, financial help, and food appeared in the analysis with extraordinary clearness. Acute pecuniary disappointments in business were frequently forgotten with the help of a "consoling" good meal and drinks, among which the rich and substantial "Tom and Jerry" was a favorite. Similar oral needs appeared when he suffered any rebuff. In his emotional relation to the analyst, the repressed demanding wishes began gradually to manifest themselves in numerous demands for exceptional favors. One of them was to be totally released from the modest fee which, at first, the patient himself had fixed, at a rate too high with respect to his income. During the course of the treatment there was generally no evidence of dyspepsia in spite of the fact that the patient took average meals without any dietetic restrictions. Acute stomach complaints, however, could be observed many times occurring precisely when he was exposed to hardship or frustrated in his dependent receptive wishes. This correlation became extremely clear when, on the request of the analyst, the patient checked the times he had to take milk of magnesia tablets. Also it became obvious that stomach symptoms occurred whenever, for external reasons, he had to cancel a badly needed analytic hour.

To summarize briefly: after a period of early spoiling by the mother, when the birth of a brother caused an abrupt frustration of needs for care and love, the patient turned his affection to his father, which caused trends of a passive nature in him. Further, the intense hostility (oral envy) which he had developed against the baby necessitated a strong defense mechanism. This consisted of displaying a generous motherly attitude towards the brother, which again reinforced, regressively, his own oral receptive cravings. The passive and dependent wishes, however, were even in their sublimation so obnoxious to the patient that they had to be overcompensated as much as possible by exaggerated ambition and drive toward independence. The repressed tendencies seemed to have found their expression in the somatic area in the excitation of the stomach functions. The gastric symptoms occurred particularly when the compensatory efforts were excessive and the gratification of his oral wishes thwarted.

It is obvious that in our patient the repression and overcompensation of the receptive-demanding attitude were not always successful in keeping it from consciousness. Alexander (2) found this to be even more outstanding in two cases which showed "early and extreme deprivation in childhood." In the case here described there was not such an extreme oral deprivation in childhood. Yet the strongest objection which the patient ever made against his mother was that she always failed to prepare the meals carefully, rather neglected them, so that the boy felt envious of the superabundance which he supposed his schoolmates got at their homes.

Better established and more rigid were the defense mechanisms dealing with the same conflict in another patient about ten years older.

CASE 2. This man, married for more than seven years, was referred because of impotency and several hypochondriacal complaints. Although conspicuously neurotic and having since puberty suffered from feelings of depression and inferiority, he had gone through a university successfully and kept a good position as an industrial director. The medical history revealed a gastric ulcer diagnosed ten years ago, but at the beginning of the analysis the patient suffered only from occasional slight dyspepsia; this complaint ceased almost entirely after one year.

Somewhat previous to the analysis, after the death of his parents and a brother-in-law, all of whom passed away in a short period of time, the patient (who did not have brothers) had felt obliged to take over a number of consequent responsibilities. Among them, the care of an elderly maternal aunt and the guardianship over the son of his only sister appeared to be special burdens. However, he welcomed such duties, took them for granted, and performed them with the utmost reliability in a generous and self-sacrificing way. In the analysis it became clear that this trend to assume responsibilities dated far back in his childhood. When the patient was about eleven years of age, his father, a tall, once mighty and commanding man, developed an eye disease in addition to his serious deafness which, after an operation, blinded and wrecked him definitely. At that time the patient had to give up his boyish pleasures and had to assist his mother in financial matters. Eager to have full responsibility, he hurried through the university and graduated at an exceptionally young age. He acquired the reputation of being unselfish, painstaking, exact in the administration of the estates of others, of supporting unsuccessful members of the family, and secretly granting help for the study of the children of his and his father's employees, to whom he acted as a just and severe guardian.

His impotency, mostly an impotentia ejaculandi, was the final outcome of a highly disturbed sexual development, dominated by extreme passive trends. Neither masturbation nor coitus attempts could ever bring about an ejaculation; only rarely did he ejaculate through certain passive masturbatory practices or in dreams. This disturbance was based upon a deep-seated fear connected with the female sex organ and a strong narcissism. The analysis revealed a period of uninhibited sexual activity in infancy, consisting chiefly of urination in front of, and upon, the one and a half year younger sister and mutual masturbation with her, which behavior ended quite suddenly at about the age of 6. At that time the vague threats of the mother (because of his masturbation) were dramatically materialized by a tonsillectomy without anesthesia (in this procedure, still in use on the continent, a single instrument pinches and cuts off a part of the tonsil). Consequent to this trauma, the boy developed enuresis and fear of darkness, became docile, shy, and virtuous. Thus after the renouncement of his aggressive tendencies and the assumption of such a passive and feminine attitude, it was only natural that he became envious of his sister. Later the patient went through a similar emotional sequence. At the approach of puberty his pity for the defectiveness of his father inhibited the development of natural competitive feelings and increased his unconscious sense of guilt, but besides, made him renounce all demands on his mother, who gave all her devotion to her blind and deaf husband. Under these conditions the patient became easily the object of the activity of a much older homosexual cousin.

Meanwhile, because an overcompensatory mechanism began to operate, the envy towards the sister gave way to a devoted protective attitude towards her. During university years the patient kept in close contact with her and had vivid fantasies of establishing a home to live with her in the future. Consequently, when she surprised him by getting married, he felt very unhappy and forlorn. Shortly afterwards he graduated and developed an affection for a maternal cousin. He was too inhibited in his sexuality to marry her, however, and gradually settled down to a bachelor's existence; (later he did not fail to support the same cousin and her husband). During this period one of the directors, an efficient but happy-go-lucky man, had won the patient's admiration and attachment, and now this man became the object of his latent passive homosexual wishes. Although he violently rejected them, these feelings made the patient's social adjustment difficult. Thwarted in every emotional gratificatiqn, his cravings for affection became more and more intense.

The gastric complaints, heartburn and typical pains after meals, occurred at that time. Finally, when occult blood in the feces was found, a gastric ulcer was diagnosed and the patient underwent a Sippy cure. He moved into his sister's home and was taken care of by his brother-in-law, a well-known physician. Those two months under the tender care of his sister meant a real gratification of his strong needs for attention, care, and love, which the patient could not satisfy in his usual life. During this happy period the ulcer healed completely, but true to his nature, the patient could not remain in debt, and before he returned to work he treated his benefactors to a long and expensive trip. Two years later, after much doubt and hesitation, he married a cool and reticent girl who was not, and could not be, in love with him.

The patient's relation to his sister's son was most revealing in showing the deep-seated conflict between his wish to be spoiled and loved by his sister alone, to the exclusion of his nephew, and his tendency to assume a responsible and adult role. He did many favors for this nephew, but his hostility against him came to expression in the form of a neurotic symptom; he developed writer's cramp while writing a letter of recommendation on behalf of the nephew.

Superficially the patient showed an extreme modesty; for example, on his birthday he refused to see relatives or friends for fear they would give him a present. Also, in the beginning of the analysis, his behavior was characterized by modesty and complaisance. Occasional outbursts of hostile feelings served as a defense against too much passivity, a reaction to the psychoanalysis, described by Lewis Hill (22), in persons who in early infancy had experienced an acute and painful rejection of their needs for love and dependence by a mother.

Summarizing, we may say that early in life, under the influence of several factors, this patient renounced his aggressive impulses, becoming extremely passive and repressing strong oral receptive and aggressive tendencies. Later he was well defended against his sexual impulses by feminine identification and consequent impotency, but against his oral tendencies he had to build a complex system of defense mechanisms in the form of overcompensatory generosity and responsibility.

In the neuroses of the two male patients, the typical emotional conflict and character traits, as described by Alexander and his co-workers, were outstanding. Obvious in different phases of life, this could be observed over and over again in the course of the psychoanalysis. The following common features were particularly striking:

1. Both patients withdrew quite acutely from infantile sexual activity and became passive, submissive children, attached to their fathers without evidence of much identification with them, rather competing with their mothers.

2. The growing strivings for affection from the father created a mounting tension through a conflict with the so highly different standard of the environment which required the opposite of being a sissy. A reorientation on a more primitive stage, therefore, took place, consisting of a regressive reinforcement of oral trends. Thus the passive-feminine attitude was pushed into the background in favor of an oral dependent one.

3. Those inner changes required a definite renouncement of aggressive impulses, but in the unconscious the aggressive tendencies were maintained and expressed in dreams in the form of fantasies of grabbing and taking hold of things in a forceful aggressive manner (oral aggression).

4. When the passive-dependent wishes were directed towards men, a homosexual coloring was the result; although they were not overtly perverse, both patients showed obvious latent homosexual tendencies in later life.

5. Finally the guilt about the grasping tendencies and the intense rejection (out of prestige) of the wishes for dependence led into a strong overcompensation which brought about the described character traits of generosity and sense of responsibility.

6. Stomach complaints, preceding the occurrence of an ulcer, occurred in both patients when the incongruity between the overt behavior (struggle and ambitious efforts for accomplishments) and the repressed longings for dependence became excessive.

Discussion

Concerning the psychogenic factors in gastric ulcer, there still remain a number of questions to be answered. Among them prevail: the possibility of other factors involved, the clinical differences between the presumed psychogenic and nonpsychogenic peptic ulcers, and the significance of a preceding gastric neurosis in some, but not all cases. However, there seems to be no longer any doubt about the role of the autonomic nervous system as the transmitter between emotional disturbances and the stomach function, as stated in 1932 by Harvey Cushing (15): "vagotonic persons, through emotion or repressed emotion incidental to continued worry or anxiety and heavy responsibility, combined with other factors such as irregular meals and excessive use of tobacco, are particularly prone to have chronic digestive disturbances with hyperacidity often leading to ulcer." He suggested that stimulation of the interbrain ("a long overlooked station for digestive impulses, easily affected by psychic influences") and, in particular, of the tuberal nuclei of the hypothalamus, may disturb the autonomic innervation of the stomach in such a way that hypersecretion, hypermotility, hypertonicity, and local anemia render the mucosa of the stomach digestible by its own juice.

Cushing mentioned "vagotonic persons" as predisposed to this mechanism, but, pointing at the surgical stimulation of the parasympathetic nucleus tuberis, he said: "or what theoretically amounts to the same thing, a functional release of the vagus from paralysis of the antagonistic sympatheticus fibres." Without entering into a discussion of the concept of so-called vagotonia, it may be stated that not all individuals with peptic ulcers have such a vagotonic constitution, and also that the significance of a "local vagotonia" of the stomach (regarded by some authors as a constitutional-etiological factor) seems questionable. Comparing the Javanese with other races, Brummelkamp (9) found that their more stable vegetative-autonomic constitution (25) is accompanied by a local, vagal hypertonus manifest in a hyperacidity and quicker emptying of the stomach, although, as said, in the Javanese, gastric ulcer is rare.

The Balfour lecture of Cushing on the interbrain and peptic ulcers paved the way for numerous studies in neurophysiology, focusing on the pathogenetic problem. Some of them clearly show the importance of disturbance of the sympathetic innervation for the development of peptic ulcers. Watts and Fulton (34) and Hoff and Sheehan (23) succeeded in causing multiple hemorrhagic lesions in the gastric mucosa of monkeys through hypothalamic injuries. According to them the affection of the first in "the complex balance between sympatheticus and parasympatheticus" would result in a local vasoconstriction, gradually considered as a pathogenetic condition not less important than the vagal hypersecretion and hypermotility.[2] Keller

---

[2] Donald Sheehan (The hypothalamus and gastrointestinal regulation, Research Publication, Association for Research in Nervous and Mental Disease, Vol. 20, 1940) concluded "It is suggestive but not proven that the gastrointestinal changes are due to an overactive sympathetic center in the hypothalamus, probably caused by irritation from the adjacent injury." He also discussed certain differences between the true peptic ulcer and the gastric lesions through hypothalamic injury, but stated that the motility of the gastrointestinal tract and the amount and nature of the digestive juices are under the direct influence of the hypothalamus.

(24) showed that cerebral lesions do not cause bleedings in the stomach wall if the sympatheticus chain is removed beforehand. Thus it becomes more and more probable that in the pathogenesis of the peptic ulcer, rather the autonomic innervation of the stomach as a whole is upset. This also follows from the experiments of Orndorff (28) and co-workers who, by means of pilocarpine intoxication of dogs, caused hypersecretion and hypermotility but failed to obtain ulcers. The authors admit that whereas they did not implicate the sympathetic innervation of the stomach directly, vascular changes in the stomach wall were lacking. George Draper (19), studying the electrocardiogram of ulcer patients, also states that even in people "with ulcer-constitution the whole autonomic nervous system is highly tense and labile, although the slow pulse, sinus arrhythmia, and prolonged P. R. interval possibly indicates a peculiar vagotonicity."

The experiments of Silbermann (32) who succeeded in causing gastric ulcers in dogs by sham feeding (esophageal fistula) were repeated in 1937 by Schmidt and Fogelson (31). In spite of strong acid reaction, their ten dogs did not develop ulcers. In accord with the observation of so many patients with hyperacidity and no ulcers, the authors are inclined to believe that other factors than hypersecretion must be involved, and they attribute the findings of Silbermann to malnutrition and vomiting of his animals.

Brummelkamp (10) observed pyloric ulcers through starvation in rats; alkalinization prevented them. Fasting of cats, however, did not cause ulcers unless, by means of hydrochlor-morphini, a pylorospasm and a hypersecretion were simultaneously effected. The author gives the following explanation for the different effects of fasting in rats and cats: the first, being rodents, are accustomed to chronic digestion, whereas to the beasts of prey intermittent hunger is an experience to which their organism is adjusted. The last distinction reminds us of the need for frequent feedings in sucklings and small children in whom, because of the process of growth, the oral-receptive function is so predominant. The regression which was shown to have taken place in our ulcer patients causes a continuous unconscious longing for dependence and special cravings for getting by mouth. This is believed to stimulate the stomach continually, which then finally acts similarly to that of the starving rodents and thus becomes particularly prone to the development of peptic ulcers.

Still more comparable to what supposedly goes on in persons with "ulcer conflicts" are the experiments done by Wilhelmy and co-workers (35). By means of a stomach pouch in dogs, they examined an intragastric process, i.e., the local inhibition of the gastric secretion by the presence of 0.1 norm. hydrochloric acid in the empty unstimulated part of the stomach. They not only tested this inhibition during digestion when food was in the other part of the stomach (gastric phase) and during the intestinal phase, but extended the research to the "psychic phase" by presenting to their animals food which only after a period of time could be taken in the mouth and swallowed. It was found that the gastric secretion during this phase easily can break through the inhibitory effect of the presence of hydrochloric acid which in the same concentration totally prevented the acid secretion during the gastric phase. They concluded, therefore, that the secretory energy of the psychic phase causes a degree of hyperacidity unobtainable by one of the two other phases.

In view of the complexity of the human psychic conditions, the work with animals, on the whole, does not offer a satisfactory imitation. Nevertheless the last described Tantalus experiment, in the psychosomatic respect, comes closer to the mechanism of an intensified "ulcer-conflict." The frustration of the cravings in the animals was, of course, purely externally determined, but the experiment proves that under high specific psychic tension the stomach behaves quite differently than in its more usual function.

If not conclusive, it is at least presumptive that similar somatic processes including local vascular and muscular changes—in other words, functional disturbances of the stomach effected by means of the autonomic nervous system—may be originated in men by the typical emotional conflicts described, which, in general, are based upon special childhood experiences. If such disturbances lead sometimes into a peptic ulcer, it would be only logical to recognize, next to the neurogenic, a psychogenic ulcus pepticum.

The value of these considerations for the practical physician is still a complicated matter. Since the care of the ulcer patient remains his privilege, in certain cases it would be of use to him to keep in mind that special nursing, as dictated by the Sippy cure, or the continuous milk drip into the stomach throughout the day and night [Winkelstein (37)], affects not only the acidity but the unconscious as well. Also, evaluating a low nocturnal acid curve in a patient with a gastric neurosis [Winkelstein (38)], the emotional consequences of hospitalization should be taken into consideration. Occasional hypersecretion in quite different psychic conditions is of course not excluded.

Individuals with peptic ulcers, however, are not psychiatric patients, and those who should see the psychiatrist many times never get to him. The psychiatrist, on his part, if he considers, with Alexander, some ulcers as the organic, final result of a psychogenic functional disturbance, certainly will prefer to be called earlier rather than later when less reversible tissue changes have already developed. The present situation is still inadequate in many respects. Psychotherapeutic generalities offering the patient a better mental hygiene (less work, more rest, etc.) are of little permanent value for anyone who suffers from a deep-seated personality conflict which has led finally to such organic changes as peptic ulcer. On the other hand, far-reaching interpretations by a psychiatrically-minded physician, although correct, are just as unsatisfactory if administered without adequate preparation. With all this, of course, it is not maintained that every ulcer patient needs a psychoanalysis, but rather that those cases in which the psychogenic factor appears to be important require an expert psychotherapeutic handling just like any other psychoneurosis.

Summary

A report was given on the history of two male patients who had suffered from peptic ulcer. Psychoanalysis, in both cases, enabled a more detailed observation of the relation between certain conflicting (oral) needs and the gastric disorder. An oral regression, following earlier female identification, and a sudden renunciation of aggressive tendencies were found to have been of definite importance for the development.

The most recent literature dealing with psychogenic factors in peptic ulcer was reviewed, and, in accordance with some physiologic and psychoanalytic observations, special consideration was given to gastroduodenal ulcer as the final result of psychogenic functional gastric disturbances, effected by means of the autonomic nervous system and dependent on specific emotional conflicts, the basis for which is laid in childhood.

BIBLIOGRAPHY

1. ALEXANDER, FRANZ. The medical value of psychoanalysis. (2nd Ed.) New York: W. W. Norton & Co., 1936.
2. ALEXANDER, FRANZ, AND CO-WORKERS. The influence of psychologic factors upon gastrointestinal disturbances: a symposium. *Psychoanal. Quart.*, 1934, 3, 501. (In this volume, p. 103.)
3. ALEXANDER, FRANZ. Functional disturbances of psychogenic nature. *J. Amer. med. Assn*, 1933, 100, 469.
4. ALEXANDER, FRANZ. Psychological aspects of medicine. *Psychosom. Med.*, 1939, 1, 7.
5. ALVAREZ, W. C. Light from the laboratory and the clinic on the causes of peptic ulcer. *Amer. J. Surg.*, 1932, 18, 207.
6. ALVAREZ, W. C. Ways of improving gastroenterology. *Rev. Gastroenterol.*, 1937, 4, 160.

7. BERGMANN, G. VON. *Funktionelle Pathologie.* (Qte Aufl.) Berlin: Julius Springer, 1936.
8. BOND, E. D. Psychiatric contributions to the study of the gastrointestinal system. *Amer. J. digest. Dis. Nut.,* 1938, 5, 482.
9. BRUMMELKAMP, R. Maagulcus en vegetatief zenuwstelsel bij den Javaan. *Geneesk. Tijdschr. Ned.-Ind.,* 1933, 73, 770.
10. BRUMMELKAMP, R. Over de veelvuldigheid van de maagzweer bij de Chinees in het licht van het dierexperiment. *Geneesk. Tijdschr. Ned.-Ind.,* 1934, 74, 1710.
11. CHAPPELL, M. N., STEFANO, I. J., ROGERSON, D. S. AND PIKE, F. H. The value of group psychological procedures in the treatment of peptic ulcer. *Amer. J. digest. Dis. Nut.,* 1937, 3, 813.
12. CROHN, B. B. Functional and nervous disorders of stomach and alimentary tract. *Amer. J. digest. Dis. Nut.,* 1935, 1, 773.
13. CROHN, B. B. Gastroduodenal ulcer. *New Engl. J. Med.,* 1938, 218, 148.
14. CUSHING, HARVEY. The possible relation of the central (vegetative) nervous system to peptic ulcers. *New Engl. J. Med.,* 1931, 205, 979.
15. CUSHING, HARVEY. Peptic ulcers and the interbrain. *Surg. Gynec. Obstet.,* 1932, 55, 1.
16. DANIELS, G. E. Neuroses associated with gastrointestinal tract. *Amer. J. Psychiat.,* 1934, 91, 529.
17. DAVIES, D. T., AND WILSON, A. T. M. Observations on the life history of chronic peptic ulcer. *Lancet,* 1937, 2, 1353.
18. DRAPER, GEORGE, AND TOURAINE, GRACE ALLEN. The man-environment unit and peptic ulcer. *Arch. intern. Med.,* 1932, 49, 615.
19. DRAPER, GEORGE, BRUENNER, H. G., AND DUPERTIUS, C. W. Changes in the electrocardiogram as criteria of individual constitution derived from its physiological panel. *Amer. J. med. Sci.,* 1937, 194, 514.
20. EMERY, E. S., AND MONROE, R. T. Peptic ulcer: nature and treatment based on a study of 1435 Cases. *Arch. intern. Med.,* 1935, 55, 271.
21. EUSTERMANN, G. B. Modern concepts of the etiology of peptic ulcer and their bearing on therapy. *J. med. Soc. N. J.,* 1939, 36, 369.
22. HILL, L. The use of hostility as defense. *Psychoanalyt. Quart.,* 1938, 7, 254.
23. HOFF, E. C., AND SHEEHAN, D. Experimental gastric erosions following hypothalamic lesions in monkeys. *Amer. J. Path.,* 1935, 11, 789.
24. KELLER, A. D. Protection by peripheral nerve section of gastrointestinal tract from ulceration following hypothalamic lesions, with preliminary observations on ulcerations in gastrointestinal tract of dog following vagotony. *Arch. Path.,* 1936, 21, 165.
25. KOUWENAAR, W. Beteekenis van het voorkomen van maagzweren in de tropen voor de studie der aetiologie. *Ned. Tijdschr. v. Geneesk.,* 1930, 74, 2321. Also Transactions 8th Congress Far Eastern Association of Tropical Medicine, Bangkok, 1930, 1, 587.
26. LIGHT, R. N. Experimental observations on the production of ulcers by pilocarpine. *New Engl. J. Med.,* 1931, 205, 980.
27. MENNINGER, W. C. Functional disorders of the gastrointestinal tract. "The gastrointestinal neuroses." *Amer. J. digest. Dis. Nut.,* 1937, 4, 47.
28. ORNDORFF, J. R., BERGH, J. S., AND IVY, A. C. "Peptic" ulcer and the "anxiety complex." Failure of pharmacologically sustained hypersecretion and hypermotility of stomach to produce chronic gastric ulcer in dogs. *Surg. Gynec. Obstet.,* 1935, 61, 162.
29. RIVERS, A. B. Clinical considerations of the etiology of peptic ulcer. *Arch. intern. Med.,* 1934, 53, 97.
30. ROBINSON, S. C. On the etiology of peptic ulcer. Analysis of 70 ulcer patients. *Amer. J. digest. Dis. Nut.,* 1935, 2, 333.
31. SCHMIDT, C. R., AND FOGELSON, S. J. The effect of physiologic hypersecretion on the gastroduodenal mucosa. *Amer. J. Physiol.,* 1937, 120, 87.

32. SILBERMANN, I. S. Experimentelle Magenduodenalulcuserzeugung durch Scheinfüttern nach Pavlov. *Zbl. f. Chir.*, 1927, **54**, 2385.
33. STEIGMANN, F. The peptic ulcer syndrome in Negroes. Clinical and statistical evidence on psychogenic as against racial factors in the etiology of this syndrome. *Amer. J. digest. Dis. Nut.*, 1936, **3**, 310.
34. WATTS, J. W., AND FULTON, J. F. The effect of lesions of the hypothalamus upon the gastrointestinal tract and heart in monkeys. *Ann. Surg.*, 1935, **101**, 363.
35. WILHELMY, C. M., McCARTHY, H. H., AND HILL, F. C. Acid inhibition and cephalic (psychic) phase of gastric secretion. *Amer. J. Physiol.*, 1937, **120**, 619.
36. WILSON, D. C. Gastric neuroses. *South. Med. & Surg.*, 1935, **97**, 433.
37. WINKELSTEIN, ASHER. A new therapy of peptic ulcer. *Amer. J. med. Sci.*, 1933, **185**, 695.
38. WINKELSTEIN, ASHER. One hundred and sixty-nine studies in gastric secretion during the night. *Amer. J. digest. Dis. Nut.*, 1935, **1**, 778.

THE TRANSITION FROM ORGAN NEUROSIS TO CONVERSION HYSTERIA[*]

By George W. Wilson, M.D.

In the course of analyses of patients with gastrointestinal symptomatology, it has repeatedly come to my attention that the symptom for which a patient entered analysis was at times replaced by another symptom or symptoms. Often a conversion symptom of hysterical nature was concurrent with and incident to at least temporary cessation of the original organ neurosis. The present paper represents an attempt to trace the transition from an organ neurosis to conversion hysteria and an analysis of the material at the time of the replacement. It is realized that such a separation of organ neurosis from conversion hysteria cannot be considered a fixed one. However it is customary to restrict conversion hysteria to symptoms occurring in the voluntary and sensory systems, and to speak of organ neurosis in reference to function disturbances of organs whose functions are autonomic and under normal conditions not subjected to voluntary influences. It has been observed that in organ neurosis the psychological factors involved are usually very definitely pregenital in character,[1] whereas in conversion hysteria later phases of instinctual organization are prevalent, more specifically the phallic phase. I shall attempt to trace the progress of the dynamic structure during psychoanalytic treatment from early pregenital to the phallic level, coincident with the change from gastric symptoms (peptic ulcer) to conversion symptom in the following case.

This patient is a 41-year-old female attorney who came to analysis for recurrent duodenal ulcer, agoraphobia, handwriting difficulties, and a feeling of social maladjustment. She is the youngest of three children, having a brother 7 years her senior and a sister five years older. Her brother is a successful attorney. The sister, who was unmarried and with whom the patient made her home, is a forceful, ambitious, and competent schoolmistress who married during the

[*] *International Journal of Psycho-Analysis* XIX: 1-18, 1938.
[1] Alexander, F., Bacon, C., Levey, H., Levine, M., and Wilson, G. The influence of psychogenic factors upon gastrointestinal disturbances: a symposium. A report on research carried on at the Chicago Institute for Psychoanalysis. *Psychoanal. Quart.*, 1934, 3, 501-588.

224

analysis. Her father is a well-known rabbi. The mother is an ambitious but entirely ineffective person, who during the patient's childhood suffered continuously from gastrointestinal symptoms which were diagnosed as psychogenic in origin. She had been very attached to her mother as a child, and found it impossible to leave home until after she was thirty years of age. As a child she took great pride in being her mother's nurse, caring for her, waiting on her, and rarely leaving her side, for she had fears that her mother would die and leave her. These almost constant fantasies, together with her mother's continuous illness, kept her in a state of anxiety for several years. Her ulcer was inactive at the time of beginning the analysis, but became active and demonstrable through roentgen-ray examination in a phase of the analysis which I shall describe later.

This patient exhibited certain personality trends described as frequent in ulcer personalities.[2] Specifically I refer to the intense incorporating tendencies which are repressed and lead to overcompensation through increased activity and ambitious effort in life. She was an aggressive, hard-working, efficient, and successful attorney. She maintained a very independent attitude towards other members of the firm and refused to accept favors from anyone. The deeper oral receptive and aggressive tendencies were almost but not entirely denied. In relationship to her sister, she did live out some of these tendencies by living with and permitting the sister to feed and treat her as in a distinctly mother-child relationship. That this relationship produced considerable unconscious guilt, and also attempted to relieve the guilt, was demonstrated in her attitude towards her sister and other members of her family. She spent money in entertaining her sister, assumed the financial responsibility for their household, and sent money and other gifts to her parents and her brother's children. To these children she felt a particular responsibility and, in addition to her gifts, fantasied financing their musical education, something which she herself had been denied, and their college careers.

Much of the material of her analysis revolved about seduction by her brother. This occurred when she was ten years of age and consisted in her being masturbated by him at irregular but rather frequent intervals until she was fifteen, when he married and left home. Before this rejection she began to masturbate herself, and continued this until just before beginning her analysis. There were many periods during this time when, out of fear and an obsessive belief that she was "damaging" herself, as she in fact believed herself to have been

² Alexander, F., Bacon, C., Levey, H., Levine, M., and Wilson, G., *loc. cit.* This patient may be identified as patient "A" in Quantitative dream studies by Alexander, Franz, and Wilson, G. W. *Psychoanal. Quart.,* 1935, 4, 371-405.

"damaged" by her brother, she would discontinue this practice. The same idea was prominent throughout her analysis, for she soon began to accuse the analysis and the analyst of injuring her. Many times she made the accusation that the Institute and the analyst had promised to relieve her of conflicts, and this had not been accomplished. In fact she found herself much worse than before she began the procedure. Before the analysis everyone thought of her as a well-adjusted person, but after coming to analysis she had great difficulty in handling her work as well as her social adjustments. Although she insisted that her ulcer did not have a psychogenic basis, nevertheless she blamed the analysis for its recurrence. She pointed out that it was healed when she began and became active during the process.

During these intervals she consulted countless male and female gynecologists for the purpose of receiving assurance that she was not damaging herself and that she had not been damaged, as well as for a means of aiding her in discontinuing this practice. She received all kinds of advice, ranging from that of using her "will power" to one suggestion that she undergo an operation which was described as similar to circumcision and consisted in rotating a piece of mucous membrane over the clitoris.

The patient successfully blackmailed her brother during most of her life. It was he who paid for her education, financed her frequent trips to physicians for her gynecological complaints and her gastric symptom. But more than mere finances were involved in the manner in which she expressed her hatred for him. He was blamed for all her symptoms, as well as her failures in heterosexual adjustments and her lack of success in life. (Actually she was quite successful unless asked to assume responsibility.) Her inabilities in any given direction were directly attributed to her experiences with him and therefore to him. Very early in the analysis she became conscious of the wish to make him suffer as she believed herself to have suffered. She wanted him to feel guilty, and was intensely envious of his success and his obviously good adjustment in life. She hated his wife and was pleased when she had a miscarriage. Many times she succeeded in arousing his guilt feelings through complaining of illness, of her inability to concentrate on her work, her need to take vacations, etc. On at least two occasions he was summoned from some distance to her bedside because of somatic symptoms which she admitted were used as a means of punishing him as well as a way of receiving attention.

Although the most of her hostility for men was expressed towards her brother, she frankly confessed a hatred for most men. She constantly depreciated her father and described him as being weak and ineffective, a sentimental old bookworm who was at the same time cruel and sadistic. She complained that he gave her much affection when she was a small child, but later completely rejected her. She complained of his religious intolerance. At the same time the patient greatly admired his intelligence, his knowledge of literature, history, and music. She had been very attached to him as a child, followed him about and enjoyed his company a great deal, but later detested him, blamed him for most of the family quarrels, which were frequent, and felt he was the bad influence in the whole family situation. She had fantasies of his beating her, and much of her early material offered a striking example of what Freud has described in "A Child Is Being Beaten." [3] However most of this hatred was lived out in reference to her brother. Obviously she turned from her father to her brother for affection and physical contact, as well as making him the object of her vengeance. This fact becomes of paramount importance in analyzing the development of her conversion symptom.

The stage setting for the seduction is also of importance to the understanding of later developments. She claimed this took place while they were lying on her parents' bed in a room overlooking a hospital watching ambulances going in and out. She said they had spent many hours passing the time this way while alone in the house. Her brother often stroked her back and patted her hip, and it was following such common practice that he, on this occasion, exposed and masturbated her.

From the very beginning she exhibited an intense fear of the analysis. She canceled the first three hours because of the sudden development of acute respiratory symptoms which resembled a common cold.[4] She was late for her first hour and felt a strong disinclination towards coming. She appeared very frightened and complained of the difficulty about having to talk. She also expressed her dislike of having a male analyst, that she would have much preferred coming to a woman. She thought it would be much easier because many of her difficulties she believed were probably sexual in character, and her early training had probably produced inhibitions against telling those things to a person of the opposite sex. Then she immediately referred to fears of her father and said that she had always been afraid of him. She followed this with a confession regarding her masturbation episodes with her brother and her fears of having been damaged. Her early dreams contained distinct references to her castration wishes toward men and her fears of the feminine role.

---

[3] Freud, Sigmund. A child is being beaten. In *Collected papers,* Vol. 2. London: Hogarth Press, 1924.

[4] In this connection see Menninger, Karl, Some unconscious psychological factors associated with the common cold. *Psychoanal. Quart.,* 1934, 3. Also Saul, Leon, Psychogenic factors in the etiology of the common cold. *Int. J. Psycho-Anal.,* 1938, 19 451-470.

This transference situation continued for about 40 analytic hours. Then her whole transference attitude changed and she began to neglect her work, her compensatory giving to her sister and other members of her family practically ceased, and she began to express with increasing frankness her passive dependent relationship to her sister and to me. She spent entire days in bed during which time her sister prepared the meals and waited upon her as a mother would. She complained bitterly of the necessity of earning her own living, and wanted to become totally passive and dependent. For her the ideal solution would be to spend the rest of her life in bed, reading, resting, and daydreaming, removed from all contact with reality. This frankly expressed infantile attitude illustrated a commonly observed fact: that when a symptom or a behavior pattern becomes threatened by the analytic procedure, it may become intensified as a defense reaction.

Obviously, beginning the analysis had for her a meaning similar to that of the original seduction by her brother. She was afraid of the analysis, afraid of a male analyst because this constituted to her unconscious a reproduction of the original intimate relationships with her brother. There was not only the fear of having her genital desires aroused as they were at that time, but there was the added fear of her castration wishes towards him which she unconsciously realized would be reproduced in the analytic situation. Obviously then she took flight into the mother-child transference relationship.

At this point, because her oral dependent relationship to her sister had been thoroughly analyzed in the transference situation, it seemed advisable to recommend the discontinuance in real life of the gratification of these tendencies. The analytic situation seemed opportune for such advice for the reason that these exaggerated indulgences had an obvious defense significance for her. Therefore she reacted violently to this advice, refused to make any change whatever, and became more dependent and demanding than before.

Immediately following her refusal to cooperate, she began to have gastric symptoms similar to those which had been active during her "ulcer" periods. She found it impossible to eat anything except bland foods and began to restrict her diet to milk and soups. Severe epigastric pains were complained of after eating, as well as insomnia and more or less constant nausea. She consulted her former gastroenterologist, who advised a rœntgenological examination. This was done, and an active duodenal ulcer with pylorospasm was demonstrated. At the same time she admitted an intense jealousy of her sister, who had become interested in a man whom the patient considered inferior. She did everything possible to prevent their proposed marriage. She transferred some of her dependent attitude to other more sympathetic mother-substitutes and succeeded in getting a great deal of attention from them. In this way she offered an excellent demonstration of exacerbation of gastric symptoms coincident with her stubborn determination to hold on to her oral incorporating tendencies, at the moment when the analyst not only through interpretations but through recommendations interfered with their gratification.

She attempted to frighten me with the severity of her gastric symptoms and suggested that she take a vacation both from work and from analysis and remain at home attended by her sister. Coincident with my discouraging this and the actual setting of a wedding date by her sister, she suddenly developed a new symptom. This consisted of intense pain starting in the upper lumbar region, continuing down the spine, and radiating into the left hip. This was accompanied by a lateral scoliosis causing her to lean towards the left. The spinal condition became so painful that she could not walk and had to be assisted from her bed. She consulted several orthopedic surgeons, who expressed varying opinions, but a diagnosis of spinal arthritis was finally made. Her brother was, of course, immediately notified and came to Chicago to aid her. She remained at home for two weeks after the onset of this symptom. During this time she was treated with the common remedies for arthritis—rest in bed and applied heat, but her condition did not improve. On the contrary the pain and scoliosis became worse, and it was finally decided to take her to the hospital for rœntgen-ray examination, after which she was to be mechanically stretched and a plaster of Paris cast applied to her back. Then all of her gastric symptoms disappeared and she could eat anything, but out of fear restricted herself for the most part to a bland diet.

I was informed of her intention to undergo these drastic therapeutic measures and therefore asked her by telephone if she would like to have me come and see her. Her answer was, "No," but that *if* I came she would have to receive me out of courtesy. I called immediately, expressed an attitude of friendly interest in her illness, and then inquired about her mental condition. She replied by telling me a dream of the previous night which had disturbed her considerably.

> *Dream:* She saw several soldiers with fixed bayonets. They all belonged to the same army. Suddenly they began to attack and fight each other. She feared that in the confusion she might get hurt.

Without actual confirmatory associations, I told her I believed the dream represented what she was doing in reality to the several doctors (including myself), playing one doctor against another; and that in the dream there was a fear of being hurt and an obvious need for punishment as a reaction to the wish to injure others. Her reaction to this interpretation was a negative one. She replied that she needed competent medical advice, that analysis could probably straighten her out mentally, but she had a real physical, pathological illness which I was ignoring or at least minimizing.

I advised an immediate rœntgen-ray examination of the vertebral column to determine further what pathological state actually existed and attempted to discourage both stretching and application of the cast, at the same time offering to have her transported to and from my office each day if she wished to continue her analysis. She reserved her answer and two days later I received a letter from her. She was in the hospital, the rœntgen-ray examination had not demonstrated any vertebral lesion whatever, but the stretcher had been applied and the cast was to follow. In the same letter she complained that her friends (mother-substitutes) were really her enemies. I replied to this letter by again recommending that she discontinue her attempts of getting herself "damaged" and return to the analysis. I also indicated that probably she was her own worst enemy. These were only reiterations of former interpretations.

However this letter seemed to have the desired effect, because she left the hospital and returned to the analysis. Her posture was very stiff, with distinct deviation to the left. She walked with difficulty She gave three definite reasons for returning. The first was my interpretations in regard to her being her own worst enemy, the second some insight into the manner in which she was "fooling" the doctors, and the third was that her gastroenterologist told her he believed her back symptoms were largely psychogenic and that she had better return to analysis.

For several succeeding hours her material contained repeated accusations that everyone wanted to damage her, that doctors were all incompetent, that the sooner psychoanalysis and medicine got together the better it would be for the innocent victims of both. She insisted her pain and deformity were due to some spinal pathology and that the doctors simply could not find it. However her condition continued to improve.

The development of the new symptom was coincident with thwarting of her last desperate attempt to maintain her passive dependent relationship to her sister. When I began to force her out of this situation, not only with interpretations but also with a recommendation that she discontinue the relationship, she evidently made an emotional effort to abandon the pregenital attachment to the sister and face the problem of heterosexuality. An added incentive for such an attempt was that of her sister's impending marriage which drove her into competition with her sister on an adult feminine level. The internal obstacles to this progress are known from her previous analytic material. The way to a heterosexual adjustment was blocked by the intense hate and fear reactions towards men. The sexual episode with her brother intensified her aggressive and castrative wishes towards men to such a degree that it necessitated a projection of these wishes, and she attempted to place all the blame on to men. The projection solution then became: It is not she who wants to castrate men. They damage her. Her brother damaged her. I believe that this muscular spasm had a direct relationship to this conflict, a conflict centering about castration wishes towards men and the resultant fears of retaliation. The psychological circumstances under which the symptom occurred corroborate this belief.

At this time, when the symptom was at its height, I encouraged her to be more socially aggressive, because I anticipated that she was about ready to face the problem of heterosexuality and assumed that the previous analysis had blocked her escape back to a pregenital dependence upon her sister (and mother). I told her specifically that I thought it expedient for her to seek the company of both men and women, but more particularly that of men and to make some overt attempts toward friendly relations with them. She laughed at, belittled, and rejected my suggestion. She said she had no friends except women, she was out of touch with eligible men. Then she brought the following dream:

> Dream: It was all about beds. They seemed to be on a quiet beautiful street. The streets seemed to criss-cross. One was Willow Street, which seemed very soothing to her. It was a little eerie, too, because of the darkness.

It is interesting that before telling this dream in the analysis she repeated it to her sister.

In associating to the dream she stated that her sister said she wanted to retreat. Patient says this is not true. She is only interested in being straight and out of pain again. This is such a blow to her pride. She must wear a support, which she despises. The night of the dream a man and his wife were quarreling in the next apartment—and a boy had an argument with his parents. She envied this boy his ability to argue with his parents without any apparent fear of retaliation. She was always afraid to argue with her parents. There was all kinds of excitement and a radio was going full blast. The people quarreling expressed themselves beautifully, but excitedly. It reminded her of the good old days at home and her mother's and father's quarrels. She is disturbed about having so many doctors treat her. Maybe she does play one against another. She can see that she is acting like a prostitute except that instead of men in general she is using doctors. She actually lied to two of them and did not realize at the time that she was attempting to get them to quarrel with each other. She has had the feeling that she would like to sleep with several men, a different one every night. She remembers a song from the Gilbert and Sullivan opera, "The Mikado," about a little bird who sat in a tree all day and sang. When asked why he sits and sings all day, the answer is the same monotonous refrain, "Tit Willow." No matter what he is asked, the answer is always "Tit Willow." She was greatly impressed by this opera, but could only remember the song of the dickeybird who sang over and over again the same monotonous refrain.

This dream expresses clearly and dramatically the deeper dynamics of my patient's psychology in this phase of the analysis (i.e., the phase in which the transition from pregenital conflicts corresponding to the emotional background of peptic ulcer and the genital conflicts expressed in the conversion symptom, as described, took place). The dream obviously contains a threat which was only partially grasped by me at the time and was followed by the carrying out in reality of the threat contained therein. For these reasons I have chosen to examine and interpret the dream rather thoroughly, not only in relation to its manifest and latent contents but also in respect to material previously obtained during the analysis.

The dream expresses an intense spite reaction to my advice that she abandon the oral dependent relationship to her sister and mother-substitutes and that she mix with the opposite sex. To this she reacted as though it were a rejection by me, toward whom she had an oral dependent transference similar to the relationship to her sister, and all the fury of a rejected girl is contained in the dream. In the dream she accuses me as a girl might accuse her mother. She says, "You drive me into the street, into prostitution." (This is expressed by the beds in the dark street.) The depreciation of a sexual life is clearly shown in the associations. The crisscross streets to which she associated the quarreling couple refer to the parents' quarrels and a sadomasochistic conception of intercourse. At the same time the dream also expresses the wish to regress to the security of the analytic situation which is treated as analogous to a mother caring for her child. Willow Street had for her a soothing significance, and the tit willow, as well as the monotonous refrain, refer to the soothing effects of a lullaby.

It is of interest to observe that every element of this dream contains such a double and opposing meaning. Sexuality is referred to as being prostitution, and at the same time the reference to the security of the parental home and the wish for a mother-daughter relationship is clearly shown. The dream also contains a reference to another type of reaction, namely, fear of the female sexual role as shown in her identification with the boy previously mentioned in the associations. The main content of this dream is the rejection of heterosexuality because of its danger. Verbalized it would be, "You refuse me, reject me, want me to become a woman. That means you really want me to be a prostitute like my mother." The opposing meaning is the wish to retreat from the danger of sexuality to the protection of the mother. Also the analyst's interpretations are felt as soothing lullabies. This is shown in her association to Willow Street, which had a soothing influence.

But this, too, has a negative meaning. The analyst's interpretations, particularly those referring to her oral receptive and aggressive desires, likewise the monotonous repetition about being damaged by her brother and by the analysis, are monotonous refrains. It is not impossible that she also accuses the analyst, as she accused her brother. Verbalized it would be, "You force sexuality upon me just as my brother did." This, as we shall see, is at least partially a projection of her own wish to damage first her brother and later men in general. Her fear of the darkness (the street in the dream was eerie too) is a reaction to her fear of seeing her prostitution wishes. This may also express the wish to keep the analyst in the dark.

The dream, as well as the symptom, expressed a drastic defense against genital desires: desires so active and so feared for the reasons stated that she had to build up some defense which would render heterosexuality impossible for her. The complaint against the brother also contained this defense element.

In this phase of the analysis, when she is confronted with the problem of sexuality, she feels driven into it. She repeats the same reaction which she experienced when her brother "forced" a sexual relationship upon her. This reaction was one of retaliation fear because of the castration wish, and resulted in rejection of the feminine role and an identification with men to avoid the suffering role of a woman. The oral-dependent attitude toward the mother was transferred to a wish to incorporate the penis orally. The previous material showed that the wish to incorporate her father's (and brother's) penis was due not only to resentment and fear but also to the wish to own something, the possession of which pleased the mother.

We see that she had two methods of escape from the problem of heterosexuality. One was a regression to the oral level, the resumption of the oral-receptive, dependent relationship to the mother; the second was an escape on the phallic level, an identification with the man by castrating him and incorporating his penis. As I have pointed out in the first part of the analysis, the transference material, dreams, etc., express castration wishes towards men which were later followed by an oral-dependent attitude towards me as well as towards her sister and represented a reliving of the defense against the genital desires. The analyst for a long period represented (in the second instance) the mother who would protect her against heterosexuality, but when the conversion symptom developed, this mother-transference had been abandoned and she not only was expressing frank sexual wishes towards me but this frank expression was followed almost immediately by carrying out of sexual impulses in life. When she was driven out of this oral type of solution she reacted with attempts corresponding to the second pattern, that of masculine identification. Concurrent with this attempt she developed the hysterical symptom previously described.

The psychological meaning of this conversion symptom cannot be fully reconstructed. However I am inclined to assume an important relationship between the anatomical localization of the symptom and the erotic pleasure-sensation which she experienced when caressed by her brother. This part of her anatomy, which was originally connected with pleasure sensations, became the seat of pain. This is obviously due to guilt feelings as a reaction to receiving pleasure from her brother, and at the same time out of revenge wishing to castrate him. A complete analysis of the symptom is not of paramount importance to the purpose of this paper. However it appears that with this symptom she symbolically made of her body a penis, a stiff but damaged one. It is not justifiable, however, entirely to separate the two solutions, masculine identification [5] and regression to the oral level.[6] The conversion symptom which led to the contortion of her body not only expressed the phallic solution, but at the same time permitted a regression to early dependent attitudes in life. She became entirely dependent, obtained satisfaction out of being nursed, fed as an infant is fed, and received a great deal of attention. She remained in bed and removed herself from all touch with reality.

That the symptom also had a further defense significance in relation to assuming an adult role in life is well illustrated in her material. The symptom developed at the time she wished to indulge her passive dependent wishes but was forced into some activity in the reality situation. She repeated many times that her back was less painful

[5] Freud, Sigmund. On the physical mechanisms of hysterical phenomena. In *Collected papers*, Vol. 1. London: Hogarth Press, 1924.
[6] See particularly, Lewin, Bertram D. The body as phallus. *Psychoanal. Quart.*, 1933, 2, 24.

when she remained quiet and inactive, that exertion increased her pain. She reasoned that, having to work, to come to analysis, to perform the ordinary daily function of life, all contributed to her discomfort. At the same time she reported dreams in which she would be sitting, lying, or standing quietly, but in danger of being *injured,* usually by something being projected in her direction, and there was always the feeling in the dream that she must *not* move. She felt secure providing she made no movement. That these dreams refer to insight in the analysis is obvious, but, in view of the fact that her fears of genitality were so intense and that this symptom was clearly a defense against progression to an adult attitude, I believe we are justified in assuming that it contained quite specifically a protest against adult feminine activity, against walking, standing on her own feet in the sense of psychologically growing up. The projectile nature of the danger in the dreams quite plainly referred to her fears of the feminine role in intercourse.

The masculine identification represented a new attempt to solve her Oedipus conflict in relation to her mother on the phallic level. Previously she found a solution through renouncing all competition and assuming towards her mother the role of the helpless, dependent child. Now she wants to possess a penis with which she can please the mother, as the father does, and in consequence continue to receive from her. With this new attempt at solution on the phallic level the hysterical symptom develops, whereas during the period of her peptic ulcer symptom the psychodynamic background corresponded to a pregenital, i.e., an oral, solution.

As previously mentioned, the patient made an attempt to carry out in reality the threat contained in the dream. She managed through her brother to meet a male friend of his in Havana during the vacation period, and with this meeting began the realization of her dream.

In the first hour following the vacation period she reported that she had had intercourse with this man and that it seemed a very ugly experience. She stated that he was exactly like her father in every respect, that he liked her, said nice things to her, and made love to her. She thought him very intellectual but not very aggressive. She said that they talked for hours about things which she had discussed as a child with her father, and that for her it was a real mental feast. He was very kind and understanding and never interrupted anything she said or did. He was very affectionate and she enjoyed kissing him, particularly his hands. They spent whole days together, and after two days decided to sleep together. They planned to stay at her hotel, but when they arrived on this particular evening she found that she did not possess a key to her room. Afterwards she learned that he had it in his pocket (an obvious reference to her lack of a penis and his possession of one). She began immediately to menstruate, which caused a postponement of the sexual relationship. After menstruation finished, they made another attempt. She was quite frigid and the intercourse was painful. She said she believed most women felt the same way about intercourse but would not admit it. It disturbed her when he called her "pal," because this had been one of her brother's pet names for her. She told in detail of her preparations for intercourse, how she undressed with a do-or-die precision, and laughed hysterically when, after undressing, she ordered the light to be extinguished and he pushed the wrong switch illuminating the whole room. She felt that the room was full of men and women watching them. What she enjoyed most in the whole procedure was his masturbating her. Then she referred to her frigidity and said that there must be some anatomical and not an emotional reason for it. Her sister told her that in the beginning of sexual relations frigidity was very common.

Following this episode she became convinced that she was madly in love with this man and wanted to quit her position, move to Havana, and live with him. This, however, he quite emphatically discouraged, and frankly informed her he had no intentions of getting married and was not at all anxious to be tied down to any permanent affair. Following this rejection she decided she wanted to return home, became very anxious to return to the analysis, and felt that anyway she had made a distinct advance toward successful adjustment. But at the same time she felt this was the only man who could possibly care enough for her to overlook her age and other believed deficiencies. She said she felt quite uninhibited in his presence, that she could "act" with him, that she enjoyed singing to him and entertaining him in other ways. In many respects their relationship assumed a homosexual flavour. She felt that he was somewhat feminine in his actions; that he was very fixated to his family, that he was passive and indecisive, that he probably was quite neurotic but very good company, and that anyway he was exceedingly kind to her. Following this recital of her Havana experiences, a major part of the analysis, as well as her fantasy life, consisted of a repetition of this experience.

It was pointed out to her that she had lived out her unconscious transference wishes in this episode, that she received from this man what she could not get from the analyst, i.e., overt manifestation of affection (physical contact), and that she did not receive the things she disliked in analysis, viz., interpretations and objective behavior on the part of the analyst. Also the evident hostile castrative wishes were interpreted. She accepted all the interpretations except the one referring to hostility. She even claimed that probably this man was hostile to her, that he used her and that he certainly misused her, but there was no hostility on her part whatever. It is obvious that emotionally she equated three experiences: (a) the masturbation episode with her brother; (b) the sexual experience in Havana; (c) the analytic situation. All three she rejected and maintained that they damaged her.

Following this she became openly hostile toward me in the analysis, and at the same time experienced a slight recurrence of her spinal symptoms. As often observed in analysis, after overtly expressing the hostility which is under pressure of intense guilt, she again attempted a flight from making conscious her hostile wishes into a passive receptive attitude. She reported a dream in which she attacked her mother, had the feeling that she had killed her, and fled in terror. The dream changed and she was passing around a bottle of liquor which someone had given her. This dream demonstrates how, when she was faced with making conscious her hostility for her mother, she again fantasied the original type of solution, i.e., repression of the hostile wishes and attempted to relieve her guilt through compensatory giving.

The oft-repeated claim that her brother and the analyst damaged her had for her the meaning that her brother in the first instance and the analysis in the second instance stimulated her sexual desires and a need for sexual satisfaction. In neither experience was this need gratified. Therefore the wish to damage, as well as the projection of that wish, became for her not only a rationally justified wish for revenge but also contributed to her difficulties when she attempted a genital solution in the analysis. She reached this level only to be thwarted and left unsatisfied; these intense fears of rejection caused her to vacillate between attempts at solution on the oral and phallic levels. The genital conflict is always active, in the conscious material it forms the center of organization, and the oral helpless dependent attitude is kept in reserve as a defense.

To summarize briefly the observations which I have discussed and the conclusions drawn from those observations: A transitory hysterical symptom characterized by a spasm of the muscles of the lumbar region with the resultant left lateral deviation of the body developed during a critical period of analysis. During this period the patient was forced, by analytic insight and some active encouragement by the analyst, to face the problem of heterosexuality from which she had previously regressed to a pregenital dependent attitude in relation to older female members of her family (mother and sister).

The patient's dreams and the association material which she produced in connection with the conversion symptom dealt with the resentment towards the brother and analyst, but more specifically with castration wishes and masculine identification. Although the specific symbolic meaning of the symptom cannot be reconstructed with actual proof as to its correctness, it probably expressed a fantasy of incorporation of the male genital with intense guilt feelings as a reaction to the incorporation. The anatomical localization of the symptom is obviously identical with that part of the body which was connected with erotic pleasure sensations experienced by the patient during the sexual episodes with her brother. If the unconscious material which was presented in connection with the hysterical conversion symptom is compared with material which appeared at the beginning of the analysis in connection with the gastric symptoms, striking differences may be observed. The character of the material connected with the gastric symptoms was preponderantly pregenital in character and centered about the dependent, demanding attitude towards the patient's older sister, and was highly charged with feelings of guilt and inferiority.

In contradistinction to this, the material which appeared in connection with the hysterical symptom belonged to the phallic period of the instinctual development. The masculine identification with rejection of the female role was the paramount aim during this phase of the analysis.

This observation is in accordance with the assumption made by Freud and accepted by most psychoanalytic authors that hysterical conversion symptoms express tendencies belonging to the phallic and genital phases of development. It also indicates that in the neuroses of vegetative organs (organ neuroses) pre-eminently pregenital tendencies are involved. In this case the hysterical conversion symptoms developed, and the gastric symptoms ceased coincident with the patient's attempt to renounce the regression to oral dependence and face the problem of heterosexual adjustment.

BIBLIOGRAPHY

1. ABRAHAM, KARL. Forms of expression of the female castration complex. *Int. J. Psycho-Anal.*, 1920, **1**, 342.
2. ABRAHAM, KARL. Manifestations of the female castration complex. *Int. J. Psycho-Anal.*, 1922, **3**, 1.
3. ALEXANDER, FRANZ, AND CO-WORKERS. The influence of psychologic factors upon gastrointestinal disturbances: a symposium. *Psychoanal. Quart.*, 1934, **3**, 501-588. (In this volume, page 103.)
4. ALEXANDER, FRANZ, AND WILSON, G. Quantitative dream studies. *Psychoanal. Quart.*, 1935, **4**, 371-405.
5. DEUTSCH, H. The significance of masochism in the mental life of women. *Int. J. Psycho-Anal.*, 1929, **11**, 48.

6. Ferenczi, Sándor. *The phenomena of hysterical materialization. Further contributions to theory and technique of psychoanalysis.* London: Hogarth Press, 1926.
7. Freud, Sigmund. The psychogenesis of a case of female homosexuality. *Int. J. Psycho-Anal.,* 1920, **1**, 125.
8. Freud, Sigmund. Hysterical phantasies and their relation to bisexuality. In *Collected papers,* Vol. 2. London: Hogarth Press, 1924.
9. Freud, Sigmund. General remarks on hysterical attacks. In *Collected papers,* Vol. 2. London: Hogarth Press, 1924.
10. Freud, Sigmund. A child is being beaten. In *Collected papers,* Vol. 2. London: Hogarth Press, 1924.
11. Freud, Sigmund. On the physical mechanisms of hysterical phenomena. In *Collected papers,* Vol. 1. London: Hogarth Press, 1924.
12. Horney, K. The flight from womanhood. The masculinity complex in women as viewed by men and by women. *Int. J. Psycho-Anal.,* 1926, **7**, 324.
13. Horney, K. On the genesis of the castration complex in women. *Int. J. Psycho-Anal.,* 1924, **5**, 50.
14. Jones, Ernest. The early development of female sexuality. *Int. J. Psycho-Anal.,* 1927, **8**, 459.
15. Jones, Ernest. Notes on Dr. Abraham's article on the female castration complex. *Int. J. Psycho-Anal.,* 1922, **3**, 327.
16. Klein, Melanie. *The psychoanalysis of children.* London: Hogarth Press, 1932.
17. Lampl de Groot, A. The evolution of the Oedipus complex in women. *Int. J. Psycho-Anal.,* 1928, **9**, 332.
18. Lewin, Bertram. The body as phallus. *Psychoanal. Quart.,* 1933, **2**, 24.
19. Mason-Thompson, E. R. The relation of the elder sister to the development of the Electra complex. *Int. J. Psycho-Anal.,* 1920, **1**, 186.
20. Menninger, K. A. Some unconscious psychological factors associated with the common cold. *Psychoanal. Quart.,* 1934, **21**, No. 2.
21. Rado, Sándor. Fear of castration in women. *Psychoanal. Quart.,* 1933, **2**, 425.
22. Sachs, Hanns. The wish to be a man. *Int. J. Psycho-Anal.,* 1920, **1**, 262.
23. Saul, L. J. Psychogenic factors in the etiology of the common cold. *Int. J. Psycho-Anal.,* 1938, **19**, 451-470.
24. Van Ophuijsen, J. H. W. Contributions to the masculinity complex in women. *Int. J. Psycho-Anal.,* 1924, **5**, 39.

PART III

DISTURBANCES OF THE RESPIRATORY SYSTEM

BRONCHIAL ASTHMA IN CHILDREN *

By Margaret W. Gerard, M.D.

Character is caught not taught. It must be built up, not by the studies in the curriculum, but by those who teach the pupils. This would seem to be a self-evident truth, but it has been too much lost from sight in America where the numbers to be handled in the public school system are so great that personal contact and influence of teachers and taught have been necessarily weakened.
        —W. W. Comfort *in* The Quaker Way of Life

Since the discovery of allergens and the disclosure of the fact that many persons subject to asthmatic attacks were sensitive to one or more of these allergens, the emphasis in the investigation of causative factors has been upon the specific allergic sensitivity of the patient (1). However, many investigators early recognized that asthmatic patients did not always develop attacks when exposed to the allergens to which they were sensitive, and, conversely, often developed typical attacks when there was no evidence of the presence of the provoking allergen (7). The psychological factor partially responsible for the development of the attack has been investigated scientifically only in recent years (4, 5, 6, 7), although as early as 1882 reports occur in the literature of asthmatic attacks which were precipitated by strong emotions (2). More recently numerous similar reports have been published, and these offer significant evidence that there is a correlation between the emotional state of the patient and the occurrence of bronchial asthma in both adults and children.

In an attempt to isolate specific emotional states as those conducive to the production of an attack, investigators have enumerated a variety of emotions observed preceding it. Fear, anger, anxious doubt have been most frequently mentioned as the causative affects; whereas several authors stated that any strong emotional conflict may be followed by typical asthmatic symptoms.[1]

It is, however, well known that severe emotional reactions and psychic conflicts occur in all psychoneuroses and are therefore not specific for bronchial asthma. Allergists have shown, also, that persons sensitive to allergens do not all develop asthma when under the

* *The Nervous Child* V: 327-331, 1946.
[1] See (7) for a more complete summary of the literature on this subject.

stress of emotions, but react with a variety of symptoms, such as urticaria, eczema, gastrointestinal disturbances, hay fever, and so forth. Therefore evidence does not support the assumption that allergic sensitivity in conjunction with strong emotional states equals asthma.

Since allergists have found no substances which are specific only for asthma and not for other allergic conditions, recent investigators have turned their interest to the analysis of the personality structure of asthmatics in an attempt to unearth the psychic conflicts, if any, from which the emotional states observed in asthmatics may arise, and which are conflicts common to all asthmatic patients. This is the approach which has proved of most value in the explanation of the production of other psychosomatic disorders such as ulcer (8), constipation, enuresis (9), and others.

An important study of the personality of asthmatic children was made by Rogerson, Hardcastle, and Duguid (3). These authors found marked overanxiety and lack of self-confidence in the twenty-three children studied. During their psychological examinations the children showed great anxiety when alone with the examiner, and the younger ones refused to be separated from their mothers. They all seemed to prefer to say nothing in answer to questions rather than risk making a mistake. In a play group they were quieter and appeared to be more repressed at first than the majority of the other children, and a few of the younger ones made frequent excursions out of the room for reassurance that their mothers were just outside the door.

The parents of these children were found by the authors to be predominantly overprotective to a pathological degree (in 17 out of 23 cases). In some instances this behavior was shown to grow out of ambivalent feelings in which the excessive protective attitude was due to an attempt to overcome the guilt feelings resulting from a deep hostility toward the child.

In the treatment of these children, the authors attempted to change the oversolicitous behavior of the parents into a more affectionate but more permissive attitude in order to allow the child a greater degree of independence. At the same time the child was encouraged to enter more independent activities to facilitate a decrease in the anxiety which he experienced when away from the mother. In a significant number of the cases treated, the number and severity of asthmatic attacks were noticeably decreased. (Of 25 cases, 10 became symptom free, 4 were much improved, and 4 showed some improvement.)

In these cases the evidence seems to indicate that the attacks were definitely correlated with a fear of separation from the mother. This correlation was also indicated by Weiss (10) whose analysis of an adult asthmatic male led him to the conclusion that the asthmatic attacks developed as a reaction to a fear of maternal separation. He compared the attack to "the shrieking, helplessly sprawling newborn child with blood-red, swollen face." In this patient the fear of maternal disapproval and rejection was aroused by the fact that his sexual impulses had been completely repressed in his early years by the mother's extreme intolerance of any indications of sexual activity or interest on his part and by a prying curiosity into his affairs. The analyst became for him a substitute who, in contradistinction to the real mother, was permissive. It was thus possible for the patient to free and accept his sexual impulses without fear of loss of the parental figure upon whom he depended.

Several of the reports in the literature cite examples of secondary utilization of the asthma attacks to gain a solicitous protection from a person upon whom the patient depended and whose loss he feared. Nabor (11) reported a case in which the attack seemed to develop from a wish to soften the dominating cruel attitude of the mother. In a case of Wittkower's (1), the patient kept her indifferent husband at home to care for her by properly timed asthma attacks.

By far the most significant scientific investigation of asthma in relation to the psychological factors involved in the disease is that of French, Alexander, et al (7). In this study a meticulous examination of the material obtained from penetrating psychoanalyses of sixteen adult patients and eleven children was made by the twelve collaborators in order to determine what basic factors, if any, could be found common to all, and to find if any correlation existed between these factors and the production of the asthmatic attack.

These authors came to the following conclusions after an evaluation of the evidence produced by the patients in analysis.[2]

1. The asthmatic attack occurred as a reaction to the danger of separation from the mother or loss of her love. The precipitating situation seemed to be not the actual fact of losing the mother but the possibility of losing her as a result of indecision and conflict between the urge to cling and the temptation to separate from her. This condition they found to be an undercurrent deeply repressed and continuous throughout the patient's life.

2. Situations which stimulated the fear of loss were found to be of two kinds: one, the prospect of actual separation from the mother; and two, a temptation situation in which repressed impulses, of which the mother disapproved, threatened to break through and estrange

---

[2] See 7 for detailed descriptions of the patients' analyses.

her. The impulses most commonly considered dangerous to the patient were sexual impulses. Other unacceptable impulses were those hostile to the mother or to rivals such as siblings, and urges for independence.

3. The patients disclosed a variety of defenses against the fear. Most common were those seeking reconciliation, such as the utilization of suffering to gain sympathy, and confession of wishes which sought maternal acceptance of the wishes.

Mastery of the fear by repetition of the traumatic event was a defense used by some of the patients and, particularly among the children, it was shown by provocative aggressive behavior which strove for reassurance that the mother would not reject them. In some instances the individual defended himself against the fear by withdrawing from the temptation situation into a fancied protection. This was dramatically exhibited in the intra-uterine dreams and fantasies of these patients, some symbolic and some frank intra-uterine wishes. The latter was beautifully demonstrated by the little girl who curled upon the therapist's lap in an intra-uterine position and said, "Now I am inside you like a little baby and all protected."

4. Attacks were found to occur when the defenses broke down. Two main situations causing the disintegration of the defenses occurred when the danger of losing the mother became acute and when the threat of estrangement took the patient by surprise.

5. The character structure of the patients varied considerably, but common to all were a lack of independence and maturity as well as a dependent attitude toward the mother and maternal figures.

6. During analysis, interruption of the asthmatic attack occurred in several situations. In some, confession relieved the attack. In others, crying caused the cessation of attacks, and this indicated to the authors that there was a correlation between the asthma attack and the inhibition or repression of a cry which arose from anxiety or rage. In many cases asthma attacks did not occur in the beginning of the therapy after a satisfactory dependent transference relation to the analyst was established, but later, as impulses first became conscious and the fear of separation from the analyst emerged, and thus psychologically repeated in the analysis situations similar to those associated with the development of the emotional conflict in childhood. Cure of the condition in some cases and considerable decrease in the number and severity of the attacks in others occurred after resolution of the conflict, which allowed the patient to exert his own independence. With this new security in his own power he no longer needed the dependent relationship to a mother figure and consequently lost his fear of separation.

7. In attempting to explain why asthma rather than some other symptom develops in an attempt to solve the basic personality conflict found in asthmatics, several theoretical possibilities were offered. The cry in some instances may be suppressed because of parental prohibition, and in other instances from parental shaming at the time when the child yielded to a wish to retreat to maternal protection; while a third possibility may lie in the universal rejecting attitude of the mothers of these patients which might have led to a tendency on the child's part to refrain from appealing to the mother in order to avoid the traumatic experience of rejection. A final possibility is that, due to the parents' ambition for their child's maturity, the patient may have been forced into an early pseudo-independence which went beyond his emotional resources and which caused an insatiable longing for maternal protection. Finally, all of the factors may have operated in unison to maintain a continuous, strong, dependent need within the child.

A constitutional factor in the allergic sensitivity of asthmatics is not ignored. Since it was proved that, under certain circumstances, the asthma attack did not occur when the patient was exposed to the allergens, and, conversely, attacks did occur when the patient was thrust into specific conflict situations in the absence of allergens, it was suggested that the basic emotional conflict operated to make the patients less resistant to the allergens. This theory was supported by the discovery that the patients, through the aid of therapy, became more resistant to the allergens after they had succeeded in overcoming their emotional conflict relative to emancipation from the mother or her substitute.

Since the publications of the monograph, to which the present author contributed case discussions, five more asthmatic children have been studied and treated with psychoanalysis by the author. All of these children presented basic conflicts similar to those described in the monograph. All of them revealed, in fantasy and in play, an exaggerated fear of separation from the mother. This anxiety was relived in the transference relationship. Because the therapist showed an accepting rather than rejecting attitude toward the patients, they were able to resolve the fear, to develop courage in their own independence, and finally to give up the longing for infantile dependency. In four of these cases, the asthmatic attacks ceased and have not returned in periods of two to five years since treatment. In one of the cases, although acute asthma does not occur, slight wheezing develops coincident to severe bronchial colds. This fifth child was 12 at the onset of treatment and already had developed secondary body changes as evidenced in a barrel chest. It is also probable that a secondary thickening of the bronchioles had occurred, as is often found in asthmatics of long standing. This thickening may account for the persistence of the wheezing.

In all of these cases marked maternal rejection had begun at an early age. In one case it resulted from the mother's disappointment that the child was a boy rather than a girl, which she had longed for. After a girl was born, when the patient was 2, the mother transferred him to the care of a rigid, perfectionistic nurse and devoted herself to the girl. In the second case the mother was an alcoholic and frequently beat the child and railed at her for crying. In a third instance the child had been abandoned by the mother when she was 2, and had been brought up by a stern, rejecting aunt who was excessively punitive at any sign of sex interest. In the other two cases both mothers were ambivalent, ambitious parents who held the children to a standard of maturity and achievement far beyond their years.

In connection with the role of allergens in the production of asthma, all five children were examined for sensitivity before and after psychotherapy. All of them reacted strongly to substances: two, to several foods; one to house dust; and two to pollens, house dust, and less strongly to food substances. After analytic treatment, and the cessation of the asthma, all five reacted to tests with the same substances to which they had reacted previously and with the same strength as formerly. And in no instance did they present other allergic symptoms which might have been considered as substituted for the asthma. These findings seem to offer strong evidence that the specific emotional condition of the patient is at least of equal importance to the allergic sensitivity in production of asthmatic attacks.

BIBLIOGRAPHY

1. WITTKOWER, E. Studies on the influence of emotions on the functions of organs. *J. ment. Sci.*, 1935, **81**, 533.
2. SALTER, H. G. *On asthma. Its pathology and treatment.* New York: Wm. Wood & Co., 1882.
3. ROGERSON, C. H., ET AL. A psychological approach to the problem of asthma and the asthma-eczema-prurigo syndrome. *Guy's Hosp. Rep.*, 1935, **85**, 289.
4. OBERNDORF, C. P. Psychogenic factors in asthma. *N. Y. J. Med.*, 1935, **35**, 41.
5. FRENDENBERG, S. Asthma and life difficulties. *Fortschr. d. Med.*, 1935, **53**, 392.
6. CLARKSON, A. K. The nervous factor in juvenile asthma. *Brit. med. J.*, 1937, **2**, 845.
7. FRENCH, T. M., ALEXANDER, FRANZ, ET AL. Psychogenic factors in bronchial asthma. *Psychosom. Med. Monograph No. 2*, 1941.
8 ALEXANDER, FRANZ, AND CO-WORKERS. The influence of psychologic factors upon gastrointestinal disturbances: a symposium. *Psychoanal. Quart.*, 1934, **3**, 501-588. (In this volume, page 103.)
RARD, MARGARET W. Child analysis as a technique in the investigation of mental mechanisms. *Amer. J. Psychiat.*, 1937, **94**, 3.
s, EDOARDO. Psychoanalyse eines Falles von nervösen Asthma. *Int. Z. f. Psychoanal.*, 1922, **8**, 440.
J. Asthma Bronchiale: allergische Behandlung und Psychotherapie. *d. Gegenw.*, 1929, **70**, 437.

PSYCHOTHERAPY IN BRONCHIAL ASTHMA *

By Thomas M. French, M.D.,
AND
Adelaide M. Johnson, M.D.

A study of the psychogenic factors in bronchial asthma was made several years ago by the Chicago Institute for Psychoanalysis. Of the dynamic relationships uncovered by this research, one of the most significant was that between asthma attacks and confession. Throughout the lives of patients subject to psychogenic asthma attacks, there seems to run as a continuous undercurrent, more or less deeply repressed, a fear of estrangement from the mother. The cause of this fear is usually the patient's own forbidden impulses which he thinks will offend the mother. One device, of which the asthmatic patient makes extensive use to protect himself against this danger of estrangement, is confession of the disturbing impulse. If the mother or mother-substitute accepts the confession without being shocked, then all is well for a time. If, however, the patient is too uncertain of the mother's tolerance to dare make his confession, then an asthma attack is likely to be precipitated.

This dynamic relationship between confession and asthma attacks has obvious implications for psychotherapy. The psychotherapeutic situation offers, first of all, an opportunity for the patient to confess what is disturbing him. If the asthmatic patient can gain confidence to confess fully and freely the impulses that are at the moment responsible for his fear of estrangement from some mother-substitute, then we may expect relief from his asthma attacks until some new forbidden impulse arises to disturb him. This period of relief may be quite prolonged. When attacks occur again, the therapist's problem is to discover what is the new disturbing impulse and to encourage the patient again to find relief by confessing it.

This is an important principle in every psychotherapy. Many cases of psychogenic asthma, however, differ from other more complex psychotherapeutic problems in that the relatively uncomplicated cases of psychogenic asthma require little or no treatment other than that which aims to make the patient more and more secure in the

* *Psychosomatic Medicine*, Part II of *The Proceedings of the Second Brief Psychotherapy Council*, 1944. Chicago Institute for Psychoanalysis, pp. 14-21.

confidence that nothing he may need to confess will be disturbing or offensive to the therapist.

The effect of such a therapy is at first merely symptomatic. By confessing what is disturbing him, the patient gets relief for a time from his asthma attacks. Such symptomatic relief tends gradually to diminish deep underlying insecurity and dependence.

This theory suggests that we should be able to obtain satisfying therapeutic results with at least a considerable number of cases of bronchial asthma by means of briefer methods of psychotherapy. The objective in such therapy is to discover and help the patient to confess the particular matters that are disturbing him at the time of exacerbation of asthmatic attacks, and then, as soon as relief is obtained, to diminish the frequency of treatments until other asthmatic attacks occur.

The following case, reported by Karl Hansen in 1930,[1] is a very nice illustration of the efficacy of this kind of therapy. The patient was an English woman of 49, married, and living in Germany. She had suffered periodically from asthma attacks since she was 10 years old. Hansen reports the circumstances of original onset of the asthma attacks as follows: Just prior to the onset the patient's mother had become ill and died. During the mother's last illness the patient had had the sole responsibility of her care. The actual onset of the attacks seem, however, to have been precipitated by another incident. The patient was attending a school in England where standards of honor were very high. She was the best student in the class. One day identical mistakes were found in the school work of both the patient and the girl who sat next to her, and the patient was suspected of having copied. Even as an adult she could not remember for sure whether she had been guilty. As she put it, "I didn't copy, but my intelligence tells me that is the only way the identity of the two papers could be explained." In any case much pressure was put upon her to confess, but she stubbornly refused.

It was at this time that her asthma attacks began. They continued for about four years, until she was 14 years old. About this time an American friend of her father, S., a man of considerable character, visited the family, won her friendship and confidence, and took her walking frequently with him in the country. In the course of her conversations with him the school incident and her feelings about it came to be talked over very freely. After that she ceased to have asthma attacks for a period of about five years.

1 Hansen, K.   Zur Frage der Psycho- oder Organogenese bei allergischem Bronchialasthma und den verwandten Krankheiten. Uber psychische Bedingungen des Bronchialasthmas. *Nervenarzt*, 1930, 3, 513.

Then at the age of 18 she fell in love with F., whom she could not marry because he had other ties. Apparently, in reaction to this situation, she became engaged to G. She described G. as a "splendid animal" whom she did not like but to whom she was strongly attracted sexually. A sexual relationship developed, but she found this distasteful and was unable to decide either to marry him or break with him.

Immediately after becoming acquainted with G., the asthma attacks began again and continued for the three years she was engaged to him. They stopped when she broke off the engagement.

Then she married a German musician of great talent to whom she was attracted because of his many fine traits. The husband, however, was already ill at the time of the marriage, and is described as a weak and dependent personality to whom the patient felt herself from the beginning in the role of sympathetic protectress and mother rather than wife. He was pictured as living in continuous high spirits, never tired or depressed, but under pressure to tell his wife everything that he felt. This made it necessary for her to maintain a continuous and often forced gaiety. She described the first months of the marriage as completely happy but never thoroughly free of the impressions made upon her by her memory of F. Even in the first months of her marriage she was thinking of F.; she felt there was no one else like him.

A year later she gave birth to a son and was very happy. In her son she felt the first justification for her marriage. When the son was 6 months old she took a trip to England and stayed not far from G. She avoided G., but was pursued by him. She had no feeling for him, she said, but began to feel critical of her marriage. She began to suspect that her husband's illness was hereditary and decided therefore to have no more children by him.

After she had broken off her engagement with G., the patient had no more asthma attacks for about four years, but immediately after meeting G. again the attacks returned. They continued to be severe for another four years and then gradually diminished.

During the World War the patient was so busy with her household, and so cut off from England that there was little to remind her of F. After the end of the war she entered into correspondence with S., the American friend of her childhood, and presumably continued in correspondence with him until he died a number of years later. Following his death and immediately after she had again seen F. in England, her asthma attacks returned. They continued for three years until she first consulted Hansen.

In the first interviews Hansen was surprised by the amount that the patient was able to tell him and the freedom with which she could talk about herself. She said that since her youth she had longed for someone to whom she could tell all this.

On physical examination Hansen found evidence of chronic asthma, bronchitis, and functional emphysema, but no temperature. There was a 4 per cent eosinophilia. There was a strong positive allergic reaction to bed feathers and to horse hair.

After the patient had told her story to Hansen, there were no more asthma attacks for several months, but then there was a severe recurrence of attacks when she met F. again. The attacks disappeared again after an interview with Hansen. After this the patient had been without attacks for two years at the time Hansen's article was written.

It will be noted that this individual had had prolonged periods throughout her life when she was free of asthma attacks, and that the periods of severe asthmatic attacks had their beginning in every instance in reaction to quite definite situations which brought to the surface her latent conflict. Such a case is obviously well suited for a method of psychotherapy that depends upon confession alone to achieve its results.

Our Institute case was not quite so favorable for this very simple method of therapy because this patient, at the age of 24, had already given in to his illness to the extent of renouncing the profession for which he had prepared himself, so that he was thoroughly dependent upon his father at the time he sought treatment. In accordance with this dependent attitude he immediately developed a very strong dependence upon his therapist, which made necessary a continuous therapeutic contact.

The following account of the therapy in this second case is based upon a summary prepared by Adelaide Johnson, who treated him.

When he first consulted Dr. Johnson the patient was 24 years old and single. He had recently graduated from a medical school, but felt himself quite unable to practice because of severe asthmatic attacks. Four years previously skin tests had found him allergic to beef, pork, and chicken.

He had a history of asthma since the age of 14. Before this age he had weighed over 200 pounds, but then went on a diet, reduced his weight to 155, and at that time began to develop asthmatic attacks. When he came for treatment the patient was living with his father, a physician, his mother having died when he was 3. Of this event he recalled only the mother's leaving home on a stretcher, fighting with the attendants, and crying as they took her to the hospital, where she died of pneumonia.

After the mother's death the patient and his brother moved next door to live with their father's sister and her husband. They lived there until the patient was 9. At this time the father married again —a young woman 19 years his junior. The patient states that they were married six months before anyone was told. He resented the new wife and mother very much, and at first he fought with and was very mean to her, but as he came to know her he grew fond of her.

Four years before the patient came for treatment the stepmother died of ulcer. At the time he began treatment he was extremely frank about his intense dislike for his father, which he attributed chiefly to the father's misuse of funds belonging to the patient's mother and stepmother. The patient also recalled that before the father's second marriage he had always sided with his aunt against his uncle, but rather early in the treatment he came to realize that the aunt was really a complaining, begrudging, and resentful person.

The aunt was very fat and the patient had always told her that he wished to be fat like her. At the time of the treatment, however, he resented her obesity and looked upon her refusal to diet as part of her greediness and infantilism. His own impulse to be fat like her throws some light upon his own obesity in early adolescence before he began to diet. This attitude toward the aunt's obesity may probably be taken as an indication of a relationship which became plain later, that his obesity served the function of a defense against the conflict arising out of the attraction to his aunt and to his stepmother.

The patient was treated for a total of 45 interviews, for the most part at weekly intervals. Almost immediately the analyst had opportunity to point out the patient's tendency to develop a relationship of great dependence upon her. In the second hour the patient told how for 8 years he had warded off attacks of asthma by rising late in the morning, leisurely sitting on the toilet where he drank coffee slowly for an hour or so. If anything interrupted or rushed him, he was certain to get an attack. Later in the same interview, however, a topic came up which was related to his anxieties about sexual impulses. He said that the only kind of girl he liked was an older girl who would take full responsibility for any sexual relations entered into, and would not nag him afterwards for attentions! Immediately after this statement he said, "I hope you will be critical of me and tell me just what to do so I don't do the wrong thing." The therapist said, "In other words, you want me to be like the older girls who know what they are about, who see things clearly, who

face the facts and relieve you of any responsibility for their acts."
The patient laughed and said, "That's exactly what I want. You
see, I'm being dependent on you right away, and I want you to be
frank because I can't stand people to go round about things. I want
to know where I stand with people."

The first asthma attack reported after the beginning of the treatment was attributed by the patient to the fact that he had to take
his coffee rapidly and hurry around after he got up. He said he was
watching himself to see whether he would have an attack and "sure
enough he did." Later on in the same hour, however, he told of his
extreme embarrassment with girls from the time he was 6. Eventually he related this to the embarrassed, uneasy feeling that he had
when his uncle teased him about being snuggled by his obese aunt.

When the therapist asked how his aunt accepted his efforts to be
more independent, he said she would not stand for it. Any attempt
on his part to "talk up" met with a whipping. She thwarted any
adventurousness on his part. She "stuffed him with food."

At this point the therapist told him it seemed that his asthma came
when his dependence was threatened, whether in relation to women
or when he was left alone on a job (as will be reported later). She
pointed out that his asthma began at 14, after he had reduced his
weight and was therefore more attractive in appearance, and she
wondered whether the asthma had something to do with impulses in
him that might threaten a pleasant relationship with a mother-person.
After this interpretation the patient recalled that when he was 9 he
realized that his stepmother was very pretty and nineteen years
younger than his father. She encouraged him to fondle her breast
and rest his head on her bosom. She would draw him closer and
closer until the father, in a rage, would order him off to bed. From
the age of 9 to 14, when he was so obese, this seductive situation
continued, associated on the patient's part with intense conscious
sexual desire for the stepmother. He did not think of her as a
mother, and longed to get into bed with her, but feared that she would
tell his father. In these years there was extreme fear of his father
and of dogs. At 14, when he reduced drastically and felt more attractive physically, all the sexual play with his stepmother ceased and
he had no further sexual feeling for her. It was at this time his
asthma began to be disturbing.

Two months after treatment started the patient took a job in a
department store under his brother's supervision. An asthma attack occurred the first night when everyone went off and left him at
midnight and he was alone at his work. To him this job signified an
extension of the home with dependence on the brother, although it

did furnish an independent income. Attacks continued at night for some weeks when he was left alone.

The patient continued to feel elated about his treatment hours. He said nothing could make him leave them. The therapist at this point warned him about the possibility of later resistance. He protested, however, that he had told the therapist more than any other patient in so short a time. This the therapist interpreted as a wish to be the most cooperative of her patients and to confess all to her.

The patient failed to tell the therapist that he had had a mild asthmatic attack on the way to the office before the ninth hour, but he recalled this in the tenth hour. In discussing this attack, the analyst finally elicited from him the following confession: "Well, last Wednesday before I came here, when I felt the attack coming on, I thought of sexual feelings in connection with the red-head and the Jewish girl and my aunt and my stepmother and practically every woman I know, and nothing clicked." The therapist pointed out that it was significant he should have thought of sexuality in relation to practically every woman except herself. This, however, he energetically denied. He emphasized, instead, his great dependence upon her.

At this point, three months after treatment began, the patient was very dependently attached to the therapist, was avoiding all girls and having almost no asthma. A month later he came in furious about having to meet his Draft Board. He was certain the men on the board would have no patience with the emotional basis for asthma. He felt all these men were as "dumb" as his father, and he would die of asthma if he had to leave the therapist now. His asthma became worse. The analyst suggested that possibly he was angry at her for not intervening on his behalf with the Draft Board. In discussion of his intense anger, which soon appeared, he confessed that he had wished the therapist would "risk her reputation" in order to "save his life." The therapist's frustration of his dependence and her acceptance of his rage constituted one of the two major steps in his treatment. As a result, the patient felt more independent.

It was after this hour that the patient for the first time was able to ask a "respectable girl" for intercourse, accept her refusal, and ask for another date. Never before had he approached a girl who he thought might refuse him. He now began steadily dating an attractive girl.

Soon he mentioned that his girl had a former beau whom she sometimes thought about. He did not want to be a "second fiddle," and he asked what the therapist thought about the girl. The therapist suspected that by means of this question the patient hoped to find out something about her own sexual experiences and her attitude toward them. This suggestion apparently took him by surprise, but he immediately recognized its validity. "By George," he said, "that's right. I wouldn't have thought of it." For several hours after this the patient was preoccupied with the faithlessness of women, as illustrated by stories of married women with whom he had had intercourse. To this the therapist commented, "I doubt if you have as much conflict about women who are unfaithful as about women who are faithful to their husbands." He felt this to be true, but added that he was not so easily downed by a rival as formerly. He went on for two or three hours to say that he could not be in conflict with the therapist because she was too old for him. When a friendly opportunity arose, the therapist wondered if it were that he feared he was too young for her. He was evasive; blocked and expressed amazement that he could not think of a thing to say for ten minutes. He said "only rarely" did he feel so uneasy talking to men or women as now. The therapist asked if it were necessary to bring the "men" in now, and with great heat he said, "Why not?" He was breathing heavily. The therapist mentioned some possible concern in relation to her husband. The patient appeared startled, but immediately became more relaxed and said he had wondered about him.

About this time the therapist went on vacation. The second hour after she returned may be regarded as the turning point in the treatment. On this day the patient came to the office breathing heavily, perspiring somewhat, and obviously having a rather severe asthma attack. He had had several attacks during the week, always at night, and had taken ephedrin. Several mornings he felt his breathing a little impaired but no real attacks developed. He wanted to explain all this on the basis of his having had to rush around in the morning, especially that morning.

The therapist listened to him for a few minutes. He said he had not been out with the girl that week, and he thought that could not be a factor. He mentioned nothing about the therapist. She commented that she thought his feelings toward her had been relatively flat since she returned from her vacation, and he said that this was true. She wondered if there were some feelings about her having gone away that were not just clear. He said that he was sure this was not so, that he could not even remember one thing they talked about before she went away. Thinking that he was probably very angry at her, the therapist merely said that she was thinking of the fact he had mentioned that when he found that the girl with whom he had been falling in love was still somewhat attached to a former beau, he had dropped her immediately. At this point the patient said, "Oh, yes, and probably that brings up your husband now. I was talking about your husband just before you went away, and I felt he was too much of a rival in the picture. I felt that was one of the big factors inhibiting me in my feelings toward you."

At this point the asthma completely stopped. The patient breathed quietly, his face was no longer flushed, and he began to laugh. He said, "I can't believe it. I have never had an attack stop so suddenly even with ephedrin." He said, "You mentioned that thing, and I thought of your husband and what we were talking about before you went away, and in 30 seconds the attack had stopped." The patient was amazed. He said that at last he was convinced the therapist was involved in his attacks, and when he had the asthma attacks in the morning or at night it must be that there were some thoughts of her he was not conscious of.

Hours followed full of resentment toward the therapist, with fears of humiliation and speculations about her husband. He would like to marry her in order to have her take care of his attacks; there could be a sexual life also, but he would not be in love with her. His bitterness and anger were mentioned briefly to him. At this time he wanted to call the therapist by her first name and to have her call him Dr. X. The feeling that the therapist would not be willing to concede him all his rightful prerogatives and respect as Dr. X. was pointed out, and after this competition was worked through the patient and the therapist were both "Doctor."

After this he realized that he had begun to want to do things for women and to go out with them without any special interest in sexual intercourse. He finally came to tell the therapist that he could no longer be in love with her. There was much angry depreciation of her, which she accepted without comment. After this he said he no longer felt the anxiety he used to feel when indicating to some girl he did not love her, whereas previously he had always feared this would throw the girl into a rage. From now on he felt a great sense of freedom, talked and acted with increased masculinity and independence, and was no longer hostile but friendly.

The patient has now been in the Army for almost two years. He came to see the therapist two weeks ago. He looked fine. He had one slight attack of asthma in a difficult situation a year and a half before. He is engaged and expects to marry soon.

It will be noted that this case differs from Hansen's in that this patient's dependence made necessary a more continuous contact between patient and therapist. As a result of this the therapist had to do more interpretation than Hansen. The interpretations were directed primarily toward relieving the disturbance arising out of the frustrated dependence and out of the sexual wishes that the patient developed toward the therapist.

This case, however, illustrates, as Hansen's case did, the great relief that the patient received from confessing disturbing impulses; in fact the therapist's interpretations in the main served the purpose of anticipating and thereby facilitating the patient's confession.

REPORT OF A CASE OF ACUTE LARYNGITIS OCCURRING AS A CONVERSION SYMPTOM DURING ANALYSIS *

By GEORGE W. WILSON, M.D.

I was prompted to report this case after reading an article by Karl A. Menninger [1] in which he discusses certain conversion symptoms referred to the respiratory tract occurring during an analysis. In his report Menninger demonstrates how much may be learned regarding the psychogenic background of his case which simulated in all respects that of a common cold. The case I want to report is one of an acute laryngitis which appeared a few hours after an analytic session and almost completely disappeared during the following one. A medical examination revealed a simple congestion of the vocal cords. The patient had had several similar attacks before coming to analysis.

The patient is a 35-year-old single man who came to analysis with the predominating symptom of constipation. He is a fairly successful salesman who had been considerably more successful up until about five years ago, at which time his overt aggressiveness in relation to other members of his firm caused him to be discharged, but after a few months re-employed at considerable reduction in salary. He is the third of four children, having two older brothers and one younger sister. His father died when he was 12. He has been the main support of his mother and has continued to live with her since his father's death.

At the time of this occurrence he was in the third month of analysis and was in a period of severe resistance against becoming conscious of his hostilities, particularly toward his father and two older brothers. During the analytic session, just preceding the onset of the laryngitis, the patient began the hour by telling me that he had no desire for breakfast and had not eaten because his mother was not at home to prepare the meal for him. Also he found it impossible to eat lunch. Then he tells me of a conference he had to attend which

* The Psychoanalytic Review XXI: 408-414, 1934.
[1] Menninger, Karl A. Some unconscious psychological factors associated with the common cold. Psychoanal. Rev., 1934, 21, No. 2.

involved all the members of his firm, and that these conferences irritated him a great deal because the speakers—particularly his immediate superior—talked for hours without saying anything. Then he speaks of his father's death and refers to a question which I had asked him a few days previously regarding his emotional reactions at the time, and says, "Apparently you thought I should become melodramatic about an incident which happened more than 20 years ago. I do not have a guilty conscience about anything, and therefore have no reason to feel emotional. I could understand having a guilty conscience if I went to bed with the wife or daughter of a friend, but that I have not done."

He goes on to tell me that his father's death was caused by pneumonia, and that he was present when his father died. He remembers being very upset and having fainted three times during the funeral. He then recalls his father's pride in hearing him sing; that, as a boy, he sang very well and often entertained his father in this way.

After some superficial associations about riding horseback, he remembers that when he was 4 his brothers were playing baseball and set him down on the curb. Later they missed him, looked all day, and prepared to drag the river. At dusk they found him on the edge of the town with an old man who was "breaking" horses. He thinks they were all stallions. He says he watched this man all day. The thing that impressed him most was the ease with which he controlled the horses without ever touching them with the whip—that the trainer only "cracked" it to obtain obedience. This brings up another memory, at the age of 7, when he received a severe whipping from his father because he whipped a horse to make him run faster, at the suggestion of an older cousin with whom he was riding. I asked him his reaction to the punishment and he said he could not remember. If he had resented it, he probably would have remembered, and that it was not his desire to whip the horse anyway, that it was entirely prompted by his cousin's handing him the whip. At the end of the hour I asked him if he thought it was possible that he identified the horses with some person or persons.

He immediately associates again to his father's death and says, "I have discussed him more in the last few days than I have for 17 years." I asked him why he mentions the figure 17 and he replied that this was the year he tried to get into the army and the marine corps. Also, at the age of 7, he was accidentally shot in the mouth by an older boy, that one tooth was broken, and the nerve killed in another. This bothered him a great deal again when he was 13, and it became necessary to remove a piece of bone in his jaw, and occasionally he still has trouble which requires surgical attention.

The next hour he begins by telling me of his efforts to secure for a relative two pictures which had appeared in a newspaper. This relative wanted very much to possess them. After considerable effort he succeeded and secreted the pictures in his desk. When this relative asked him to send them immediately, seeming not to recognize the great difficulty with which they were obtained, he became very upset. He now decides that he will never send him the pictures at all, that he will return them to the newspaper or throw them away. At this point I asked him if these two pictures did not refer to something in the analytic situation which he did not want to recall or to give to me. His immediate reply was, "I know what you mean. You are referring to the two episodes about the horses. If you want me to talk about it, I will. What impressed me was the complete mastery this man had without using a whip. *I know I do not identify myself with the horse, and you with the ringmaster, and I am not protesting too much, either.* I told you the story of the pictures only because it irritated me, but you reach way down to Oshkosh and tie it up with something which happened at the age of four. Incidentally, why does one find so much profanity among horsemen? You certainly don't find it among automobile mechanics. It must be a safety valve —an outlet." At the end of the hour I said, "Possibly profanity serves the purpose of vocally expressing hostilities which could not be successfully handled, and might also aid in relieving inferiority feelings through depreciation of others."

As I mentioned earlier, the acute laryngitis with complete loss of the use of his vocal cords occurred about two hours after this session. It is of some interest to note that on this particular evening he had planned to go to the theater to see Dennis King in "Richard of Bordeaux," and to escort a woman who is an obvious mother-substitute, who constantly mothers and entertains him to the fullest extent. She had recently returned from Canada, and as soon as he met her he had made the remark that he "supposed he would have to listen to an evening devoted exclusively to her Canada experiences." His throat condition became so severe during the evening that he found it no longer possible to converse with her, and went home immediately after the play.

During the hour immediately following the attack he tells how he enjoyed the show; that Dennis King put on an exceptional performance; that just previous to the show he had been in the office of George Kaiser (his immediate superior), who irritated him very much; and that during the night he dreamed something about Frank Kaiser (an old friend). In the dream there was some activity, turmoil, and then something was going to be done, but further than that he cannot remember. He tells me that in the play he felt sympathy with the king when they threw him into jail, but that it was inevitable; that the king was succeeded by his cousin, who in turn was succeeded by his son. At this point I asked him if it were not true that he had succeeded his father in the family situation, to which he replied, "I followed him; I did not succeed him. My father has entered into my conversation more the last few days than in the last 15 years. Had he lived, he would have had more influence on me probably. I must confess I know all the profane words that are to be known."

In attempting a reconstruction of this conversion episode (and I shall only interest myself in the conversion symptom), I think it well to do so with reference to the patient's outstanding more or less constant symptom, viz., constipation, the dynamic background of which became clear in many details. Both unconscious factors, which have been described by Alexander [2] in cases of constipation, played an important role here. Alexander describes in such cases a typical attitude toward the environment: "I do not take or receive and therefore I need not give." Abraham [3] mentions the same attitude: anal retention in connection with oral deprivation, as frequent in cases of neurotic parsimony. As the dynamic background producing this surface attitude, Alexander distinguishes two unconscious factors: (a) retention because of fear of loss; (b) retention because of fear of doing damage. The latter unconscious attitude (b) we see quite clearly in this case, i.e., deeply repressed hostility for the father and brothers. Despite the fact that he recalls his sorrow at the time of his father's death, he does so entirely without emotion. The screen memories which he brings up during the analytic hour just preceding his attack are related to the earlier feelings of envy toward the brothers. He remembers his brothers playing baseball and leaving him at the curb. It is not difficult to reconstruct the psychological situation of the little boy watching the game of the older brothers. His envy causes him to walk away and he finds great satisfaction in watching the horse trainer, fantasying himself in the superior posi-

---

2 Alexander's formulation for the constipation type is as follows:

Typical conscious attitude toward environment schematically verbalized.	"I do not take or receive, and therefore I do not need to give."
The deeper dynamic background of the symptoms.	1. The rejection of the obligation to give on account of fear of loss (castration fear) and
	2. the inhibition of anal sadistic impulses (to give spitefully in a destructive way) are the chronic inhibitory stimuli leading to constipation.
The content of the psychic stimuli which cause the dysfunction.	Retaining because of 1. fear of loss; 2. fear of doing damage.

3 Abraham, Karl. The anal character. In *Selected papers*. London: Hogarth Press and The Institute for Psychoanalysis.

tion of the trainer dominating the horses. The profanity of the trainer, to which he makes reference in the same connection, expresses his mental attitude: the wish to attack his older brothers with profane words and cursing. These hostile feelings against the brothers are linked up with similar emotions toward the father, as shown in his reference to his father's death. Also his reaction to the play in which the king is put in prison shows clearly the same emotions toward the father, which the analysis has stirred up. The transference attitude runs parallel with these memories. His losing his voice is obviously a reaction to the wish to attack the analyst with profane words—the same wish which he had as a child toward the older male competitors in the family and which he repressed, probably out of fear of retaliation.

Parallel with his laryngitis he developed a severe attack of constipation. I am inclined to assume that both forms of constipation (inability to give out words and feces) are determined by the same unconscious mechanism: rejection and overcompensation for aggressiveness expressed by the aggressive use of the excrements (soiling) and vocal expression ("filthy words").

Meeting in the evening his friend, who in many respects plays the role of a mother-substitute, probably aggravated his conflict situation. He could not use his voice in her presence (a form of anal self-castration), the same voice which he wanted to use aggressively against the father-substitute, the analyst.

Less clearly, but still quite obviously, the other unconscious factor mentioned, under (a), can be seen as active in producing the symptom. Voice and words have also a positive evaluation for him. He sang to his father and gave him pleasure with his voice. The hostile component of his father-relation leads to the spiteful reaction: "I do not need to give positive value (sing to father); I want to use my voice to produce filthy words (give spitefully)." It is quite obvious that for the unconscious the attitude toward the excrements and words have the same double meaning for him: gift, singing, and soiling (attacking with profane words). His symptom has the double meaning: (a) refusal to give words, and (b) inhibition of the use of profane words.

The previous analysis of the patient suggests that the same two unconscious factors are active in the causation of his constipation. It is quite impressive that the whole attack was introduced by his refusal to eat because his mother did not prepare breakfast for him. This self-imposed deprivation produced in him a mental condition in which he could freely assume the spiteful attitude: "I do not receive (food) and therefore I am entitled to refuse to give (words and

STUDIES IN PSYCHOSOMATIC MEDICINE

feces, as gift) but use them for attack." These anal sadistic tendencies arouse fear and lead to constipation in both levels, i.e., in the throat (loss of voice) and in the rectum (fecal retention).

This same characteristic reaction is particularly well demonstrated in the transference situation. For example, in the hour preceding the vocal disturbance he speaks about his constipation and asks me if I do not think he should take a large dose of oil or at least an enema. Possibly if he drank buttermilk that would relieve him to some extent. He believes that psychoanalysis cannot entirely dispense with medicines. When I ask him why he prefers to use palliative measures rather than to analyze his symptoms, he replies that he cannot analyze them for the reason I do not show him how. I know all the answers but I will not give them to him. I could point out the way for him and then if his symptoms *are psychic* they would automatically disappear. We see that he explains his failure to give (associations, valuable material) because I do not give to him (medicines and explanations which to him equal mental food).

This observation also contributes to the frequent anal cathexis of words and speech, and has been described by various authors in cases of stuttering,[4] and by Ferenczi in the psychogenesis of tic.[5]

Regarding the displacement of the anal aggressive tendency to speech, i.e., producing profane expressions, the following observations appear instructive. The patient throughout his analysis revealed a peculiar sensitiveness to "acoustic attacks" upon himself. He became irritated at having to listen to the speeches of others, to the radio, and he spoke irritatedly about the long and futile speeches of his business associates. He anticipated with obvious hostility the necessity of listening to a long story about his friend's Canadian trip. Previously in the analysis he had complained of the annoyance in having to listen to his mother's, sister's, and brothers' troubles. In the transference situation he becomes irritated when I speak for any length of time, taking the attitude that my interpretations are critical and often will interrupt to argue their fallacy. When he does not do this he impatiently awaits conclusion of my statements to begin his refutation. The screen memory relative to his admiration at observing and listening to the horse trainer is also of interest in this connection.

---

[4] See especially Coriat, Isador H. Stammering: a psychoanalytic interpretation. *Monograph No. 47* by the Nervous & Mental Disease Publishing Co., 1928. In this paper Coriat observes a relation between stammering and constipation, both expressing "stoppages" but involving different ends of the intestinal canal. See also Ferenczi, Sándor. *Further contributions to the theory and technique of psychoanalysis,* Ch. 28, pp. 250-251.

[5] Ferenczi, Sándor. Psychoanalytic observations on tic in his *Further contributions to the theory and technique of psychoanalysis.* London: Hogarth Press and The Institute for Psychoanalysis, 1926.

We see that he is sensitive to and rejects, assuming the passive role in listening to others or in being told things by others, that he would prefer to be the one who attacks others vocally (with words and profanities). This sadistic reaction to the passive attitude of listener is inhibited, probably through guilt and fear, and leads to his laryngitis.

The whole conflict, rejection of the role of the passive listener, is superimposed upon the rejection of passive homosexual tendencies which were stirred up in his unconscious. When he associated to the memory of the horse trainer dominating the horses, he suddenly exclaims, "I am not the horse and you the trainer." To listen, to be told things, to be attacked vocally, has the obvious meaning for him of assuming the suffering role of the woman; to attack with words means to be masculine like the trainer. This vocal attack, however, on account of the anal sadistic features, he has to repress and in consequence he develops his aphonia.

A STUDY OF STRUCTURAL AND INSTINCTUAL CONFLICTS IN CASES OF HAY FEVER *

By George W. Wilson, M.D.

It is reasonable to believe that man's assumption of the upright position was the beginning of greater utilization of the visual and auditory sensibilities and a lessening of olfactory perceptions. This produced a corresponding increase in the visual and auditory acuity, accompanied by a diminution in olfactory sensitivity. It is a well-established fact that primitive vertebrates rely primarily upon olfactory perception for maintenance of existence and as the stimulus for reproduction.[1] Danger, food, and sexual stimulation are all perceived by the olfactory centers before perception takes place in either the optical or auditory spheres. Grinker (6) in a personal communication states: "The importance of primitive olfaction as the first receptor of distant stimuli is further enhanced because it gave rise to the evolutionary trend from which the neocortex arose. Danger perceived from considerable distance permitted a slower and more adaptive response, which characterizes cortical activity, than stereotyped immediate reflex activity of lower levels of the neuraxis. As olfaction became less important in the primates and least in man, the large olfactory areas of the cortex, the massive subcortical system of connections and the olfactory portion of the diencephalon became more concerned with central regulation and adaptation of visceromotor activity and the visceral expressions of certain emotions. Chief among these is the regulation of flight or fight reactions, or the expressions of fear or anger. The preparedness of activity in these spheres constituting a tonic activity of old olfactory diencephalic centers find expression in the universal state of anxiety,

* *Psychosomatic Medicine* III : 51-65, 1941.
[1] In a footnote in his book *Civilization and its discontents,* Freud writes: "The diminution in importance of olfactory stimuli seems itself, however, to be a consequence of man's erecting himself from the earth, of his adoption of an upright gait, which made his genitals, that before had been covered, visible and in need of protection and so evoked feelings of shame. Man's erect posture, therefore, would represent the beginning of the momentous process of cultural evolution. The chain of development would run from this onward, through the diminution in the importance of olfactory stimuli and the isolation of women at their periods to a time when visual stimuli became paramount, the genitals became visible, further till sexual excitation became constant and the family was founded, and so to the threshold of human culture."

normally conditioned into appropriate and preservative fear of dangers in reality, morbidly internalized in neuroses. Thus, centers concerned with responses to dangers perceived through the sense of smell became concerned with preparedness and emergency responses to dangers perceived by all the sense organs and from inner instinctual drives provocative of dangerous retaliatory reactions from the environment."

Observations on children demonstrate a greater sensitivity to odors than that possessed by adults. It is also observed that children are less or not at all disturbed by what to the adult constitutes a disagreeable or disgusting odor. The offensive reaction to odors *must* be a conditioned and not an instinctive one. Young children as well as animals will often eat their own vomitus and smear their feces. This condition also occurs frequently in states of regressive psychosis. Olfactory hallucinations are very common, particularly in paranoid states. The offensive reaction to odors takes place during the child's early development and *must* be a product of the environment and an identification with the attitude of the parents toward odors.[2] Exactly this attitude of parental figures toward dirt, filth, offensive or disgusting smells, together with similar attitudes toward other biological functions, may well have a far-reaching influence upon the child's psychological development.

The present report represents a psychoanalytic study of seven cases of hay fever (five female and two male patients). The material presented by these patients during psychoanalysis led me to the assumption "that the psychological component of the hay fever symptom is a result of unsuccessful olfactory repression. Probably the first and most important factor in determining this unsatisfactory repression is that of unsatisfied, thwarted, and inhibited sexual curiosity." The failure or refusal of parental figures to enlighten and instruct the child who is attempting to satisfy and master his sexual curiosity leads to a displacement and an increase in preoccupation with other bodily functions—particularly elimination. This function is intimately associated with odors; breath, perspiration, urine, and feces. When parents and other persons in authority place a strict taboo upon the sexual curiosity, while at the same time they encourage and even seduce the child into preoccupation with the excretory functions, this

---

2 In *Civilization and its discontents,* Freud continues: "Excreta arouse no aversion in children; they seem precious to them, as being parts of their own bodies which have been detached from them. The training of children is very energetic in this particular; its object is to expedite the development that lies ahead of them, according to which the excreta are to become worthless, disgusting, horrible, and despicable to them. Such a reversal of values would be almost impossible to bring about, were it not that these substances expelled from the body are destined by their strong odors to share the fate that overtook the olfactory stimuli after man had erected himself from the ground."

displacement readily, and probably with varying degrees of intensity, inevitably occurs.[3]

All of my patients remembered being exposed, during childhood, to many experiences of seductive behavior by one or both parents, often under the guise of interest in their excretory functions. For example: The two boys were given inadequate and even false sexual information; one was given enemas by his mother up to the age of 5 and the other two up to the age of 12. Of the girls studied, all five were often attended by their fathers before and after performance of the excretory functions up to—and in one case after—puberty. None of these girls was given adequate or honest sexual information. The mothers were all sexually inhibited women who had themselves been reared and brought up according to strict, mid-Victorian patterns including a strict taboo of anything sexual. The fathers of all the patients studied maintained complete aloofness to their children's curiosity along sexual lines. It is not my intention to infer that children reared in such an environment are predestined to have hay fever. The parent-child relationship that I have indicated is fairly common, both for children who develop other types of neuroses as well as for children who make fairly satisfactory psychological adjustments. It is rather my intention to demonstrate that these patients were reared in an atmosphere that was conducive to the repression of sexual curiosity, and at the same time encouraged in the indulgence of olfactory perception.

Krafft-Ebing (8) in *Psychopathia Sexualis* states: "In beasts the influence of olfactory perception on the sexual sense is unmistakable. Extirpation of the olfactory nerve in puppies renders the male unable to recognize the female." Mantegazza removed the eyes of rabbits and found that this deficit did not in any way interfere with procreation. Some writers claim that the habit of kissing originates in the the sense of smell rather than that of taste. This would explain the ritual of nose rubbing as a form of greeting in primitive cultures. Fliess demonstrated the so-called genital spots in the noses of women, which when anesthetized with cocaine controlled painful menstruation. Brill (2), in a most interesting article, "The Sense of Smell in the Neuroses and Psychoses," discusses the relation between preoccupation with pleasant and unpleasant odors in the neuroses and psychoses and agrees with Daly (3) who claims: "The hypersexual attractive smell given off by the female in heat must have been one of man's

---

[3] This preoccupation with organic functioning by one or more parental figures during the child's developmental processes may have a far-reaching influence in determining later reaction patterns, particularly with regard to the individual's attitudes toward his or her own body and doubtless influences or may determine the choice of neurotic symptom or even the site of involvement in organ neuroses.

greatest temptations to violate the incest taboo." Daly, however, is of the opinion that the sex-attractive odor is lost to mankind. My own experience agrees with that of Brill when he states, "I am convinced that although very deeply repressed it is still quite active and occasionally comes to the surface." Dunbar (4), in her paper, "Psychoanalytic Notes Relating to Syndromes of Asthma and Hay Fever," says she observed that her asthma and hay fever cases were much preoccupied with their sense of smell.

Magnus Hirschfeld, (7) in his book, *Sexual Pathology,* makes an exhaustive—but from a psychological viewpoint quite superficial —study of perversions and writes : "The eye is especially the medium of human love. Possibly because through its use in the erotic realm, the involuntary seeking and pursuing of sexual stimuli, it has become for us the chief receptive station for beauty. With other creatures, other senses take this leading position, and always, with every animal, his most delicate organ is also erotically the most sensitive perceptive organ. . . . In the animal world, attraction through scent plays a large role, and elsewhere the sense of smell is highly developed. A great many animals have glandular organs whose secretion is solely for the purpose of attracting the male. The male will follow the scent of this perfume . . . . for unbelievable distances; . . . . Many animals become absolutely intoxicated through smelling so that finally . . . there is scarcely time for the sexual act. . . . As regards the sense of smell, I could cite a number of cases in which this sense dominated over the others. . . . Many people say that any and every perceptible body odor emitted by a person whom they love is unpleasant to them. . . . It is evident that even unsympathetic impressions, in the case of strong love, can awaken feelings of desire which, to be sure, usually have a masochistic basis. Thus I know of a case in which a girl was violently in love with an athlete who suffered from a foul-smelling ozena. In the beginning this obnoxious odor was exceedingly painful to her, but her passion was so strong that not only did she become accustomed to it, but even missed and sought for it. In another case the pungent reek of a cavalryman's sweating feet caused a strong revulsion in a lady of high standing, and later a feeling of the strongest desire. . . . From the observations of Schiff, Fliess and others it may be concluded that there are certain sexual points in the erectile tissues of the nose which are in correlation with the proceedings of the sexual sphere. From this arises the probability that there are erogenous zones in the nasal mucous membrane such as we have long known to exist in the sensory sphere of the skin."

In a further discussion of *head fetishism,* Hirschfeld quotes from the material of a case of hair fetishism as follows: "If he buried his face in the hair which attracted him, an ejaculation often resulted immediately."

In another case of hair fetishism he says: "S. himself describes the phenomenon of his aberration: 'After I have cut the lock, I go home and kiss the charming hair again and again, I press it to my nose and cheeks, and breathe in the precious fragrance of it.' "

Freud (5) in his paper "A Case of Obsessional Neurosis" states: "By his own account, when a child, he recognized every one by their smell, like a dog, and even when he was grown up he was more susceptible to sensations of smell than other people . . . and I have come to recognize that a tendency toward osphresiolagnia which has become extinct since childhood may play a part in the genesis of neuroses." In a footnote, Freud refers particularly to certain forms of fetishism as a result of olfactory repression. In "Three Contributions to the Theory of Sex," Freud states: "Psychoanalysis has filled up the gaps in understanding of fetishism by showing that the selection of the fetish depends upon a coprophilic smell-desire which has been lost by repression. Feet and hair are strong smelling objects which are raised to a fetish after the renouncing of the now unpleasant sensation of smell." Freud then goes on to explain the further overdetermination of the feet and hair as displacements above and below for the absence of the penis in women. Abraham (1), in a discussion of a case of foot and corset fetishism, says: "In the present case of fetishism I found the patient's pleasure in 'disgusting' body odors had been unusually strong originally." Abraham's patient had passed through a stage of what would correspond to smell fetishism and a moderation took place that led to repression of the olfactory sensitivity with a substitution of interest and pleasure in looking, i.e., the interest in odors had been repressed and visual curiosity substituted with displacement to another part of the body that gave off an odor.

In other words, Freud and Abraham came to the conclusion that the repression of eroticized olfactory sensation resulted in displacement to the visual field, but with a secondary displacement from the genitals to the feet or to the hair. Freud called this phenomenon "partial repression and displacement."

A study of the material collected during psychoanalysis of seven cases convinced me that the psychological component in hay fever is based upon a displacement of sexual curiosity from the visual to the olfactory sphere. This would explain the preoccupation with an anal interest in organs capable of secreting odorous substances and symbols for organs that may represent anal (olfactory) substitutes for the genitals. Displacement of interest from the genitals to other organs may also explain in many cases a similar overevaluation of a nongenital organ as observed in fetishism.

Noting this strong tendency toward anal (olfactory) displacement led me to make definite inquiries regarding sensitivity to odors in each of my patients. (On several occasions patients had informed me that their olfactory sensitivity was particularly acute during states of emotional tension, and that certain odors precipitated hay fever attacks, but the relatively extreme acuity of olfactory perception only came to light when I made specific inquiries.)

Before presenting case material to demonstrate my thesis, I should like to refer briefly to certain patterns of similarity in all of the hay fever patients studied.

CASE 1. This patient was a 26-year-old unmarried male who suffered from mild seasonal hay fever. He presented no other organic symptoms. He had had severe constipation as a child. This patient came for treatment because of a severe obsessional neurosis, with the predominant symptoms of compulsive thinking.

Sexual Information: He was given inadequate and false information by the mother; no information by the father.

Seduction Experience: Enemas were given him by the mother up to the age of 12 and on at least one occasion he gave an enema to his mother. He slept in the same bed with his mother until the age of 14.

Sensitivity to Odors: This man was extremely sensitive to unpleasant odors, particularly the decaying of nitrogenous material. During analysis he occasionally hallucinated unpleasant odors in the room.

Tendency toward Displacement of Interest: Women with red hair had always been extremely attractive to this man, (9).

CASE 2. This patient was a 23-year-old unmarried male who suffered from severe attacks of seasonal asthma and hay fever. He presented no other organic difficulties, but sought treatment for relief of his upper respiratory symptoms.

Sexual Information: He was never given any sexual information or instruction by either parent. The mother and father were divorced when the patient was 18 months of age. When the patient was 3 years of age he was kidnapped and cared for by the father for a period of about 2 months. The patient's mother remarried when the patient was about 5; the stepfather never discussed anything of a personal or sexual nature with him. The patient's grandmother, who lived in the home, gave the patient false, threatening information. (She threatened him with drowning to discourage masturbation and bed wetting.)

Seduction Experience: At the age of 5 he was seduced into sexual play with a girl of 12. This play continued over a period of several months, but was never confessed to anyone. At the age of 6 he was introduced to mutual masturbation by a boy of 12. Both the mother and the grandmother displayed an exaggerated interest in the patient's excretory functions, and gave him cathartics and frequent enemas.

Mother's Pregnancy: A sister was born when he was 8 years of age. The sister's impending birth was never discussed with the patient, and his hay fever developed during the mother's pregnancy.

Sensitivity to Odors: He was extremely fond of the smell of caves and underground passages. He spent his vacation periods exploring underground places.

Tendency toward Displacement of Interest: This boy displayed an early obsession to learn to play wind instruments, and later expanded this to an intense need to master all of the common musical instruments.

CASE 3. This patient was a 26-year-old unmarried female who suffered from severe seasonal hay fever for which she sought treatment.

Sexual Information: She was given inadequate and false information by both her mother and a grandmother who lived in the home. The mother probably lied to the patient regarding her own sexual life, claiming that her only reason for marrying was because she wanted children. The mother's attitude toward having children after the patient's birth was proof to the patient that this assertion was untrue. Both parents and the family physician exhibited an exaggerated interest in her eliminative functions.

Seduction Experience: At the age of 5, on the promise of being given a present, she was seduced into introducing her hand into the pocket of a strange man. She felt the man's erect penis and ran home frightened, but did not report this experience for several hours. At the age of 7 she had a similar experience with the janitor in the building where she lived. This experience she never confessed prior to her analysis.

Mother's Pregnancy: Although material reported during the analysis would indicate that the mother had at least one abortion after the patient's birth, this has been consistently denied and cannot be proven.

Sensitivity to Odors: This girl claimed that she had always been extremely sensitive to odors of both an unpleasant and pleasant nature.

As a young child she classified her parents and grandparents according to their "smell." She complained that her mother was very careless about laundering her lingerie and about personal cleanliness. Although she was extremely fond of her grandfather, she claimed that his breath was offensive to her. As an adult, she claimed that she could detect at a distance the odor of a menstruating woman. She also said she could detect a change in odor of a man when he became sexually excited.

Tendency toward Displacement of Interest: This patient expressed what amounted to a fixed delusion that her feet were exceptionally large, and that this marred her otherwise beautiful figure. She also exhibited considerable interest in her own hair, and once remarked that although she felt nervous and tense, she would feel relaxed as soon as she had been to the hairdresser. She was also extremely attracted to red-headed men.

Case 3 will be referred to in considerable detail later in this presentation.

CASE 4. This patient was a 35-year-old single female. She suffered from severe seasonal hay fever, nonseasonal asthma, and spastic colitis. She sought treatment because of the colitis. The hay fever and asthma were not admitted until after her analysis began.

Sexual Information: This patient received inadequate sexual information, probably without any falsification, from the mother. An attitude of complete aloofness was maintained by the father. The mother, grandmother, and several doctors, who were consulted because of frequent illnesses during the patient's childhood, expressed an exaggerated interest in her eliminative functions. She was given cathartics and enemas regularly.

Seduction Experience: The father and a maternal uncle were extremely seductive toward the patient when she was a child, and became very inhibited in their behavior when she reached puberty. The patient occupied a berth with her father on a trip to Florida when she was 5 years of age. Upon their arrival in Florida, she became quite interested in a bellboy at the hotel where they stayed. A seductive gesture, for which she was severely punished, was the placing of her hand upon her genitals and then putting her fingers up to the bellboy's nose with the remark: "Smell beautiful perfume." When the patient was 6 she developed some sort of a vaginal infection, and it was recommended that the mother use frequent douches as a treatment. The analysis revealed that the patient utilized this treatment for the purpose of being masturbated by the mother for a long period of time.

This behavior pattern was later repeated as an adult with several doctors.

Mother's Pregnancy: A sister was born when the patient was 4, and the mother had a miscarriage of twin boys when the patient was 7. The patient was not informed about either pregnancy but was told of the miscarriage after it occurred.

Sensitive to Odors: She did not exhibit an extreme sensitivity to odors, but occasionally hallucinated disagreeable and sexually stimulating odors. During adolescence she developed nasal polyps which were surgically removed, and this procedure was repeated many times.

Tendency toward Displacement of Interest: This patient reported a large number of dreams in which shoes and hats were used as genital symbols. She made an extensive study of the history and development of head coverings, became an instructor, and later the head of a large millinery establishment.

CASE 5. Patient F. was a 30-year-old married female. She suffered from severe seasonal hay fever. She sought treatment because of neurasthenia, with the predominant symptom of cardiac palpitation.

Sexual Information: She was given inadequate and false sexual information from the mother, grandmother, and the housekeeper. The patient was overprotected outside the home, but the mother relegated much of her home training to a housekeeper.

Seduction Experience: This housekeeper seduced the patient into mutual masturbation when the patient was 7. At the same time she also initiated mutual masturbation between the patient and her younger brother. The father was overly affectionate when the patient was a child, but extremely inhibited with her as she approached maturity.

Mother's Pregnancy: The patient had 2 younger brothers, one born when she was 5, and another when she was 8 years of age. She was not given any preparation or information relative to either pregnancy.

Sensitivity to Odors: This patient was extremely sensitive to both pleasant and unpleasant odors.

Tendency toward Displacement of Interest: Hairy men were very repulsive to this woman. She experienced a feeling of disgust in relation to people who were careless about bodily cleanliness. She married a man who she knew was extremely careless in this respect, and she obtained a great satisfaction in trying to reform him.

This detailed account of rather striking similarities in parental attitudes toward sexuality, as well as the reaction formations which seemed to parallel each other to a considerable extent in all of my cases, has been presented not because of the belief that all such environments lead to hay fever but because this parallelism may be of some significance in the apparently unsuccessful attempts at repression of olfactory stimulations.

I should like to present a fragment from the analysis of Case 4 of this series, and from this material to demonstrate the major part of a psychological cycle beginning with inhibited or forbidden sexual curiosity that is followed by an unsuccessful attempt at intellectual sublimation through substitution of the object and attempts at displacement from the olfactory to the visual sphere. With the failure of sublimation and substitution in *both* spheres, and the threatened emergence into consciousness of the repressed curiosity which was so intimately connected with feared sexual impulses, an acute rhinitis attack developed during an analytical session. The rhinitis soon subsided and was followed by an attack of bronchial asthma.

CASE HISTORY. Case 4,[4] an attractive, single, 35-year-old successful fashion designer, applied for analysis because of hay fever, asthma, and urticaria. She welcomed the opportunity of being analyzed as a research case because of an intense conflict over homosexual impulses which kept her in a constant state of anxiety. It had been impossible for her to establish any satisfactory heterosexual relationships, even though she had a great desire to have a home and family.

Autumnal hay fever began at the age of 7. The asthma attacks were nonseasonal, but the specific allergens were ragweed, June grass, burweed, marsh elder, sagebrush, timothy, red top, and pyrethrum.

The patient was the only living child of her parents. She had generalized convulsions at the age of 2 years, coincident with her training in bowel and bladder control. She had always suffered from constipation.

The patient described her mother as a very beautiful, intelligent, motherly person who babied her and her father. She believed that the mother was dissatisfied with her marriage, and that she reacted to this dissatisfaction by overcompensatory solicitude toward her family. It was the patient's belief that her mother suffered all of her life from unsatisfied sexual hunger, but this appears to be based upon the patient's wish and the mother's untruthfulness rather than upon fact, because once, when as an adult the patient suggested this belief to her mother, she met with instant denial and an indication that the father was not only potent but had always been quite sexually

---

[4] This is Patient Y of the asthma series. See French, T. M., Alexander, Franz, et al. Psychogenic factors in bronchial asthma. *Psychosom. Med. Monograph No. 2,* 1941.

aggressive. The mother never gave her any direct sex information, and although the subject was frankly taboo in the household, some time previous to the beginning of the patient's puberty the mother gave her a book which explained the sex life of birds and animals. The patient stated that this only served to increase her already present confusion. The mother encouraged the patient to confide in her as long as the confidences were not of a sexual nature. The mother practically demanded that the patient in her childhood give a full and complete account of her experiences when they were separated. During adult life this same pattern of behavior was continued in the form of correspondence, and the patient confessed everything to her mother with the notable exception of her sexual impulses and conflicts.

The patient first described her father as a passive, dependent, unreliable, feminine, unsuccessful business man. Later material proved this description to be untrue. The father was not unsuccessful. However, he had frequent illnesses associated with the respiratory function. As a child the patient was very attached to her father, but about the age of 12 she began to resent any overt manifestations of affection by him and at the same time resented his position as head of the household and her mother's deference to him. She resented his lack of success in life, although he was not unsuccessful, and she began at this time to fantasy rescuing the family through being very successful herself. Her attachment to her father as a child manifested itself in taking a great interest in her father's hobbies. She spent many hours with him in the woods and mountains. Her father was a great nature lover, and he taught the patient a great deal about botany and ornithology. He had wanted her to be a boy, and from the beginning encouraged her attempt to imitate boys in every possible manner.

There is no history of the father's being overly affectionate with the patient in a physical way. There was, however, a definite history of overly affectionate behavior by a maternal uncle, who was quite openly, though probably unconsciously, seductive in his attitude toward her.

The patient as a child was very aggressive and intellectually successful. She made uniformly good grades in school, and obtained a position as a private secretary to a novelist immediately after her graduation from business college. She exhibited considerable talent for drawing and painting before she was 5 years of age, at which time she began to live out in play fantasies of being a fashion designer. However her designs were always those of masculine wearing apparel. She designed every article of clothing worn by her father, and copied designs from advertisements and haberdashery windows. Many hours were spent arranging her father's ties and in designing new patterns. At the same time she was greatly interested in boys' games. She usually dressed in boys' clothes, either in overalls or Boy Scout outfits. She begged to have her hair cut short and, when this was discouraged by the mother, attempted to trim it herself. She played marbles, baseball, and tennis, and competed with boys in all of their games. She learned to shoot when still a very young child, and carried her own rifle on hunting trips with her father.

When she was 5 years of age she was seduced by another girl into exhibiting herself to a boy of about her own age; they exhibited their sex organs and then both urinated. The patient felt extremely guilty over this experience, and always connected it in her fantasies with her acne. The little boy also developed acne at adolescence, and the patient felt that the skin lesions were direct visitations of punishment upon them as a result of their behavior. A little later she discovered that she could see through an opening into the shower room used by the high school football players and she felt equally guilty about this indulgence of her curiosity. It was quite evident that she made a rather frantic attempt to sublimate her sexual curiosity in study and voracious reading. As a very young child she began to read everything she could find, spending entire days alone in her room engrossed in books.

Later, work and a career became the major interest in her life. She did, however, maintain a close relationship with several women, toward whom she felt a particularly strong homosexual attraction. One of her friends reciprocated the homosexual attraction, and after resisting great temptation to live out overt homosexual attraction, they decided to separate themselves as far as possible from each other. This attempt at a homosexual solution was unsatisfactory and proved to be so disturbing to her that it was necessary for her to abandon the association and take flight from the situation of temptation as she did from her home. The homosexual object chosen by the patient was a girl who had been partially successful in replacing her mother in her own family situation and in her father's affections. This father was a dominating figure both in the home and in the business world. There was some evidence that he was sexually promiscuous, and from the beginning of the patient's attachment to his daughter he became sexually attractive to the patient, but this she repressed and denied. When under the influence of alcohol, he often discussed sexual subjects with her and made affectionate gestures toward her. She complained that she could see the outlines of his genitals through his trousers, and that this was both fascinating and disgusting to her. This disturbed her very much and, although she admired his business ability and his aggressive behavior, she made every effort to avoid contact with him, particularly when his daughter was not present. It was this duplication of the original parental situation that made it necessary for the patient to bring about a separation from these mother and father figures.

With most men the patient attempted to play the role of a man among men. She insisted upon paying her own way. She depreciated men and felt superior to them, but feared that attention would be called to her homosexual leanings unless she was seen with them. She enjoyed the company of brilliant men, not only successful ones but those who had original ideas about sculpture, architecture, design, and other artistic productions.

In the autumn of 1938 the patient had been indulging in a very close relationship with a woman who was overtly homosexual with other women, and who was attempting at this time to seduce my patient into an overt homosexual relationship. My patient, however, was "using" this woman to further her own selfish wishes. She accepted presents, mothering, prestige in social and professional relationships without giving anything of value in return. The patient was openly seductive toward this mother-substitute, and after leading this woman to believe that she was about to accede to her sexual demands, proceeded to reject her.

This behavior was repeated several times in spite of interpretations intended to discourage the indulgence of this thinly disguised homosexual behavior. Interpretations of the patient's gratifying transference reactions outside the analysis were transmitted (confessed) by the patient to the mother-substitute from whom she obtained these gratifications and resulted in the woman's making an attempt to discontinue her interference with the patient's analysis.

Terminating this gratification of a mothering type of attention and indulgence outside the analysis produced an intense anger reaction in the patient. She withdrew from all social contacts and became quite obsessed with her work. Her employer had once asked her to make a comprehensive study of vegetable dyes, and at this time the patient began a vigorous and exhaustive study of color reactions and the blending of different dyeing products. Her analytic material was extremely sterile. She reported long, complicated dreams, and either disregarded them or complained that she could not associate to them, but attempted instead to interpret the material schematically. In most of these dreams she identified herself with a little child in a big, confusing world, or with a baby who "sees nothing, hears nothing, knows nothing." At the same time she occasionally reported dream fragments relating to seeing something growing, always with the statement that these dreams were of no importance. To these dreams she associated her fantasies of having a house and garden, of raising vegetables and flowers, and a wish to have a normal sexual life, although admitting that even the thought of heterosexual relations was distasteful to her. She complained that men were careless about exposing the outline of their penis, and expressed the wish that all men should be compelled to wear some sort of "girdle" that would completely hide the presence of the male genital. She said she hated men because they were better paid, for producing less, than women.

In addition to her intensive study of different dyes, she became extremely interested in taking camera pictures of buildings and artistic productions, and said that she was obsessed with the need to be physically active and to satisfy visual impulses. These visual impulses took the form already outlined, together with a compulsion to go to motion pictures every night and then return to her home and read everything she could find relative to dyes. She extended her interest in dyes and colors to mixing paints and observing the different shades of color that could be obtained. Then she began having difficulty with her eyes. Her vision became blurred. She broke her glasses and consulted an eye specialist who recommended a surgical operation for the purpose of opening the tear ducts to permit better drainage into the nostrils. Immediately following this consultation with the eye specialist, she reported the following dream:

> The patient was high up in a building, and someone was operating a tremendous camera just outside her window. From the window she could see an alley that was filthy with dirt, garbage, and water, all mixed together. She knew the odor must be terrible.

In a second dream:

> She was a Teddy bear without a nose.

To the camera the patient associated the analysis and the ophthalmoscope of the eye doctor. She complained of having a severe headache which she attributed to her experience with the eye specialist. She said that experts were no good—*they all wanted her to see too much.* To the tall buildings she associated ambition, although denying that she was at all ambitious, and said she would prefer a home and garden to professional success. To dirt and filth she associated sexuality, but denied any feeling that sexuality was dirty or filthy. To the odor she associated her acute sense of smell, and the use of incense in her room when, as an adolescent, she was preoccupied with reading pornographic literature. To the Teddy bear she associated childhood play with Teddy bears with whom she always identified

herself, and remarked that no nose meant "not nosey; no curiosity." [5]
An interpretation of her great need to repress and intellectualize her
sexual curiosity illustrated by the large camera, her identification
with an inanimate object without a nose, and her remark about the
experts who wanted her to see too much was made at this time with
the suggestion that this need for repression was apparently induced .
or influenced by the feeling that the repressed material was filthy
and disgusting to her.

The next hour the patient reported the following dream:

> The patient felt sexually attracted to a young man who was standing
> in front of her. The man was the patient's brother, although the
> patient was an only child. He aroused more of a sexual interest in
> her than she had ever felt for any man. He had beautiful hair, his
> clothes were dirty, his pants were not pressed, and he had "stinky" feet.

In association to this dream the patient claimed to possess an
almost unbelievable ability to distinguish different odors. She said
she could distinguish odorous foods and substances at a great distance, could distinguish people by their odor, could detect menstruation in women, could recognize the presence in the house of a dog or
cat even though unseen, and that she could detect the slightest beginning of decay in animal proteins. She said that when she had
hay fever her sense of smell was greatly impaired. To the man in
the dream she associated first herself and then her father, and remarked that his breath was now very offensive to her, although this
had not been true when she was a child. She remembered that her
father had "smelly" feet, and that he was not always careful about
his personal appearance. She recalled how male dogs sniffed at the
genitals of her female dog, and remarked that in most respects dogs
were cleaner than humans. Then she remembered another dream
of the same night:

> Some woman offered the patient two bananas on a plate. This
> woman was about to offer the patient a third banana, when the patient
> refused the plate. The bananas looked as though they had been heated
> or cooked.

The patient's first association to this dream was a memory of
having seen when she was a child the burned skin of a naked man
sunning himself. She believed that the man was entirely naked, and

---

5 In this connection, two of my other hay fever patients made identical speculative
formulations relative to this formulation. They came to the conclusion that no nose
(inflammation of nasal mucous membrane sufficient to inhibit or destroy the sense of
smell) meant "no nose, no must nots, no external prohibitions against sexual curiosity,"
but that with the threatened emergence of sexual curiosity the prohibition became internalized and constituted a super ego identification with the forbidding parent.

that she was fascinated by the sight of his penis. Then she recalled that her mother had had two miscarriages, and remarked that she was the only one of the mother's pregnancies that had not been killed. The patient said that was not because she was wanted, but that the pregnancies had probably all been accidents, that all children were accidents, and that no parents ever really wanted to have children.

The first of these two dreams is of particular interest because of the obvious reference to the conflict over visual sexual and olfactory sexual stimulation. Both the hair and the feet are, to use Freud's terminology (5), raised to a fetish, the hair is beautiful, and the feet are "smelly." However, the olfactory interest in the feet is not repressed; in the dream the patient actually hallucinates the smell of the odorous feet. The dream begins with a strong sexual interest in the man; as she states, stronger than she ever felt for any man. Her first association to the man is to herself. As we have seen in previous material, the masculine protest reaction represents her first line of defense against forbidden sexual temptation.[6] In this dream the confusion between visual and olfactory stimulation is clearly shown; the man's hair was beautiful, his clothes were dirty, his pants were not pressed (i.e., the outline of the penis was visible), but he had "stinky" feet. In her associations she referred to the sexual curiosity of dogs, and by inference indicated that both visual and olfactory sensation are determinants of sexual stimulation in the human as well as in the animal. In this dream, as in fetishism, visual curiosity is inhibited and olfactory curiosity is intensified; the patient tries to substitute through displacement both above (hair) and below (feet) strong smelling objects for the real object, particularly the father's genitals.

Following these dreams the patient reported dreams of inhibited curiosity with displacement onto buildings, landscapes, women who wore masks, tremendous parks, big lakes, and great waterfalls. She was always trying to arrive some place, but when she attempted to reach her destination she would find it necessary to wade through mud and filth. In the analysis the patient became exceedingly defiant and demanding. She threatened to have overt homosexual relations, demanded that the analyst do something to help her—the nature of which she could not state—but she wanted the analyst to tell her exactly what to do and what not to do in all her social contacts. When the analyst did not assume this protective-mother role, she developed an acute rhinitis and reported the following dream:

---

[6] The father's attitude toward her as a child, of encouraging masculine identification, probably also influenced this attempt at solution of her conflict.

The dream began in a restaurant. The patient, the analyst's wife, and the analyst were about to have a meal together. The patient was eating potatoes and meat. Then the scene changed, and the patient was eating the upholstery—particularly the hair—out of the analyst's couch. She felt that she was eating "down too low."

In association to the dream the patient expressed great hostility for a male patient, with whom she was well acquainted. She said she knew that the analyst's couch was stuffed with feathers, not with hair. Again she complained of poor vision, and said that her eyes were blurry and watery. She disclaimed any interest in people, particularly men, at the same time expressing a wish that she could be interested in some man. She complained that men and women only used her for entertainment. She said that as soon as she removed her glasses—which she had done before coming to her appointment— she began to have a headache, her eyes felt blurry, the nasal mucous membrane began to feel sensitive, and her breathing was obstructed. She also complained of severe nausea, and said that she had vomited her breakfast. She recalled an incident that occurred soon after leaving her parents' home. She was riding with a man whom she had just met. He fondled her breasts, kissed her, and attempted to pull her head down into his lap. His penis was exposed and erect. She was furious and experienced a severe attack of nausea. However, she attributed the nausea to the cocktails they had had before dinner. As this hour progressed, the patient developed an attack of rhinitis that lasted for two days, and was then followed by an attack of asthma.[7]

The dreams reported begin with those of inhibited or forbidden curiosity. The patient has a need to satisfy her visual sexual curiosity, but this is inhibited and projected. The curiosity regarding the mother's pregnancies is displayed and symbolized in terms of things growing from the ground. She makes almost frantic attempts to substitute other forms of visual satisfaction on an intellectual basis of sublimation in work, photography, visual learning, and constructive attainments. But even these attempts of substitution in the reality situation demonstrate the admixture of visual and olfactory conflict. Much of the curiosity has to do with dyes, colors, paints, and soil, and in her dreams there is always the need to go through something dirty and smelly. Sexuality is always pictured as dirty and filthy. The dream material shows a gradual progression of the thwarted and unsatisfied curiosity, reaching a climax in the dream where she finds it necessary to deny all curiosity (either

---

[7] During the analysis of patient's suffering from both hay fever and asthma, I regularly observed that a mild hay fever attack often preceded an attack of asthma.

visual or olfactory) and identifies herself with an inanimate object (Teddy bear) without a nose. In the dream of the large camera, the curiosity is all projected on to the analyst, but at a distance she can see dirt and filth. There is a great need to distance the curiosity that the analysis has mobilized, which is pictured as dirty, filthy, and as having a bad odor.

This need to distance and repress the visual curiosity and to substitute anal (olfactory) curiosity is a result of the intensely aggressive character of the impulses that are mobilized by seeing. For this patient, to see meant to wish to grab, to take, to injure, to possess.

With the confession that although her father's breath is now offensive (it was not always so), the patient remembered another dream of the same night, a dream in which she refused something a woman offered her. The symbolism of the bananas as well as the oral-incorporation impulse appears self-evident, but there is probably considerable condensation and overdetermination in this dream, because her associations refer to seeing—satisfied curiosity—in the sense that she saw the naked man's penis, but an unsatisfied sexual impulse in that it was fascinating and sexually stimulating. She also associated her mother's two abortions, and expressed the belief that her mother was a murderess. In her associations to the dream the patient confused something she remembered seeing—the man's naked, burned body and penis—with something she repressed—her hostile, oral-destructive reactions to the mother's pregnancy. She denied her destructive impulse toward baby and penis in the dream by refusing the bananas. The attempt to project the oral-destructive impulses onto the mother is unsuccessful, as shown in the last dream quoted. In this dream the patient makes a direct oral attack upon the analyst's couch eating the upholstery, particularly the hair.

In this dream the couch (bed) is the place where she spends an hour each day concentrating upon the conflict between wish and inhibition of sexual curiosity (which is so castrative in character) and sexual satisfaction; (the reference to the bed as the place where the parents had sexual relations and the place where the mother had the miscarriages is obvious). The analytic couch, like the parents' bed, is intimately associated with bodily odors, and the male patient toward whom she developed so much feeling of antagonism occupied the couch each day just before the patient.

Several times during the analysis, the patient brought dreams in which the analytic couch was identified with a toilet; to use her own expression, "a place to defecate," a place to get dirt and filth out of her system. As an adolescent the patient also lay on a couch reading sexually stimulating literature while inhaling burning incense. In the dream the analytic couch is stuffed with hair but, she says, she knows very well it is stuffed with feathers. As a child the patient often went duck shooting with her father, and during the analysis she reported several dreams in which the parents (particularly the mother) were identified with ducks. It would appear then that the oral attack is directed toward the genitals of both parents. The patient also associated an experience in an automobile in which the temptation to orally attack a man's genitals was denied with a marked, nausea reaction. She had experienced nausea and loss of appetite during this period of the analysis, which makes it probable that in the dream the patient's sexual impulse takes the form of an oral attack upon the analyst's genitals, but out of fear of retaliation and loss of love the impulse is repressed and the symptom of denial is substituted. It would appear then that the visual curiosity is intensely sadistic in character, and that the olfactory displacement of sexual interest represents a masochistic attempt at solution of the sadistic impulse.

The bodily odors remaining in the couch are equally as stimulating as the sight of the genitals, and it is probably significant that, with the failure of sublimation and substitution in the visual sphere, the olfactory sphere becomes overcharged and this leads to inhibition. When this occurs the eyes and nose (the organs of sexual curiosity) assume the character of sexually stimulated genitals with congestion and increased mucous secretion. This results in a diminution of both olfactory and optic sensitivity.

Summary and Conclusion

An attempt has been made to demonstrate certain psychological similarities with particular emphasis upon the persistence of preoccupation with olfactory stimuli in five cases of hay fever that were psychoanalytically studied. Significant unconscious material reported by one patient who suffered from severe seasonal hay fever preceding the advent of an attack of severe acute rhinitis is presented and discussed.[8] In this case, material is presented to show that, when repressed *sexual* curiosity relating to the function of reproduction became mobilized in the analysis, the patient made an extreme attempt to sublimate the curiosity along visual, intellectual lines. This attempt represents and may be considered a normal process of sublimation. It was not the manner in which the patient tried to solve this conflict, but the intensity of the effort and the emotional need to

---

[8] An analysis of the motor manifestations of this symptom, particularly sneezing, has been deliberately omitted in this discussion because this aspect should constitute the basis for a separate study.

sublimate the curiosity that is significant. The material reported during this period shows that efforts at sublimation in the visual sphere did not succeed because the aggressive character of the visual curiosity necessitated the substitution of a more primary olfactory curiosity. The dreams demonstrated that external olfactory stimulation remained as an effective source of stimuli and conflict. This led to the establishment of a vicious circle that was temporarily terminated in the production of a conversion symptom which in varying degrees of intensity produced membranous congestion with a corresponding diminution in both olfactory and visual perception.

An analysis of the unconscious material reported by the five cases studied by the psychoanalytic method makes it possible to hypothecate the specific psychological factors in patients suffering from hay fever. The interplay between these inner conflicts, attempts at their solution and the external agents (specific pollen allergens) which precipitated the actual hay fever attack remains unknown. Either a specific constitutional hyperosmia leads to the sense of smell as a regressive solution to dangerous curiosity, or the regression itself produced the hyperosmia and nasal sensitivity to pollen. The physiological principle relative to summation of external and internal stimuli may solve the problem of the interaction of psychological and allergic factors in hay fever. Patients who as a result of their psychosexual development have substituted olfactory for visual sexual curiosity may, because of this, become more sensitive to pollens. Olfactory curiosity that has never been relieved may be considered to be a constant irritant to the mucous membrane of the nose. An added irritation from an external agency, such as pollen, may produce an attack. It is possible that there are cases in which the local sensitivity alone, in the absence of psychological stimulation, may be sufficient to precipitate an attack. It may be assumed that sometimes, as in this case, when the psychological stimulation was increased by the mobilization of repressed sexual tension, this alone sufficed to produce an attack of rhinitis. This would explain the resistance to pollens that was obtained by patients who were exposed to psychoanalysis. When the genital inhibitions and the chronic psychological stimulus were eliminated, the pollen irritation could no longer precipitate an attack.

BIBLIOGRAPHY

1. ABRAHAM, KARL. Remarks on psychoanalysis of a case of foot and corset fetishism. In *Selected papers.* London: Hogarth Press, 1927.
2. BRILL, A. A. The sense of smell in the neuroses and psychoses. *Psychoanal. Quart.,* 1932, 1, 42.

3. DALY, C. D., AND WHITE, R. S.   Psychiatric relations to olfactory stimuli.   *Brit. J. med. Psychol.*, 1930, 10, 70.
4. DUNBAR, H. F.   Psychoanalytic notes relating to syndromes of asthma and hay fever.   *Psychoanal. Quart.*, 1938, 7, 25.
5. FREUD, SIGMUND.   A case of obsessional neurosis.   In *Collected papers.* London: Hogarth Press, 1925.
6. GRINKER, R. R.   A comparison of psychological "repression" and neurological "inhibition."   *J. nerv. ment. Dis.*, 1939, 89, 765.
7. HIRSCHFELD, M.   *Sexual pathology.*   (Rev. Ed.)   New York: Emerson Books, Inc., 1940.
8. KRAFFT-EBING, R. v.   *Psychopathia sexualis.*   (Rev. Ed.)   New York: Physicians & Surgeons Book Co., 1924.
9. WILSON, G. W.   The red-headed man.   *Psychoanal. Rev.*, 1938, 25, 165.

PART IV

CARDIOVASCULAR DISTURBANCES

EMOTIONAL FACTORS IN ESSENTIAL HYPERTENSION *

PRESENTATION OF A HYPOTHESIS

By FRANZ ALEXANDER, M.D.

The view presented in the following pages is an attempt to integrate a number of diversified observations of clinical, pathological, physiological, and psychological nature into a consistent etiological picture of essential hypertension. These etiological conclusions do not claim final validity, and should serve merely as a basis for further systematic studies which may lead finally to an etiologically founded therapeutic procedure. Speaking of essential hypertension, I refer to the clinical condition, which is defined in the article of Katz and Leiter, in this symposium, a clinical condition consisting of a chronic elevation of the systolic and diastolic blood pressure which cannot be retraced as a secondary result to known pathological changes in the kidneys, the vascular system, or other organs.

Since in other articles of this symposium the somatic aspects have been dealt with extensively, I shall restrict myself only to a brief summary.

The Clinical Course

Perhaps of greatest importance for the problem of etiology is the typical course of hypertensive disease. In most cases one can differentiate an early phase in which the blood pressure shows great fluctuations, and a later phase in which the blood pressure becomes stabilized on a higher level. This was most convincingly demonstrated by Fahrenkamp (5). It can be validly suspected that in this initial period the blood pressure temporarily may return to normal or fluctuate around the normal level and for shorter or longer periods around a higher level. Further thorough observations of such incipient cases over a longer period of time would be of greatest importance in order to establish the primary causes. Only in the second irreversible phase does the blood pressure become stabilized at

* *Psychosomatic Medicine* I:173-179, 1939.

a high level. This typical course of essential hypertension makes the assumption improbable that degenerative changes in the blood vessels are the primary causative factors. The first fluctuating phase seems to be definitely a functional one.

Pathological Findings

This assumption is favored by the conclusion of most authors that organic findings such as left ventricle hypertrophy, pathological changes in the large vessels and in the arterioles, when present in cases of essential hypertension, should be considered rather the result than the cause of hypertension because they rarely can be found in early cases.

Physiology

In discussing the problem of etiology it is important to differentiate between mechanisms and causes. It is generally accepted that the chronic elevation of the blood pressure is the result of an increased tonus of the arterioles. Vasoconstriction in the splanchnic area, because of the vast blood capacity of this region, probably contributes most to the elevation of the blood pressure. As causes of this chronic increase of tonus, different possibilities are considered, none of them established with certainty. The increased tonus may be the result of stimulation of the vasomotor centers. This is the neurogenic theory. It may be the effect of pressor substances in the blood stream. This is the humoral theory. For this latter some experimental evidence has been furnished lately by Harry Goldblatt (7) who artificially produced hypertension of longer duration in dogs by creating local ischemia of the kidneys by clamping of the renal arteries. He assumes that due to this ischemia a pressor substance is retained, which, however, has only a pressor effect in combination with cortical adrenal hormone. Of course the neurogenic and the humoral theories are not contradictory. Both mechanisms may be at work.

It is obvious that neither of these explanations answers the question of etiology proper. They concern merely intermediary mechanisms. The etiological problem is: What is the cause of the chronic vasomotor stimulation, or, if the humoral theory is correct, what is the cause of the renal ischemia responsible for the retention of pressor substances?

As has been mentioned before, the typical clinical course of hypertensive cases makes it seem improbable that in early cases generalized pathological changes in the blood vessels, or local pathology of the renal vascular system, are causative of the renal ischemia. If local renal ischemia should turn out to be the intermediary cause of chronic hypertension in the early phases of the disease, this ischemia must be due to a functional spasm of the renal vessels rather than to irreversible histopathological changes. In any case, if further investigations would corroborate the assumption that a vascular spasm resulting in renal ischemia is the intermediary cause of chronic hypertension, the essential etiological problem would still remain unsolved, namely, the origin of the local spasm of the renal vessels.

In the following, the question of intermediary mechanisms—humoral or neurogenic—will be disregarded, and I shall concern myself merely with observations which might throw light on the primary causes of essential hypertension.

General Psychological Observations

A large majority of authors agree that the clinical manifestations of essential hypertension are greatly influenced by the emotional state of the patient. I mention only the observations of Goldscheider (8), O. Mueller (16), Mohr (13), Heyer (9), Moog and Schürer (14), Fahrenkamp (5), Alkan (1), Fishberg (6), Schultze and Schwab (18), Wolfe (20), Soma Weiss (19), Moschcowitz (15), Karl and William Menninger (12), Karl Menninger (11), and Lewis Hill (10). Ayman and Pratt (2) and Riseman and Weiss (17) emphasize the coincidence of neurotic personality traits with hypertension, and K. Menninger suspects the importance of inhibited aggressive impulses. Also Hill mentions the role of inhibited hostile tendencies. Some of these authors observed that under acute emotional strains the blood pressure rises and remains elevated for a shorter or longer period. These elevations are usually superimposed upon an already heightened blood pressure. After the patient has calmed down again the blood pressure may drop, but remain on a higher level than normal, characteristic for the patient.

The influence of acute emotions upon the blood pressure has also been experimentally reproduced in animals by Cannon (3) and his co-workers under the influence of rage and fear. According to his experiments, elevation of the blood pressure is one constant element of a complex physiological syndrome characteristic for the emotional state of rage and fear. This syndrome (increased adrenalin production, mobilization of sugar, shortening of the clotting time of the blood, increased blood pressure) is a utilitarian reaction of the organism preparing it and making it fit for flight or fight.

Psychoanalytic Observations

The psychoanalytic study of cases as described in the previous articles of this symposium allows a more continuous comparison of chronic and not only of acute emotional states and blood pressure. Moreover the psychoanalytic method makes possible a detailed evaluation of the psychological material. This offers an approach to the question of whether or not the emotions which influence the blood pressure are of a specific nature. The comparative study of a series of cases suffering from essential hypertension indicates that chronic, inhibited, aggressive hostile impulses, which always appear in connection with anxiety, have a specific influence upon the fluctuations of the blood pressure. Furthermore, it suggests that patients suffering from hypertension have a characteristic psychodynamic structure. This consists in a very pronounced conflict between passive, dependent, feminine, receptive tendencies and overcompensatory, competitive, aggressive hostile impulses which lead to fear and increase a flight from competition towards the passive dependent attitude. This vicious circle in itself is, however, extremely common, being the central emotional conflict of a large number of neurotic individuals who have normal blood pressure. Characteristic for the hypertensive patient is, however, his inability to relieve freely either one of the opposing tendencies: neither can he freely accept the passive dependent attitude nor freely express his hostile impulses. A kind of emotional paralysis can be observed which results from the two opposing emotional attitudes blocking each other.

Confronting these psychological observations with the clinical, pathological, and physiological facts, and with the results of animal experiments, the following etiological assumptions can be made.

In normal animal life, fear and rage find their expression in physical flight or attack, for which the body prepares itself under the influence of these emotions. One important element of this preparation consists in the increased blood pressure. Human beings living in a competitive civilization are equally and perhaps even more permanently exposed to fear and hostile impulses, yet have much less opportunity to give expression to these feelings in physical combat. Social life requires an extreme control of these hostile impulses. A neurotic form of this control is unsuccessful attempts at repression. One of the best founded discoveries of psychoanalysis is that impulses which are inhibited in their expression sustain a chronic tension which is apt to have a permanent—or we may call it a tonic effect upon certain physiological functions. This is the etiological theory of the psychogenic organ neuroses. An acute elevation of the blood pressure is part of the normal reaction to acute rage and fear. Our assumption is that a *chronic* inhibited rage may lead to a *chronic* elevation of the blood pressure. Such inhibited rage never finds its natural consummation in physical aggression which is followed by fatigue when the heightened blood pressure returns to normal. Such accumulated and never adequately expressed hostile aggressions are like a foreign body which is the source of a permanent irritation. The organism is constantly in preparation to fight. Typical of this state of apprehensive preparedness is a heightened blood pressure. Of course we know that these hostile impulses are not permanently at the same level. In the course of life, during contact with the environment, they become frequently stimulated; at other times they become repressed and retreat from the psychic surface into the deeper layers. This comes to expression in the fluctuations of the blood pressure.

According to this assumption the typical course of essential hypertension might be described as follows: The maturing individual in the course of his life gradually becomes more and more confronted with the complex problems of maintaining his and his family's existence, his social position and prestige. In our present civilization all these tasks unavoidably involve hostile competitive feelings, create fears, and require at the same time an extreme control of these hostile impulses. Those who through constitution or through early life experience have acquired a greater amount of inhibitions will handle their aggressions less efficiently than others and will tend to repress them. On account of their inhibitions they cannot find socially acceptable legitimate vents for their aggressive feelings, and thus these hostile impulses become accumulated and increase in intensity. It must also be borne in mind that the neurotic individuals who are more than normally blocked in relieving their hostilities and aggressions usually become inhibited also in many other respects, particularly sexual expression. All these inhibitions make them, in their struggle for life, less effective, create feelings of inferiority in them, stimulate their envy, and increase their hostile feelings toward their more successful, less inhibited competitors. These hostilities again require a greater amount of control and thus lead to greater inhibitions, greater inefficiency, and in turn again stimulate hostile, envious, and competitive tendencies. This vicious circle is one of the best known mechanisms revealed by psychoanalytic study of neurotic personalities. Our experience is that the chronic hypertensives belong to this group of overly inhibited yet at the same time intensely hostile and aggressive individuals. Of course not all of these persons are necessarily hypertensives. The same neurotic conflict situation may find other entirely different expression. I refer to such well-known clinical entities as manic depressive states, compulsion neuroses, paranoia, and criminal behavior. It seems that essential hypertension develops when circumscribed neurotic symptoms which serve for the draining of pent-up hostile impulses are absent. This assumption is substantiated by such observations as that of George Draper, (4) who observed the return of a longstanding elevation of the blood pressure to the normal, coinciding with the patient's developing certain neurotic symptoms.

It is probable that in the first phase of this disturbance—when most cases are not yet under medical observation—these patients, if studied, would show in their everyday life a greater than normal degree of fluctuation and frequent transient elevations of their blood pressure. I assume that this instability of the vasomotor system is the expression of a specific psychoneurotic conflict situation characterized by the inability to handle accumulated hostile impulses. The hostile impulses are neither thoroughly repressed nor adequately expressed. This psychological tension serves as a constant vasomotor stimulus and leads to a functional overtaxation of the circulatory system, which, lasting over a long period, may result in vascular changes, possibly in the first place in the renal vessels. These secondary vascular changes may account for the stabilization of the blood pressure on a high level. In this second phase the disturbance has become irreversible. Of course a constitutional vasomotor instability must be also considered. The familial nature of essential hypertension is well established.

Essentially, this concept is not new. A number of authors have come to the same conclusion: namely, that essential hypertension is in its early phase a functional disturbance gradually leading to those pathological changes which are responsible for the irreversible stabilized malignant phase. Whereas Fishberg (6) and many other internists are chiefly impressed by the hereditary familial nature of the disturbance, others—like Riseman and Weiss (17), Ayman and Pratt (2), Alkan (1), and Wolfe (20) emphasize, in addition to constitution, also the etiological importance of psychic factors for the early phase of the abnormally fluctuating blood pressure. What our psychoanalytic observations add to this general psychogenic concept is a working hypothesis regarding the precise nature of the emotional factors. The affinity of hostile impulses to blood pressure elevation is well established by experiment. What is assumed is that the excessive and inhibited hostile tendencies which are typical of hypertensives have a continued effect upon the blood-pressure-controlling physiological mechanisms, and through years may lead to permanent histological changes.

The question of heredity is then reduced to a more general problem. If it is true that the vasomotor instability is a manifestation of a psychoneurotic condition, the question is, to what degree this psychoneurotic condition should be considered as inherited or acquired.

Concerning this question the most interesting observations are those of Schultze and Schwab (18), who point out on the basis of extensive statistical studies that Negroes in Africa very rarely suffer from chronic hypertension, whereas Negroes living in America show it in a very high percentage and supply a surprisingly large number of malignant cases. These observations indicate that—not the racial constitution—but different environmental and cultural conditions are responsible for this frequency : namely, the difficulties of adjusting to the new conditions of life which require an unusual amount of self-control. The difficulty of adjusting to the complex conditions of cultural life is the essence of psychoneurosis.

The undeniable fact that neurotic traits run in families does not necessarily require a hereditary explanation. Psychiatric experience shows that, apart from heredity, there is another perhaps even more common form of transmission of neurotic trends from generation to generation, namely, through the psychological influence of neurotic parents upon their children.

Conclusions

We come to the conclusion that the early fluctuating phase of essential hypertension is the manifestation of a psychoneurotic condition based on excessive and inhibited hostile impulses. As such it is a reaction of the individual to the complexities of our present civilization. Since the same psychological condition is extremely widespread and finds expression in different forms of neuroses, the question of specificity still requires further investigation. The assumption of a constitutional instability of the vasomotor system therefore cannot be discarded. It is to be hoped, however, that further psychological investigations on hypertensives will make it possible to discriminate a specific neurotic handling of hostile impulses which necessarily leads to extreme fluctuations of the blood pressure and then secondarily to its later organic consequences.

The therapeutic possibilities of the psychoanalytic method in essential hypertension cannot be as yet conclusively formulated. It is obvious that in all those progressed cases in which one has to reckon with histopathological vascular changes one cannot hope that through psychotherapy the blood pressure can be brought back to a normal level. Of course, also in these cases, it is possible that the diminution of emotional conflicts may at least reduce the fluctuation superimposed upon a high-average level. However, psychotherapy has its greatest chances during the early fluctuating phase and therefore will have primarily a preventive value.

At present I must refrain from any definite therapeutic conclusions because most of our cases are still in the process of treatment. Some observations, however, made during the psychoanalytic treatment of such cases are quite encouraging; for example, that a patient during an emotionally calm period of several weeks' duration showed a definitely lower systolic and diastolic pressure and minimal fluctuations. Lewis Hill (10) reported a cessation of the hypertension in a case of a successfully analyzed patient.

Life seldom allows even emotionally well-balanced people to remain always calm and poised. Much less can it be expected that psychoneurotic individuals, to which the majority of the hypertensives seem to belong, even after successful treatment will always be free from apprehensions and aggressions. Under the influence of their daily life they will show at least the same amount of emotional upsets as anybody else. If the assumption is correct that the hypertensives have a constitutionally less stable vasomoter system, these emotional fluctuations will necessarily come to expression in fluctuations of their blood pressure. What psychotherapy can hope for is a better emotional adjustment, and, as a result of this, less daily fluctuation of the blood pressure; that is to say, less taxation of the cardiovascular system. Thus psychotherapy may prevent the development of those secondary organic changes which are probably responsible for the malignant stabilized forms of essential hypertension.

BIBLIOGRAPHY

1. ALKAN, LEOPOLD. Anatomische Organkrankheiten aus seelischer Ursache. Stuttgart: Hippokrates Verlag, 1930.
2. AYMAN, D., AND PRATT, J. R. The nature of symptoms associated with essential hypertension. Arch. interm. Med., 1931, 47, 675.
3. CANNON, W. B. Bodily changes in pain, hunger, fear and rage. New York: D. Appleton-Century Co., 1934.
4. DRAPER, GEORGE. The common denominator of disease. Amer. J. med. Sci., 1935, 190, 545.
5. FAHRENKAMP, KARL. Die psychophysischen Wechselwirkungen bei den Hypertonieerkrankungen. Stuttgart: Hippokrates Verlag, 1926.
6. FISHBERG, A. M. Hypertension and nephritis. Philadelphia: Lea & Febiger, 1934.

7. GOLDBLATT, HARRY. *Studies on experimental hypertension.* V. The pathogenesis of experimental hypertension due to renal ischemia. *Ann. interm. Med.,* 1937, 11, 69.
8. GOLDSCHEIDER, K. *Z. f. ärzt. Fortbildung Nr. 1,* 1926. (Quoted from Fahrenkamp)
9. HEYER, G. R. *Das körperlich-seelische Zusammenwirken in den Lebensvorgängen.* München: J. F. Bergman, 1925.
10. HILL, LEWIS, B. A psychoanalytic observation on essential hypertension. *Psychoanal. Rev.,* 1935, 22, 60.
11. MENNINGER, K. A. Emotional factors in hypertension. *Bull. Menninger Clin.,* 1938, 2, 74.
12. MENNINGER, K. A., AND MENNINGER, WILLIAM. Psychoanalytic observations in cardiac disorders. *Amer. Heart J.,* 1936, 11, 10.
13. MOHR, FRITZ. *Psychophysische Behandlungsmethoden.* Leipzig: Hirzel, 1925.
14. MOOG, D., AND SCHÜRER, F. Ablauf der Hypertonie bei der Kriegsnephritis. *Deut. med. Wchschr.,* 1919, 455.
15. MOSCHCOWITZ, ELI. Hypertension: Its significance, relation to arteriosclerosis and nephritis, and etiology. *Amer. J. med. Sci.,* 1919, 158, 668.
16. MUELLER, OTFRIED. *Die Kapillaren der menschlichen Körperfläche.* Stuttgart: Hippokrates Verlag, 1922.
17. RISEMAN, J. E. F., AND WEISS, S. Symptomatology of arterial hypertension. *Amer. J. med. Sci.,* 1930, 180, 47.
18. SCHULTZE, V. E., AND SCHWAB, E. H. Arteriolar hypertension in the American Negro. *Amer. Heart J.,* 1936, 11, 66.
19. WEISS, SOMA. The interaction between emotional states and the cardiovascular system in health and disease. *Emanuel Libman Anniversary Volumes,* 1932, 3, 1181.
20. WOLFE, THEODORE. Dynamic aspects of cardiovascular symptomatology. *Amer. J. Psychol.,* 1934, 91, 563.

PSYCHOANALYTIC STUDY OF A CASE OF ESSENTIAL HYPERTENSION *

By Franz Alexander, M.D.

The observations described in this article were made in the course of a systematic clinical investigation conducted at the Chicago Institute for Psychoanalysis. The objective of this clinical study was to explore the psychological processes and the personality structure of patients suffering from essential hypertension. This investigation was undertaken in the hope that a systematic study of the emotional life of hypertensive patients by the psychoanalytic method, continued over a long period, would throw some light upon the still open question concerning the etiological role of emotional factors in the development of this widespread condition. At the same time the aim of this study was to establish the possibilities of psychotherapy in essential hypertension.

It is common clinical knowledge that acute emotional tensions have an influence upon the height of the blood pressure. A common experience is that a patient who is in an apprehensive mood while having his blood pressure taken shows higher readings than after he has been calmed down by the physician's reassurance. Animal experiments have corroborated the clinical findings, and have shown that under the influence of rage and fear the blood pressure rises (3). The influence of acute and intensive emotions on blood pressure can be observed in patients whose blood pressure is normal, as well as in those whose blood pressure is chronically elevated. It has also been observed in hypertensives whose condition is caused by renal disease. These observations in themselves do not allow any etiological conclusions concerning the role of emotions in the causation of chronically elevated blood pressure. They account only for the transient fluctuation of the blood pressure.

Another important clinical finding described by different authors is that most essential hypertensives show marked neurotic personality traits. Neither does this observation allow any definite etiological conclusions because the neurotically disturbed emotional life and high blood pressure may be parallel manifestations of a third factor

* Psychosomatic Medicine I: 139-152, 1939.

(constitution) ; or the hypertension might contribute to the development of neurotic tendencies; or the hypertensive state may be the result of a long-standing neurosis. The opinions of different authors are divided on this subject.

We expected to obtain different kinds of information from the psychoanalytic study and therapy of such patients. In the first place the psychological observations obtained by the method of psychoanalytic technique promised a more intimate insight concerning the influence upon the blood pressure, not only of acute emotional states but also of chronic emotional tensions as they can be observed in neurotics. Furthermore, the psychoanalytic study of cases gives a detailed picture of the personality development from early childhood which might throw light upon the development of the hypertensive state. Finally, a comparative study of a series of patients suffering from essential hypertension may answer the question whether or not there is a definite personality structure which is characteristic for these patients. Apart from these theoretical objectives, we hoped to find a therapeutic approach based on etiological knowledge. In the following an attempt will be made (a) to give a dynamic picture of the personality make-up of a hypertensive patient; (b) to correlate the fluctuations of his blood pressure with his changing emotional states; and (c) to establish whether or not there are specific emotional tensions which have a specific influence upon the blood pressure.

The Patient's Personality and Its Development

The Present Picture. The following observations were made during the analysis of a 47-year-old male patient who was suffering from a pronounced though not excessive essential hypertension of the fluctuating variety. The patient's systolic blood pressure fluctuated between 175 mm. and 136 mm., and the diastolic between 120 mm. and 92 mm. This condition is of two years duration.[1]

The patient was a married business man of Swedish descent with a distinctive educational and family background. He had four children, two older boys and two girls. He occupied an important and responsible (but not the highest) position in a large concern.

The patient's father died young of an acute infectious disease, his mother of a stroke when 73 years old. The patient drinks coffee occasionally and smokes from 20 to 40 cigarettes a day. The physical examination of the patient revealed a well-developed, well-nourished, somewhat obese, middle-aged man weighing 209 pounds.

---

[1] Compare with the article by Leon Saul where the typical personality structure of seven analyzed hypertensives is summarized. (Page 345.)

There was a distinct odor of alcohol on his breath. There was a moderate arcus senilis of both eyes. Liver dullness was two to three fingers below the costal margin, but no evidence of liver tenderness. The second aortic tone was moderately accentuated. There was a questionable enlargement of his spleen. His urine showed a trace of albumin and a considerable number of pus cells in the centrifuged specimen. Hemoglobin was 90; white blood count 7600. There was a not undue, very moderate arteriovenous nicking in the retinal vessels, with no increased tortuosity of the capillaries. Electrocardiographic examination showed a slow, regular heart beat with a slight tendency to left axis deviation, and a moderate amount of slurring and notching in QRS in the 4th lead.

When I saw the patient first, he showed an extremely pronounced self-consciousness, with a vivid sense of inferiority. He constantly compared himself unfavorably with others, had little confidence in himself, tended to undervalue his efficiency, and was always doubtful about the merits of his accomplishments. At the same time he was very ambitious to excel and turn out perfect work. He was definitely a retiring type, inconspicuous, a conformist, always polite, avoiding contradiction. His ambitions to progress and to outdo the others remained restricted to his fantasy and did not appear on the surface. It soon became evident that this overt attitude of modesty and compliance put him under an extreme pressure and created intense inferiority feelings in him. These became most tormenting in relation to his chief. The patient never would contradict his chief, would follow his suggestions, accept blame while talking with him; but after he left the office, he was filled with self-contempt and would tell himself, "You should have answered. You should have said no! You should have demonstrated to him that he was not right. You are no good and you never will be any good." This self-depreciatory attitude usually became so unbearable that he would have the urge to drink. Alcohol dissipated his sense of weakness and inefficiency. As soon as the alcohol began to make its effects felt, his spirit was lifted; he felt courageous and strong. But apart from the effect of the drug, the act of drinking itself had the significance of a rebellious act for him. He secretly enjoyed the feeling that in the middle of the day during office hours he escaped his duties and indulged in a forbidden activity. In this alcoholic mood he would also indulge in promiscuous sexuality in a rebellious spirit against limitations imposed upon him by external social standards and by the voice of his otherwise so strict conscience. Obviously these alcoholic and sexual escapades relieved his sense of inferiority because under the influence of alcohol he dared to commit such offenses as he would never have ventured upon without alcohol. But, soon after he thus successfully escaped the pangs of inferiority feelings, he ran into a new conflict, that of guilt. For after he had committed all these forbidden sexual and nonsocial acts in order to show his independence and thus escape his inferiority feelings, his conscience began to work and made itself felt in the form of remorse.

The patient's attitude in his professional life closely paralleled his attitude towards his wife. Here, also, overtly he subjected himself to all requirements of the marital state but he secretly rebelled against its restrictions. His promiscuity to a great extent was rebellion against the marital chains. At the same time he had a deep affection for his wife, which no other woman had shared. His extramarital relationships were all of a superficial nature.

In brief, the most conspicuous feature in his make-up was this double attitude of overt subjection to external code and to his conscience, with an extremely strong emotional rebellion against this submission. This internal rebellion, however, did not show itself in any other way than in his drinking and occasional promiscuity, both of which had the emotional significance of a short circuit or a vent to relieve emotional tension—particularly his rebellious feelings against every external and internal restriction to which he submitted himself otherwise to an extreme degree.

The Unconscious Dynamic Background of the Overt Picture. During the course of his psychoanalysis the deeper dynamic background of this surface picture has been worked out. His rebellious, aggressive attitudes against the social restrictions of marriage, against his boss, against routine—aggressive attitudes which he never could express openly and freely—were the reactions to a strong passive, masochistically colored, feminine tendency and wish for dependence. With the progress of the analysis, more and more unconscious passive homosexual material came to the surface both in dreams and in the transference. This feminine tendency had a definitely masochistic tinge. In his dreams he was usually attacked. In other dreams women appeared in the masculine role, even equipped with male anatomy. These masochistic and feminine attitudes also came into expression in day fantasies in which he imagined his chief attacking, rebuking, and abusing him. In this passive masochistic attitude two elements were clearly discernible—(a) a guilt component, and (b) a feminine element. The masochistic passivity was a combination of guilt and feminine submissiveness. By being abused and attacked he relieved his guilt feelings and at the same time obtained feminine passive gratification. The guilt feelings came from his rebellious aggressiveness and extreme destructive competitiveness which were reactions to the deep passive feminine attitude. The well-known neurotic vicious circle was solidly established in him; his unconscious, masochistic feminine wishes hurt his masculine pride and drove him to rebellion, increased his competitiveness and ambition. These overaggressive tendencies, however, created guilt and fear which made the struggle of life too strenuous, exhausting, and repulsive for him, and thus intensified his longing for dependence and retreat. The thus increased passive dependent wishes, however, could not be accepted by his ego, which was educated according to the accepted standards of his environment, namely, to consider success and efficiency and victory in the race of life as the highest virtues. Under the pressure of this deeply entrenched ideology of success he had to struggle relentlessly against his deep longing for relaxation and dependence and continue the competitive game of social life. However, in distinction to many other cases who show the same vicious circle of emotional life, he was unable to give expression either to his aggressive ambitions or to his wish for passive dependence. Fear and guilt blocked the expression of aggressiveness, and the internally accepted social standards prohibited him from giving in to his wish to escape the struggle of life. His aggressiveness and his protest against passive submission found a feeble expression in the adolescent behavior pattern—in surreptitious drinking and forbidden sexual acts. To some degree he gratified some of his submissive and dependent longings in giving his wife full control of their social life, expecting her to make all important decisions and assuming toward her the role of an adolescent towards his mother, a peculiar mixture of obedience and surreptitious revolt. In his dreams, however, he regressed even further back than adolescence, way back to the early dependent attitude of the child toward the mother (oral dependence). A typical expression of this tendency was dreams in which he escaped the difficulties of life by seclusion and returning to mother nature in a somewhat Rousseau-ic manner. Some of the dreams were classical examples of womb fantasies; he saw beautiful and mystical wild spots in nature, deep pits filled up with crystal clear water where big penguin-like birds rested peacefully and he together with them. The analysis of these regressive dependent tendencies led us back to a period of his life in which he must have reacted with great rivalry towards his 11-year-younger brother, envying the mother's care for the baby and the passive gratifications of the little child.

The dynamic picture was one of an extreme polarization of the emotional life; on the one hand, a wish towards the infantile role of dependence and the feminine role of submissiveness and passivity, counterbalanced by the opposite attitude of ambition, perfection, and masculine superiority. These two opposite tendencies mutually reinforced each other. The passive regressive tendencies hurt his pride and stimulated his aggressiveness, whereas the aggressive competitive tendencies created fear and a longing for the security of the passive situation of being loved and cared for.

The here described polarization of these two opposing psychological attitudes reinforcing each other in a vicious circle is a picture very commonly found in neurotic persons. It has been described by my collaborators and me in peptic ulcer cases (1) and in certain delinquent types (2). The same emotional conflict was most elaborately and convincingly described by Horney (6), who even went so far as to postulate this conflict between competitive ambition versus the wish to be loved and taken care of to be a nuclear conflict, typical for the contemporary neurotic in our competitive Western civilization. The ubiquity of this conflict in our times does not mean, however, that all neurotics have the same personality structure. The psychoanalytic study of a great variety of neurotic patients taught us to recognize many different ways and means by which different personalities succeed in relieving the emotional tension resulting from this central conflict. Thus, for example, we have learned that peptic ulcer patients usually succeed in expressing their ambitious drives toward accomplishment and responsibility, frequently in aggressive business activities or in administrative or organizational work. The opposite tendency, which is a reaction to this strenuous ambition— their longing for dependence and being loved and taken care of—is drained by organic symptoms, namely, by the increased functions of the stomach. The stomach is stimulated by the repressed unconscious tendencies to be fed which since early childhood are emotionally linked with the wish to be loved. Also certain delinquent types freely express their aggressiveness and the wish to be tough and independent which they amply gratify in their adventurous life. Only the careful exploration of the depth of their emotional life can reveal the soft nucleus, the wish for dependence and security. This unconscious wish they satisfy when captured and imprisoned; then they freely indulge in the wish for shelter and retreat. Many prisoners' peculiar attachment to the prison, their unconscious wish to be recaptured and thus to escape from the struggle of life into the security of the prison, has been amply demonstrated by the psychoanalytic study of prisoners (2), and has also been recognized by the intuition of novelists (4 and 5).

What made this hypertensive case so different from the peptic ulcer personalities or the delinquent types and other neurotics, in which this same vicious circle is a central issue, was the patient's extreme inhibition to satisfy either of his two opposing major trends; apart from the two inadequate vents, promiscuity and drinking, he was unable to express any aggressive independent wish, but at the same time he was equally unable to satisfy freely his longing for passive dependence. This strong inhibition to satisfy either of the two opposing major sides of his nature, his rebellious independence as well as his dependence, accounts for the impression which he made on the observer of being in a permanent emotional tension: a boiling volcano before eruption but never erupting.

This inability to express these two opposing attitudes explains the peculiar neutrality which was so characteristic for his human relationships: always polite and modest yet not extremely submissive and humble, outwardly complying but always giving the impression of a tacit resistance. The analysis revealed that whenever he complied with the request of another person, especially of a superior, he immediately afterwards in fantasy rebelled against it without being able to give free expression to this internal revolt. It is no exaggeration to say that he was paralyzed in every emotional expression, each of the two polar opposing tendencies blocking the expression of the other.

This emotional paralysis accounts for certain recurrent characteristic dreams in which he undertook to do something (to catch a train, to go play golf, etc.) and was unable to do so. (His feet did not respond, or he could not put on his shoes, etc.).These dreams were accompanied by a feeling of utter futility. The deeper inquiry showed that even the only vents by which he could express his rebellion and independence, his drinking and sexual escapades, were condensation products of the two opposing tendencies. In his sexual relationship to women there was a great amount of secret passive gratification (mainly through identification with the sexual partner), and his drinking, apart from its surface significance of an adolescent forbidden act, at the same time gave him the possibility to flee from all responsibilities of life and indulge in a carefree Nirvana-like sensation. It is no exaggeration to say that the alcohol bottle was the direct substitute for the mother's breast. Like feeding in his childhood, now drinking was able to relieve all unpleasant sensations, dissipate all worries, and give him a deep feeling of relaxation and happiness. Because it served both purposes to express rebellion and also to gratify his flight from responsibility to passive relaxation, drinking became a dangerous symptom. This explains why his conscious struggle to give up drinking had to remain ineffective.

How the Present Psychodynamic Structure Came About—Bird's-Eye View of the Life History. As will be seen, this emotional tension, resulting from two equally strong opposing tendencies blocking each other, was the psychodynamic situation which could be brought into correlation with this patient's high blood pressure. Therefore it might appear irrelevant for this study to enter the genetic problem as to how this emotional impasse came about during his life history. If it were true that such a chronic emotional tension might produce a chronic elevation of blood pressure, the history of this condition is of secondary importance. In different cases the same emotional blocking might come about in different ways; the important question is, whether or not, if present, it necessarily leads to high blood pressure. In order to decide this latter question above all it must be established whether or not this type of chronic emotional tension is characteristic for hypertensive patients. *Saul* (page 345) summarizes our observations concerning the characteristic personality structure of hypertensives. His summary shows, however, not only that the actual emotional situation prevailing in adult hypertensives shows great similarities in different cases, but also that the developmental history shows certain parallel features.

Only the most important facts of the life history will be mentioned, only those occurrences and emotional experiences which apparently have contributed to the development of the above described psychodynamic situation.

The patient came of an intellectual, refined family, and was born in Sweden. The family came to the States when the patient was 3 years old. He was one of six children; an older brother died before the patient was born. The patient was the second of three brothers who were born in three successive years. Then came a five-years-younger sister, and finally his youngest brother, 11 years younger.

As a young boy the patient was in every respect the outstanding member of the family. His brothers looked up to him more or less as a hero. He would fight the battles of the younger boys. He was inclined to extreme outbreaks of rage, was absolutely fearless, played as astonishing game of football and baseball. In his first two years of public school he resented the routine which was then required and rebelled against one of the teachers quite violently. His being sent home from school for unruly behavior became a regular occurrence. He still retained for a long time his superiority over his brothers and other boys. He was not only the best student in his grade, but probably the best student in the school. The whole family and everybody who was in contact with him had the greatest expectations of him.

When he was 12 years old his father died. He felt he should cry as all the other members of the family did, but he had no true desire for it.

Gradually the patient lost his leading position in the family. Already in the first college years, he began to slip, both in athletics and in scholastic achievements. As a result he developed a severe depression. He was still an excellent student and a good athlete, but both of his brothers began to catch up and even surpass him. In his high school and college days the patient made friendships with socially outstanding boys much wealthier than he was. When he finished college he obtained a position in a concern owned by one of his friend's families. Leaning over backwards, he accepted in this company a menial position which was connected with extreme discomfort and even degradation. During this time he developed his second severe depression. Soon after he recovered from his depression he married a socially outstanding girl, and through this marriage he entered into a group much wealthier than his family was. Although he obtained a very excellent business position, the patient had to struggle desperately to live up to the standards of his circle. In about the twelfth year of his marriage he started to drink, which was the only means of getting rid of his apprehensive depressive moods, which with great regularity, every morning after awakening, began to torture him. Looking back on his life, back to adolescence, the patient was never free from a strong self-critical depressive state of mind which gradually grew worse and worse.

Viewing this history from a distant perspective we see the gradual metamorphosis of an overaggressive, successful, domineering young man, determined for leadership, into a shy, inhibited, conforming, overly modest, and unexpressive person. The aggressive and courageous spirit of his early years appears in the adult only in the form of two neurotic behavior patterns—in promiscuity and drinking—in this typically adolescent way of showing masculinity and a tough independent spirit.

The explanation of this metamorphosis will be found in the analytical material by means of which we have in part recovered and in part reconstructed those emotional experiences which deflected the course of the patient's masculine development and broke the spirit of this promising young man.

The History of the Emotional Development. For a long period during his treatment the patient's memory material consisted mostly of recollections of defeats and failures, intimidations and inhibitions. The early period of aggressive leadership did not appear in his associations, and was obviously overshadowed by gloomy memories dealing mostly with his internal insecurity, with a continuous struggle against his inhibitions. Although the intimidating experiences which gradually led to the development of an extremely inhibited personality go back to his early childhood, it was not before puberty that they visibly influenced the overt picture and changed his relationship to his brothers from leadership into a slow but continuous falling back.

For a long period the patient did not recall at all the extreme rage outbreaks characteristic of his earliest childhood. This free expression of anger in childhood is in such a contrast to his later inability to express any hostile feeling that it can only be explained by a later extreme repression of all hostile impulses. This might account for the fact that he forgot this early aggressive attitude to an astonishing degree and that memories about his early aggressive behavior and temper tantrums were recovered only in the progressed phase of his analysis.

One of his earliest memories is that when 3 or 4 years old he climbed up on his father's back, fell, and suffered a concussion. About in the same age he remembered the first spanking by his father, who punished him for his violent temper. After this punishment the patient felt extremely humiliated. It was mentioned before that in the first school years he openly rebelled against school routine and was continually punished.

Right at the beginning of his treatment he recalled a series of external events of intimidating nature.

When he was 4 years old he fell into water and was almost drowned. From this incident he retained up to the present date some fear of diving.

When he was 5 years old, in kindergarten, he locked himself into a closet with another boy, could not get out, and became extremely panicky.

When he was 5 he locked himself out on a playing porch on the third floor, and when he tried to climb down he fell down one story.

One of his most outstanding memories is of an older man who took him and his brothers out fishing, but then, because of his unruly behavior, wrapped him up with a fish line. He never could forget the impotent rage which he felt at being bound up in this way. Struggle against external pressure was one of the leading motives in his associations.

The most serious intimidations were, however, connected with his sexual feelings. His sexual curiosity appeared early in the prepuberty period and occupied most of his interest. As long as he can remember he always felt extremely shy and timid toward girls. Everything connected with sex he considered low and dirty, but at the same time he had an extreme longing for it. As an adolescent he did not dare to touch even the hands of a girl. His first sexual intercourse was with a prostitute when he was 17 years old. Afterward he felt morally soiled. He confessed immediately to his mother, and did not dare to give in to his sexual impulses again until he was 21 years old. After this time he had casual sexual relationships but after them always felt terrifically degraded.

In a later period of his analysis he was able to remember probably his first sexual trauma. When 3 or 4 years old his father caught him masturbating and reprimanded him. About the same time he had a recurrent nightmare of an ogre which appeared at the end of a dark corridor and threatened him.

His father, who died when the patient was 12 years old, played apparently the most important role as an object of fear and hostility. He thought that he ought to break the boy's aggressive spirit and rebelliousness against every external pressure and routine, and made a point of teaching him how to lose. Patient was about 8 years old when his father began to take him out to the golf course, beat him at golf repeatedly, and tried to make him like to be beaten. Patient remembered his senseless rage when he was beaten in any competitive game. It is interesting that even at his present age the patient has the greatest dislike to go out to play golf with his chief. Whenever the chief asked him to go out to play golf, he wanted to refuse, did not dare to, accepted the invitation, but for days after the analytic hours would be filled with broodings of the following kind: "Why did I accept? Why couldn't I say to the boss—'No, I won't go'?" In spite of this overt rebellion his dream material gave ample evidence of the fact that this submission appealed deep down to his passive feminine longings and was a source of unconscious gratification for him.

The most important factor, however, which contributed to breaking his spirit was unquestionably the extreme inhibition of his premature and intense sexual desires by the very strict moral code of his environment and particularly of his family. The so common puritanical rejection of everything related to sex was unusually pronounced in his childhood attitude.

Gradually the external intimidation by his father, school discipline, and the moral pressure of his environment became internalized in the form of a severe conscience, the source of his intensive and continuous guilt feelings. Every manifestation of sexual interest, of aggressiveness and competition, became connected with a sense of guilt. He could not win without feeling guilty for it; as a result of this guilt feeling a powerful internal self-thwarting attitude has developed in him. These unconscious guilt feelings explain why, when he later became a business executive, he never could discipline or dismiss anyone without the most severe remorse and self-accusation. He had several dreams in which he first was in the superior position and then compulsively had to identify himself with the underdog.

This self-thwarting attitude was the basis of his extreme self-consciousness, insecurity, inhibition about speaking publicly, and persistent fear of losing his leadership. Only this self-inhibiting influence of his overly severe conscience can account for his gradual slipping back in scholastic achievements and athletics in relation to his brothers. From early puberty on his life consisted of a desperate struggle against this internal self-thwarting tendency, trying in vain to retain his former superior position. When his younger brother once made a remark that on one day of the year they are the same age, he threw him on the floor, shouting at him, "You may be the same age, but you never will have my physical power."

In school and college this struggle centered around scholastic and athletic achievements, and later during his married life around income and social prestige. In his adult years his social circle took over the role of the competitor which his two brothers played in his youth.

It is not my purpose to give the full case history, only as much as is necessary to substantiate the following dynamic reconstruction of his emotional development.

This aggressive and intellectually and physically outstanding young boy reacted to the external pressures he met in his early life, such as school routine and other customary restrictions of the latency period, with rebellion. This provoked his father, who rationalized his emotional reaction to his son's aggressiveness with some educational theory and who tried to break this little rebellious Oedipus. It seems that he succeeded only too well. As has been mentioned before, this submission to his father, to which the little boy first gave in under external compulsion, gradually became erotized, or, in other words, a source of a feminine gratification. As can so often be observed, the ego made the best out of a painful situation. At first he was forced to submit, and did it under protest; later, gradually he began to like it. It must be emphasized, however, that this feminine masochistic attitude remained always unconscious in him. His conscious ego, dominated by masculine pride, never would admit it openly. This unconscious, masochistically colored, feminine, dependent attitude, in combination with the more diffuse and intangible but equally powerful moral pressure mainly represented by his mother, prepared the ground for the extreme sexual inhibitions and guilt feeling which the boy began to show after his eighth year. These sexual inhibitions hit his masculine self-confidence in its core.

As a continuation of the external intimidations, his guilt feeling toward his brothers forced him toward the *inferior position* which already previously had become erotized in relation to his father. Yet the previous position of superiority and leadership developed in him a sense of obligation to live up to the high expectations which everyone had toward him. Tired by these permanent efforts to maintain his leading position, he developed a keen longing for the comfortable dependent though inferior role of the small child. The birth of his younger brother, when he was 11 years old, unquestionably contributed to this regressive longing for the carefree position of the small child. While he had to make desperate efforts to hold on to his leadership and continue to play the role of the hero, there was the example of his little brother, pampered by the mother and enjoying a comfortable carefree existence. His alcoholism—as became fully evident during the analysis—served the purpose of solving this conflict by satisfying both of the conflicting tendencies. On the one hand, drinking meant for him a rebellious act, gave him a spurious feeling of superiority, eliminated his inhibitions, enabled him to give in to his promiscuous sexual tendencies; but on the other hand, the alcohol bottle represented the milk bottle and the feeding mother. Intoxication gave him the same relaxed Nirvana feeling which he probably experienced in his earliest infancy during the act of suckling.

Relation Between Emotional Tensions and Fluctuations of Blood Pressure

Among all the dynamic forces which participated in this complex dynamic equilibrium, the rebellious aggressive tendencies and the concomitant anxiety stood in direct relationship to the fluctuations of the patient's blood pressure. Although he never could express freely these hostile aggressive impulses, they were not deeply repressed into the unconscious. They appeared in aggressive fantasies or during his depressions in self-destructive attitudes. Whenever they were mobilized, his blood pressure rose, whereas in those periods in which he was relatively calm, the blood pressure fell.

I shall submit now the observations concerning the relationship of emotional status and blood pressure readings.

At the beginning and the end of every analytic session, the blood pressure of this patient was measured by a mercury sphygmomanometer and compared with the emotional state of the patient and the

TABLE I

I Emotional State: Very Disturbed	II Emotional State: Somewhat Disturbed		III Emotional State: Calm
1937	1937	1938	1937
Mar. 1...160/120	Mar. 4...150/104	Jan. 5...150/108	Mar. 19...138/ 92
Mar. 2...158/112	Mar. 5...168/118	Jan. 10...152/104	Mar. 22...136/ 94
Mar. 8...162/104	Mar. 16...140/ 96	Jan. 11...152/104	Mar. 26...138/ 96
Mar. 24...160/104	Mar. 17...160/106	Jan. 12...136/ 98	Apr. 1...142/ 96
Mar. 31...158/112	Mar. 18...146/ 98	Jan. 28...158/106	Apr. 2...140/100
May 7...160/110	Mar. 23...152/102	Feb. 1...156/102	Apr. 3...140/ 94
May 17...164/128	Apr. 23...140/106	Feb. 8...148/100	Apr. 6...136/ 92
May 25...174/124	Apr. 25...138/102	Feb. 9...150/104	Apr. 22...150/110
May 27...160/110	Apr. 28...152/102	Feb. 10...140/102	Apr. 27...164/120
June 1...154/114	May 4...136/106	Feb. 11...144/ 92	May 8...132/ 98
June 2...164/104	May 5...144/104	Feb. 14...148/100	May 24...142/106
June 10...172/122	May 6...154/110	Feb. 15...148/102	June 7...148/108
June 15...154/104	May 18...160/110	Feb. 16...146/100	Sept. 10...128/ 90
June 17...160/106	May 21...150/110	Feb. 21...150/108	Sept. 14...152/106
July 2...142/102	May 26...147/103	Feb. 23...142/ 94	Oct. 4...140/100
Sept. 28...168/112	June 3...136/ 96	Feb. 25...140/ 94	Oct. 12...142/106
Sept. 29...174/120	June 4...150/110	Feb. 28...140/ 98	Oct. 18...146/ 98
Sept. 30...164/110	June 8...148/106	Mar. 1...158/106	Oct. 19...142/100
Oct. 1...158/112	June 9...148/108	Mar. 4...148/ 98	Nov. 2...142/102
Oct. 11...156/110	June 11...154/104	Mar. 7...150/100	Nov. 5...146/ 98
Nov. 3...158/110	June 14...146/116	Mar. 16...144/ 98	Nov. 8...138/ 94
Nov. 17...160/110	June 16...144/106	Mar. 21...138/100	Nov. 11...140/ 98
Nov. 18...160/108	June 18...156/110	Mar. 22...146/ 98	Nov. 12...140/ 98
Dec. 13...166/112	June 29...158/106	Mar. 28...142/102	Nov. 15...140/ 98
Dec. 14...160/112	June 30...146/104	Apr. 6...148/110	Nov. 16...144/102
Dec. 23...170/118	July 1...156/106	Apr. 13...144/104	Nov. 29...148/106
1938	July 4...152/106	Apr. 15...142/100	Dec. 3...148/100
Jan. 6...168/114	Sept. 9...146/104	Apr. 18...150/112	Dec. 15...148/110
Jan. 14...156/106	Sept. 13...146/106	Apr. 22...156/108	1938
Jan. 24...166/112	Sept. 16...150/104	Apr. 23...150/106	Jan. 4...140/108
Feb. 4...150/106	Sept. 20...152/110	Apr. 24...154/106	Jan. 17...140/ 90
Feb. 7...150/106	Sept. 21...162/112	May 5...152/108	Jan. 18...146/ 96
Apr. 20...158/104	Sept. 27...152/106	May 9...144/108	Jan. 19...140/ 96
Apr. 25...152/102	Oct. 25...170/120	May 11...152/106	Jan. 20...136/ 98
Apr. 27...158/106	Oct. 26...156/114	May 19...154/104	Jan. 21...136/ 92
May 1...166/116	Oct. 27...154/110	May 20...154/106	Feb. 2...144/ 92
May 2...156/112	Oct. 28...152/108	May 24...152/120	Feb. 17...134/ 92
May 21...162/110	Oct. 29...146/108	Oct. 3...158/108	Feb. 18...142/100
Oct. 11...166/110	Nov. 4...150/108	Nov. 3...146/104	Feb. 24...142/ 96
Oct. 12...146/104	Nov. 9...146/100	Nov. 7...156/102	Mar. 8...146/100
Oct. 13...170/110	Nov. 10...144/102	Nov. 8...166/108	Mar. 10...146/ 98
Oct. 14...148/106	Nov. 19...162/112	Nov. 9...144/ 96	Mar. 11...142/ 96
	Nov. 22...148/102	Nov. 14...148/ 96	Mar. 17...144/ 98
Average: 160/111	Nov. 24...148/104	Nov. 16...146/104	Mar. 18...136/ 92
	Nov. 26...148/104	Nov. 17...150/100	Mar. 29...136/ 98
	Nov. 30...152/106	Nov. 18...150/112	Apr. 14...136/100
	Dec. 1...150/108		Apr. 19...138/104
	Dec. 2...140/108	Average: 150/105	May 4...138/106
	Dec. 6...152/104		May 10...142/104
	Dec. 16...152/110		May 12...142/100
	Dec. 20...164/112		May 16...146/102
	Dec. 21...164/102		May 26...132/ 96
	Dec. 24...152/108		May 31...132/100
			June 1...148/102
			Sept. 8...132/100
			Sept. 9...138/106
			Oct. 4...140/ 98
			Oct. 5...140/ 98
			Oct. 6...144/ 96
			Oct. 7...132/ 92
			Nov. 4...140/102
			Nov. 15...150/106
			Average: 141/ 99

details of the analytic material. The blood pressure was taken at first by a physician who did not treat the patient, and then by the analyst in order to establish the influence of special emotional reactions towards the analyst. However, in the vast majority of readings there was no noticeable difference between the two readings. Furthermore, both observers took several readings.

These observations in Table I can be summarized as follows: In 201 sessions the patient's blood pressure was taken and compared with his emotional state. In 41 interviews the patient's emotional state was *very disturbed,* in 99 interviews *somewhat disturbed,* and in 61 interviews the patient was subjectively *calm.*

His average blood pressure on the basis of all readings was 149/105. During the very disturbed interviews, the average blood pressure was 160/111, and in the calm interviews, 141/99. There were only two very disturbed sessions in which he had a relatively low blood pressure, and both occurred on a day after he had consumed a considerable amount of alcohol. Otherwise the blood pressure functioned almost as a barometer of his emotional state, being high when the patient was emotionally disturbed and lower when he was calm.

Because the patient came to a great number of the analytic sessions after consuming alcohol, the question arose as to the direct effect of alcohol upon the blood pressure. In order to eliminate this complication, in the following chart only those blood pressure readings are considered which were taken when the patient was entirely sober.

As is seen in Table II, here there is no exception from the rule, namely, that during the very disturbed sessions his blood pressure is relatively high (average 161/110 mm.), during the calm sessions considerably lower (average 142/98 mm.).

These observations show a clear correlation between emotional disturbances and change of blood pressure. It is important that in those days when the patient felt calm, and did not show emotional conflicts, his blood pressure was only a little above normal. Therefore one is justified in saying that whenever a marked elevation of his blood pressure above normal was observed, it regularly coincided with a disturbed emotional state.

During the majority of the interviews the blood pressure remained about the same at the end of the session as it was at the beginning. In a number of sessions the blood pressure dropped or rose considerably—15 to 20 points. It is noteworthy that the examination of the analytical material during the sessions when the blood pressure dropped showed marked relief from emotional tension, whereas in the hours when it rose it showed increased resistance and discomfort. The nature of the emotional state which was connected with elevation of the blood pressure can be briefly characterized as a depressed, tense, apprehensive mood, sometimes mixed with some aggressive irritation which, however, the patient never expressed openly but only referred to in a descriptive, calm fashion. When depressed, the patient turned against himself, depreciated himself and his work in many different ways. Such depressive states usually were connected with fearful apprehension. He was concerned lest on account of his inefficiency—which to be sure was merely imagined—he would lose his job and would not be able to support his family. Then his

TABLE II

In Sober State

I Emotional State: Very Disturbed	II Emotional State: Somewhat Disturbed		III Emotional State: Calm
1937	1937	1938	1937
Mar. 1...160/120	Mar. 4...150/104	Jan. 10...152/104	Mar. 19...138/ 92
Mar. 2...158/112	Mar. 5...168/118	Jan. 28...158/106	Apr. 1...142/ 96
Mar. 31...158/112	Mar. 16...140/ 96	Feb. 1...156/102	Apr. 2...140/100
May 25...174/124	Mar. 17...160/106	Feb. 8...148/100	Apr. 3...140/ 94
May 27...160/110	Mar. 18...146/ 98	Feb. 9...150/104	Apr. 6...136/ 92
June 2...164/104	Apr. 25...138/102	Feb. 10...140/102	May 24...142/106
June 15...154/104	May 6...154/110	Feb. 11...144/ 92	Nov. 2...142/102
June 17...160/106	May 18...160/110	Feb. 14...148/100	Nov. 5...146/ 98
Sept. 28...168/112	May 21...150/110	Feb. 15...148/102	Nov. 8...138/ 94
Sept. 29...174/120	May 26...147/103	Feb. 16...146/100	Nov. 11...140/ 98
Sept. 30...164/110	June 3...136/ 96	Feb. 23...142/ 94	Nov. 12...140/ 98
Nov. 3...158/110	June 4...150/110	Feb. 25...140/ 94	Nov. 15...140/ 96
Nov. 17...160/110	June 8...148/106	Mar. 1...158/106	Nov. 16...144/102
Dec. 14...160/112	June 11...154/104	Mar. 4...148/ 98	Nov. 29...148/106
1938	June 14...146/116	Mar. 7...150/100	Dec. 3...148/100
Feb. 7...150/106	June 16...144/106	Mar. 22...146/ 98	Dec. 15...148/110
Apr. 20...158/104	June 18...156/110	Apr. 13...144/104	1938
Apr. 25...152/102	July 4...152/106	Apr. 22...156/108	Jan. 17...140/ 90
Apr. 27...158/106	Sept. 20...152/110	Apr. 23...150/106	Jan. 18...146/ 96
	Nov. 4...150/108	Apr. 24...154/106	Jan. 19...140/ 96
Average: 161/110	Nov. 9...146/100	Nov. 7...156/102	Jan. 21...136/ 92
	Nov. 10...144/102	Nov. 8...166/108	Feb. 2...144/ 92
	Nov. 19...162/112	Nov. 9...144/ 96	Feb. 13...134/ 92
	Nov. 22...148/102	Nov. 14...148/ 96	Feb. 18...142/100
	Nov. 26...148/104	Nov. 16...146/104	Feb. 24...142/ 96
	Nov. 30...152/106	Nov. 17...150/100	Mar. 8...146/100
	Dec. 1...150/108	Nov. 18...150/112	Mar. 10...146/ 98
	Dec. 2...140/108		Mar. 11...142/ 96
	Dec. 6...152/104	Average: 150/104	Mar. 17...144/ 98
	Dec. 16...152/110		Mar. 18...136/ 92
	Dec. 20...162/112		Apr. 14...136/100
	Dec. 21...164/102		May 12...142/100
			Oct. 6...144/ 96
			Nov. 15...150/106
			Average: 142/ 98

only escape would be suicide. In other sessions his self-destructive attitude was mixed with anger and embitterment directed against his superior, but he never expressed these feelings in an emotional, dramatic fashion. Ideas of physically attacking his chief were not uncommon. In the course of his associations these aggressive thoughts regularly led to anxiety and then to self-accusations and self-depreciation. The consecutive phases of this emotional process could be clearly observed, how his hostile impulses created guilt and fear, then became inhibited, and then like a boomerang turned back against his own self.

There is no doubt that the dynamic nucleus of his emotional difficulties consisted of hostile impulses. These led to fear and guilt, and, as the next step, to his depressions. His emotional condition could be best characterized as a state of inhibited hostile aggressive impulses.

In the last part of his analysis the patient entirely lost his depressions, and his emotional tension appeared only in the form of a tense feeling and some vague irritability. Most significant is the fact that during a period of two months, during which the patient's emotional difficulties were reduced to a minimum, when he had no apprehensions about his job, felt calm and contented, his blood pressure did not show the usual extensive fluctuations; his systolic pressure, with the exception of one day, did not surpass 150 mm.; in the last three weeks of this period his diastolic pressure, with the exception of one day, never exceeded 100 mm. This is therefore significant, because, viewing the whole period of the analysis, the variations of his systolic pressure were between 175 mm. and 136 mm., and of the diastolic pressure between 120 mm. and 92 mm.

This analysis is still in progress. One cannot, therefore, as yet draw definite therapeutic conclusions from it, especially not concerning the hypertensive state. So much can be stated, however, that in the course of the analysis the patient has almost entirely recovered from his depressions and has his alcoholic tendencies under much better control. The analysis still cannot be considered as completed because, although the depressions and apprehensions have disappeared and the irritation towards his chief has completely subsided, the patient is still under considerable emotional tension, the ideational content of which is much less defined, however, than it was before. This tension consists mostly in a rebellious feeling against every external routine and limitation. This emotional tension is definitely less than it was before; it has more openly an aggressive connotation and is not turned against himself in the form of depressions and self-accusations. So far as the blood pressure is concerned, in the last eight months the trend was toward a slow but definite decrease of both systolic and diastolic pressures. The day-by-day fluctuations have been around a somewhat lower level, and their range is definitely smaller, with the exception of a period of a few weeks when an extremely traumatic external event upset the patient's emotional equilibrium to a considerable degree. A definite therapeutic conclusion will be possible only if the analysis succeeds in further diminishing the patient's chronic emotional tensions.

Summary

The day-by-day blood pressure fluctuations of a 47-year-old male suffering from a chronic depression, chronic alcoholism, and essential hypertension, have been compared with the daily psychoanalytic material. The patient's overt personality has been described, and the underlying psychodynamic personality structure reconstructed and explained in the light of the emotional development which led up to the adult personality.

A definite correlation has been found between emotional tensions and fluctuations of the blood pressure. The nature of the emotional tensions has been identified as inhibited but not deeply repressed aggressive impulses directed partly inward against the patient's own person in the form of depressions, partly turned outwards in the form of hostile feelings. These emotional states were mixed with an apprehensive worrisome state of mind. Finally it was observed that during a period in which the patient was in an exceptionally calm state, his blood pressure was definitely lower and showed considerably smaller fluctuations. During the last period of treatment, with the diminution of the emotional tensions, there was a slow but definite decrease of the day-by-day fluctuations, and a slow downward tendency of the average blood pressure level.

BIBLIOGRAPHY

1. ALEXANDER, FRANZ, AND CO-WORKERS. The influence of psychological factors upon gastrointestinal disturbances: a symposium. *Psychoanal. Quart.*, 1934, 3, 501-588. (In this volume, page 103.)
2. ALEXANDER, FRANZ, AND HEALY, WILLIAM. *The roots of crime.* New York: Alfred A. Knopf, 1935.
3. CANNON, W. B. *Bodily changes in pain, hunger, fear, and rage.* New York: D. Appleton-Century Co., 1934.
4. DOSTOEVSKY, FEODOR. *Crime and punishment.* New York: Grosset & Dunlap, 1927.
5. FALLADA, HANS. *The world outside.* New York: Simon & Schuster, 1934.
6. HORNEY, KAREN. *The neurotic personality of our time.* New York: W. W. Norton & Co., 1937.

BLOOD PRESSURE FINDINGS IN RELATION TO INHIBITED AGGRESSIONS IN PSYCHOTICS *

By MILTON L. MILLER, M.D.

The study of the psychopathology of repressed hostilities in relation to essential hypertension, by Franz Alexander and his collaborators, suggested to me the possibility of finding elevated blood pressure in two groups of psychotics where there is a high degree of repressed hostility: (a) the depressed group who are self-accusatory and turn the hostility against themselves, and (b) the paranoid group who defend themselves against their hostility by accusing others of aggressive tendencies toward them. Altogether, 193 psychotic patients were studied. Initially a group of 116 psychotics were studied: 60 paranoid, 33 depressed, and 23 schizophrenics. A second group of 77 cases, in which the blood pressure was predicted on the basis of psychological examination before being taken, was used as a control and will be discussed later.

Review of Literature

One finds numerous contradictory reports of both high and low blood pressures in the various mental disorders. None of the following workers gave adequate statistics or adequate psychological descriptions of the patients and of their predominant emotional state at the time when the blood pressure was taken. M. Craig (5) found low blood pressure in cases of patients with excitement, and high pressure in those with depression. In women with acute melancholia he found an average pressure of 150 mm. systolic, in men slightly lower. Excited patients ranged from 95 to 110 mm. H. Alexander (3), in "A Few Observations on the Blood Pressure in Mental Diseases," found elevated blood pressure in melancholia; he found somewhat higher readings in acute mania than Craig reports. Longworth (16) found no constant modification of blood pressure in maniacal and melancholic states in other mental disorders. W. R. Dunton (6) arrived at similar conclusions, again, however, without any correlation with the emotional states of the patients. John Turner (19)

* Psychosomatic Medicine I: 162-172, 1939.

does not agree with the above findings. S. Clark (4) found no characteristic change in average blood pressure in mania or melancholia, and no constant alteration with recovery unless recovery was accompanied by marked improvement in general health. Systolic blood pressure rose after acute excitement in a manner comparable to that of normal individuals after exercise. Sometimes he found a fall due to fatigue. He felt that finer, purposeless movements of the chronic maniac or of agitated melancholia did not influence blood pressure. He makes this statement : "Any changes in mental or emotional state alone, unaccompanied by marked restlessness or energetic motor activity, as a rule did not influence the average blood pressure but occasionally a small rise was observed." His observations and those of Turner coincide in their statement that there was no relation between various forms of mental disorders and blood pressure except in cases of congenital deficiency.

M. C. Hawley (13), without giving case material, concluded that the blood and pulse pressure become raised and are more marked as the restlessness becomes more marked. He found low blood pressures in stuporous cases. The pressure in manic cases was higher than in depressions, while in melancholia the pressure was relatively high in patients in middle life. C. J. Enebuske (7), in discussing manic cases, concluded that the blood pressure is higher than 150 mm. (which he considers the normal level). After the disease has run its course, the tension is then around 150 mm. In manic attacks the pressure may rise to 210 or 250 mm. He found that manic cases in young persons have a higher pressure than depressives of the same age, but that the latter may develop hypertension values over 150 mm. He noted low blood pressure in catatonia, and that some cases of dementia praecox may run a consistently high pressure of 210 to 320 mm. or a consistently low pressure from 90 to 110. He concluded that the elevations are due to (a) presence of vasomotor irritant in the blood producing contraction of peripheral arteries, (b) psychogenic causes such as "false ideas, visual and auditory hallucinations, commands, psychomotor impulses, hypervigilance, strained attention, and efforts of will." The author does not give case histories nor does he discuss the emotional states of the patients. H. Freeman (8) found consistently low blood pressure in a prolonged study of 50 schizophrenics.

From the foregoing account we see that a number of workers have reported considerable elevation in other groups besides acute excitements. These observations have hitherto received no satisfactory explanation. However, N. Reider (17), in a study of the reactions of the blood pressure in psychiatric cases to the cold pressor test, cites three case histories and mentions the connection between repressed aggressions and blood pressure elevation.

Method

The emotional state of each case was determined by a personal interview with the patient before taking the blood pressure, and by the attendants' or nurses' observations. A study of the patient's record also was made. The interview was usually brief and was an attempt to get a dynamic view of the patient's illness by encouraging the patient to discuss his ideas in his own words. Usually leading questions were confined to such remarks as, "Can you tell me why you are in the hospital?" . . . . "What is your opinion as to the reasons for your illness?" Specific stimulus words and attempts to stimulate the patients were avoided. Each interview included a question as to the patient's own reactions to his illness and to the hospital environment. The blood pressure was determined with a standard mercury sphygmomanometer after a period of rest in bed (in most cases) and the average taken of 5 consecutive readings. The physical condition of all patients was noted from the record of the examination. No cases were accepted in this study where there was any evidence of heart disease, arteriosclerosis, renal or any other organic factor which might influence the blood pressure. In all cases urine and Wassermann examinations were negative. In this study care was taken to avoid measuring the blood pressure of psychotic individuals who showed transient emotional flare-ups. Instead, patients were selected in their typical emotional states which had been persisting for some time. A list of suggested patients with various types of emotional disturbances was obtained from the physicians and attendants. Then many of these patients were selected for the study after they were seen by the writer in their typical emotional attitude. Many of the cases displayed the same attitudes weeks and months later. It is a generally accepted fact that in patients with essential hypertension but without mental diseases, the emotional reactions to the doctor influence the blood pressure. In this study special care was taken to avoid such emotional reactions.

It was possible to subdivide the paranoid and depressed psychotics into three groups for each division. The predominant trends were ascertained from an interview with the patient, from the attendants' and nurses' observations, and from a careful study of the history with particular attention to content. The dynamic concept of inhibited aggressions is fully described by Alexander (2) in this symposium, and does not need further elaboration here except to state that the paranoid defends himself against his own hostility by accusing someone else of the aggressive tendencies. In the Paranoids, classification was based on the following criteria:

Paranoids

Group I.—Irritability, anger, suspiciousness, and well-organized persecutory delusions, with intense affect.

Group II.—Clear-cut reduction of the same affective expressions, with a certain amount of complacency.

Group III.—Grandiose megalomanic trend, affording a high degree of narcissistic satisfaction.

It was also possible to classify the Depressions into three groups, as follows:

Depressions

Group I.—Expression of extreme self-deprivation, self-accusation, tension, and obvious severe depression, with considerable anxiety and fear.

Group II.—Hypochondria, moderate tenseness, some anxiety and restlessness, and sadness, but to a less degree than in Group I.

Group III.—Retardation of speech and motion, little ideation; also the stereotyped "crying jag" in which masochistic attitudes are obviously highly erotized. Also characteristic passive, complaining attitudes, showing little fight in relation to the illness —literally "giving up." Hypochondria.

Examples of each type in the Paranoids and Depressed groups follow.

Paranoid I, Case #21, a man of 39, blood pressure 162/113, showed marked distrust of the doctors, the barbers, his relatives, and others in a typically paranoid manner. As shown in his case history as well as present attitudes, his aggressions toward those around him were projected, and therefore constantly stimulated his fears and gave him an apparent excuse to express resentment and anger. In the interview he was suspicious, irritable, evasive, tense, and tremulous. He had a bad taste in his mouth, he said, because his sister put poison in the food. He was sarcastic and angry at the physicians in the receiving hospital who committed him to the State Hospital. He said, "They said I drank and beat my wife. I never drank in my life."

The attendant's observations are as follows: "He is seclusive and hallucinates. He complains of trouble with his digestion (delusion of being poisoned) and constantly wants to go home. He does not give his right name and complains that the attendants annoy him.

He is always trying to make a good impression and insisting there is nothing wrong with him."

A brief abstract of his history reveals the following facts: His work is sporadic, consisting of a series of failures in attempting to earn a living. Twelve days before admission he jumped out of a window and ran through the rain to his sister's house. He waved a crucifix and prayed and talked to Jesus, then ran through the house thinking that someone was going to poison him by gas. He thought all of his family were against him, even his mother, and that people were surrounding the house in order to kill him. He heard men's and women's voices, but could not remember what they said. It is interesting to note that a second examination a week later showed no change in his emotional state or blood pressure—his average blood pressure was 160/105.

An example of Paranoid II is the following: Case #13, a young man of 26, who is tense, somewhat suspicious, ill at ease, and constantly fidgets with his hands. He says spontaneously, "I had several shocks. I lost some money by pickpocketing and robbery. That was just after a nervous experience I had at the city hall when I had to serve on a jury. That gave me a shock. I had planned to go to college. Strange people were acting in a queer way and looking at me peculiarly."

The attendant's observations are: "The patient is quite cooperative but extremely tense and nervous. He is a good worker and gets along fairly well with others."

He was admitted for observation in 1931 because he had been acting strangely, following heat exhaustion a year previously. In 1937 he became irritable, seclusive, and antisocial and showed fear, tension, apprehension, and evasiveness. About 8 months before admission he became angry at his parents and walked out in the rain in his best clothes. His history discloses that for years he had been fearful, apprehensive, seclusive, and suspicious—thinking other people talked about him. Shortly before admission he attacked his sister with a knife. He was admitted voluntarily because he was afraid he would harm someone. The average blood pressure at the time of the writer's examination of him was 145/91.

An example of Paranoid III, Case #16: This 30-year-old woman says, "I am Christ." She claims that she can read the doctors' minds, and that the superintendent of the hospital communicates with her by radio to tell her that she is going home. The patient was the third of 5 children. She was always jealous of the others and felt that she was being discriminated against by her family. She felt superior to most people, and in the hospital claims she is another person, a superman. She thinks she has sexual powers of both man and woman. She maintains a superior attitude in the hospital. Her average blood pressure is 127/90. Such patients as this have regressed to a megalomanic state in which their conflicts have reached a partial solution and their aggressions are not continually being stimulated.

In the depressed patients the intensity of the repressed hostilities was determined by the evidence of self-accusatory ideas and guilt, which indicate the presence of unconscious aggressions that are turned inward against the individual, a familiar psychoanalytic concept (1). The amount of tension accompanying self-accusations seems to measure the strength of the hostility which is repressed. These factors, rather than any others, are from the dynamic point of view found to be diagnostic of an intense depressed state. It was occasionally found, for example, that while a patient may be classified as depressed from the hospital diagnosis, which is usually made a few weeks after admission, a close scrutiny of the patient's emotional state years later might reveal on the one hand a marked withdrawal of the patient from the environment, similar to a schizophrenic state, or on the other hand a matter-of-fact adjustment to somatic delusions unaccompanied by any affect. An example of a depressed patient with intense repressed hostility producing marked guilt is as follows:

Depressed I, Case #63: This patient is a young woman of 30, a college graduate, who had been rather moody during the last four years since the appearance of an inactive goitre. After the death of her roommate at college some months ago, who died as a result of an operation for carcinoma of the breast, the patient has talked about her continuously. She has become increasingly depressed, feels that she is dying and going to hell, that she has committed too many sinful sexual acts and so abused her body that God will never forgive her. She feels that she is paying for the sins of everyone because she denied God, and she has expressed the wish to crack her own head open with a knife or hatchet. The blood pressure was 153/91.

Another example of considerable self-accusation with hostility turned inward is Case #81. She is a 47-year-old married woman who has been depressed for several years. Her statement is, "I killed myself. I blame myself for everything I have done. I hope they don't put it in the papers. I hear mother's voice saying you will still be sorry. Everything I eat makes me sick. I know they don't want me at home. Wherever I go everybody looks at me. I don't look right." The blood pressure was 148/103.

An example of Depressed II, is Case #77, a 45-year-old woman who is cooperative and seems rather passive, sad, and dejected. After the blood pressure was taken she was a little tearful. Her blood pres-

sure at admission in July, 1937, was 120/80. Three weeks later, at
the time of the examination by the writer, the average pressure was
140/105. She had been depressed since her mother's death five years
previously. She complained that she had failed to mix with people
all of her life. Her mother's death was a great blow to her because
they had always been together. The father had died before the patient was born. Increasing irritability toward her husband and increasing depression after the mother's death resulted in frenzied
scratching of her body and frequent crying spells. After about two
weeks in the hospital there was some improvement in the marked
restlessness and crying.

Depressed III: Occasionally one finds depressed patients like
Case #116 who have a low blood pressure (100/80). At first glance
his blood pressure reading would seem to contradict our theory, but
a closer study of the case reveals a psychological state which can be
correlated with the blood pressure. The patient is a 27-year-old unmarried man who for the past two years has had fluctuating depressions and excited, grandiose episodes. The present illness followed
an expansive period of several months' duration in which he felt that
he had an unusual capacity to make large amounts of money and
entered into foolish, grandiose, financial operations in which he ran
up huge bills, etc. In previous hospitalizations he has been euphoric,
irritable, hyperactive, and talkative. From his history it appears that
his mood changes followed difficulties in jobs or business reverses.
His record reveals that he never had any real interest in girls, that
he chided his married brothers for their marriages, was passive and
slow, and showed a lack of initiative. An attack of gonorrhea a year
ago gave him much concern. Six months before the present admission he lost his job, and for the next four months lay in bed and refused to talk to anyone. Just as suddenly a few weeks before admission he became alert, overactive, and grandiose. As he is observed on
the ward, he appears to be extremely passive, deeply preoccupied,
somewhat sad in appearance, and has little to say. He is not agitated
or tense; he is docile, does what he is told by the attendants, sleeps
quite well, but has a poor appetite. About all he says in response to
questions is that he wants to go home. He has no idea of what may
be wrong with him. One gets the impression that this patient has
given up the battle and is getting considerable satisfaction from hospitalization. He has advanced to a state in his psychosis in which he
has renounced competition, withdrawn interest in reality, and is getting satisfaction from a rich fantasy life. There is more than a little
resemblance to the catatonic reaction here. Although the pros and
cons of diagnosis in this case could be discussed at length, from the

dynamic point of view there is no question that his emotional state is one in which there is a "hibernation" so that he undergoes relatively little stimulation of the hostilities against which he is protecting himself. In other words, the patient seems to have "given up," psychologically, for the time being, and in this way avoids his conflicts.

A different type of regression in the depressed emotional state (Depression III) is illustrated in Case #83. This is a woman of 48 who has been hospitalized for several years. Her constant complaint is that she has no bones in her body, has no nerves, and is unable to account for the fact that she exists. She is unusually pleasant, passive, and cooperative. The attendant, who has known her during her entire stay, describes a "rutlike" pattern in which the patient is rather quiet, passive, and withdrawn. She often laughs and talks about her ideas. There is evidently little conflict over her hostilities, which have become diffused and generalized. She indulges in a relatively meaningless expression of somatic delusions which seem to be a partial solution of her conflict. Her blood pressure is low.

In contrast with the more acute emotional disturbances of depressions and paranoia, a group of relatively withdrawn schizophrenics was studied. As has been noted by numerous authors [Freud (11), Tausk (18), and others], in this psychosis conflicts are avoided by means of a marked withdrawal of the ego from painful reality and a return to a relatively early infantile state, the narcissistic state.

Not only the schizophrenics but the other types of cases, as illustrated by the above examples, showed a lower blood pressure when a fair solution of the conflicts was achieved. As was to be expected from the foregoing considerations, the blood pressure was below normal in the majority of schizophrenic cases. This finding of course has been noted in the literature, beginning with the work of Kraepelin (14), by the group working at the Worcester State Hospital (10), and by others, but no dynamic psychological explanation has hitherto been offered. In the narcissistic stage of withdrawal from reality there is little frustration, and consequent diminution or absence of stimulation of hostilities. This would suggest a reason for the "unresponsiveness of the sympathetic system," as expressed by Gottlieb (12). This state could be compared to that of a hibernating animal whose cardiovascular system does not have to respond to rage reactions. Nolan Lewis's (15) findings of hypoplasia in the aorta of dementia praecox patients suggests some connection with the fact that the load on the cardiovascular system has been greatly reduced in these deep states of regression. The slow circulation time [Freeman (9)] might also be explained on the same basis.

Examples of Blood Pressure Correlation with Chronic Emotional States

It is obvious that the blood pressure will fluctuate, depending on the state of the emotions, so that the same individual may show a range of fluctuation. In this study some observations of blood pressure and emotional state were made over a period of several weeks by the writer. A number of cases were found in which the history showed a record of observations of blood pressure over a period of years. When these were correlated with the emotional states as noted also in the history, one could see considerable fluctuation of pressure, varying directly with the emotion. It is obvious that not much can be concluded from single blood pressure observations; nevertheless even these show striking correlation with the emotional states of patients over a period of years. Those observations, taken in 1937, were made by the writer, and are the average of five readings.

For example:

Case #1 admission
    8/34 blood pressure 105/75, passive, cooperative.
    11/25/35 blood pressure 130/80, passive, daydreams a lot.
    5/22/36 blood pressure 126/80, continues passive.
    6/1/37 blood pressure 150/100, tense, sullen, angry, irritable, complains of family persecuting him.
    6/17/37 blood pressure 130/86, passive, cooperative, smiles in silly fashion.

Case #27
    1928 blood pressure 125/60, emotional state not recorded.
    2/34 blood pressure 120/80, pleasant, cooperative.
    8/24/34 blood pressure 170/90, hears voices; hears a boy talking to her; thinks her son was killed.
    1/5/36 blood pressure 144/80, somewhat irritable.
    9/15/37 blood pressure 180/103, tense, angry, intense delusions of persecution.

On the other hand, in Case #37, a depressed man, whose blood pressure was taken several times at different intervals, at each examination the emotional state was approximately the same, and so was the blood pressure.

(Examined by the writer)
    5/31/37 blood pressure 144/90, depressed.
    6/8/37 blood pressure 143/100, depressed.
    6/17/37 blood pressure 136/93, depressed.

In order to test the validity of the hypothesis concerning the relation between repressed aggressions and blood pressure, a control experiment was undertaken. A prediction of the blood pressure was made after an interview was held with the patient in order to determine the state of his hostile emotions. The predicted blood pressure and the classification of the emotional status, according to the groups outlined, were noted on a card. Then the actual blood pressure was taken and checked by another observer. Depressed and paranoid patients were classified into three groups for each disease. The same criteria were used as already described.

The lower limit of predicted blood pressure for the first Paranoid Group was arbitrarily set at 150/100. In the second group the predicted range was 120 to 150 systolic and 80 to 90 diastolic. Under 120/80 was the range used for the third group of predictions.

The following tables will show the results of the predictions as well as the average blood pressure findings in the original group studied.

INITIAL STUDY OF HYPERTENSION IN PSYCHOTICS

PARANOIDS

Age 20–30

Case No.	Age	Sex	Delusions of Persecution	Megalomania	Group	Blood Pressure (average of 5 readings)
1.	24	f	+	−	I	150/100
2.	28	f	+	−	I	138/104
3.	21	m	+	−	I	161/ 82
4.	28	m	+	−	II	135/ 90
5.	27	f	+	−	I	161/ 90
6.	29	m	+	−	II	145/ 90
7.	27	f	+	−	II	140/ 86
8.	27	m	+	−	II	139/ 84
9.	25	m	+	−	I	159/ 98
10.	27	m	+	−	I	154/102
11.	26	m	+	−	I	134/102
12.	25	m	+	−	III	127/ 87
13.	26	m	+	−	I	145/ 91
14.	22	f	+	−	I	142/ 96

Age 30–40

15.	32	f	−	−	II	140/ 80
16.	30	f	−	+	II	127/ 90
17.	33	f	−	+	II	120/ 85
18.	33	f	−	−	II	122/ 90
19.	36	f	+	−	I	125/100
20.	37	f	−	+	II	122/ 89
21.	39	m	+	−	I	162/113
22.	32	m	−	−	III	110/ 80
23.	32	f	+	−	I	140/100
24.	37	m	+	−	I	158/103
25.	39	f	+	−	I	145/ 95

PARANOIDS—Continued

Age 30–40

Case No.	Age	Sex	Delusions of Persecution	Megalomania	Group	Blood Pressure (average of 5 readings)
26.	30	f	+	−	I	153/101
27.	37	f	+	−	I	180/103
28.	39	f	+	−	I	144/ 93
29.	33	f	+	−	I	148/102
30.	38	f	+	+	II	147/ 91
31.	32	m	−	+	III	120/ 86
32.	38	f	+	+	III	134/ 82
33.	37	f	+	+	III	128/ 83
34.	38	f	+	+	II	134/ 95
35.	38	f	+	−	I	172/ 99
36.	34	f	−	+	II	134/ 87
37.	31	m	+	−	I	158/101
38.	33	f	−	+	III	120/ 85
39.	34	m	+	−	I	134/103
40.	40	m	+	−	II	133/ 94
41.	47	m	+	+	II	146/ 86
42.	47	m	−	−	II	137/ 91
43.	40	f	+	−	I	156/ 92
44.	47	f	+	−	II	148/ 85
45.	40	f	+	−	I	156/ 96
46.	44	f	+	−	I	134/103
47.	40	f	+	−	II	145/ 92
48.	41	f	+	−	I	159/ 97
49.	43	m	+	−	I	186/112
50.	49	m	+	−	I	182/110

Age 40–50

51.	40	f	+	−	II	140/ 97
52.	49	f	+	−	I	166/101
53.	41	m	+	−	II	107/ 79
54.	41	f	−	−	II	145/ 86
55.	43	f	+	−	I	197/114

Age 50–60

56.	52	f	+	−	I	155/ 89
57.	52	f	+	−	I	160/ 85
58.	50	m	+	−	I	159/ 96
59.	51	f	+	−	I	150/ 99
60.	60	m	+	−	I	145/ 80

DEPRESSIONS

Age 20–30

Case No.	Age	Sex	Self Accus.	Tense	Somatic Delusions	Guilt	Passive Regression	Group	Blood Pressure
61.	22	m	+	+	−	+	−	I	146/ 80
62.	25	m	+	+	−	+	−	I	140/ 91
63.	29	f	+	+	−	+	−	I	153/ 91
116.	27	m	−	−	−	−	+	III	110/ 80

DEPRESSIONS—Continued

Age 30–40

Case No.	Age	Sex	Self Accus.	Tense	Somatic Delusions	Guilt	Passive Regression	Group	Blood Pressure
64.	30	f	+	+	−	+	−	I	145/ 90
65.	34	f	+	+	+	+	−	I	182/117
66.	35	f	+	+	−	+	−	I	135/102
67.	37	m	+	+	−	+	−	I	143/100
68.	37	f	+	+	−	+	−	I	137/101
69.	38	f	+	+	−	+	−	II	131/ 95

Age 40–50

70.	40	f	+	+	+	+	−	II	142/ 99
71.	40	f	−	−	−	−	+	III	121/ 93
72.	40	f	−	−	−	−	+	III	110/ 77
73.	42	f	+	+	−	+	−	I	142/100
74.	42	m	+	+	−	+	−	I	139/ 90
75.	44	f	+	+	−	+	−	I	144/100
76.	44	f	−	−	−	−	+	III	124/ 80
77.	45	f	+	+	+	+	−	II	140/105
78.	46	f	+	+	−	+	−	I	148/ 98
79.	49	f	+	+	−	+	−	I	191/102
80.	49	f	−	−	−	−	+	III	105/ 78
81.	47	f	+	+	−	+	−	I	148/103
82.	41	f*	−	−	+	−	+	II	138/ 91
83.	48	f	−	−	+	−	+	III	113/ 80
84.	41	f	+	+	−	+	−	II	139/ 86

Age 50–60

85.	52	f	+	+	−	+	−	I	157/104
86.	52	f	+	+	−	+	−	I	210/114
87.	53	f	−	−	−	−	+	III	96/ 73
88.	55	f	−	−	−	−	+	III	100/ 60
89.	57	f	+	+	−	+	−	I	195/112
90.	58	f	+	+	+	+	−	II	158/ 94
91.	60	f	+	−	−	+	+	II	140/ 85
92.	60	f	+	+	−	+	−	I	160/107

* Negress.

SCHIZOPHRENICS (All regressed, passive)

Age 20–30

Case No.	Age	Blood Pressure
93.	25	116/88
94.	23	121/89
95.	26	122/87
96.	23	122/89

Age 30–40

97.	37	125/93
98.	33	106/82
99.	38	122/83
100.	35	104/59
101.	37	116/90
102.	38	127/88
103.	37	113/80

SCHIZOPHRENICS (All regressed, passive)—Continued

Age 30–40

Case No.	Age	Blood Pressure
104.	30	121/80
105.	30	110/90
106.	32	119/60
107.	36	99/36
108.	37	77/55
109.	37	117/88
110.	36	111/86
111.	31	113/80
112.	32	99/80
113.	30	110/90
114.	34	126/75

Age 40–50

115.	41	99/75

CONTROL STUDY

Classification	Case No.	Predicted B.P.	Observed B.P. (Average of 5)
Paranoid I	118	above 150	117/ 80
	119		110/ 90
	120		155/109
	121		154/ 80
	122		168/ 89
	123		158/ 90
	124		163/ 94
	125		168/107
	126		138/ 84
	127		205/115
	128		177/ 88
Paranoid II	129	120 to 150	142/ 82
	130		157/ 87
	131		155/ 91
	132		145/ 87
	133		101/ 78
	134		140/ 82
	135		147/ 89
	136		138/ 82
	137		123/ 79
	138		119/ 79
	139		144/ 76
	140		126/ 73
	141		137/ 88
	142		130/ 98
	143		132/ 90
	144		132/ 83
Paranoid III	145	below 120	97/ 70
	146		110/ 80
	147		107/ 74
	148		133/ 91
	149		107/ 74
	150		94/ 75
	151		110/ 76
	152		114/ 77

Classification	Case No.	Predicted B.P.	Observed B.P. (Average of 5)
Depressed I	153	above 150	165/105
	154		170/ 92
	155		122/ 80
	156		172/112
	157		124/ 70
	158		158/100
	159		163/ 80
	160		168/112
	161		177/105
	162		120/ 84
	163		162/116
	164		162/100
Depressed II	165	120 to 150	128/ 83
	166		143/109
	167		113/ 90
	168		130/ 80
	169		126/ 80
	170		99/ 80
	171		131/ 90
	172		125/ 75
	173		167/114
	174		97/ 70
	175		123/ 82
Depressed III	176	below 120	109/ 72
	177		118/ 90
	178		134/ 86
	179		138/ 85
	180		95/ 60
	181		110/ 76
	182		97/ 79
	183		113/ 83
	184		116/ 80
	185		112/ 86
	186		113/ 70
	187		110/ 70
	188		107/ 71
	189		110/ 80
	190		100/ 76
	191		92/ 75
	192		105/ 80
	193		123/ 84
	194		96/ 70

PREDICTIONS OF BLOOD PRESSURE IN PSYCHOTIC PATIENTS ON BASIS OF ESTIMATION OF REPRESSED HOSTILITY (Systolic)

Classification	No. of Cases	No. Correctly Predicted	% Correctly Predicted
Paranoid I (above 150)..................	11	8	72.7%
Paranoid II (120–150)...................	16	12	75%
Paranoid III (below 120)................	8	7	87%
Depressed I (above 150)................	12	9	75%
Depressed II (120–150).................	11	7	63.6%
Depressed III (below 120)..............	19	16	84.4%
	77	57	74%

AVERAGE BLOOD PRESSURES

Classification	Original Study		Controls		Total	
	No. of Cases	Av. B.P.	No. of Cases	Av. B.P.	No. of Cases	Av. B.P.
Paranoid I..........	34	155/95	11	155/93	45	155/94.5
Paranoid II.........	20	136/88	16	135/84	36	135.5/86
Paranoid III........	6	118/83	8	109/77	14	113/79
Depressed I.........	18	157/100	12	155/96	30	156/98
Depressed II........	7	141/93	11	126/86	18	132/88.7
Depressed III.......	8	110/78	19	110/77	27	110/77
Schizophrenics......	23	112/79				

Discussion of the Tables. In discussing the results of the predictions of blood pressures in the various groups, it is pertinent to ask whether or not the accuracy is higher than might be arrived at by chance. With the help of a statistician, Dr. M. W. Richardson, of the Department of Psychology at the University of Chicago, it was shown that the correlations are much higher than chance would warrant.

An estimate was made of the standard error of the systolic blood pressure, in the original study and in the predicted cases, for the three group classifications; the differences between the means of the group classifications are clearly within the accepted level of statistical significance. Thus, for example, the standard error for the average finding of 155 mm. of systolic pressure in the original and the control Paranoid I group is 1.0. The standard error for Group II in the Paranoid series was 1.3 for the initial study and 1.4 for the controls. The standard error of the difference between the average systolic blood pressure of Groups I and II is 1.7. This includes the predicted group. The remainder shows similar close correlations.

In the control group of the 11 individuals who, from the clinical examination of the emotional status, belong to the group of Paranoid I, 72.7 per cent are correctly placed in the systolic blood pressure category. This percentage is to be compared with 28.6 of the total paranoid individuals falling in this class, that is, a prediction of 150 mm. systolic or over. The essential or correct prediction over chance is 44 per cent, with a standard error of 13. This figure, then, becomes highly significant, since 44 per cent is over three times the standard error. In the second group of paranoid individuals it is plus or minus 9.8. The excess over chance in this group is four times the standard error. In the third group of Paranoids the standard error is plus or minus 4.

In the Depressions the excess percentage of correct cases is a little less than three times the standard error, and in the third group, that is, Depressed III, the excess is five times the standard error.

It will be noted that there is a much higher correct prediction rate when systolic pressure only is used as an indication. Predictions had also been made on the basis of diastolic pressures, but it was found that the percentage of correct predictions showed a great deal of variation and that it was impossible to make consistently correct predictions. The findings seem to indicate that there is a functional correlation between the emotional status and the systolic pressure.

It was possible to subdivide the depressed and paranoid patients into three groups according to the intensity of the emotion, as already outlined. It will be noted, however, that fewer successes in predictions were made in Group I Paranoids and in Group II Depressed. Actually it is quite difficult sometimes to distinguish a depression of moderate degree from an intense depression because of the fact that external manifestations may be rather similar. Further study is needed to work out more exact criteria for differentiation.

From the empirical observation of the patients' emotional states, a classification was made into three groups which were correlated with the blood pressure. The interpretation was made that it is the state of the repressed aggressions which is the main factor in stimulating the blood pressure elevations. Of course it is possible that anxiety may also be a factor in producing blood pressure elevation, but this anxiety probably is connected with repressed aggressions.

In the 193 cases studied, there appears to be a significant correlation between the repressed hostile emotion and the degree of elevation of blood pressure. The study suggests that where there is a chronic psychological tension arising out of chronic inhibited hostile impulses, chronic elevation of blood pressure may result. Further studies of similar groups continued over a long period of time are needed to show the extent of variations and fluctuations of the blood pressures of psychotics. It is suggested that in psychotics with an intense degree of repressed aggression, permanent damage to the cardiovascular system occurs as a result of long-sustained hypertension (2). Conversely, those patients with a high degree of passive regression throw little strain on the cardiovascular system. It would appear from the above findings that the study of the blood pressure of a psychotic individual could be utilized in a practical way. For example, if an active paranoid or depressed patient's blood pressure drops considerably, it would be a good indication that a considerable amount of regression is taking place, and that the patient is making a passive infantile adjustment to the hospital. On the other hand, a rising blood pressure in a paranoid patient might be a danger signal of an impending disturbed state. Similarly, an elevated or rising pressure in a depressed patient would be a warning that the repressed hostilities are being directed inward and that a suicidal danger is present.

Summary

A study of the correlation between the emotional status and the blood pressure of 193 psychotic individuals was made. A significant degree of correlation was found. It is possible to divide both paranoid and depressed psychotic individuals into 3 groups on the basis of a clinical examination of their emotional status. This offers a ready and convenient estimate of the dynamic state of the emotions in these groups. The blood pressure findings may be significant in diagnosis and prognosis.

BIBLIOGRAPHY

1. ABRAHAM, KARL. Selected papers: manic-depressive states and the pregenital levels of the libido. London: Hogarth Press, 1927.
2. ALEXANDER, FRANZ. Emotional factors in essential hypertension. Psychosom. Med., 1939, 1, 173. (In this volume, page 289.)
3. ALEXANDER, H. A few observations on the blood pressure in mental diseases. Lancet, 1902, 163, 18.
4. CLARKE, S. The blood pressure in mental disorders. J. ment. Sci., 1910, 56, 96.
5. CRAIG, M. Lancet, 1898 (June 25).
6. DUNTON, W. R. Some observations upon blood pressure in the insane. Boston med. surg. J., 1903, 149, 422.
7. ENEBUSKE, C. J. On vasomotor unrest in the insane; studies based on 20,000 measurements of the tension and the radial pulse in 250 cases of various forms of insanity. Boston med. surg. J., 1917, 176, 385.
8. FREEMAN, H. Effects of "habituation" on blood pressure in schizophrenics. Arch. Neurol. Psychiat., 1933, 29, 138.
9. FREEMAN, H. Variability of circulation time in normal and in schizophrenic subjects. Arch. Neurol. Psychiat., 1938, 39, 488.
10. FREEMAN, H., HOSKINS, R. G., AND SLEEPER, F. H. The blood pressure in schizophrenia. Arch. Neurol. Psychiat., 1932, 27, 333.
11. FREUD, SIGMUND. On narcissism: an introduction. In Collected papers, Vol. 4. London: Hogarth Press, 1925.
12. GOTTLIEB, J. S. Relationship of systolic to diastolic blood pressure in schizophrenics. Arch. Neurol. Psychiat., 1936, 35, 1256.
13. HAWLEY, M. C. Studies of blood pressure in states of excitement and depression. Arch. interm. Med., 1913, 12, 526.
14. KRAEPELIN, E. Dementia praecox. Edinburgh: Livingstone, 1919.
15. LEWIS, N. D. C. The constitutional factor in dementia praecox. New York: Nervous & Mental Disease Publishing Company, 1923.
16. LONGWORTH, S. G. Blood pressure in mental disorders. Brit. med. J., 1911, 1, 1366.
17. REIDER, N. Blood pressure studies on psychiatric patients. Bull. Menninger Clin., 1938, 2, 65.
18. TAUSK, V. On the origin of the "influencing machine" in schizophrenia. Psychoanal. Quart., 1933, 2, 519.
19. TURNER, J. Observations on the blood pressure and vascular diseases in the female insane. J. ment. Sci., 1909, 55, 418.

THE STATUS OF THE EMOTIONS IN PALPITA-
TION AND EXTRASYSTOLES WITH A NOTE ON
EFFORT SYNDROME *

By Milton L. Miller, M.D.,
AND
Helen V. McLean, M.D.

For centuries it has been recognized that the heart is particularly susceptible to emotional stimuli. One of the earliest cardiac diagnoses in accordance with this recognition was made by Avicenna (1) in the tenth century:

A certain young man of Gurgan, by the Caspian Sea, lay sick of a malady which baffled all the local doctors. Avicenna (his identity being then unknown) was invited to give his opinion, and, after examining the patient, requested the collaboration of someone who knew all the districts and towns of the province, and who repeated the names while Avicenna kept his finger on the patient's pulse. At the mention of a certain town he felt a flutter in the pulse. "Now," he said, "I need someone who knows all the houses, streets, and quarters of the town." Again a certain street was mentioned, and the same phenomenon was repeated, and a third time, when the names of the inhabitants of a certain household were enumerated. Then Avicenna said, "It is finished. This lad is in love with such and such a girl who lives at such and such an address; and the girl's face is the patient's cure." They were brought together and married and the cure was completed.

In this case the patient had repressed the entire conflict, even his awareness of love for the girl. The physician perceived a part of his patient's conflict (love) but not the fear which it engendered.

Extrasystoles produced as a result of emotional stimuli are mentioned by Wittkower as having been first observed by Nasse (13) in 1818. During the past two decades the development of diagnostic methods has made for much greater precision in differentiating organic from functional heart disease, and has led to a recognition that at least 50 per cent of the patients who consult a physician because of heart symptoms have no demonstrable organic lesion of the cardio-

* The Psychoanalytic Quarterly X: 545-560, 1941.

vascular system, and that even where actual cardiopathology can be proved there are 30 to 35 per cent of these symptoms which cannot be explained on an organic basis but which are functional in character.

Among the numerous cardiologists who have studied cardiac neuroses alone or in conjunction with organic heart disease, outstanding contributions have been made by Ryle (14), MacWilliam (12), and MacKenzie (11) in England; Connor (4), White (17) and his co-workers, Kilgore (8), Christian (3), Boas (2), and Weiss (15), in this country. In such contributions the physiopathological aspects of the problem are dealt with exhaustively. The psychopathological descriptions, however, are in general terms such as, "emotional disturbance," "worry," "grief."

In *Emotions and Bodily Changes,* Dunbar (5) has summarized the psychological findings in the literature pertaining to cardiac neuroses up to 1938. From all the attempts to delineate the emotional situation which may be in causal relation to the cardiac symptoms, up to that date, of chief interest are the findings of MacWilliam (12), Wolfe (19), Karl Menninger (9), and William Menninger (10).

MacWilliam (12), in studying the effect of dreams on circulation, noted marked palpitation, increased heart action, increased pulse rate, and greatly raised blood pressure in an individual who awoke after a dream "in which he felt lively resentment at the irritating conduct of an official on a public occasion." From his studies Mac-William (12) concluded that such an emotional disturbance in sleep may cause hemorrhage, anginal attacks, or even ventricular fibrillation.

Lewis Gunther and Karl Menninger (7) made electrocardiographic records of a female patient who had intermittent attacks of extrasystoles when she was being prepared for a pelvic examination and while the examination was being made. Her history showed that she had considerable conflict over sexuality. While the case was not explored in great dynamic detail, the authors suggest that the anxiety connected with sexual stimulation contained an element of hostility, and that both fear and hate were "expressed autoplastically." Psychoanalytic observations upon cardiac disorders are reported by Karl and William Menninger (9), and in a later paper by William Menninger (10). They stress the importance of unconscious factors which may be associated with the production of cardiac symptoms. In a summary of their observations the authors state that "the heart disease and heart symptoms are sometimes reflections of strongly aggressive tendencies which have been totally repressed, and appear characteristically in a man who is strongly attached to the father and hostile to the mother." The hostility to the father is repressed, and if the father has heart disease or heart symptoms the patient "includes these symptoms in his identification with the father to carry out the inexpressible patricidal impulses reflexively by unconscious focal suicide."

William Menninger (10), in a later paper, points out the connection between cardiac symptoms and repressed unconscious hostilities.

In a paper entitled "Effort Syndrome," published by Wittkower, Rodger, and Wilson (18), in Lancet in April, 1941, the findings in 50 cases of soldiers between the ages of 20 and 50, all suffering from effort syndrome, are described and classified. This study is in harmony with our own psychoanalytic findings and corroborates impressions we received regarding the unconscious conflicts of our own 4 psychoanalyzed patients suffering from similar functional cardiac symptoms.

In the soldiers studied by Wittkower and his associates (18), cardiac symptoms were among the most prominent and consisted of cardiac pain, palpitation, "fluttering in the chest, as if the heart was going to stop or burst—usually connected with fear of impending death." They found that the soldiers fell into five personality groups: those in Group I (twenty) were characterized mainly by "a keen sense of duty and by a rigid superficial and deep morality, and with severe repression of their aggressiveness"; Group II (eleven) showed a similar structure, but were less inhibited in their aggressiveness, and particularly tended to be defensive of the "underdog"; Group III (only three) apparently overcompensated with overaggressiveness, but then took flight into illness; Group IV (twelve) were constitutionally of inferior physique, too much attached to their mothers; Group V were quitters who seemed to have inadequate egos and to have given up the battle in their early years. Although these five groups present superficial contrasts, fundamentally they all appear to present the same basic structure—conflicts about the same issues which were a source of difficulty in our own four patients. All of these fifty soldiers had chronic personality difficulties which seemed to bear directly upon their cardiac illnesses.

Before we give the specific emotional setting in which palpitation, precordial pain, and extrasystoles occurred in our own patients, we wish to digress in order to mention a dream of Freud (6), which he quotes in *The Interpretation of Dreams,* and from which he awoke with palpitation.

I tell my wife I have some news for her, something very special. She becomes frightened, and does not wish to hear it. I assure her that on the contrary it is something which will please her greatly, and I begin to tell her that our son's officers' corps has sent a sum of money (5,000 k.) . . . something about honorable mention . . . distribution . . . at the same time I have gone with her into a small room, like a storeroom, in order to fetch something from it. Suddenly I see my son appear; he is not in uniform, but rather in a tight-fitting sports suit (like a seal?) with a small cap. He climbs onto a basket which stands to one side near a chest in order to put something on this chest. I address him; no answer. It seems to me that his face or forehead is bandaged; he arranges something in his mouth, pushing something into it. Also his hair shows a glint of grey. I reflect: Can he be so exhausted? And has he false teeth? Before I can address him again, *I awake without anxiety but with palpitations.* My clock points to 2:30 A.M.

In his associations Freud (6) recognizes his own competitive attitude towards his son and the envy of his son's youth.

CASE 1. A conscientious young business man of austere upbringing came to analysis because of hypochondriacal fears, especially related to his heart. He was afraid that he might die of heart disease. For six months he had felt a dull ache over his heart, and occasionally mild pains in his left arm as well as palpitation and extrasystoles. A physical examination prior to the beginning of his analysis was negative. A recent electrocardiogram showed some slurring of the R-S complex and a left axis deviation. There was a slight sinus arrythmia but no extrasystoles. The cardiologist interpreted the electrocardiographic findings as a result of childhood diphtheria and scarlet fever.

In the initial interviews, the patient, who is very intelligent, seemed unduly meek and subservient. This paralleled his attitude of passive submission to his father. Later, when he mentioned his father, he gave an important clue to the unconscious origin of his difficulties by a casual remark. His father had died three years before of a second attack of coronary occlusion preceded by a period of angina pectoris. The patient mentioned the first coronary occlusion, and added in an offhand manner, "That didn't finish him, he lived for six months after that."

The patient's cardiac symptoms, which had been especially prominent for six months, coincided with the beginning of his work in a minor capacity in the business concern which his father had been instrumental in founding and which bore his father's name. The symptoms coincided also with the time of year of his father's coronary attack.

In his life to date the patient had been passive, compliant, and had always preferred the easy way. He had been unable to decide on a career, and at college had been most interested in precisely those subjects about which his father knew little. When he finished college he wanted his father to arrange a sinecure in the business for him, but he was refused. He was employed in a bank for several years, where he did poor work and felt bitter about the fact that his father's partners were getting good jobs in the business for their own sons. After his father's death the patient went to work in the family business but harbored resentment towards the president, formerly his father's partner, because he offered the patient only a minor position.

The patient's unconscious competitive attitude towards his father is dramatically illustrated in a dream which recurred several times at the beginning of the analysis.

His father is not quite dead, but, over a long period of time, is suffering, writhing and groaning.

His associations refer to his fear and resentment of his father, his feeling that the father never helped him enough, and his worry over his own cardiac symptoms, namely, palpitation, extrasystoles, and numbness of the left arm.

During an interruption in the analysis, the patient had two dreams which he reported when the analysis was resumed. The first was accompanied by several weeks of extrasystoles, the second by intense palpitation and fear of imminent death.

First Dream: I thought father had heard about my having an automobile accident, running into another fellow's car, after I had had a few drinks. I tried to keep it a secret. Father tried to get me to meet him face to face and have it out. I didn't want to.

His associations referred to his learning that he was to be a candidate for the presidency of a tennis club of which he was a member. This news preceded the dream. He reacted with intense fear, violent palpitation, and extrasystoles at the thought that he might be elected and have to make a speech at the banquet. He unconsciously equated the possibility of his election with a victory over his father, hence the intense fear and the guilt in the dream. This dream also represented his wish to resume analysis.

The second dream, which occurred a few weeks later, gives us further insight into his unconscious attitude towards his father.

Second Dream: On the ceiling of the family's summer cottage there were two spiders together in some kind of movement. The male was a hairy tarantula, the female was beautiful like a dove.

The patient awoke with violent palpitation and fear, and thought of his father's death. He associated his father as the tarantula and his mother as the female spider. He had often felt his father was dirty, crude, etc., and had always felt the same attitude towards sexual intercourse. He had a lifelong fear of spiders. Further associations referred to the first dream of the automobile accident. The second dream reveals one of the important sources of the patient's unconscious hostility towards his father, namely, envy of the father's sexual relation to the mother, which he actually witnessed repeatedly since he slept in the parents' bedroom until he was seven or eight years old.

In a later hour he was fearful, tense, felt his face alternately flush and grow pale, and experienced some extrasystoles. These symptoms occurred during a session in which he related a dream in which he won in a competition with another man, had intercourse with a girl, and then felt guilty. He recalled his fear of his father and his confusion at 6 years of age when he learned that his mother was going to have another child and vaguely realized the role his father played.

For a few weeks following the resumption of the analysis the patient continued to experience frequent extrasystoles daily. An interesting example was the patient's response to an interpretation with an extrasystole. During this hour he was expressing his anger at his wife's recent pregnancy and his unwillingness to take on the added responsibility, by depreciating and criticizing her. When the interpretation was made that he avoided analysis of his attitude towards his wife, since it is connected in his mind with his previous attitudes towards his mother, he immediately responded with an extrasystole and remembered his fear of his father as well as his envious hostile attitude towards his superiors.

CASE 2. A college student came to analysis because of marked tenseness, inability to choose a career, and a history of previous nervous breakdowns. His father was a strict, stern, intensely competitive, Napoleonic type of business man with whom the patient felt unable to compete. However he tried to outdo him in scholarly achievement, and in his daily life was exceedingly submissive to his father. He tried to repress his passive homosexual attitude, but it found expression towards other men in his efforts to exhibit himself intellectually. This patient's hostility was nearer to the surface than that of the first patient described. He got into trouble frequently but always took flight into ill health.

During the analysis he often experienced palpitation and sometimes extrasystoles connected with his feelings towards his father, especially when he was becoming conscious of death wishes towards him. On one such occasion he perspired, felt anxious, noticed some tachycardia, marked dyspnea, and pounding of the heart.

Such an emotional situation is clearly illustrated by a dream during this period.

> My father was lying down in great distress physically. He had a heart attack, and his pulse was very rapid.

The patient associated his father's attacks of gastrointestinal distress and recalled his father's fear of death. Then he recalled that he was told by the family physician that he was a replica of his father. He wished his father would die, then remembered that he himself had always had fears about his heart. He added, "Maybe I was afraid he would die and maybe I felt he would bring some kind of attack on me because I wished it on him."

CASE 3. A 40-year-old chemist sought treatment because of generalized dissatisfaction with his personal life, frequent periodic drinking, and repeated attacks of extrasystoles. He had been brought up in a pious atmosphere. All of his conscious anxiety was related to his fear of the consequences of his drinking bouts and to the extrasystoles. At certain periods showers of extrasystoles would recur during one to several days. Then for no apparent reason they would disappear. His heart had been examined several times by cardiologists and had been found organically sound. In spite of reassurance he continued to be obsessed by the fear that he would die of heart disease as his father had.

The patient was the fourth of six children. Neither the patient nor any of his siblings had ever married. Consciously he depreciated marriage and emphasized the disadvantages of being tied down to one woman and a responsible relationship. Unconsciously he revealed intensely rivalrous hostility against any man with a wife and a well-established home. In his profession he had as his immediate superior a man really inferior to the patient in intellectual capacity. Whenever his competitive urges began to interfere with his passive relation to this superior, he would begin drinking. The self-destructive nature of the drinking was clearly shown by the fact that he would drink himself into unconsciousness in his laboratory, where he could have been discovered and discharged. Occasionally his work and his own narcissism required that he equal or excel his superior in a way calculated to arouse the anger of this man. During such periods the extrasystoles occurred, subsiding when the patient could once more slip back into a passive submissive relation to his superior. Whenever the patient was struggling against a sexual interest in the analyst's wife, and against a wish to marry a woman who represented his mother, he would have showers of extrasystoles during the time such matters were under discussion. Unconsciously the patient felt positively identified with his father. His hostility towards any father figure arose whenever he felt propelled to engage in a rivalrous struggle with a loved father. He attempted to hide his sexual interest in a mother figure by a conscious depreciation or scornful attitude towards her. When this failed, and when he was becoming conscious of his jealous rage against a father-substitute, he expressed autoplastically symptoms similar to those which had caused the father's death.

CASE 4. A conscientious, ambitious woman, who had been brought up in a strictly moralistic household, had been under treatment for some years when she reported that three weeks previously she had for the first time in her life begun to suffer pain around her heart associated with single or multiple additional heartbeats. She was frightened that she might have some form of organic heart disease, although she told herself that the cardiac symptoms were undoubtedly caused by some emotional tension. She consulted an internist, who, after a thorough physical and electrocardiographic examination, reassured her that her heart was organically sound. The precordial pain and extrasystoles continued, however, for several days following the internist's reassurance. After the patient awoke from a dream, the meaning of which was in part clear to her, the cardiac symptoms disappeared and had not recurred up to the time of consultation with the woman psychiatrist. Two days later the patient wrote to the psychiatrist giving further associations to the dream. While writing this letter the precordial pain momentarily recurred. The essential history of the patient is as follows. She is a 48-year-old unmarried woman who had been successful in the nursing profession. She had been a rather withdrawn, slightly eccentric individual, but, viewed superficially, her professional and social adjustment seemed adequate. During 1931–1932 she had her first sexual affair. Her lover was a man six years younger than the patient. In many physical and mental characteristics he resembled the patient's father. His given name was even the same as her father's name. The patient had developed increasing anxiety which made her withdraw from all professional and social contacts, but during the past eight years a gradual process of rehabilitation had taken place. Later the patient was offered an excellent position. She became immediately anxious, predicting that she would only fail. While she was attempting to reach a decision about the job, her psychiatrist went away for ten days. It was then that the cardiac symptoms appeared.

During the recent consultation she said, "I've always been afraid of heart disease because I remember as a small child hearing a doctor say, 'That one will die of heart disease.' Then I always thought mother died of heart disease. [The patient's mother died when she was 8 years of age.] That's why I was so worried over the pain and extrasystoles. In the dream you were a French woman, not very tidy and a little too fat. You were singing songs in some place like the Institute where there were a lot of men around you. You were singing, '*Je ne sais pas ce que je suis.*' You were French, immoral, and loose. From what you were singing you must also have been me or my mother." The patient gave further associations in a letter written two days later: "I must write to add what I know I did not include in the dream. The woman was diseased, venereal, or leprous —also infectious, and the skin was white like your skin, like camellias. I tell myself this and try to convince myself it is not like funeral or wedding flowers. They are a carnage. I think of my mother after she died. Perhaps when much affected one feels she is placing a spell by thinking a thing and in wishing a mother dead; one killed her. Once was enough without doing so to you. After all, the woman in the dream was a prostitute. In writing this sentence I had a pain in my heart for the first time in several days. I wish all social workers, teachers, and especially nurses, exploded and blown away."

The meaning of the dream is clear. In re-establishing herself in her profession, the patient felt that she was competing not in a professional sense alone but also in a sexual way with her psychiatrist. If the psychiatrist were dead of heart disease, like her mother, she could then be in her place surrounded by men. At the very moment when her hostile competitive attitude was becoming conscious, fear of retaliation and fear of loss of her psychiatrist's love overwhelmed her. As a punishment for her hostility she identified herself with her mother who died of heart disease. A temporary relief from her cardiac symptoms came as a result of spontaneous insight into the sexually competitive meaning of the dream. With the complete confession, not alone of her sexual rivalry with the psychiatrist but also of her death wish, intense fear of retaliation again caused momentary cardiac disturbance.

Discussion

It is clear that the appearance of palpitation and extrasystoles in the patients we have described is connected with anxiety. What are the specific emotional situations with which this anxiety is connected?

An outstanding feature in our cases is the fact that the symptoms always appeared at a time in the analytic situation when the defenses had been worked through and the strong competitive attitude towards the parent of the same sex appeared. In each case our patients gave the impression that the parent of the same sex represented an overwhelming, fearful adversary with whom they had always unconsciously been engaged in a desperate struggle—a struggle which they wished to avoid at all costs because this parent was also unconsciously a loved person; in life they expressed this love in the form of a strongly submissive attitude. To submit rather than to fight was the keynote of their lives.

As the analysis proceeded to the exposure of the conflict with the parent of the same sex, the patients were impelled towards a more active and aggressive attitude. This did not necessarily express itself directly in sexual competition, but the patients felt that they must prepare to engage in competition with a powerful rival. The active attitude, as the analysis brought it nearer to consciousness, was blocked for the following reasons: (a) the competitive aggressive attitude aroused too much guilt, and the punishment for such hostility was often expressed by means of identification with the cardiac symptoms of the parent; (b) the competitive urge threatened dependence upon the loved parent and aroused fear of losing the parent's love. This strong attachment inhibited the patient's flight.

Identification with a parent of the same sex who had cardiac symptoms has been mentioned as a feature of three of our four cases, and in two cases which Dr. Thomas French mentioned to us in a verbal communication. The ambivalence in our patients expressed in the identification with the heart symptoms of a parent is characterized by the dominance of the unconscious love for the rival parent, and dependence upon him, as opposed to concomitant hostility. Although functional cardiac symptoms also occur when neither of the parents have had heart disease, cardiologists have long noted the frequency of their incidence in relatives or close associates of patients with cardiac neuroses. However, although our patients identify with the parent's heart disease in connection with a specific emotional situation, they do not have the same symptoms as the parent. For instance the business man (first case), whose father had died of a coronary attack and who previously had suffered with angina pectoris, had palpitation and extrasystoles. The onset of such cardiac symptoms mobilizes hypochondriacal fear which then contributes further to the anxiety and is used by the patient as a rationalization for the anxiety.

Upon going over the case records summarized in the paper of Wittkower, Rodger, and Wilson (18), we observed in the majority of them the following similarity to our own patients: when an increased competitive drive was demanded of these individuals, they were unable to direct aggressive energy toward the competitive goal and instead of being vented in actual muscular activity the stimulated energy apparently was transformed into cardiac symptoms. Especially in Group I, there was a "fear of showing fear," and it would seem that the superego conflict apparently blocked the impulse towards flight as well as the impulse to fight.

Wittkower and his associates (18) emphasize the strong sense of morality, religion, conscience, and duty found in so many of their effort syndrome patients, and contrast the stern, religiously moral type with the colitis type whose conscience demands overcleanliness, and the peptic ulcer patients who are conscientious about earning their "bread and butter." [2]

Palpitation is a biological manifestation of fear in the face of danger. The increased pulse rate and intensified heart action make the individual subjectively aware of the increased activity of the heart. Situations which produce palpitation involve an immediate urge to activity and at the same time fear of it. Common examples are: palpitation experienced upon receiving a rebuke from one's superior, taking an examination, going to a forbidden amatory rendezvous, and the like. In all these situations the individual is driven by his active, ambitious attitude into an apparent danger which at the same time he feels an urge to avoid. His flight is blocked.

Our patients react to competitive situations similarly. The competitive activity, if it had been carried out, would normally have been discharged in muscular movement; instead, it appeared in the form of cardiac responses. Their analyses pointed clearly to the origin of the conflict in the oedipal situation. While all of our cases experienced extrasystoles as well as palpitation, it is not clear just why extrasystoles occur in the specific emotional situation described; perhaps further physiological studies may throw light on this question.

In the psychoanalytic treatment, the dangerous situation had to

---

[2] Connected with the effort syndrome, they found breathlessness and depression very frequently present. Respiratory illness was frequently associated with onset of cardiac symptoms. We believe it is possible that the breathlessness and respiratory symptoms are associated with fear of separation from an object upon whom the patient is dependent, and the depression may be connected with guilt over hostility to the loved person. See French, Thomas M., and Alexander, Franz et al. Psychogenic factors in bronchial asthma. *Psychosom Med. Monograph* 4, 1941.

be faced, and when the relation betwen the symptoms and the emotional situation became clarified, the symptoms improved.

It is interesting to compare our cases of palpitation and extrasystoles with hypertensive cases studied psychoanalytically at the Chicago Institute for Psychoanalysis. The hypertension cases appear to be fixated at a constant, strongly rebellious attitude towards the rival parent. As French has stated, they appear to be fixated on an obstacle which prevents them from approaching their goal but from which they cannot retreat. In the hypertensive cases the emphasis is on rebellion as a protest against a strong unconscious passive submissive attitude. By contrast our patients suffered from palpitation when they were much nearer to tackling the competitive situation but were inhibited at the point of expressing competitive hostility.

BIBLIOGRAPHY

1. AVICENNA. Quoted in WHITWELL, J. R. *Historical notes on psychiatry.* London: Lewis & Co., 1936.
2. BOAS, E. P. Neurogenic disorders of the heart. *Amer. J. med. Sci.,* 1928, 156, 789.
3. CHRISTIAN, H. A. Diagnosis and treatment of diseases of the heart. *J. Indiana med. Assn.,* 1928, 21, 51.
4. CONNOR, L. The psychic factors in heart disease. *J. Amer. med. Assn.,* 1930, 94, 447.
5. DUNBAR, F. H. *Emotions and bodily changes.* (2nd Ed.) New York: Columbia University Press, 1938.
6. FREUD, SIGMUND. *The interpretation of dreams.* London: Allen & Unwin, 1932.
7. GUNTHER, L., AND MENNINGER, K. A. Intermittent extrasystole directly associated with emotional conflict: a case report. *Bull. Menninger Clin.,* 1939, 3, 164.
8. KILGORE, E. S. The nervous heart. *Amer. Heart J.,* 1929, 5, 9.
9. MENNINGER, K. A., AND MENNINGER, W. C. Psychoanalytic observations in cardiac disorders. *Amer. Heart J.,* 1936, 11, 10.
10. MENNINGER, W. C. Functional cardiovascular disorders: "cardiac neurosis." *Southwestern med. J.,* 1937, 21, 281, 324.
11. MACKENSIE, SIR J. *Diseases of the heart.* (4th Ed.) London: Frowde & Hodder & Stoughton, 1925.
12. MACWILLIAM, J. A. Blood pressure in man under normal and pathological conditions. *Physiol. Rev.,* 1925, 5, 303.
13. NASSE: Quoted in WITTKOWER, E. Studies on the influence of emotions on the functions of the organs. *J. ment. Sci.,* 1935, 81, 665.
14. RYLE, J. A. Visceral neuroses. *Lancet,* 1939, 2, 407.
15. WEISS, S. The interaction between emotional states and the cardiovascular system in health and disease. *Emanuel Libman Anniversary Volumes,* 1932, 3, 1181.
16. WHITE, P. D. Cardiac neuroses. Nelson's Loose Leaf Med., 1929, 4, 447.
17. WHITE, P. D., AND CRAIG, H. R. Neurocirculatory asthenia. *Arch. int. Med.,* 1934, 53, 633.
18. WITTKOWER, E., RODGER, T. F., AND WILSON, A. T. M. Effort syndrome. *Lancet,* 1941, 1, 531.
19. WOLFE, T. P. Emotions and organic heart disease. *Amer. J. Psychiat.,* 1936, 93, 681.

HOSTILITY IN CASES OF ESSENTIAL HYPERTENSION *

By Leon J. Saul, M.D.

Introduction

It has been known for a long time that acute emotional states can cause transient elevations of blood pressure (2), and it has been suspected that emotions may be of etiological importance in the chronic condition of essential hypertension (4). Just how critical a role the emotions play etiologically in this condition is not known, although some cases have been reported in which chronically elevated blood pressure has returned to normal after the patient experienced emotional relief (9). Nor is it known whether or not any specific emotional situation is correlated with essential hypertension, i.e., whether any specific psychology of essential hypertension exists. Anger is the emotion connected with high blood pressure by the laity, an impression which is confirmed by scientific investigation (1) (5) (10) (11) (12). This communication describes the main psychological features of seven psychoanalyzed cases of essential hypertension. This series is, of course, very small, but the uniformity of the psychology is at least suggestive, and receives support from other cases, studied more briefly, and from the short reports of cases in the literature. The more thoroughly studied cases were two men and two women with essential hypertensions which ranged from 140 to 200 systolic over 80 to 130 diastolic. The blood pressures were recorded by mercury manometer before and after every analytic session. Correlations between the fluctuations of blood pressure and the psychological material are dealt with by Alexander. Besides these four cases, psychoanalytic material was also available on three more psychoanalyzed cases whose pressures ranged lower. The patients were all examined medically.

This paper is a report of an effort to determine whether or not any specific psychological features could be found in a small series of essential hypertensives. The conclusion is that such a correlation probably exists, but further study is required on these and on more

* *Psychosomatic Medicine* I : 153-161, 1939.

cases before a clear-cut answer can be given. The common findings in these few cases were (a) the status of a particular conflict situation, and (b) the status of the hostilities.

The Conflict Situation

The central conflict situation was strikingly similar in the four cases. This conflict situation is a widespread one, and its distinguishing features in these cases lay in its status and the way in which it was handled. In brief this conflict situation consisted of (a) a masochistic submissive and an oral-dependent attitude, originally toward a dominating parent, leading to a masochistic submissive attitude to a dominating conscience, to the parent of the same sex, and to parent-substitutes in later life; (b) chronic, unsuccessful, unsatisfied rebellion, and hostility in protest against this submission. The rebellion and hostility were conscious or near to consciousness, and not expressed directly because of fear of loss of love. The submissiveness was not conscious, and bitter hostility opposed making it conscious in the analyses. There was also rage at not getting the desired passive oral-dependent gratification. Another prominent feature was excessive fear of heterosexuality, which was to some extent indulged despite the anxiety. The most characteristic general feature of all the cases was that both the oral-dependent wishes and the hostile aggressive impulses were internally inhibited and were never satisfied in life or in symptoms. These patients were neither passive and dependent nor hostile and aggressive. They could give in to neither trend. During periods when they could and did, their blood pressures were markedly lower.

Clinical Data

Mr. A came with a complaint of anxiety. He was in his forties, with a hypertension fluctuating from 160 to 200 systolic over 110 to 130 diastolic which had been increasing for the preceding 10 years. He was the only patient of the series with marked arteriosclerosis and somewhat impaired renal function, 65 per cent phenolsulphonthalien excretion. He was one of a number of children and had been spoiled and dominated by his mother, who also dominated the physically strong father. His mother made him work from the age of 6 to contribute to the family, who lost their money at that time. He reacted with lifelong bitterness to being thus prematurely forced to work after the earlier extreme spoiling. She forbade sports as dangerous, and later forbade the patient to see girls other than those of his own faith. He obeyed despite his envy of the boys who engaged in athletics and in sexual play with girls. She set him the ideal of wealth, inspired him with excessive ambitions and great expectations, and forced him into marriage against his will with a girl of her own choosing. Thus his whole life, his work, his religion, his marriage, came to mean submission to the mother—"bending the knee," as he put it—and also being forced out of the earlier situation of maternal spoiling and protection into excessive ambitious activity. He tried in vain for many years to escape or rebel against this unconscious attachment to the mother. Finally he actually got a divorce and tried to indulge in sexual promiscuity and alcoholism. He even took a girl to the Orient in an effort to escape his fears and be free sexually. But the anxiety was too great and he was forced to give up the rebellion. The patient's hypertension always increased during these periods in which anxiety frustrated his attempts at heterosexuality.

Apparently in an effort to escape the conflict with his dominating mother, this patient turned to his father. But although on the surface his relations with men were less acutely disturbing, the dependence and submissiveness toward them was even more intolerable than toward women. Again the patient rebelled, using unconscious hostility as his defense. This was most clear toward his boss to whom again he would not "bend the knee." Besides his hostility from rebellion against his dependence and submissiveness, he would rage at not getting the passive receptive satisfaction he demanded, i.e., at not being able to be dependent on others, but being forced to ambitious independent exertion and responsibility. But his rage from rebellion and from frustration was never directly expressed. He was quiet and gentlemanly withal. His rage at his mother was conscious and at his boss nearly so, though he knew nothing of the source (the submissive dependent wishes). The unconscious structure is that of paranoia. In a typical dream he is in bed with a woman when a big man enters with a flashlight, and the patient tries to flee in anxiety. It is a nightmare. The big man is the analyst, the flashlight the analysis. The patient tries to flee from his tendency to give up heterosexuality and to become dependent upon the analyst. The positive Oedipus conflict was also overt and intense in this case. The unconscious masculine competitiveness was intense, and there were dreams of direct sexual advances to the mother. The mother had evidently been seductive as well as dominating. Her domination and seductiveness intensified the patient's feelings of inferiority and hostility to the father, and drove him to further dependence upon the mother and to an anxious, submissive, masochistic attitude to the father.

A full description of the second male hypertensive appears in Alexander's paper (p. 298). It is typical of the male hypertensives studied. The female cases are not so clear. Briefly, Mr. B was in early middle age. His hypertension was of two years' standing and ranged from 135 to 175 systolic over 90 to 120 diastolic. He presented a picture almost identical with Mr. A's. Mr. B. also had a domineering mother who drove him into a dependent (oral) attitude to her and into fear of her, and into an anxious, submissive attitude toward the father, who in this case also dominated the patient. This patient, like Mr. A, conformed perfectly, was a model citizen, and compliant, obedient, subordinate. But although he never showed it, his wish to defy the father, repeated clearly in his relationship to his boss, was close to consciousness. Like Mr. A, he dared not express it in the slightest degree for fear of losing the love of his boss, business associates, and social set. He expressed it privately by promiscuity and solitary drinking. These activities were compulsive reactions to situations in which he overtly submitted to a man but wished to defy him. For example, he would accept orders from the boss with complete obedience, but feel rebellious and hostile and on the verge of attacking the boss. He would then go out and indulge in alcoholism and promiscuous sexuality. Once the boss invited him to play golf. He dared not refuse, accepted graciously, but cursed himself violently for complying. His sexuality was compulsive and indulged in under the influence of alcohol, so that he wished to be cured of these episodes. He had no personal interest in these women, who were almost impersonal agents for indulging his sexuality. In fact he was potent with them only when under the influence of alcohol. He too showed very clearly, later in the analysis, his rage when his receptive wishes were not satisfied.

Both of these patients were chronically pessimistic, anxious, and mildly depressed. They tried to escape by recourse to alcohol and promiscuity, although they were really very inhibited sexually. Drinking and promiscuity were to them symbols of defying conventions and means of escaping from dependence and submissiveness, and resulted in feelings of deep guilt and anxiety. When in the country, away from women, bosses, and obligations, both were much relieved.

The psychoanalytic material showed that both had struggled against strong wishes to be in second place, passive, submissive, dependent, and that both were in a chronic state of hostile rebellion against these wishes, since their pride demanded that they be first—independent, at the top. Hence their chronic defiance and hostility to bosses. This passive dependent trend was seen in their strong oral attachments to their mothers, and in their feminine identification with the women who were their sexual partners. Every attempt at intercourse resulted in acute anxiety. From childhood they felt intense guilt about sex. The parents had great expectations for their futures, and they were driven by high ambition, but at the same time resented this drive and longed to give it up, be cared for, escape. Marriage was from duty, and both rebelled against it. In both analyses the siblings were almost never mentioned or alluded to, so strong was the hostile rivalry with them and the oral attachment to the mother. A number of their early dreams were almost identical, namely dreams of being in a sexual situation with a woman and being seen by a man with consequent anxiety, and dreams of being inhibited in doing something. These dreams reflect the inhibition of the masculinity by the submissiveness to the father, which therefore causes much anxiety in the dreams, and is so fought against in life. Both men showed clearly the oral dependence on the mother and the masochistic passive submission to the father, and then the unsuccessful abortive efforts at hostile rebellion and defiance against the submissiveness. Mr. B's defiance found greater outlet, since he actually could indulge the alcoholism and promiscuity which Mr. A wished to do but could not because of anxiety. It may be significant, therefore, that Mr. B's blood pressure was more fluctuant and averaged lower than Mr. A's. Both male patients were masculine looking, tried to use sexual promiscuity and alcoholism as outlets, and showed the chronic unexpressed rebelliousness particularly in relation to their bosses. Both showed well-developed positive Oedipus complexes as well as the negative, i.e., masculine competition with the father, as well as submission to him.

Another male patient, seen only in a few interviews, presented a psychological picture strikingly similar to these two. He was mild-mannered and submissive. He was strongly attached to his mother in an oral form, as was seen by his indulgence in periodic candy jags. His rage from rebellion against his own submissiveness and oral dependence, and from the thwarting of these wishes, was expressed early in life by temper tantrums which lasted until after adolescence. Threatened with loss of love because of them, he succeeded in controlling them and became milder in personality. Within a year after suppressing them his blood pressure rose from normal, on repeated examinations, to 160 over 100, and went slightly higher during the next decade. Physical examination was negative. This case shows clearly the importance of the oral trend and how suppression of rage was followed by increased external mildness of manner and submissiveness, and by the development of essential hypertension. Compare Alexander's case report, pages 299-315.

Miss C was in her thirties, unusually quiet and charming. In her own words, she had "retired in favor of" (8) her mother and sisters. She felt that they were so much more attractive that she could not compete with them, and she never had a single date until her middle thirties. She then began going with a man her own age, and just when the affair threatened to become serious, her blood pressure, hitherto normal on repeated tests, rose sharply to more than 200 systolic over 130 diastolic. (Compare with Mr. A whose hypertension increased when his anxiety blocked his attempts at sexual intercourse.) She had had no sexual experience. She gave up men and stayed close to her mother, to whom she took an oral-dependent attitude, as shown in her dreams as well as in life. The mother was the strong, dominating personality of the family, and the patient had no one else upon whom to depend for love, having relinquished men. The patient was of fine type, gentle, and conventional, with a strong sense of duty and obligation. She was the only one of the patients whose rebellion against her submission to her mother and to her conscience was not very largely conscious. For example, she went off on a trip, but could feel no more free than she did at home, like Mr. A. Thus she was the most inhibited patient of the series and her blood pressure was the highest. This greater repression may have been due to her father's violent death in a probably purposive accident. This intimidated her and increased her dependence upon her mother. As an example of her submissiveness in the transference, she once thought the analyst had suggested that she do something that she did not want to do. She felt compelled to obey, although she hated to (like Mr. B, when the boss invited him to play golf), and wept with impotent rage at her inability to resist complying, due chiefly to fear of loss of love.

Miss D, a patient of Miller's, like Miss C, consciously retired in favor of her sisters. She was in her early twenties, quiet and sweet in manner and expression. Her blood pressure ranged from 150 to 180 systolic over 80 to 110 diastolic and was of at least 3 years' standing. She was the breadwinner for the family, working to support them and to send her sisters to college. She spent most of her time at home in an oral relationship to the mother who fed her and cared for her when she returned from work in the evening as though she were the man of the family. She had many unsatisfied dreams of being fed by the mother. Like the other patients, she was overly generous to those dependent upon her, and pleasant and gentle in personality with a sense of duty so great that she was overworking and sacrificing her own life in order to contribute to the family. But she had constantly to control a conscious bitter rebellion against her submission to her mother, to her boss (a man), and to her own conscience, which forced her to relinquish pleasure, sex, and independence in favor of excessive work. She had temper tantrums, especially against her boss, which she barely succeeded in concealing. This consciously controlled defiance of the boss was exactly like the two male patients.

Two other patients, in connection with whom less complete psychoanalytic data were available, were women. Miss M, a patient of Grinker's, was about 30, with an essential hypertension averaging 175/100. Most characteristic of her was her naïveté and the fact that she never got angry. In this case, too, the mother was the dominant member of the family and ran the family, and the patient formed a strong predominantly maternal superego. She felt she ought to have the mother close by, but always felt better when the mother was away. The patient had had no sexual relations, and very few social relations with boys, and still did not know where babies came from. The extreme repression of the heterosexuality seen in the other cases, especially of the women, is also conspicuous here. However, in this case, so far as was apparent after several months of analysis, the hostility seemed to be due less to rebellion against the submissive attachment to the mother than to oral thwarting by the mother, i.e., to anger at the mother for not satisfying all of the patient's demands upon her.

A mild fluctuating hypertension, frequently reaching 150/100, was found during the analysis of Mrs. O, a patient of MacDonald's. She was married, with two children, and developed anginal pains, panic, and mild agoraphobia when her younger sister came to live with her. As in all the preceding cases, a dominating mother was prominent in the history and in the psychoanalysis. She sought constant approval from the mother, catered to her, had many oral demands upon her for care and attention, and also, largely in defense, death wishes toward her and sexual wishes for men which for a period developed into nymphomania, with demands for intercourse many times a day. Her psychoanalytic material was unusually overt. Thus the drainage of her hostility and her protest against the attachment to her mother was relatively successful, although at the cost of agoraphobia, nymphomania, and considerable disorganization of her personality.

The patients who showed the same conflict situation, but whose protest was comparatively successful and whose hostilities and sexuality were freer, showed some, but much lower, hypertension. A study is now in progress of the psychological correlations with the rises of blood pressure in these cases in which the pressure is normal some of the time.

Controls

It is clear that dominating parents are common, and that the conflict described is a general one and is not peculiar to cases of essential hypertension. However, pending further study of these and many more cases, the present material suggests that the *status* of the conflict may be peculiar to cases of essential hypertension. These patients submit, but they stifle intense hostility which is near to consciousness. As controls, it is easy to observe patients without hypertension who have this same conflict situation but who solve it in other ways. For example, one patient shunned situations in which his submissiveness would be stimulated by doing independent free lance work, saying frankly that he was unable to work for a boss. He relieved unavoidable tensions by gambling, in which he indulged with very little conflict. In other cases the submission is accepted with very little protest or with some narcissistic compensation. A comparison has not yet been made of the psychology found in essential hypertension with that found in angina pectoris and in the cardiac arrhythmias. The first impression is that the hostilities in the latter cases are freer, as seen in the dreams. In a small series of eight controls I have not found hypertension in patients who have the same conflict as the hypertensives but who have workable solutions for it. Thus, so far as the control series has been examined, no essential hypertension has been found in cases in which (a) the submissiveness is accepted, (b) the problem is avoided by shunning submissive situations, (c) the rebellion and hostility are adequately repressed and bound by organized neuroses or find adequate outlets in life behavior or sexual activity by assuming forms which are not too conflictful and anxiety producing for the individual, or, *possibly* (d) the hostility does not arise from this protest situation but from another source, for example, direct oral thwarting, but this is questionable.

Status of the Hostilities

The following was the status of the hostilities in the cases studied: The hostility was (a) intense and (b) chronic. However gentle the exterior, the analyses made it clear that these individuals were chronically boiling with rage.[1] (c) The hostility was in all these

---

[1] One patient reported the following dream: "I heard the hissing of steam all around me and then realized it was within myself. I became tense and trembling with the

cases the central issue of the analysis, the pathogenetic element, so to speak. (d) The psychological level of the hostility may be of importance, since in all these cases it was close to consciousness. There is reason to suspect that the crucial point here may be the proximity of the hostilities to motility. (e) The hostility was in all cases very inhibited. On the surface these individuals were nonhostile and even overly gentle, but did not lack energy. They worked, in fact often overworked, and succeeded, while protesting against doing so. The hostility found no adequate outlet in behavior in life, through drainage by sexual activity (which often discharges unconscious sadistic impulses) or even in dreams, although there was apt to be considerable conscious hostile fantasy. (f) Although inhibited, the hostility in these cases was not adequately bound in an organized chronic neurosis, for example, paranoia, compulsion neurosis, chronic alcoholism, etc. Cases have been reported by Draper (3) and Eisler (6) in which the hypertension disappeared when the patient developed neurotic symptoms. The hostility was never adequately expressed but never relinquished. The regressive wishes to give up the struggle and accept a passive, dependent emotional situation were also not accepted. Both were blocked.

The Common Psychological Features

Surveying these seven cases grossly, the following similarities are conspicuous. The first is the prominence of the conflict with a dominating parent, especially the mother. This was central in every case, but in that of Mr. B the father also dominated the patient. Two main reactions were seen in the patients. The one was a submissiveness to the mother, transferred in part in the male patients to the father, thus producing in all cases a submissive situation against which the patient was in constant, hostile, unsuccessful rebellion. This rebellion, when it broke through, took the form in the two men of promiscuity and alcoholism, and in the women of sexual wishes which were overtly indulged only by Mrs. O. In these few cases those with the freer outlets had lower blood pressure levels. The other main reaction to the mother, prominent in all cases, was the oral dependent attachment to her which formed part of the submissiveness and was rebelled against, but which, when not satisfied, due to both external thwarting and internal inhibition (guilt, pride, am-

---

pressure. An elderly woman called me 'the boss.' But I said: "No, that man is the 'boss.' " In his associations the patient brought out his rebellion against his boss and against the analyst, and to the steam associated a machine trembling with the pressure of steam within. This pressure was his rebellious hostility against the boss and the analyst, chronic and unvented.

bition, and narcissism), lead to chronic rage at the frustration, and was a component of the alcoholism. The oral material and the anger from unsatisfied oral wishes were conspicuous in the material of all the cases.[2] In the case of Miss M, the hostility from thwarted oral wishes to the mother was the main theme, and the component of rebellion against the mother attachment not so important as in the other cases, at least so far as the analysis had progressed in several months. (It may be that hostile rebellion against the mother will appear later in the analysis.)

The second similarity was the repression of the heterosexuality with attempts to indulge it despite anxiety. Mr. A, after his compulsive attempts at sexual freedom, wished to give up heterosexuality entirely because it caused him so much conflict and anxiety. Mr. B had no interest in the women with whom he was promiscuous, and usually never saw them before or afterwards. They were only part of the bouts of alcoholism and promiscuity which relieved the tensions from rebellion against his boss. In contrast is an anginal patient without hypertension. He was of the Don Juan type with real appreciation of feminine charms, found great pleasure in his relations with women, and could freely indulge his sexuality. The three women with the high blood pressures were strikingly similar in their repression of sexuality. Thus Miss C never even had a date until she was past 30. Miss D had a very rare date, as a duty, at the behest of her mother. Miss M, nearly 30, claimed such innocence of sexuality that she did not know where babies came from. In contrast was Mrs. O. When her impulses broke through she made excessive sexual demands. But her blood pressure only irregularly rose above normal.

The third similarity was in the status of the hostilities, as already described.

Other similarities are less definite. All these patients were "nice" persons, as has often been noted. The reason for this has not been worked out. Probably it is due to a combination of the guilt and submissiveness. In general it seems especially difficult for essential hypertensives to come for psychoanalysis, probably because of their guilt and their fear of the oral and submissive wishes.

In all cases the problem was a very deeply ingrained and repressed one, intimately organized into the whole personality. Whether or not the progressive rise in the level about which the blood pressure

---

2 This checks with Karl Menninger's statement that it is common to find in the histories of essential hypertensives that in childhood they have been thrust prematurely into situations of self-reliance (10).

fluctuates is connected with progressive organization of the personality into a less flexible form, and what the interrelationships are, is a question of great theoretical as well as practical importance. The therapeutic aspect of it is discussed in Alexander's paper. Probably once the pressure ceases to return to normal levels in its fluctuations, both psychological and physiological therapy becomes more difficult. However our observations indicate that psychoanalytic treatment has at least some effect in reducing or arresting the progress of the hypertension in these cases, but it is too early to draw definite conclusions as to the therapeutic results.

Comment

As stated at the outset, this communication is a report of the preliminary phase of this study. Many essential problems remain untackled and unsolved. An important problem at this point is whether the essential hypertension is connected with hostilities from *any* source, such as oral thwarting, depending only upon their intensity, and status, or whether the conflict situation found in these cases is an essential part of the picture.

Another important question is that of the role of the anxiety. The hostilities have been examined thus far without special attention to their direction and relationships. It may be that the hypertension is most directly connected with fear, particularly of the conscience.

The roles of the heterosexuality and of the oral demands are also not worked out.

Two other approaches are promising. The one is a study of the psychological material in connection with the fluctuations in blood pressure and in connection with the level about which the pressure fluctuates. Such correlations are reported in Alexander's paper and are being studied in the other cases. Some of the records contain daily blood pressure recordings and analytic material over periods of several years. In one case, Mr. A, the level of fluctuation clearly fell after two months of psychoanalysis, as the patient accepted and enjoyed the passive situation. But after another six months, when it became conflictful, the level rose and was high for nearly a year during intense hostile transference.

The other approach is that of a "microscopic" study of the dreams as done by French (7). This technique reveals elements not otherwise discernible. A lead is the impression of French that the proximity of the hostilities to motility may be critical.

Summary

An attempt is made to describe the common psychological features in seven cases of essential hypertension. The prominent similarities are (a) the prominence in every case of a dominating mother, with submissiveness and oral dependence toward her, transferred in the cases of the two men to their fathers, with consequent chronic, hostile, unsuccessful, nearly conscious rebellion against the submissiveness, and chronic unexpressed rage at unsatisfied oral demands and at independent activity and work; (b) marked inhibition of heterosexuality, although indulged to some extent despite anxiety; (c) the status of the hostilities—intense, chronic, inhibited, near to consciousness and perhaps to motility, not adequately expressed, and not adequately repressed, and bound as by an organized neurosis; (d) the inability to accept and satisfy either the passive dependent wishes or the hostile impulses, so that these individuals were neither weak and dependent nor aggressively hostile but were blocked in both directions. During periods when either trend was more satisfied, the blood pressure was markedly lower.

These results are more than suggestive, but the series is too small as yet to establish conclusively whether or not these psychological features are generally typical for cases of essential hypertension.

BIBLIOGRAPHY

1. ALEXANDER, FRANZ. Emotional factors in essential hypertension. *Psychosom. Med.*, 1939, 1, 173. (In this volume, page 289.)
2. CANNON, W. B. *Bodily changes in pain, hunger, fear and rage.* New York: D. Appleton-Century Co., Inc., 1934.
3. DRAPER, GEORGE. The common denominator of disease. *Amer. J. med. Sci.*, 1935, 190, 545-558.
4. DUNBAR, H. FLANDERS. *Emotions and bodily changes.* New York: Columbia University Press, 1935.
5. DUNBAR, H. FLANDERS. Physical mental relationships in illness, *Amer. J. Psychiat.*, 1934, 91, 541-562.
6. EISLER, EDWIN. Verbal communication to the author.
7. FRENCH, T. M. Reality and the unconscious. *Psychoanal. Quart.*, 1937, 6, 23-61.
8. FREUD, SIGMUND. *Collected papers,* Vol. 2. London: Hogarth Press, 1924.
9. HILL, LEWIS. A psychoanalytic observation on essential hypertension. *Psychoanal. Rev.*, 1935, 22, 60-64.
10. MENNINGER, K. A. Emotional factors in hypertension. *Bull. N. Y. Acad. Med.*, 1938, 14, 198-211.
11. SAUL, L. J. *Institute for Psychoanalysis Annual Report,* 1933-1934.
12. WOLFE, T. P. Dynamic aspects of cardiovascular symptomatology, *Am. J. Psychiat.*, 1934, 91, 563-574.

PART V
ENDOCRINOLOGY AND METABOLISM

A PSYCHOSOMATIC STUDY OF HYPO-
GLYCEMIC FATIGUE*

By Franz Alexander, M.D.,
AND
Sidney A. Portis, M.D.

About a year ago we began a psychosomatic study of a well-defined group of psychoneurotic patients whose psychological condition appeared in association with a peculiarity of their carbohydrate metabolism manifested by a flat intravenous glucose tolerance test as found in cases of hypoglycemia. Psychologically these patients are characterized by what best can be described as an asthenic syndrome. The outstanding feature is apathy, a loss of zest, a general letdown feeling of aimlessness, a repulsion against the routine of everyday life, be it occupational activities or household duties. Seldom is this apathy connected with anxiety or a pronounced depression. Another constant feature is fatigue, chronic or appearing in acute attacks. The fatigue has certain fairly constant features. It is present as a rule on awakening, slightly more severe in the midmorning, temporarily improved after luncheon, and most marked in the midafternoon. There is practically always a complete relief after the heavy evening meal. The patients may awaken with a severe headache which is also manifest during the midafternoon fatigue. Along with this more chronic fatigue there may be acute attacks of extreme weakness, tremulousness, sweating, and vertigo. At times a feeling of lightheadedness may be manifest. The acute attacks may be associated with anxiety of fainting or free floating anxiety.

Somatically the condition is characterized by a flat intravenous glucose tolerance test. The fasting sugar level in the blood may be normal, somewhat low, or definitely low.

Our study had two objectives: (a) To establish the relationship between the psychological syndrome and the changes in the carbohydrate metabolism; in particular to find out whether the psychological syndrome is a secondary result of the changes in the carbohydrate metabolism or the metabolic changes are produced by an emotional disturbance, or—which we thought most probable—whether there is

* Psychosomatic Medicine VI: 191-206, 1944.

a reciprocal interrelationship between metabolic changes and emotional factors. (b) To work out a combined psychotherapeutic and somatic approach for the treatment of such cases.

In the last 10 to 15 years spontaneous functional hypoglycemia has been described by various authors. In these studies, as far as the psychological manifestations have been considered, the authors' interest was to describe the psychological effects of the hypoglycemic state. After the introduction of insulin shock therapy, these psychological sequelae of hypoglycemia became generally known, and therefore we may here refer to the summaries of observations dealing with the psychic manifestation of hypoglycemia contained in the articles of Joseph Wilder (7), Thomas A. C. Rennie and John Eager Howard (4), John Romano and Gaylord P. Coon (5), and Harold E. Himwich (2). For example, Wilder mentions in minor hypoglycemic attacks, apart from the bodily symptoms (fatigue, hunger, perspiration, tremor), psychological symptoms such as mild dullness of consciousness, weakness in concentration, abulia, and depressive and anxious moods; in medium attacks, mannerisms, changes of speech, double vision, ataxia, ("striopallidary symptoms"). John Romano's and Gaylord Coon's patient, who was suffering from an adenoma of the pancreas, showed in his hypoglycemic attacks confusion, disconnected movements, and uninhibited emotional behavior.

The most recent review of the literature of this problem, which has been attracting more and more attention, has been published by Harold E. Himwich (2). Himwich classifies the psychological sequelae of hypoglycemia in five definite successive stages and ascribes this sequence to the different metabolic rates in the various regions of the brain, the highest being found in the newest portions and each succeeding part possessing a lower rate. The first, or cortical phase, is characterized by sweating, salivation, muscular relaxation, and tremors, accompanied by gradual clouding of consciousness. The second, the subcortico-diencephalic phase, appears in the form of motor restlessness, manifested by primitive movements such as snarling, grimacing, and grasping. In the third, the mesencephalic phase, tonic spasm can be observed and the Babinski reflex becomes positive. In the fourth, the premyelencephalic phase, the tonic spasms become mostly extensor spasms. The phase resembles the picture of the decerebrated dog of Sherrington. In the last, the myelencephalic phase, the patient is found in a deep coma. There is a predominance of parasympathetic tonus. These phases can be best observed during the insulin treatment of schizophrenia.

In the great majority of cases of functional hypoglycemia, only the first phase can be observed and its most conspicuous clinical manifestation is a feeling of weakness, tremulousness, sweating. Anxiety may or may not be present. Our studies include a number of cases in which this acute syndrome was lacking and only chronic apathy, aimlessness, and fatigue were present, similar to a group of patients described earlier (1929) by L. Szondi and Heinrich Lax (6). Their careful clinical study is most pertinent to our own investigation. They established beyond doubt the coincidence of a flat glucose tolerance curve with a neurotic state, which in the older psychiatric literature is usually called neurasthenia, characterized by fatigue, prostration, and apathy often combined with sleepiness, headache, palpitation, vertigo, anxiety, tremulousness, perspiration, and vasomotor lability. This syndrome can be produced by excessive insulin dosage and is also the classical sign of neurasthenia.

To begin with, the authors established the average blood sugar level in 26 normals and 31 neurasthenics, and the average values were identical. The authors' conclusion is that *neurasthenics are not hypoglycemic individuals*. They also emphasize that the hypoglycemic syndrome can be observed in people with a high blood sugar level (0.20%), and on the other hand the symptoms of hypoglycemia may be absent at very low blood sugar levels. Hence the hypoglycemic symptoms cannot be explained from low blood sugar concentration, and another phase of the carbohydrate metabolism must be disturbed. To find this was the authors' aim. They studied 31 neurasthenics and a group of 26 normals. The sugar tolerance of these groups was determined by giving 50 grams dextrose per os and the blood sugar was determined ½ hour, 1 hour, and 2 hours after the intake of sugar. The average rise was: in normals 69%; in neurasthenics 31%. The range of the rise in the normals was from 56% to 111%; in the neurasthenics from 0.4% to 50%.

A similar relationship was found between a group of 24 neurasthenic plus hypogonadic patients compared with 34 nonneurasthenic hypogonadic patients. The relationship was again similar, but even more pronounced between a group of nonneurasthenic hyperthyroid patients as compared with a group of hyperthyroid patients who at the same time suffered from neurasthenia.

On the basis of these studies the authors postulate a close connection between the asthenic syndrome fatigue-apathy-hypothony and a flat sugar tolerance curve. They consider a flat curve as pathological and postulate that in neurasthenic individuals the regulatory mechanism of the alimentary glycemia is destroyed. Their final conclusions are: (a) the most conspicuous symptoms of neurasthenia, the so-called asthenic syndrome, is analogous with the hypoglycemic syndrome. (b) The asthenic (neurasthenic) symptoms are not in a causal relationship with hypoglycemia because neurasthenics do not show hypoglycemia. (c) The asthenic syndrome appears together with a pronounced flat sugar tolerance curve. In the neurasthenics the test raises the blood sugar only 31% in average, in contrast with a 70% raise in normals. The flat tolerance curve is a pathognomic concomitant of the asthenic syndrome. The presence of neurasthenic symptoms in other organic cases also appears, together with a flat tolerance curve.

As stated above, the earlier literature, so far as psychological factors were considered, dealt exclusively with the influence of hypoglycemia upon the emotional life. In 1942 Thomas A. C. Rennie and John E. Howard (4) were the first to describe the influence of emotional factors upon the development of hypoglycemia. They have studied seven patients of which six displayed a psychiatric condition which the authors call "tension depression," characterized essentially by a motor tension "but occurring also with states of depression." These cases showed flat glucose tolerance curves during the symptomatic period. Three of these cases were observed again after their emotional difficulties had been resolved, and they showed normal glucose tolerance curves. The authors came to the conclusion that the hypoglycemia is secondary to the psychiatric disorder since it disappears with management of the psychiatric condition.

Our first prompting to this investigation came during the psychoanalytic treatment of a 45-year-old married woman who was suffering from periodic attacks of diarrhea, headaches, and overwhelming fatigue. (Patient 1.) The patient's diarrhea reacted favorably to psychoanalytic treatment, but the fatigue, which the patient ingeniously called her "pernicious inertia," resisted the psychoanalytic approach more than her other complaints. The patient spent literally the major part of her waking life on a day couch. She dreaded all the efforts of daily life, household duties, charities, social obligations, the visits to and from her children. The only activity she indulged in was voracious reading while lying on her comfortable couch. Suspecting that her fatigue had a physiological basis, particularly those violent, acute attacks of weakness, which appeared at physical exertion, one of us made a metabolic study. A flat intravenous glucose tolerance curve was found, and on this basis relative hypoglycemia [1] due to hyperinsulinism was assumed to be the cause, both of her chronic fatigue and acute attacks of weakness and exhaustion. This patient improved rapidly under the atropine and diet management, described by Drs. Sidney A. Portis and Irving H. Zitman in their

---

[1] See definition of the term "relative hypoglycemia" on page 380.

article, "A Mechanism of Fatigue in Neuropsychiatric Patients" (3) (Figure 1). As seen in Figure 1, the glucose tolerance curve, too, became normal.

We shall not go into a psychodynamic portrayal of this patient (No. 1), as her condition improved before the relationship of her fatigue to psychodynamic factors could be studied in detail. The one outstanding factor which seemed of etiological significance was the patient's complete lack of aim, zest, or spontaneous interest in any activity or in any phase of her life. It was not so much a depression as a condition which could best be described as apathy, an aimless drifting along. The therapeutic success of our combined psychiatric

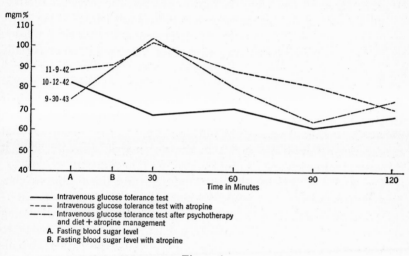

- Intravenous glucose tolerance test
- - - Intravenous glucose tolerance test with atropine
- ·- Intravenous glucose tolerance test after psychotherapy
  and diet + atropine management
A. Fasting blood sugar level
B. Fasting blood sugar level with atropine

Figure 1

and somatic treatment in this case prompted us to take up more systematically the study and theory of similar cases.

Eight additional cases have been studied, four of which gave opportunity for prolonged observation. The other four yielded primarily anamnestic material, but two of them supplied also valuable therapeutic information. In each of these nine cases the asthenic syndrome was present either in a chronic form of prolonged exhaustion and apathy or in acute attacks of weakness in connection with tremulousness, sweating, and often anxiety. In some cases both types were present. In all the diagnoses, hypoglycemic fatigue was made on the co-existence of the clinical asthenic syndrome with a flat intravenous glucose tolerance curve. In every case ⅓ gm. of glucose per kilogram of body weight (using 50% solution) was injected after the fasting rate blood sugar concentration had been established. Blood samples were withdrawn ½ hour, 1 hour, 1½ hours, and 2 hours after an intravenous administration of glucose. In a number of cases the test was repeated after a hypodermic injection of 1/75 grain of atropine sulfate. In all these cases under the influence of atropine the previously flat curve assumed a normal quality. (See Figures 1, 2, 4, 7.)

Psychodynamic Observations

In none of our psychosomatic studies have we encountered a greater conformity in the psychodynamic constellation in patients suffering from a given psychosomatic disturbance. Without exception in the nine cases, the presenting emotional situation was a lack of zest and interest in whatever activities the patients were engaged in; a picture resembling that of a depression but still different from it in certain respects. Most patients came with the complaint that life had lost all meaning for them, that they lacked an aim in life, that there was a complete absence of zest or interest in their daily activities, whether this was routine office work, teaching, preaching, study, administrative duties, or household and social obligations. In most of the cases the fatigue had developed after a gratifying occupation or a cherished goal or hope had to be abandoned on account of compelling circumstances, and the patient was forced to engage in a distasteful routine activity against which he revolted intensely.

The *first patient's* condition has been briefly described above.

The *second patient* was a 37-year-old married businessman, the favorite of his employers because of his enthusiasm, loyalty, and efficiency. Before his breakdown he was an indefatigable worker, full of zest and energy, a good provider for his family, a gay, outgoing fellow, the life of every party, who was not averse to occasional drinking, moderate gambling, and promiscuity. Then rather suddenly this bright picture changed. He came for psychiatric consultation in a state of emotional turmoil. He had lost all interest in his work and social activities, had frequent weeping spells for no visible reason; he had to force himself every morning to go to his office, was continually so exhausted that he was finally forced to interrupt his work. He suffered also from lack of appetite, some epigastric distress, and a compulsive tendency to sigh. This condition had developed shortly after his mother's death, and after he had been promoted to a more responsible position. The psychodynamic constellation behind his sudden breakdown can be given now only in briefest outline. For the last thirteen years the patient had lived an extremely sheltered existence. He had been employed all these years by the same firm and had slid easily into a successful business career in which he made steady progress, always working under the tutelage of the two owners of the firm, who were favorably inclined toward him. The patient's whole personality structure fitted into this situation. He basked in the sun of the paternal interest and appreciation of his superiors; he had, in short, the psychology of the white-headed boy. The emotional atmosphere of the office was a continuation of that of his home in which he was the youngest of six siblings. Both parents were very proud of his accomplishments and liked to brag about him to relatives and friends. Just as his main desire had been to please the parents, so now it was to please his employers. He liked freedom only as it was combined with the security of supreme providence, that of God, the parents, and the employers. Under a strong leader he was a good soldier. Though he became the first among the employees, every move was made under the criticism and guidance of his employers. While his salary was moderate, he received a large bonus every Christmas, often larger than his yearly salary. Thus even his financial compensation came in the form of a paternal gift, the expression of recognition and love of his employers. He had great joy when he could put down a substantial order on the employer's desk or when he arranged a successful, gay party for the business friends of the firm. He took care of every detail of these parties, food, wines, and girls, and was allowed to participate as an equal. Thus even his illicit pleasure could be enjoyed with the sanction of his superiors. He had been married for sixteen years to a maternal, unassuming woman and had one son. His wife cared for his comforts, put up with his moods and demands without burdening him with her demands.

After the war started everything changed. With the shrinking of business the future of the company for a long while did not look promising. While the feverish activities, solicitation of new business stopped, he was, at the same time, pushed toward more responsibility. It was the tacit expectation of the employers that he should gradually take over the greater part of the executive work. At the same time financial rewards diminished. One day the patient, with tears in his eyes, showed a small bonus check which he did not even cash. "It is not the money itself which counts," he said. He would not have wanted a larger bonus check, since he knew that it was not justified, but the old glory of the business which reflected on him was gone and the future looked uncertain indeed. About this time his mother died and he had to take care of the old and decrepit father. On top of all this his wife became ill and began to be demanding. This was the situation in which the patient emotionally collapsed. Life lost all meaning for him. There remained only duties, responsibilities, hard fight, and nothing of the early glamour. The patient began to detest getting up in the morning and going to the office, where every demand upon him appeared as a tremendous task. He became irritated with his inferiors who came to him for advice; he had to use all his will power to go through the daily routine of his office work. Bringing in new business became almost impossible, but in any case he detested all the effort which would have been required. Furthermore, the employers retrenched for the duration and seemed satisfied with a kind of hibernation. As soon as the patient developed a con-

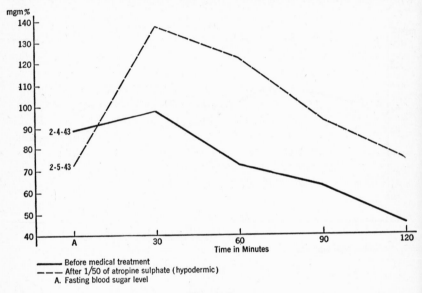

Figure 2

fidence in the analyst and transferred to him his dependent attitude, he began to pour out his secret longings for security and love. A typical fantasy was to run away and go to one of his married sisters and live with her. He wished to escape from business, to go to a sanitarium, on a vacation, or even to run away entirely. Most curious was an unconscious wish which gradually became fully conscious, to go to another part of the country and start again as a young employee with a small salary. This desire, more than anything else, showed the patient's emotional need to work under parental protection. As soon as he reached the status of leader he had to run away and start the whole process again. This was the background of his emotional collapse when his fatigue developed. A flat intravenous glucose tolerance curve was found (Figure 2).

Patient 3, a 36-year-old physician, developed attacks of fatigue which usually came two or three hours after eating. The feeling of weakness, combined with sweating and lightheadedness, was so severe that he had to stop his activities and sit down, or stop when he was walking on the street. The attacks were connected with anxiety. His anxiety became so intense that he developed a phobia which prevented his exposing himself to any situation that might bring on a fatigue attack when he was away from home. This condition developed shortly after he entered private practice. He had always been the center of interest of his overindulgent parents, a spoiled only son, who could not bear separation from the parental home. Only pride

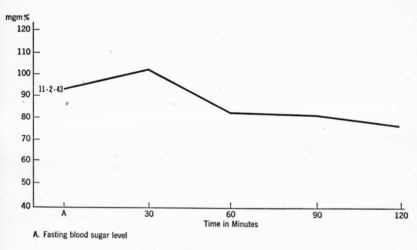

A. Fasting blood sugar level

Figure 3

and external necessity had induced him to go into practice and become more independent. Though he married an indulgent woman, he remained emotionally attached to his former family. The idea of becoming a busy practitioner appealed to him so little that for the first five years he made no serious efforts to build up a practice; in fact, he did much to avoid it. Under the influence of his pride, and later, after he married, of external necessity he forced himself to build up a practice. His acute attacks of weakness and his phobia seriously interfered with his work and he remained satisfied with working on a restricted schedule. Twice formerly he had been diagnosed as a case of functional hypoglycemia. The diagnosis was confirmed by another examination and intravenous glucose tolerance test (Figure 3).

Patient 4, a 39-year-old housewife, came with the following complaint: "Life has become entirely meaningless to me. I have no aims to strive for. The daily household duties are a chore. Visits to and from relatives are distasteful. I do not know what to do with myself. I have a terrific letdown feeling and from time to time I am so weak and fatigued that I cannot move." This condition had developed after she had finally abandoned a desire to have a child of her own and had given up the wish to adopt a child in the face of her husband's adamant objection to adoption. The diagnosis, relative hypoglycemia, was made after an intravenous glucose tolerance curve showed the typical flatness (Figure 4).

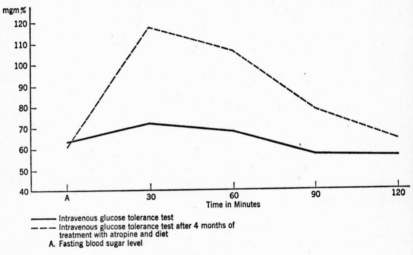

—— Intravenous glucose tolerance test
— — — Intravenous glucose tolerance test after 4 months of
        treatment with atropine and diet
A. Fasting blood sugar level

Figure 4

Patient 5, a 30-year-old artist, developed acute attacks of weakness with sweating and tremulousness five years before, shortly after he had given up his career as a creative artist and accepted a business position under pressure from his father. When he was engaged in creative work, he had been an indefatigable worker. "Without art, life lost all meaning for me," he said. As a business man, he worked under great internal protest, and finally, because of his attacks of fatigue, had to give up office work. After this, his condition soon improved. A flat intravenous glucose tolerance curve confirmed the diagnosis of relative hypoglycemia (Figure 5).

Patient 6, a 50-year-old architect, a bachelor, came to one of us in a despondent and confused state of mind. Life lost all meaning for him after an unsuccessful attempt to change his occupation, in which he had lately lost interest. In the pursuit of his hobby, nature studies, he was indefatigable. He had never had any sexual relation;

he had no intimate friends. Financially independent at 50 years of age, he stood alone in the world without any aim to strive for. For therapeutic reasons he was urged to take a job in his own field in

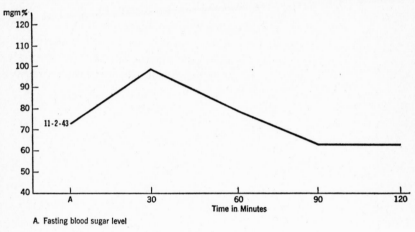

A. Fasting blood sugar level

Figure 5

which he had won recognition, but he had to force himself to the daily duties of the new job, and from time to time felt utterly exhausted. He was referred for examination and a flat intravenous glucose tolerance curve was found (Figure 6).

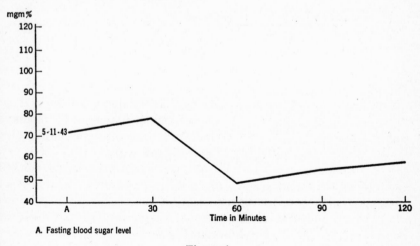

A. Fasting blood sugar level

Figure 6

Patient 7, a 58-year-old minister, complained of extreme weakness which developed during convalescence from a not very serious upper respiratory infection. He felt continually tired and had difficulty in assuming his routine activities after prolonged summer vacations. On his return from vacation this year the respiratory infection had kept him in bed for a few weeks. Although months had passed he could not recover from the feeling of fatigue, which was so overwhelming that he could not force himself to resume his activities. This complaint was particularly impressive since it came from a man of extreme ambition and will power who had driven himself into a compulsive hyperactivity all his life. A deeply rooted insecurity reaching far back to his childhood was responsible for an insatiable craving for prestige, which he tried to achieve by methodical, incessant, hard work, forging ahead in his career. His genuine interests, however, were of a philosophical and scientific nature. His break-

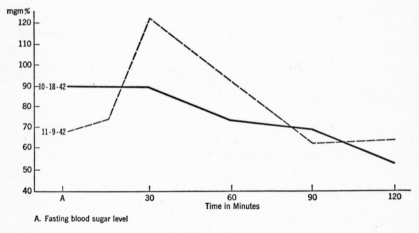

A. Fasting blood sugar level

Figure 7

down came at the height of his career. His insecurity, however, did not allow him to relax until finally a vacation, prolonged by illness, gave him a real taste of a life of contemplation. The internal unconscious rebellion against going back into the harness resulted in a fatigue so extreme that he could no longer master it by sheer will power as he had in the past. The patient showed a flat curve in the intravenous glucose tolerance test (Figure 7).

Patient 8, a 20-year-old university student, was the only son of overindulgent parents. He showed many pronounced schizoid traits, inability to concentrate, extreme shyness, and emotional flatness, and an inclination to daydreaming, in which he pictured himself as a great inventor and benefactor of humanity. His parents' chief complaint was that since his early childhood he had never showed any spontaneous interest in anything. Lately, however, since he started his university studies, he had struggled desperately for adequate grades, which in spite of good intellectual equipment he could not make because of his lack of ability to concentrate on his work and because of constant physical exhaustion. His intravenous glucose tolerance

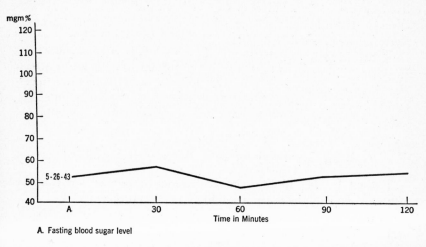

A. Fasting blood sugar level

Figure 8

curve was the lowest seen in any of our series. Unfortunately, external reasons prevented a psychotherapeutic follow-up in this case (Figure 8).

Patient 9, a 25-year-old unmarried woman, a university student, developed fatigue attacks while she was forcing herself to serious

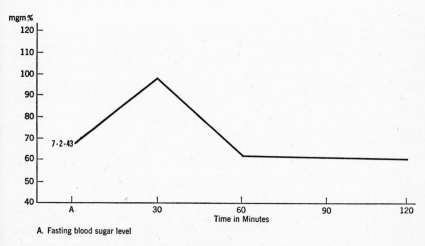

A. Fasting blood sugar level

Figure 9

pursuit of her studies in preparation for a career. She was torn between two desires: to continue her studies and to go back to her parents and follow their plans, to marry and have children. She envied deeply her girl friends who married one after the other and lived the conventional life. A deep-seated conflict concerning sexuality had driven her away from marriage toward a career. Although she tried to persuade herself that she was above a stupid bourgeois existence, in reality her studies represented nothing but enforced labor. In this condition her chronic fatigue developed, punctuated with occasional acute spells of utter exhaustion. A flat intravenous glucose tolerance curve supported the clinical diagnosis of relative hypoglycemia (Figure 9).

A Brief Summary of the Precipitating Conditions

Patient 1. The highly sensitive woman developed her condition after she gave up the hope of solving a marital problem.

Patient 2. The enthusiastic business man developed his fatigue attacks when the main incentive in his work, guidance and approval of his superiors, ceased, partly because of slowing down of the business, and partly because of his promotion to a fully responsible job.

Patient 3. The physician suffering from phobias developed his fatigue attacks shortly after he went into private practice much against his own inclinations.

Patient 4. The housewife developed her fatigue attacks when her wish to have her own child or adopt one finally had to be abandoned.

Patient 5. The artist developed his attacks immediately after he had accepted, with great internal protest, a position in a business office and at the same time had given up the career of an artist to which he was deeply devoted.

Patient 6. The architect developed his fatigue attacks while working in a responsible job which he accepted at the psychiatrist's request, although he had no desire to do so. He wanted to devote himself exclusively to his hobby of making studies of wild life.

Patient 7. This case appeared at first as an exception. The patient, a minister, professed to have the greatest interest in his regular activities. However the psychotherapeutic interviews revealed that although he had always been driven by an insatiable thirst for prestige, his genuine interests were along different lines, which he could not fully admit.

Patient 8. The schizoid university student developed his excessive fatigue while he was struggling desperately to improve his grades, although he lacked all interest in his studies.

Patient 9. The woman university student developed her fatigue attacks while she was forcing herself to engage in a career, at the same time envying the life of her girl friends who married.

The outstanding common denominator in the psychological picture of these cases is a lack of spontaneous urge toward the activity in which the patient was then engaged. It was only under the compulsion of external necessity, or under the pressure of duty, pride, or insecurity, that the patients forced themselves to sustained efforts, although they had no genuine interest or enthusiasm in their work. At the same time, in most cases, the patients were compelled by external conditions or internal reasons to give up the pursuit of activities or aims in which they had a real spontaneous interest and which in some instances had occupied the central role in their lives previously.

In all cases studied in detail the emotional syllogism which led to the emotional situation in which the fatigue developed could be formulated as follows: "If I cannot have the gratification or activity upon which I insist, I refuse to make any effort." This emotional situation is similar to a sitdown strike. Frustrated in their natural inclinations, these patients develop a protest reaction against perfunctory activities. Often they indulge in regressive fantasies and give up all real effort and ambition. The relative hypoglycemic state is the physiological counterpart or concomitant of this emotional impasse. The resulting fatigue gives further excuse for regressive wishes, and thus a vicious circle is initiated.

A detailed discussion of the psychodynamic constellation in which the relative hypoglycemic condition develops must be reserved for further publications. So much can be stated: In every case, fatigue developed when a well-functioning goal structure collapsed, or, in other words, when that type of adjustment failed which Freud originally called the "reality principle." In his "Goal, Mechanism and, Integrative Field," Thomas M. French (1) has investigated more closely the nature of adaptive goal-directed behavior and demonstrated the hierarchical system of goals based on subordination of subsidiary goals to a supreme goal which requires compromises between conflicting aims. He emphasized the significance of hope for sustaining the goal structure. Hopelessness concerning the main goal, on the other hand, is apt to disrupt the whole goal structure. In all our cases a disintegration of the patient's goal structure can be demonstrated. The emotional syllogism, "If I cannot have what I want I will not play anymore," the all-or-nothing attitude, is characteristic of the emotional background of psychogenic hypoglycemia.

TABLE I

Patient	Clinical Picture	Other Symptoms	Precipitating Factors	Laboratory Findings
1. 45-year-old married woman.	Chronic fatigue and occasional acute attacks of weakness. Withdrawal from social activities. Apathy. Mild depressive state.	Diarrhea. Migraine.	Loss of hope for solving marital problem.	IV. glucose tolerance test. Relative hypoglycemia.
2. 37-year-old married business man.	Loss of previous zest; weeping spells, depression, fatigue. Fantasies of retirement.	Epigastric distress, loss of appetite. Compulsive sighing.	Mother's death. Change in occupational situation: promotion to increased responsibility, slowing down of business, and less financial reward.	IV. glucose tolerance test. Relative hypoglycemia.
3. 36-year-old married physician.	Circumscribed phobia. Acute attacks of weakness, lightheadedness, 2-3 hours after meals, with anxiety. Withdrawal from practice.		Leaving of parental home; assumption of private practice.	IV. glucose tolerance test. Relative hypoglycemia.
4. 38-year-old married woman.	Lack of interest in everything. Rebellion against daily routine. Chronic fatigue and acute spells of exhaustion.	Colitis in past history.	Giving up hope to have or adopt child.	IV. glucose tolerance test. Relative hypoglycemia.

Patient	Clinical Picture	Other Symptoms	Precipitating Factors	Laboratory Findings
5. 30-year-old married male artist	Acute attacks of tremulousness, exhaustion, and perspiration. Slight phobia.		Giving up creative art and accepting against his own inclination a routine business position.	IV. glucose tolerance test. Relative hypoglycemia.
6. 50-year-old bachelor architect.	General despondency and apathy, lack of interest in any activity. Lonesomeness. Fatigue while working.		Frustrated longing for intimate human companionship; rebellion against routine job.	IV. glucose tolerance test. Relative hypoglycemia.
7. 58-year-old married minister.	Chronic fatigue. Moderate depression.	Headaches. One epileptic (?) seizure in the past.	After vacation and illness increased resistance against resuming routine activities.	IV. glucose tolerance test. Relative hypoglycemia.
8. 20-year-old single male university student.	Inability to concentrate, lack of spontaneous interest, shyness, emotional flatness, daydreaming. Extreme form of chronic fatigue. Picture of schizoid prepsychotic state.		Struggle under external pressure for improving scholastic grades.	IV. glucose tolerance test. Extreme relative hypoglycemia.
9. 26-year-old single female student.	Circumscribed phobia, depression, chronic fatigue.		Analytic treatment increased the conflict between continuing career or returning to parents and marrying.	IV. glucose tolerance test. Relative hypoglycemia.

The condition develops when those compromise solutions break down which life requires from every struggling human being and the hope dwindles that the cherished aims in life ever can be obtained.

The histories of our cases which led up to the final emotional impasses show great variation; no common features could be detected. The personality types also show wide difference. One patient, No. 8, was a definitely prepsychotic schizoid personality, while Patient 2 was outgoing, hyperactive, enthusiastic, given to open expression of emotion and subject to mood swings, definitely a cyclothymic personality.

These differences show that it is not a type of personality, nor even a type of history, which predestines a person to the development of this fatigue syndrome. It seems, rather, a certain psychodynamic constellation which occurs in certain life situations in personalities of all kinds that may lead to this type of physiological sequelae. The condition appears when an adaptive equilibrium becomes disturbed. It is not a question of activity and passivity or the degree of intensity of dependent or independent attitudes. The condition develops when that intricate hierarchical system of goals based on subordination and compromise of divergent impulses collapses, which every individual has to make to harmonize his conflicting aims, gratifications, and standards with each other and with the given external circumstances. As a rule an external change of life circumstances is responsible for such a collapse. When a person loses the hope of obtaining a cherished goal and gives up realistic efforts to rescue his major strivings and genuine interests from emotional shipwreck, when life begins to appear nothing but a sequence of meaningless exertion and killing routine, then the emotional sit-down strike sets in. This, in many cases, seems to lead to a disturbance of the carbohydrate metabolism in the form of relative hypoglycemia. (Table I.)

Therapeutic Remarks

Of the nine cases studied, five had been treated psychotherapeutically or psychoanalytically before they were put on atropine and diet management. Two received medical treatment before psychotherapy was started. In two cases only a psychiatric anamnestic study was made and the glucose tolerance curve established, but no psychotherapy initiated. Our therapeutic discussion, therefore, deals only with seven cases. The bodily fatigue syndrome in all the seven cases either greatly improved or completely disappeared within a week after atropine and dietary management was instituted. The patients received 1/200 to 1/75 grain of atropine three times daily, together with 2-7 mgm. of thiamin chloride and ¼-½ gr. of phenobarbital, and were put on a diet containing no free sugar, only complex carbohydrates. They had three intermediary feedings in addition to three regular meals daily, and a feeding before retiring.

In detail the therapeutic results are as follows:

Patient 1. In this 45-year-old married woman, the diarrhea attacks and fatigue attacks practically disappeared. In the year after treatment the patient had only a few light attacks following unusually strenuous activity. She is still under the same management. Psychotherapy with this patient was discontinued ten weeks after she was put on a medical management. As a result of her analysis the patient was ready to accept her present life situation with less inner revolt. The medical management, however, contributed also to the improvement of her emotional status. Freed from her inertia, she could resume her social and communal activities, which made her life less empty and meaningless. Although her basic problem remained unsolved, she accepted her life conditions with less internal rebellion. Further evaluation of this case from the therapeutic point of view will be possible only after the drug and diet management is discontinued.

Patient 2. This 37-year-old business man had been in psychotherapeutic treatment for four months before medical management was instituted. In the initial phase of psychotherapy his emotional condition, particularly his depression and tendency to weep, was considerably improved, but his revulsion against office work and the accompanying fatigue were unchanged. The initial effect of the medical treatment was an improvement in his physical fatigue, but the emotional rebellion against work, and his regressive fantasies, became even more pronounced. Psychotherapy was continued in order to make him conscious both of his tendency to escape and of his tremendous attachment to his superiors. Gradually he regained much of his old enthusiasm. After six months of psychotherapy the patient was taken off the medical management, a new intravenous glucose tolerance curve was taken and was found to be less flat than the original. Seven months later another tolerance test showed even further improvement. This patient continues to feel well and to work hard at the same time. He is again his old self, has neither weeping spells nor lack of interest nor fantasies of resigning from his job. (Figure 10.)

Patient 3. This 36-year-old physician improved considerably after five months of psychotherapy. His disinclination toward his practice disappeared, his phobias improved. There remained, however, a great anxiety of the recurrence of his fatigue attacks, which have been kept under control by medical management begun two months after he started psychotherapy. Since this physician lives out of town, the psychotherapeutic interviews have been interrupted in the last five months because the patient felt rather contented in his present condition. On account of the residue of symptoms it is

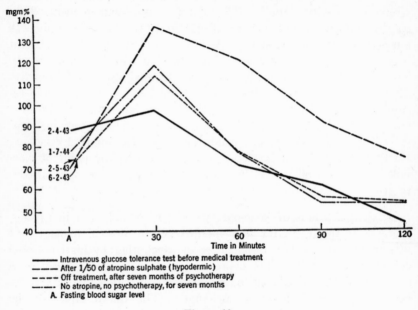

Intravenous glucose tolerance test before medical treatment
After 1/50 of atropine sulphate (hypodermic)
Off treatment, after seven months of psychotherapy
No atropine, no psychotherapy, for seven months
A. Fasting blood sugar level

Figure 10

planned to resume psychotherapeutic interviews. At present, without the knowledge of the patient, the daily dose of atropine has been reduced to 1/150 grain three times daily and at bedtime from a previous 1/75 grain dose.

Patient 5. This artist came to psychotherapy after he had been on medical management for two weeks. Soon after medication and diet were started, the patient's fatigue attacks ceased. However he did not return to his office job and at present he is following his natural inclination toward creative art. His emotional problem has become more pronounced since his fatigue attacks diminished. Since psychotherapy has just begun, any further therapeutic remarks in this case are premature.

Patient 6. The 50-year-old architect, from the psychotherapeutic point of view, responded most successfully to treatment. Medical management was started because of his excessive fatigue in his daily work after two months of psychotherapy, which averaged only two weekly interviews. Within seven to ten days after the beginning of the medical treatment, the symptoms of physical fatigue improved, but this was not followed immediately by any marked change in his emotional condition. An improvement took place only after the patient became able to have more social contact and to give up his

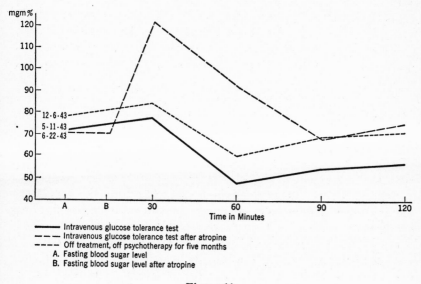

Figure 11

isolated existence. Insight into his emotional situation has gradually increased during the treatment. After four months of psychotherapy the treatment was interrupted for four months, and at the same time the medical management was discontinued. The fatigue syndrome, however, did not return. At the same time the patient became interested in a woman and a close friendship developed. After resuming his psychotherapy the patient became involved in a great conflict between the wish to withdraw from the woman and to marry her. An intensive working through of his attitude toward sexuality was followed by a resumption of his friendship; he became engaged, has married, and at present is on his honeymoon. At the time of his decision to marry, a second sugar tolerance test was taken. This test showed an improvement over the first one, six months before, which was taken at the height of his emotional withdrawal (Figure 11).

Patient 7. This 58-year-old minister had been on drug and diet management for three months before he was referred to psychotherapy. At that time he had been relieved of his fatigue symptoms to a great extent. The symptoms did not return, however, after discontinuation of his medical management.

In all cases the physical fatigue improved or disappeared completely under medical management and psychotherapy. In almost all cases the disappearance of the fatigue syndrome brought the underlying emotional situation more sharply into consciousness and facilitated the psychotherapeutic approach to the basic personality problem. In all cases the disappearance of fatigue counteracted the regressive, escaping tendencies of the patient, and in the majority it strengthened the patient's hopes and created a more optimistic outlook.

The interaction of psychotherapy and medical management is extremely complicated and we are far from understanding the dynamics of their interplay. This much, however, can be said with a fair amount of certainty. A condition of emotional letdown, manifesting itself in a loss of enthusiasm and hope and based on the disruption of the patient's goal structure, influences the vegetative balance. This manifests itself in a disturbance of the regulatory mechanism controlling the sugar concentration of the blood. This produces the asthenic symptoms and particularly the fatigue. Now a vicious circle becomes initiated. The fatigue favors the patient's tendencies toward withdrawal, impairs his efficiency, and discourages new effort to continue or resume his activities. The fatigue syndrome gives the patient a powerful secondary excuse for further withdrawal. Thus the initial emotional situation in which the patient lost all his original interest in activity and life in general becomes reinforced by the relative hypoglycemic condition, or, more precisely, by the disturbed regulatory mechanism of the carbohydrate metabolism. This disturbance for brevity's sake we may call "relative hypoglycemia." [2]

According to our present experience, in many cases, the somatic treatment is most useful in breaking up this vicious circle, thus allowing a psychotherapeutic attack on the basic emotional problem. In some cases the medical management is indispensable to insure the success of psychotherapy. Our therapeutic experience extends to six cases. In the seventh, psychotherapy has just been started. We have come to the conclusion that the unusually good therapeutic results

---

[2] Relative because the absolute level of blood sugar concentration may not be low, but the adaptation of the blood sugar level to the actual needs of the tissues is disturbed.

obtained in a relatively brief period in all six cases, in which a combined therapy has been employed, is so encouraging that we are warranted in further experimentation in cases of relative hypoglycemic fatigue.

Theoretical Remarks

The following working hypothesis seems to account for our observations. In certain emotional situations characterized by a loss of spontaneous zest and a revulsion against routine activities, a disturbance of the regulatory homeostatic mechanisms of the blood sugar concentration is likely to develop and cause the chronic asthenic syndrome and occasionally acute attacks of weakness and fatigue described in our cases. Our hypothesis is that the emotional tension to which one ordinarily refers as zest, enthusiasm, or interest keeps up a certain tonus in the vegetative innervations, a certain balance in the sympathetic adrenal and parasympathetic insular tonus. In extension of Cannon's fundamental views we assume that outwardly directed activity of the organism in which it participates with enthusiasm, zest, spontaneous striving has a tuning up effect upon the sympathetic adrenal system qualitatively similar to that of fear and rage. The sympathicotonic effect of zest is probably less intensive but more prolonged than that of fear and rage. The conditions of fear and rage are extreme cases in which the organism is tuned up for an outwardly directed activity in an emergency situation. The main function of the autonomic nervous system is to adapt the internal vegetative functions of the organism to these external tasks which the organism is called upon to perform. On the basis of our preliminary observations we assume that, like rage and fear, a keen enthusiastic striving for a goal may have a similar, more prolonged but less intensive tuning up effect upon the internal vegetative processes. It is probable that without such a vegetative tuning up sustained effort cannot be carried out with the same economy. It is well known that perfunctory activity performed without emotional participation is more fatiguing than even strenuous activity performed with emotional participation. Our clinical observations seem to indicate that fatigue and apathy developing during routine activity without interest are not merely subjective emotional states but are based on the lack of adaptation of the carbohydrate metabolism to the effort required from the organism. Without emotional participation the tuning up of the vegetative processes and the shifting of the sympathetic-parasympathetic balance in favor of increased sympathetic tonus does not take place. Hence the organism is engaged in a continued activity without the corresponding metabolic adjustment necessary for sustained effort. Probably just as important as the lack of emotional participation is a definite emotional rejection of compulsory activity in which the patient is not interested. This emotional rejection creates the emotional state of flight and increases the desire to give up. The emotional flight reaction creates a condition in the vegetative processes which we have called "vegetative retreat." The internal processes become attuned to a state characteristic for relaxation in which the vago-insular tonus is preponderant over the sympathetic adrenal tonus. This is a most paradoxical situation. The organism engages in activity while its vegetative metabolic processes are attuned to a state of relaxation. One aspect of this condition is that under the influence of vagal excitation, or at least of vagal preponderance, a condition of hyperinsulinism develops and leads to a disturbance of the regulatory mechanisms which control the sugar concentration of the blood.

Not the absolute lowering of the sugar concentration but the inability of the organism to raise the sugar concentration of the blood as it is required during activity (particularly during mental activity, because the exclusive fuel of the brain cells is sugar) is the immediate cause of the subjective feelings of fatigue and exhaustion as well as in the acute cases of tremulousness, lightheadedness, and weakness. The occasional anxiety state, which sometimes accompanies the attacks, is a subjective reaction to the acute feeling of weakness and has no specific etiological significance.

This view accounts fully for the beneficial effects of atropine and of diet containing complex carbohydrates. The atropine diminishes the vagal insular tonus and shifts the balance in favor of the sympathetic tonus. This counteracts the tendency toward a presumed hyperinsulinism and allows the organism to raise the blood sugar concentration to the level required by increased activity. A diet without sugar and including complex carbohydrates is calculated to eliminate the homeostatic reaction provoking increased insulin production and to maintain a steady supply of carbohydrates to the blood stream. The essence of this hypothesis is the extension of Cannon's view concerning the influence of rage and fear upon metabolic process via the autonomic nervous system. We assume that zest and enthusiasm, just like fear and rage, create an excess of sympathetic-adrenal tonus and mobilize carbohydrate from its depots, while the desire for relaxation favors an excess of vago-insular tonus and thus the storing of sugar. We are planning extensive animal and human experiments to test the validity of these physiological views.

BIBLIOGRAPHY

1. FRENCH, T. M.   Goal, mechanism, and integrative field.   *Psychosom. Med.*, 1941, 3, No. 5.
2. HIMWICH, H. E.   A review of hypoglycemia, its physiology and pathology, symptomatology and treatment.   *Amer. J. digest. Dis.*, 1944, 2, No. 1.
3. PORTIS, S. A., AND ZITMAN, I. H.   A mechanism of fatigue in neuropsychiatric patients.   *J. Amer. med. Assn.*, 1943, 121, No. 8.
4. RENNIE, T. A., AND HOWARD, J. E.   Hypoglycemia and tension-depression   *Psychosom. Med.*, 1942, 4, No. 3.
5. ROMANO, JOHN, AND COON, G. P.   Physiologic and psychologic studies in spontaneous hypoglycemia.   *Psychsom. Med.*, 1942, 4, No. 3.
6. SZONDI, L., AND LAX, HEINRICH.   About the alimentary glycemic reaction in neurasthenia.   *Z. f. d. ges. experiment. Med.*, 1929, 64, 274-280.
7. WILDER, JOSEPH.   Psychological problems in hypoglycemia.   *Amer. J. digest. Dis.*, 1943, 10, No. 11.

CORRELATION BETWEEN EMOTIONS AND CARBOHYDRATE METABOLISM IN TWO CASES OF DIABETES MELLITUS *

By Albrecht Meyer, M.D., Ludolf N. Bollmeier, M.D.,
AND
Franz Alexander, M.D.

Carbohydrate metabolism is one of the most complicated mechanisms in metabolic physiology. Many questions are still unexplained, and many workers are interested in their final solution. In this paper we will report two cases of diabetes mellitus that were treated by psychoanalysis, and at the same time were under the close clinical observation of Dr. Rollin T. Woodyatt who controlled the diet and the insulin therapy. Our clinical laboratory made frequent blood-sugar and quantitative urine analyses which enabled us to correlate the change in the carbohydrate metabolism of the patients with their emotional reactions.

We adopted the technique of daily urine analysis by making four to six quantitative urine examinations every day. This method of observation allowed us to correlate the psychoanalytical material with the fluctuation of the sugar output in diabetes mellitus cases.

In the two cases we will describe the patients were intelligent and cooperative, keeping to their diets strictly and carrying out the laborious collection of their urine in small specimens for almost two years, so that we feel that the results of the investigation are reliable.

CASE 1. The patient was a young man, 29 years of age, good looking, well-mannered and of high intelligence. He came of a healthy family in which no case of diabetes had been known. His mother died of a benign tumor operation when the patient was 20 years old. She was a very sensitive woman with a decisive sense of order and cleanliness, who apparently suffered much during her marriage to the patient's father, a strong husky man of rough manners and quarrelsome disposition. He frequently came home drunk, on which occasions the patient was exposed to violent scenes of

* Psychosomatic Medicine VII: 335-341, 1945.

marital discord. His sister, three years older than the patient, showed more resemblance to the father and dominated her younger brother, who reacted with the same sensitiveness as his mother and avoided quarrels, suppressing his anger to the utmost.

There was a strong attachment between brother and sister which continued also after the sister's marriage. At the same time the patient felt a strong jealousy toward her on account of the greater affection the father showed to his daughter. As a compensation the patient developed a technique of winning people for himself by always being a good child, doing things for others in the most polite manner, carrying packages for older people for instance, and becoming the beloved and praised child of the community, in contrast to the sister who often was criticized or punished for her behavior. This attitude became a distinct character trend during his later life. Through his pleasant manners and charming personality he gained many friends, and he was one of the best liked teachers in the high school where he taught.

To be loved by everyone became a constant craving in him, and he controlled carefully any manifestation of anger and resentment. The roots of this behavior pattern probably lay in his earliest life experiences. He was seriously ill between the ages of one and two years, starving under a strict diet for almost a whole year on account of a severe gastrointestinal disturbance, very likely with insufficient medical care. He recovered and was in good health until his diabetes developed. However, a strong craving for all sorts of sweet food persisted from childhood to adulthood, which consequently overburdened his carbohydrate metabolism. It seems likely that the anxiety a child experiences under the threat of starvation brings out strong inhibitions in later life against expressing natural emotions. It is highly significant that a very strong affectionate tie remained, in later life, between the patient and his mother's sister. This aunt took care of him during his childhood illness, always giving him the surplus affection he craved, while his mother, too preoccupied with her marital problems and her compulsive cleanliness, did not respond in the same way. It seems that his early traumatic experiences during his illness were not sufficiently compensated by his mother's expressions of love. The subsequent development of an insatiable craving for sweet food, a desire to be loved, praised, and to receive presents may have been a compensation for his mother's love of which he felt deprived. He learned to hide all manifestations of his hostile impulses, since this was necessary in order to ingratiate himself with everyone in his environment. Whenever he was involved in a conflict he withdrew and sank into a mood of self-pity and depression.

This role of being the charming, beloved child was seriously disturbed by the onset of puberty. His first sexual experiences consisted in continuous homosexual play with other boys. During this period of two years duration the patient was in a state of depression. His first heterosexual experience occurred at the age of 18, and was followed by others, frequently with older women. At the age of 24 the patient was engaged for two years to a woman who was ten years older than he. Apparently there was too much responsibility involved in this relationship; he dissolved the engagement and had numerous heterosexual experiences on a very playful level, alternating with homosexual experiences from time to time which were always connected with anxiety and self-reproach afterwards. He stated once that homosexuality was so easy, was always available among his friends, and involved no feeling of responsibility. All this gives us a good picture of the patient's inclination to retain an immature, childish, dependent attitude and his refusal to adopt the responsibilities of adult life. Homosexuality, however, was far from being a satisfactory solution to his problem, and involved him in another serious conflict. In the fall of 1935 he was seriously confronted with an emotional problem which he could not solve by his previous method.

His love object was an unstable young man who forced the patient into a submissive position, let him do all the kitchen work, kept him always waiting and in constant suspense. In this relationship he did not occupy his usual, dependent role and had to cope with all the difficulties of a man having a spoiled, demanding mistress. He did not even have the narcissistic compensation of playing the leading position in this affair. For the first time in his life he did not succeed in keeping the relationship on a playful, casual level. He became very attached to this friend, waited for his letters impatiently, and craved his love, but suffered at the same time because of the lack of affection the friend showed. He had to renounce all his receptive wishes and tried to disregard the resentment which developed simultaneously on account of this. He tried to break away from the friend by attaching himself to an older woman who already had adult children, and who overwhelmed him with attention and presents, tolerating at the same time all his erratic outbreaks of rage. But in spite of all the conflicts involved in the relationship with his friend his desire for him continued very strong until he broke down with diabetes.

The outbreak, or more precisely, the discovery of his diabetes took place under the following circumstances: At Christmas, in 1935, the patient went home to his father and stepmother, and became ill with flu. He never actually recovered from extreme tiredness, and was in poor health during the whole winter. In the spring almost all his teeth showed cavities and a serious furunculosis developed. He lost about fifty pounds, and in May, 1936, he was brought into a hospital almost in a state of coma. Here his diabetes was discovered and he remained under clinical observation for about three weeks. He was put on a diet and left the hospital under the regime of 150 gram carbohydrates, 75 gram fats, 75 gram protein, and 40 units of insulin daily. After he left the hospital he gave up all contact with his friend and continued the attachment with the older woman. In this relationship, which assumed a thoroughly sadomasochistic character, the patient received gratification from actually attacking her, and also from receiving attention and presents from her. No matter how gratifying this relationship might have been in satisfying both his demanding-receptive wishes and in providing an outlet for his aggression, it soon became intolerable for certain external reasons. The woman threatened his whole social existence in the small town, causing open scandals and forcing herself on him continuously. He then consulted the psychoanalyst.

Brief Description of Analysis

The first impressive material was the intensive conflict about his relationship to the older woman. After three months of treatment he gained the courage to give up this relationship, which was a source of such suffering for him. However, this break deprived him of a certain equilibrium. The relationship had satisfied his strong receptive tendencies and had given him a target for his rage. Deprived of these vents he became restless. As a result he again became susceptible to the old homosexual solution to the same instinctual cravings. A letter from his former boy friend found him in this frame of mind. He wrote that he wanted to come back and live with him again. The temptation to find relief for his receptive wishes in a passive homosexual way was great, but so was the fear of the frustration which he had experienced during his affair with this man. The anxiety blocked the possibility of a homosexual solution. Dreams appeared in which hostility was expressed toward the homosexual partner. He refused to live with the friend and turned to a woman who had outspoken masculine trends, and thus could serve as a substitute for a man. She presented a suitable object toward whom he could assume a passive-receptive attitude. He wanted to marry her but was rejected, and the relationship terminated in April, 1938, i.e., after psychoanalytic treatment of 8 months. It was around this period that for the first time in his life he could express the angry tension which always lay beneath his pleasant surface.

Finally, the greatest progress toward normality in his sexual life occurred when he chose, in the summer of 1938, a healthy young girl and had a satisfactory relationship with her. There was no responsibility involved in this relationship and he could therefore tolerate it. His relationship with his father became a much freer one, and he spent a very happy summer.

When he returned from home he fell in love with a young girl just graduated from school, who had high emotional and intellectual qualities. Through this love his main conflict between a dependent, demanding attitude and a more responsible mature relationship to a woman came to the surface, together with all the hostilities which he harbored toward mother-substitutes who thwarted him. In this phase of analysis it did not yet appear safe to advise marriage, but the patient felt that he was so much in love that he wanted to go through with his marital plans in spite of the restriction of his analyst. Finally the analyst consented. He had the impression that the girl was a good object choice, and a more stable life would be a definite advantage to the patient's physical and emotional health. The couple married at Christmas and the adjustment was a very good one. A short period of friction and violence developed when the analysis touched again the patient's aggressive oral biting tendencies toward his mother and sister. In fact, one night he physically attacked his wife. The most difficult part of the analysis was to bring out his deeply hidden murderous tendencies toward his mother. It was unavoidable that some acting-out should take place. All the hate toward his mother, accumulated probably during the sickness and starvation period of his infancy, came to his consciousness and could be worked out in analysis. This hostility appeared in dreams, mainly expressed in omnipotent biting fantasies, together with the deep anxiety of an utterly helpless child. After this early stormy period of the marriage the patient gradually developed much greater freedom, greater interest in life, and a good sexual adjustment. He finished his analysis in 1939 and is now, after an additional 6 years, well adjusted in his marital life, successful in his profession, and very much attached to his child which was born a year after he married. During the past 5 years the patient's urine has been free of sugar and he is in good physical health.

Correlation Between Carbohydrate Metabolism and Emotional Tendencies

Figure 1 shows great changes in the amount of sugar eliminated during 24-hour periods, expressed in grams of sugar. The patient was actually sugar free for 1½ years, including the first four months of analysis. At the end of December, 1937, he gave up the relationship with the older woman and was exposed, as described before, to his homosexual conflict. On January 22, 1938, he had a sudden surprising peak of the curve to 80 grams of sugar in 2000 cc. of urine. Two days before this he had unexpectedly received a letter from his friend who announced his return to town. The patient did not open the letter at once, was very excited, and when he finally did read it the urine specimen showed the high amount of sugar during the following 24 hours. The emotional conflict to which he was exposed was the anticipation of having to play the mother to this friend instead of indulging in a dependent relationship to him. He retreated from this homosexual temptation, led a very withdrawn life during the following weeks, and remained at home in a depressed self-pitying mood, a withdrawal which he had used very often even in childhood. (Note low sugar level during this withdrawal period.)

The highest peaks in the whole curve were on April 6th and 20th of 1938—almost 100 gram sugar output. They were related to rejection of his marital proposition by the homosexual girl, and were connected with a tremendous rage he did not dare to verbalize or transfer into motor activity. This rage was a reaction to being thwarted. The masculine girl who was wealthy did not want to play the mother to him, rejected him as a husband, and decided to continue in a homosexual relationship. The low point on March 12, 1938, is again connected with neurotic symptom formation and withdrawal after an indulgence in his homosexuality two days before. The lowest part of the curve, with almost no sugar, was during June, 1938, when he had his first satisfactory heterosexual relationship which did not involve responsibility. The conflict turned up again at the end of August when his attachment to his fiancée brought up deeper conflicts between his receiving wishes and a more mature sexual attitude.

Most instructive are those detailed examinations which show the fluctuations of the carbohydrate metabolism during one and the same day. The examination of the sugar output on August 25, 1938, brought the most revealing insight into the structure of the patient's conflict and allowed us to draw more definite conclusions in regard to the conflict and its effect on the sugar output. He voided his urine during that day in five portions, the total volume of which was 2715 cc. In the analytical material of the day before, the receptive and demanding tendencies of the patient were very strongly expressed. He had a dream in which there appeared an older woman who had a restaurant and supported younger boys. In the dream he inquired where this woman lived. Anxiety came up, together with the thoughts of marriage. The first specimen was negative. The second showed

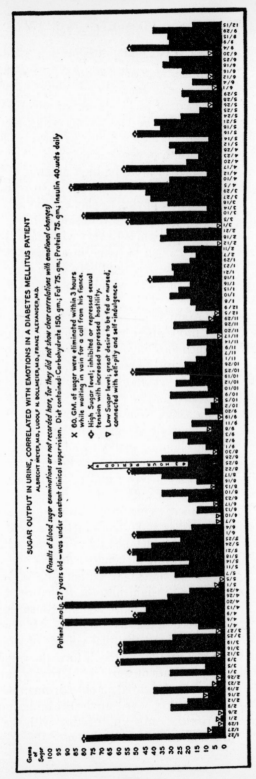

Figure 1

4 grams of sugar. Increased anger developed toward his fiancée during the afternoon, with the conflict about marriage and responsibility in the foreground. The anger was especially provoked through the wish of his fiancée to give up her position on account of the intended marriage. This anger can be characterized as a childish, aggressive, demanding claim to be given what he wanted. The specimen from 6:30 to 11 p. m. showed *61 grams* of sugar. He spent this time alone in an angry tension, expecting from her a telephone call which did not come. Here we see very clearly the frustration of his wish to be taken care of by the girl he loved, as the child by the mother. At the same time he was in a sexual tension, wanting to marry the girl; but this would involve adult responsibilities in contrast to his regressive infantile tendencies. On August 29, 1938, he had almost no sugar in the morning, but had a sugar output of 14 grams in 340 cc. later in the day when a friend came, as a very unwelcome guest, to visit him. He was forced to make lunch and the friend ate a great deal in an uncouth manner. He was in a state of rage and was not able to express his tension at all. Again we see his original conflict coming out, being forced to be the feeding mother instead of the receiving child. On March 6, 1939, the sugar output was 2 grams during the night and 7 grams in the morning. During the night a violent physical attack upon his wife occurred, connected with rage because his wife had given up her job. After this fight they became reconciled and had sexual relations. The corresponding sugar output was minimal. The next afternoon, however, he and his wife went to see the friends who had been present when the attack took place. The patient had to control himself, play a responsible role, and repress his demanding attitude. The sugar output went up to 33 grams in a couple of hours.

Following the diagram during the next months, we see that as a whole the sugar output during the time he spent at his work was greater than the sugar output during the night or at other times outside his work situation. The same tension as described above developed when he had to earn money for his wife and provide instead of receive. For instance, on a day of physical and mental rest there was no sugar eliminated, but during the working hours of the following Monday the sugar output was again 18 grams. On April 21, 1939, 6 grams of sugar were eliminated during a Sunday spent on vacation, in contrast to 21 grams of sugar eliminated on Monday morning during a few hours in school.

There were, however, Sundays and Saturdays with a high sugar output in all urine specimens. For example, on the 10th of March, 1939, the sugar output was almost 80 grams. On this day his psychoanalytic material showed the usual conflict about his biting and incorporating tendencies. This also became manifest in the behavior toward his wife, who at this time began to demand a great deal of attention, and expressed jealousy of his former friends, who spoiled the patient with attention and presents. It is thus evident that the presence of emotional tension is responsible for the fluctuation of carbohydrate metabolism. Physical relaxation on Saturdays and Sundays have a beneficial effect only if they are combined with an even emotional state. In the summer of 1939, when, as a result of his analysis, he was able to accept a more responsible adult attitude without internal revolt and live in good marital adjustment, the sugar output decreased substantially.

One year after the termination of his analysis, a son was born, and his fundamental conflict about his receptive dependent wishes came up again. Correspondingly there is a rise of the sugar level to a high peak. During the last years the patient remained sugar free and has continued so to date.

In Summary

The patient, who suffered a severe trauma at the end of his nursing period, retained much of his infantile dependent and demanding attitude and was never able to accept the responsibilities of adult existence. He always felt frustrated and responded with hostilities because no one could gratify his demands for attention and love. These hostilities revived his old anxiety that he might lose love and security, as an equivalent of milk and food of which he was deprived during the starvation period of his illness. The process of emotional maturity was blocked by this anxiety. He never reached the psychosexual attitude of adult age. His diabetes developed at the height of his emotional frustration which arose in relation to his sexual partners. Whenever they demanded of him any affection which was incompatible with his own infantile demands, he felt utterly frustrated and enraged.

In the diagram we recognize that the sugar output increased when the patient felt that his wishes to receive love and security in the manner of a child were frustrated. Low sugar levels occurred when he escaped the conflict by turning to his neurotic solution of the depression, a withdrawal from the outside world into self-pity.

CASE 2. The second patient, a woman of 26, had a psychopathic personality with many depressive trends and a tremendous drive for acting out dramatically her emotional conflicts. The roots of her illness went back to her infancy and manifested themselves in temper tantrums and outbursts toward her mother and younger siblings. She accused the mother, in her analysis, of not feeding the children carefully and sufficiently, and complained that she herself never received enough milk. As far back as she remembered the siblings took the best food away. Probably for this reason she developed an early interest in food. As an overcompensation she shared with the mother the role of feeding the younger siblings, provoking the mother at the same time through her rages. This behavior became the dominating trend of the patient's later life. Prematurely, in early puberty, she left home to take care of other people's children. In spite of good intelligence she did not finish school, but worked either to prepare or serve food or to take care of children. In this manner she lived in a constant state of frustration. She was feeding others but no one took care of her. In this she differs from the first patient, who indulged more freely in his receptive wishes. The second patient always denied herself the satisfaction of her receptive cravings. For this reason her hostilities toward her environment became very strong. This caused great anxiety and blocked her way to a psychosexual maturity to a much greater extent than in the first case. Her sexual drive appeared comparatively early and was expressed rather frankly if we consider her puritanical background. In early adolescence she had sexual experiences with older men and became very promiscuous later on. However, she remained frigid and unresponsive unless she was under the influence of liquor. It is needless to say that under these conditions her attitude did not even remotely resemble a mature reaction to her environment.

The outbreak of diabetes occurred exactly as in the first case, coinciding with exposure to sexual temptation. The patient wanted the love of an elderly man for whom she worked. To win the love of this man, who was her superior in a restaurant kitchen, she worked extremely hard and deprived herself still more of the satisfaction of the passive desires of her private life by sacrificing rest and relaxation. Her strong cravings remained unsatisfied until she became extremely restless. During this time she had a minor accident, spraining her ankle in a fall, and also had her first diabetic symptoms which were extremely severe. She was taken to a hospital almost in a coma. For 3 years she lived under a diabetic regime similar to that of the first patient, and came to analysis because her emotional problems increased simultaneously with the diabetic condition.

The most revealing part of the analysis was the transference situation of patient to analyst. Very early she developed a strong transference with expressions of her sexual desires in a most frank and demanding way, especially when the analysis, because of external rea-

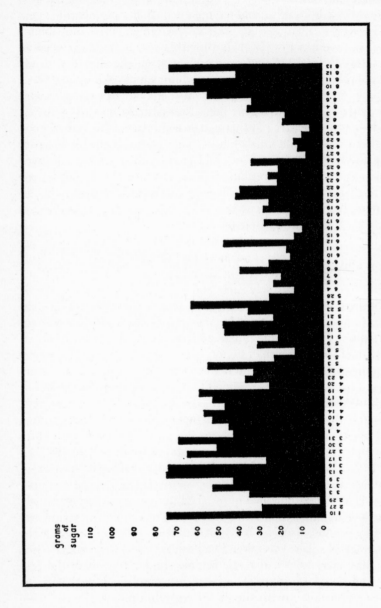

Figure 2. Sugar Output in Urine, Correlated with Emotions in a Diabetes Mellitus Patient

sons, had to be interrupted temporarily. These were emotionally of a pregenital nature which she expressed in an utterly demanding attitude toward the analyst, asking for interpretations, explanations, and immediate help in the most urgent way, just as a hungry and spoiled child demands milk and food from the mother. There were repeated periods in which the patient was under a tremendous rage which was usually connected with an extreme tension felt in her whole body. There were also frequent outbreaks of rage against the analyst toward the end of the session, especially when the analyst expected cooperation and understanding of the material from her. The patient was unable to cooperate as an adult, and being exposed to the demands for cooperation in analysis, her infantile dependent wishes increased together with frustration and resentment.

The analytic material shows clearly the sadistic coloring of her sexual fantasies and reveals that anxiety blocked gratifications and thus increased her dependent wishes.

Correlation Between Carbohydrate Metabolism and Emotional Tendencies

In Figure 2 we see that the patient had a comparatively equal elimination of sugar during the first few months in analysis. During this period there was a rather balanced emotional state. This balance was disturbed as soon as the patient became involved in an emotional conflict situation toward the analyst, transferring to him all her emotional childish demands and feeling rejected when these were not satisfied. We see that now the sugar output began to. fluctuate. Shortly after the patient returned to analysis, after an interruption of almost six weeks, the output was only 3 grams. This was on February 29, 1940. A change of analyst had taken place and the new analyst took a lenient attitude toward the disturbed and excited patient, which satisfied the strong dependent tendencies of her personality. The curve, however, soon went up again, reaching its previous level coincident with the expression of infantile demanding sexual desires toward the new analyst. These were expressed in the same manner as toward the first analyst. On March 17th there was a low sugar level of 29 grams, with corresponding analytical material of emotional withdrawal and aloofness. From May, 1940, on, there was a constant fluctuation in the sugar output which remained throughout the analysis.

An interesting observation is that of the fluctuation in the sugar output during the night, a time when there was no intake of food or insulin administration. Since dreams are an expression of emotional life during sleep, we tried to compare the emotional content of the dreams in the nights of the highest sugar level with dreams of nights when the sugar output was low. In five nights, 65 grams of sugar were eliminated out of a total of 190 grams of sugar ingested. This means that one third of the sugar output occurred during the night. The dream contents during these five nights indicated a high sexual tension, together with hostile feelings toward competitors. In five nights in which the sugar output was very low we had a total of 4.4 grams, while the sugar output of those five nights and days together was 86 grams. The dreams during these five nights of low sugar content expressed regression to passivity and playfulness, and the absence of sexual wishes.

A similar very revealing observation can be made when the patient reacted to the vacation the analyst took during the summer. She became very excited, restless, and sexually stimulated, dwelt in sexual fantasies, and masturbated frequently. During this period we have a constant rise of sugar level to a peak of 110 grams on August 10, 1940. The patient's behavior showed so many manic manifestations that the analyst had to decrease the hours. Later on he changed the treatment from analysis to psychotherapeutic interviews. The sugar level decreased considerably after this, coinciding with manifestations of depression, passivity, and withdrawal. It should be emphasized that the patient's psychosexual drives were completely of an infantile demanding nature, expressing the wish to be taken care of completely by the sexual object.

In Summary

The patient developed during early infancy strong reactions of hostility and envy toward the mother and younger siblings, together with a tremendous interest in and craving for food. In contrast to the first patient, she did not allow herself even substitute gratifications of her dependent wishes in later life on account of her strong hostilities and subsequent anxiety and guilt. Her dependent needs grew so strong that no life situation could satisfy them even to a small extent, and because of this the patient lived in a state of constant frustration and embittered anger. Her sexuality centered in the erotization of these intense demanding infantile tendencies. When the patient withdrew and indulged in self-contained passivity and aloofness, the sugar level became proportionately lower.

Summary

A report was given on two cases of diabetes mellitus—in a man and a woman—who both developed their illness under the strain of an emotional conflict of striking similarity. Both subjects showed unusually strong tendencies to receive and to be taken care of. The first patient's essential demands were stimulated by a physical trauma at the end of his weaning period; the second patient's by a traumatic weaning process. Both patients retained an infantile dependent and demanding attitude, and felt frustrated because their demands for attention and love were out of proportion to the reality situation of an adult and consequently were never adequately satisfied. To this frustration both patients reacted with hostility. Diabetes developed in both cases when these infantile wishes conflicted with the demands that were frustrated, and the sugar output decreased when they temporarily renounced their demanding attitudes.

In the diagram we see very clearly that sugar output is increased under the strain of the above conflict, and decreased when the patients indulged in self-pity and passivity.

It seems probable to us that these food-demanding drives, under the condition that nobody is there to satisfy them externally, may turn to an autoplastic satisfaction in a metabolic process which mobilizes glucose out of the glycogen stores of the body.

The observation of the increased sugar output during the night, i.e., independent of the carbohydrate intake, under certain emotional conditions described above, is consistent with these assumptions. This interpretation is in conformity with recent experimental findings, namely, that in certain cases of diabetes mellitus the rise of the sugar level is dependent not on failure of sugar utilization but on sugar mobilization.

PART VI
SKIN DISEASES

A PSYCHOLOGICAL STUDY OF A CASE OF ECZEMA AND A CASE OF NEURODERMATITIS *

By Milton L. Miller, M.D.

The psychoanalysis of patients with certain skin diseases offers a good opportunity for study, since the outbreaks are readily observable when they occur on the exposed parts and may be correlated with the patient's emotional states. This report deals with the study of the dynamic psychological factors connected with a case of eczema and a case of neurodermatitis.

In the dermatological literature there are numerous articles by such authors as Stokes (21, 22, 23), Allendy (2), Bernstein (7), Klauder (17), Barinbaum (3, 4), Gillespie (14), Blaisdell (8), Fritz Mohr (18), and others who quote case histories demonstrating that certain attacks of skin disease are connected with emotional problems. Although there are important gaps in most of the psychological pictures presented, certain similar trends run through all of the case histories. For instance, *sexual maladjustment* plays a prominent rôle in the following cases quoted:

Blaisdell (8) described a female patient who was very subservient to her father, and was married to a sexually demanding man with whom she was incompatible. Eczema developed when she was faced with his sexual demands, and was exacerbated when her husband wanted to divorce her or provoked her jealousy.

Stokes (23) cited the case of a married woman with a background of skin difficulties, whose itching increased and decreased in proportion to her husband's impotence. Also another case of a man with exfoliative dermatitis who had a terrific attack of itching after being visited by a woman friend with whom intercourse was not possible.

Fritz Mohr (18) described a woman who had sensitive skin in childhood; after marriage her skin broke out in red spots with intense itching. Separation from her husband brought about much improvement but her skin broke out again when she was reunited

* *Psychosomatic Medicine* IV : 82-93, 1942.

with him. She was not able to have orgasm, but scratched her skin with a knife or her nails after intercourse.

Another trend which appears in many of the skin cases is a strong feeling of *hatred, fear, and guilt* in regard to a cruel parent. For instance:

Deutsch (10) cited the case of a girl whose mother put braces on her arms when she was an 8-months-old infant, to prevent thumb-sucking. The patient hated her mother and later felt very guilty because the mother became insane.

Allendy (2) quoted the case of a young woman who had a harsh father, felt resentment toward men, and then later felt very guilty over a young man's suicide.

Sudden fright was followed by a skin outbreak in the following:

Heise's (15) case—a nurse who five hours after a sudden attack from behind by three female patients woke up with severe acute eczema of the face.

Blaisdell's (8) patient, described above, had one skin attack provoked by fright at a narrow escape from an auto accident.

Conflict over masturbation seemed to play an important role in many cases, for instance, in the following:

Barinbaum's (4) patient who scratched himself in the presense of his wife and at the same time masturbated.

Masochistic trends were expressed most clearly in the following:

Gillespie's (14) female patient who felt guilty for sexual desires and scratched herself as an equivalent for masturbation. She was also interested in flagellation.

Fritz Mohr's (18) patient, who was not able to have orgasm in sexual relations, and scratched her skin with a knife after intercourse.

Stokes' (23) male patient, who had had eczema and hayfever in childhood, and suffered from marked suppressed tension—he liked to be scolded by an irritable nurse and then would scratch himself ecstatically.

Exhibitionism was stressed in the case of the 18-year-old girl studied by Dr. Deutsch (10). He noted the ostentatious way in which she showed her diseased elbows to the physician.

Another important factor in several cases seemed to be the *secondary gain* of the illness.

Barinbaum (3, 4) mentioned the case of a baker who avoided work because of a skin outbreak on his hand, and of another patient who clung to his skin disease in order to receive a sick-benefit, also a third, to shirk supporting his wife by his handwork.

Stokes (21) generalizing about the psychological trends of the child who suffered from the asthma, eczema, and hayfever make-up, described him as "ceaselessly active, precocious, assertive, egocentric to a degree obtrusive even for this egocentric age." Facially, the free expression of energy and irritability, the author states, may be replaced by a peculiar, sphinxlike, poker-faced expression.

The papers referred to above describe various emotional features which the authors observed in their cases, for example, hostility or masochism, etc. The various emotions described in connection with the skin cases appear commonly in other types of individuals as well. A causal connection can only be inferred if somatic symptoms appear in connection with typical psychodynamic constellations. In most of the works referred to above, one does not know which ones, out of the variety of emotions presented, might be in direct causal connection with the physical symptoms. For instance, sexual tension has been frequently mentioned in this connection. Such a statement is not sufficiently explicit because sexual excitation may drain a large number of other emotions.

The observations which have been quoted are in no way contradictory to the recent findings of psychiatric and psychoanalytic investigators. Among the important psychoanalytic contributions to the field of dermatology are the detailed psychological studies by Dunbar (11), Bartemeier (5), Ackerman (1), and Pearson (19). All of these reports describe patients whose psychological make-up strikingly resembles the two patients to be described in the following study. Although their dermatological lesions are of diverse origin, certain character traits and problems seem to have recurred in patients with skin ailments. These patients tended to withdraw from a frustrated life to a masochistic absorption in themselves; sexual gratification was too conflictful to be attained successfully; masturbation was likewise a source of conflict; instead, release was sought through skin manipulation and fantasy.

Bartemeier's (5) patient was a senior dental student suffering from chronic exudative dermatitis; the lesion on his hand disappeared when he stayed away from school for a few weeks and recurred whenever he went back. The patient had a strong positive attachment to his mother, and a feminine identification with her. When confronted with stronger men he tended to retreat to passivity, but when unable to gratify this tendency, reacted against it by (1) pilfering (with his hands) from male patients, and (2) extraction of his teeth at the slightest provocation. Looking and grasping with his hand were early conditioned as sources of guilty gratification for him.

Analysis of his castration anxiety and exhibitionistic, sadistic, masochistic, and other conflictful unconscious drives resulted in a clearing up of the lesion on his hand.

Ackerman (1) described the case of a pathologically rebellious and intractable girl of 14, with a skin disorder originally eczematoid, that had begun at the age of two years and was generalized over the surface of her body but had tended to become especially severe at face, neck, and arms. She had had a turbulent early life. Her mother died in childbirth when she was two. Then she went through a period of submissiveness and strong attachment to her father. She also was fond of an aunt whom she regarded as her mother. She lived first in an orphan asylum and then in foster homes, and at 9 was moved again to an orphan asylum. It was then that she was told of her real mother's death. She began to think she had killed her mother and that her skin disease was a punishment for doing so. She conceived of herself as a criminal, set out deliberately to be bad, and set up a vicious circle of self-punishment and hostile action. When hospitalized at 14, she was sexually exhibitionistic and promiscuous, but she did not masturbate. She had great fear of her mother's dead body and ghost. Thoughts of killing both her father and herself were her excuse for two actual attempts at suicide. She deformed her skin with habitual scratching in what she called "fits of spite," or on occasions when she felt excessively guilty about her parents, or when she was sexually excited. She showed some slight betterment of her skin condition with medical treatment, and later, with intensive psychotherapy, showed simultaneous improvement in both skin and behavior.

Cormia and Slight (9) reported a case of a man with excoriated nodules and papules. His wife was frigid, and in the process of restraining his sex desire he had intense pruritis of the legs and arms which reached a climax in a burning sensation, equated by the patient as an orgasm with marked relief.

Pearson (19) described three analyzed cases. The first is an eleven-year-old boy who wanted to be dependent on his father at the cost of his health and made the worst of an itching eruption of his feet. The second was a man who spent much time examining and excoriating his skin. He had paranoid and obsessional symptoms which he managed to hide from his friends. In both of these cases handling of the skin was a substitute for masturbation, which had been stopped because of punishment. Both expressed defiance of their parents and a strong suicidal drive in the mistreatment of their skin. Both, during manipulation of the skin, had daydreams of what they would like to do but feared to do as successful, sadistic males. Pearson (19) also described a third case, a woman with itching eruptions of the feet. She was extremely masochistic, fearful of her mother and her husband. Unconsciously she wanted to get rid of her children, leave her husband, and defy her mother by becoming a dancer.

Pearson (19) pointed out that (1) a skin lesion due to some organic cause may be continually exacerbated by the patient's emotional behavior toward it, and (2) that "an inflammatory skin lesion may develop as an attempt to solve a difficult emotional problem."

A well-documented summary of the literature from the physiological and psychological approach has been presented by Stokes and Beerman (24). They quoted Rogerson (20) and others who describe the allergic child's conflict between dominating the parent and being overdependent on the parent. From the findings which they described, certain emotional characteristics appear to stand out as common for this type of allergic child: retarded psychosexual development, tension, guilt, anxiety, and certain contradictory motivations—dependence and hostility, dreaminess and ambition. Attention and solace are secondary gains of allergic illness. The importance of the role of repressive discipline in the emotional development of the adult "eczema personality" and the "irritative relationship often with the parent of the same sex," as well as the development of the "poker face" are stressed by these authors.

CASE 1. A short, young man with close-cropped, blond hair, shabby, collegiate clothes, a drawn, mask-like facial expression, and downcast eyes came for analysis because of lifelong feelings of inferiority and shyness. He had a hideous facial skin eruption diagnosed as eczema. Lesions also were present on the flexor surfaces of the forearm, the dorsum of the hands, and on the scalp, as well as occasional spots on the legs.

His analysis brought out the following facts about his life history: He had been much loved by his mother, a gentle person of esthetic temperament who, he felt, idolized him in preference to his two younger brothers; at the same time she was apparently unconsciously seductive. For instance he recalled his anxiety in response to his mother's often putting vaseline on his penis when he was 4. When he was 7 years old she began to have a series of pulmonary hemorrhages, and when he was 8 years old she died of pulmonary tuberculosis. During the months of her final illness he spent hours with her, but would scurry away when he heard his father returning home.

He remembered with great bitterness his father's warnings to remain out of his mother's bedroom. Her death produced such an intense emotional shock in him that he never really recovered from it. He believed that he and his father were somehow implicated in his mother's death. His father was a domineering, hard-driving, very successful business man of the "Napoleonic" type. Toward him, especially after his mother's death, the patient felt a mixture of admiration for his success, and antagonism. He felt he needed his father's protection, but his father—never very warm toward him—was quite depressed for a year, and the patient, who lived with his grandmother, felt desperately lonely. From early childhood the patient felt inferior to other boys in athletics, and succeeded in compensating for this feeling by brilliance in the classroom. However, when, at the age of 15, he entered an exclusive preparatory school, he found it impossible to adjust. When he went out for the track team, he broke his leg. He felt his inequality with the other boys so keenly that for the first time he was not able to outshine them in the classroom. That year, marked by so much tension and frustration, was followed by a stay at camp. While there, following an inoculation of smallpox vaccine, his skin broke out over his head and face. He became acutely disturbed and expressed his guilt over masturbation to everyone in camp. He spent the following year at home where he was subdued and withdrawn, maintaining a somewhat distant attitude toward his stepmother and a reserved attitude toward his father, whom he provoked by seducing a maid in such a way as to call his father's attention to it.

He spent the next four years at a western university of high standing, where he became associated with a group of eccentric, brilliant, neurotic young men who indulged themselves in "esthetic" experiences and obscenities, and might be said to have majored in schizophrenia. He managed to maintain a good scholastic standing, particularly in literary and writing courses. Very often, however, around examination time, his skin would break out, he would contract a cold and spend a few days in the hospital. On several occasions these attacks were precipitated by dates with girls. Following his graduation he spent a number of months in Europe in aimless wandering. At this period he felt depressed and confused about himself. He was worried about his skin condition and felt hopeless about the possibility of undertaking a career. He then decided upon an analysis.

In the early part of his analysis and in his daily life he tried to display himself constantly as a literary genius, a Rabelaisian cynic, and a defeated eccentric with macerated skin—or else a tragic, ruined nonentity bringing humiliation on himself and his father. He was in a constant state of frustration. He never could write successfully, he was impotent with women, and his exhibitionism failed to impress. Thus frustrated, he created a dramatic role for himself which he played alone upon the stage—his father and the analyst the audience. His job, his friendships and love affairs he permitted to have no real claims upon him or meaning to him. Reality, with its demands for conformity and sublimation, he could not accept. He was constantly impelled to attack weak, depreciated women, who were the only ones who bothered about him—and to attack himself, lacerate his own skin. At the culmination of intense periods of self-destruction, when this conflict was brought to a peak by the demands of external reality—as, for instance, when he had to make his way as a member of a boys' camp, or when he graduated from college and had to get a job—he consciously desired, and actually carried out, the solution of his conflicts by being brought home to his father sick and helpless, with severely infected skin, weeping. When he was kissed by his father on such an occasion, he fell into a coma.

During analytic hours he moved about on the couch, waved his arms continuously, and spent a good deal of time trying to make an impression with his knowledge of music, art, and literature, identifying himself with Van Gogh. He consorted with a bohemian group of young people whom he tried to impress in the same manner, and he liked to walk about the streets hatless, exhibiting his diseased skin and close-cropped hair. At times his flow of speech resembled the more salacious passages of James Joyce.

It soon became clear that his exhibitionism served many purposes. It could be turned, with versatility, into a defense against, or an expression of, his passive homosexual tendencies. He also used his intellectual exhibitionism as the solace for his wounded narcissism, since he could never expect to become a successful industrialist like his father. His excessive ambition and wish to outdo his father could only find expression in this intellectual manner.

He began to see, more and more, that his main conflict centered around the urge to compete with his father, an ambition doomed always to failure. The father, who was unusually successful, never really encouraged the patient's self-confidence. And the two younger brothers, with whom the patient competed secondarily, were more attractive and endowed with superior physique. In his dreams and in his activities he kept trying to take women away from stronger men, but always failed or expected some dreadful punishment. His attempts at masculine competition were doomed to failure, and if by chance he succeeded with some second-choice woman, he was then impotent.

He had started his analysis with great admiration of his father and an exalted opinion of the analyst. Months later he said his admiration was just another name for fear and that he had consorted with his father's enemies and tried to "rook" him in all sorts of underhanded ways. After a long confession about his hostility to his father and its effect on him, he stated that he kept disgracing himself in order to disgrace his father, and ended with the statement, "Doing away with myself would have been the ultimate revenge." He waged a subtle campaign of attack against the analyst, and spent many of his hours trying to provoke the analyst's anger so that he could accuse him of being harsh. He wept, displayed his skin lacerations, and then spent much of his time seeking a maternal atmosphere in which to recuperate, or a weaker person, preferably a depreciated girl, on whom to vent his own sadism. In order to attempt to disgrace the analyst he tried to show all and sundry how sick he was, and wandered into other neighboring offices, restaurants, etc., where he would arouse the scorn and astonishment of strangers with his unusual appearance and diseased skin. He also confessed that he had planned to simulate a shaking fit "in order to show the analyst up."

At the same time as he was provocative in the analysis, he kept expressing his desire for passive submission to strong men and his craving for their love and admiration, or at least their attention, in competition with women. He felt a sadistic curiosity about women. But he could not tolerate the active, sadistic side of his nature any more than the passive side. His life was an increasing spiral of frustration in all attempts to deal with the outside world either as an aggressive man or a submissive female; in his dreams also there was this same sense of frustration to a striking degree. Longing for the solace of the good mother, and the consequent attempt to compete with men, brought about fear of men's hostility. Then he tended to submit to men, but his masochistic femininity was too fearful—so he tried to defend himself against his fears by intense narcissism and exhibitionism, but he was too guilty to exhibit himself in a successful manner. Therefore the conflict drove him to exhibit himself, not as a successful male, but as a defeated, sick, humiliated, tragic boy, bringing punishment upon himself and his family and deserving their forgiveness because he was suffering so much already.

As the analysis of his exhibitionism proceeded, he evolved a complicated defense typical for him: having had at college about two years of psychotherapy with a psychoanalytically trained therapist, he had entered the analysis fully armed with an extensive intellectual knowledge of psychoanalytic clichés which gave him material with which to compete against the analyst. For a long time he presented never-ending theories spun around terrifying sadomasochistic fantasies in which he constructed a textbook primal scene from the point of view of the voyeur, in order to avoid talking about his daily life which was so filled with frustration. In the second six months of his analysis, which was spent in dealing with this resistance, the skin eruption became pronounced, especially because of his intense scratching.

During this phase of his analysis he had an affair with a depreciated, sick girl with whom he was impotent. At the same time he identified himself with her and abused her violently. As he lay in bed expressing his conflicting feelings and suffering the consequent tension, he would notice that his skin would become worse, and it would remain so for a number of days following. At these times he would indulge in an orgy of scratching which he would exhibit to the girl and to others. This was the acting out of his deeper conflict with his mother and father.

As his hostilities and fears increased, his desire to exhibit himself as a mental case approximated a real breakdown; in fact he actually feared he was going insane just when his hostility to the analyst was about to become fully conscious. He took refuge in a far-reaching regression, and required hospitalization because of his marked suicidal drives and delusions of a megalomanic nature—the attempts of a threatened ego to assert itself. He presented a pathetic picture of defeat. The skin on his face, head, neck, and arms was covered with a severe eczema, which was excoriated and infected. He identified himself with Christ who, although crucified, had tremendous power. At the same time his longing for the protective mother was acute. The only actual consolation he could obtain was by stuffing himself with food in the hospital. Through his sickness he unconsciously postponed facing the full force of his hostility toward his father and toward the analyst. Only after practically destroying himself could he bear to admit his aggressiveness toward the analyst. This was accompanied by such feelings of extreme loneliness that he likened his life to that of the Man Without a Country. He said the analyst was the Rock of Gibraltar and he always had wanted to smash it. Then he confessed he had lived his life in perpetual fear. He feared the world would end, feared autos, water, driving with others, etc.

Finally he admitted fear that the analyst would castrate him. He said he identified himself with his mother, and in adolescence thought he would grow breasts like a girl—this femininity he connected with his skin disease. He thought that the father's penis caused his mother's death. His skin disease expresses his identification with his mother, and the consequent danger that his father's sexual attack would bring about his own destruction as it had brought about his mother's.

The eczema had begun with mobilization of his intellectual exhibitionism in competition with his fellows in the first year at preparatory school, and was a reaction to and defense against his passive homosexual tendencies. In the analysis it appeared in relation to these conflicts. As the exhibitionistic defense had been mobilized, the skin erupted severely. This made it seem apparent that the presence of psychological conflicts were of importance in producing the eczema.

In addition to allergic reactions he had a history of childhood eczema as well as allergic sensitivity to a number of substances, particularly cat's hair. However at the time when he was dealing with the most upsetting fantasies of world destruction and his own castration, when his skin outbreak simultaneously was at its worst, the dermatologist who had been examining him could find no relation between the patient's skin condition and any allergen present at the time—only that intense scratching had led to a skin infection.

It may be that his skin ailment was fundamentally a somatic disorder of constitutional rather than psychogenic origin, but his character difficulties found in his dermatitis such a perfect medium for the expression of his conflict that at least certain periods of serious exacerbations of his skin disease may be traced to psychological causes. The paroxysms of intense scratching, which always appeared with the eruptions, were clearly psychically motivated. Also it must be noted that his skin ailment did not seem to be an entirely accidental misfortune but an integral part of his personality make-up.[1] This recalls other analyzed cases quoted in the literature, for instance the young female patient studied by Ackerman (1), as well as the dentist analyzed by Bartemeier (5) who had, like this patient, marked exhibitionistic characters, with intense guilt. This patient appears to have been fixated in his psychosexual development to a period of frustrated exhibitionism, as well as looking at the primal scene. A typical dream is: A man and woman lying in bed together, the patient is outside looking in.

Modification of therapy designed to support his shattered ego enabled him to deal with dawning insight into his hostility, his dedependence, and the motives for his exhibitionism. As the analysis continued he gradually began to understand the deeper conflicts, and

---

[1] For the last seven years the patient had, besides his skin disease, occasional mild attacks of wheezing which were nonseasonal. As the asthma cases do, he occasionally showed in the transference some compulsion toward confession, and felt very guilty about his sexual adventures—with the urge to exhibit them to his father and to the analyst. He had not a typical asthma conflict, however (12). Instead of having asthmatic attacks in the situations of sexual temptation, it was when his desire to be loved by the analyst or his father was thwarted that his skin broke out.

at the same time there was some improvement in his skin. Shortly after this it was felt that his analysis should be interrupted to give him a chance to take advantage of what insight had been gained. He was able a few months later to obtain steady employment in an intellectual occupation and to take part in social activities. His skin improved considerably.

I should like to quote two typical dreams which give composite impressions of two sides of his personality:

> 1. I was on top of a mountain in a foreign civilization. Someone put me in a concentration camp. They were cruel. I saw them break an old man's leg across a chair. I thought of escape, but I would be shot. There were girls in the dream, but they were my kid brother's contemporaries.
>
> *Associations:* He associates being in a concentration camp with fiddling with girls and passive anal desires. He thinks of falling and breaking his nose at four, operations on nose, his conviction that God was against him following that accident, and his frustrated lonely childhood. He also mentions some guilt about recent drinking since starting analysis. This dream follows frustration resulting from analyst's telling him the day before that he uses his exhibitionism as a defense against analysis of his passive tendencies.

On a day on which the skin on his face was particularly bad, he had the following dream:

> 2. He is trying to impress the president of a large corporation, but his efforts are received with contempt. Then he sees a girl who looks like a monkey with a wizened face with grey hair on it, and is disgusted.
>
> *Associations:* In his associations he talks of a letter from his father to the president of the corporation, and his desire to make an impression. He feels tortured by his limitations, tried to write last night, but it was very labored. He felt guilty about it, and his skin became worse. He remembers wanting to do to his mother "what father did" but feeling inadequate. When his mother died, he wanted to die too. He used to look through the keyhole at his stepmother taking a bath. He says, "I talked to myself last night as if I were my father talking to his son. Always had to pretend he was on my side." He resented his grandmother and mother babying him, and says, "I had a terrific blankness after mother died." When he was small, allusions to sex, he says, brought punishment from his father.

The first dream clearly shows his intense masochism. The dream was the reaction to the explanation given him on the preceding day concerning the meaning of his exhibitionism. Evidently this aroused his competitiveness and aggressiveness, which was only expressed in terms of being treated cruelly and of being inadequate sexually.

The second dream shows the particular way in which he handles his competitiveness. Since he is unable to compete successfully with his father, he is driven toward a feminine identification with his mother, which, however, arouses his fear. He expresses his frustration then by exhibiting himself as a bizarre figure with a facial skin eruption (monkey with a wizened face) and at the same time expresses his disgust for such weak figures.

The psychodynamic picture may be summarized as follows: He competes with his father in an exhibitionistic way. However this attempt to compete arouses his guilt because it is essentially destructive (breaking an old man's leg across a chair) and also his fear (I would be shot). He retreats then to a feminine masochistic attitude toward the father. This psychic position, however, produces shame and a further competitive effort as a reaction against this humiliating attitude. These conflicts seem to be causally connected with the skin lesions in the following two ways: (a) exhibitionism and masochism are constantly stimulated and the skin lesions supply an outlet for these conflicting drives. By scratching and macerating his skin he can satisfy his masochism and at the same time he exhibits the lesions; (b) the eruption of the skin actually was at its worst when the need to express these two drives (masochism and exhibitionism) was greatest, and it may be that stimulation of sympathetic nervous pathways may have contributed, along with the scratching, to biochemical changes in the skin. Further physiological and biochemical research may elucidate the latter possibility.

CASE 2. The second patient, a tall, blond young man, in his twenties, sought analysis for sexual impotence and hoped to be accepted as a research case because of chronic neurodermatitis. He was of foreign birth. The medical history of his skin disease is as follows: He was told that at the age of 3 or 5 he had had skin lesions between the toes; at 14 he had a patch behind the left knee which appeared and reappeared many times. There are still some remnants of it. There were similar lesions on the soles of both feet at 19, which still persist. Four years ago he had a patch on the dorsum of the right hand, between the index finger and thumb, which gradually extended to cover the palm. A year ago it cleared up three weeks after he consulted a female dermatologist who hinted that he should moderate his life—which the patient interpreted to mean that he should give up sexual relations and masturbation. So far the skin lesion has not returned.

He presented a veneer of cool politeness and reserve. There was little expression in his face, which seemed drawn and masklike. He walked slowly and indolently as if living in an ivory tower, and his affected air was reminiscent of the lines by E. A. Robinson:

> "The man Flammonde, from God knows where,
> With firm address and foreign air,
> With news of nations in his talk
> And something royal in his walk,
> With glint of iron in his eyes,
> But never doubt nor yet surprise . . ."

He liked to dress in odd-colored suits and wore a faded hat which he felt made him conspicuous. In a business office, where he formerly worked as a clerk, he appeared one day, to the astonishment of his colleagues, in a bright silk blouse. He had great interest in clothes, especially men's clothes of unusual design, and with much pride once showed his father some shoes with zippers that he had made. In his social contacts he was usually detached and aloof, and looked down with contempt on most of the people who lived in his hotel, classifying them as bourgeois. When he felt more congenial he was fond of quoting satirical statements of Oscar Wilde. Toward his superiors he presented a meek, compliant air, but felt keenly his lack of prestige compared with theirs. He complained bitterly that when he met his boss socially he was treated as an inferior.

While the patient was still a small child his parents separated and he did not remember seeing his mother from the time he was 5 until he was 13. In this early period he resented his mother's rejection bitterly. A few scattered early memories indicated vivid sexual curiosity with considerable guilt in relation to his sexual impulses and fear of punishment. He recalled seeing the woman who later became his stepmother standing nude in front of a mirror. He rushed up to her and put his nose into her buttocks (age about 7).

When he separated from his mother at the age of 5, his attachment to his father became even more intense, but here too he was doomed to rejection because of his father's several marriages and long absences. He recalled at this period that when his father left him for a short time he drank urine, hoping that "magic" act would hasten his father's return. He spoke constantly of the fact that his father could trace his lineage back to the Middle Ages. The father was an artistic, literary man—kind, indulgent, and apparently of a type easily dominated by women.

At 6 the patient came to this country with his father and a housekeeper who married his father when the patient was 11. His childhood was marked by a feeling that he was effeminate. He had long hair like a girl until 8, and felt inferior to other boys in athletics.

He remembered also that at 8 he wanted to keep house for his father. The housekeeper who married his father he continually described as a very brutal, domineering person, the object of his strong hatred. When he was 10 he was angry with her, and threatened her with intercourse. After his father married her, the patient and she were openly hostile to each other.

At this period the family, for business reasons, moved to a South American country; this increased the patient's feeling of inferiority because he had to learn a new language. At about 14 he formed an association with an older boy who was extremely aggressive and used to go about carrying a loaded pistol. At 16 his stepmother died, and he put salt in his eyes at her funeral in order to pretend that he felt some grief. When he was 18, his father, who was then in his sixties, married for the third time over the patient's violent protests. However, he became fond of the second stepmother, who was 35 years her husband's junior, and he made advances to her openly in such a way as to arouse the father's jealousy.

Since puberty he was quite conscious of his impotence and sought help by electric treatments, hypnosis, and finally at the age of 19 by circumcision for long standing phimosis.

In his late teens he had a great desire to be an actor, and had such conflicting ego-ideals as Dorian Gray, Nietzsche, and Napoleon. He consistently sought after prestige, and through his father managed, in his early twenties, to join some exclusive social clubs where he met his bosses, although he still held an inferior position as a clerk.

In his attempts at sexual affairs he showed a preference for much older women, usually divorcees, and always assumed a very passive role. At 17 he began to have the fantasy of being raped by a woman on a fine silken bed. In addition to his sexual affairs with women, he usually formed an attachment to a man—either an older man with prestige or a younger man with strong exhibitionistic drives, latent homosexual trends, and literary, pseudo-sophisticated interests like the patient himself.

His analysis at first was characterized by breaking down the defenses against the strong, passive homosexuality which was one expression of his urgent desire to be loved and cared for by some fatherly person. He maintained obstinate intellectual defenses against the understanding of his feminine attitude toward men, and concentrated on exhibiting himself as a sort of fascinating foreign nobleman. In his dreams, however, he repeatedly expressed conflicts about hiding or being seen in embarrassing situations with regard to the analyst—for instance in one dream he was a seductive girl in a red dress. In his dreams and in his daily attitude he maintained a parasitic attachment to the analyst and to other men with prestige, similar to the way he had felt toward his father. When this was interfered with he reacted with rage which he projected to the analyst by attempting to prove in dreams and in dealing with his own daily problems that the analyst treated him badly. It was later disclosed that he had begun the analysis without revealing his total financial assets, and then it became clear that this represented the wish to make the analyst take him for very little, to single him out for indulgence as he once wished his father would. His reluctance toward paying for the analysis paralleled that of Bartemeier's (5) skin patient.

Analysis of his coming late or of missing hours showed that he felt guilty about his strong wishes to receive love and attention from the analyst, whose attentions he really wished to monopolize without reimbursement—so that he could not bear to accept the degree of attention to which he was entitled. His guilt, because of the suppressed rage at the thwarting of his dependent, receptive drives, resulted in a distant, overpolite attitude, and consequently great difficulty in dealing with his transference feelings, as well as his feeling toward his boss and towards other authoritative figures.

His relation to women at the beginning of the analysis presented a picture of an attempt to satisfy a strong receptive urge, and again the result was frustration. He became engaged to a wealthy girl in whom he first became interested only after he had seen her with a man whom he envied and toward whom he felt attracted. This girl served as a vehicle for a fantasy which he had since his adolescence, namely, that he would marry a wealthy girl who would support him, then have a number of children toward whom he could devote his life and whom he would bring up to be supermen. He treated the girl coldly and depreciatingly. In order to justify the sadistic attitude toward her he looked for opportunities to feel jealous of her attentions to other men. His anger then interfered with his ability to receive from her, and was vented upon the men toward whom he felt great jealousy.

He had the fantasy of having ten children—all boys—by ten different women. The boys would be raised by him and developed into supermen who would then govern the nations of the world. Still another fantasy was equally a favorite of his, because he felt unable to develop a satisfactory career, he planned to work in order to invest in the stock market, accumulate enough savings to retire at the age of 35 and devote the rest of his life to dilettante pursuits. These fantasies parallel the manifestations of the functionally restricted ego and megalomanic trends in the first patient discussed.

Coitus to this patient, as to the other also, was a sadistic act. It represented (a) revenge for rejection by his mother as well as by his father, and (b) an attempt to prove his superiority over his father. As already mentioned, on several occasions when he was nine or ten, he threatened his stepmother, when he was very angry at her, with intercourse. Similarly his adolescent fear of getting syphilis from sexual contact with women during intercourse was probably based on fear of punishment for the fantasied sexual attack on women. In his affairs he very soon lost interest if women showed too much enjoyment of his company. He always got pleasure out of treating them shabbily and frustrating them.

The attack of dermatitis on his hand, which began a few years ago, coincided with the beginning of an affair with a divorcee with whom he was impotent. During the analysis he had a dream which throws some light on the psychogenic factors connected with the outbreak of dermatitis:

> There was a priestlike man carrying a casket of steel like a cradle. A young woman lifted up the cover and looked in. There was a baby in it, and the baby's face was eaten up—a black color. I looked in and saw the remainder of the baby—all blackish as if it had been worm-eaten. I was afraid of catching a disease and tried to pull rubber gloves over my hand, but before I could, saw a scratch on my right hand at the same place where I had the skin disease. Blood was dripping; also, there was a brown spot and I knew I had caught the disease. There was a large corpse lying on a bench in the garden.
>
> *Associations:* His fear of contracting syphilis and his fear that other people would look upon his skin disease as syphilis; the gloves used by a surgeon in operating, and the blood spot with cut flesh. He once saw an attractive girl in a syphilitic clinic. Corpse he thinks of as his dead stepmother who often warned him about the dangers of catching syphilis. When he was 13 he was worried about his phimosis and smegma, and was told by a friend he had venereal disease. He remembers that when he consulted a professor about his impotence, when he was 16, he was told that masturbation caused it. He talks about his sadistic attitude toward girls, and how he loses interest if they respond; also of his great interest in watching burlesque shows. He remembers that when he was very small, his father told him that in the city where they were, there were bodies on the street on account of an influenza epidemic. He thinks of himself as the child in his dream and the man and woman are his parents—the woman not his real mother, but his stepmother. He remembers also that he once read in Freud that a woman who was frightened at the sight of blood had this fear as a result of defloration when she noticed blood on the sheet during the wedding night.

In the dream he expresses the same attitude as he wishes to express in the analytic situation. He connects himself with a pontifical figure ("the man Flammonde") who, however, always carries with him his own feminine receptive tendencies (the diseased baby) which constantly cause conflict. At the same time the priest represents the father, and, during the course of the treatment, the analyst, toward whom he felt passively submissive. When, however, longing for love, for a father-figure, was not gratified, he reacted with frustrated rage which he turned on to himself. The dream also shows clearly his feminine identification, which he cannot fully accept because of his sadistic attitude toward women. He is afraid he will experience in coitus what he wishes to do to them (the disease in the dream). His conflict over masturbation, which is connected with these sadistic, masochistic, and exhibitionistic-voyeuristic fantasies, produces intense guilt. The space between thumb and index finger on the dorsum of the right hand which he actually uses for masturbation seems to become "punished" in a sense by being contaminated with neurodermatitis. The locale of the lesion on the hand also suggests a symbolic representation of the female genital. This is well substantiated by the analytic material. Bartemeier's (5) patient showed a similar mechanism.

If he is active sexually, then he must hurt the woman. His hope is to be passive and receptive, and still to avoid injury, but reality, his competitive conflict with father-figures, and his masculine narcissism do not permit this. Just as in the first case, his attitude toward women and toward men both provoke too much guilt for the expression of his genitality; masturbation likewise is guilt-ridden, and he feels the need to expose and expiate his guilt by way of exposing, not the genitals which he must safeguard, but the other offending organ, the hand.

It is clear that in contrasting this patient with the previous one discussed, we deal here with a personality in which the functional capacity of the ego is greater. It seems also apparent that in Case 2 there is more latent capacity to sublimate these conflicts. He had less fixation on the mother and a more yielding attitude of passive submission to the father than Case 1. Since he is more able to express positive feelings toward stronger men, and always associates himself with men of prestige, he is able to get more narcissistic satisfaction and support than Case 1. He is not forced to take quite such depreciated objects of heterosexual interest as the former patient, and is less self-destructive.

Discussion

In Case 1 we saw the patient's hopeless struggle to defy his father, to outdo him in achievement, without ever accepting the necessity for the real development of his capacities. In a parallel way he wished immediately, by a brilliant flow of associations, "to make a world's record" by analyzing himself in a few weeks. In Case 2 the same narcissistic need is evident, but expressed in a more realistic way. In these patients the skin disease apparently offers an expression of chronic unsatisfied emotional tensions which cannot be discharged genitally because of deep conflict. The inhibited masculine drives and the inhibited feminine, masochistic drives in both cases recall those of the other skin cases in the psychoanalytic literature. In both of my cases there happens to be identification with a dead or diseased mother, as well as with a depreciated prostitute type of mother who in the second case overtly rejected the patient since infancy. Both patients were impotent, passive men, sadistic toward women, dependent upon their fathers, and tremendously guilty about their hostility. The skin lesions served as a medium for the expiation of their guilt. The hostility was turned inward and was expressed in a masochistic form upon the skin—in Case 1 by actively injuring it, and in Case 2 by a more symbolic expression. The exhibitionism which, as has been shown, expressed their competitiveness, ambition, and defiance, in an infantile manner, also served their need to impress, startle, and command attention (in a self-destructive way) by showing others their diseased skin.

It might be that these individuals, through their early experiences, have developed a considerable degree of erotic conditioning of their skin so that when the sexual impulses were impeded from expression through genital channels, because of severe conflicts within the personality, the easiest outlet for the sexual tension was an autoerotic one previously established (Freud, 13). Perhaps the eczema of childhood (usually an allergic response) which the first patient had was an important factor in reenforcing early erotism [2] of his skin, thus preparing a convenient site for the later expression of his tension.

Scratching of the skin as an outlet for unsatisfied tension is an important symptom in many skin diseases. In Case 1 the tension seemed to be the result of a number of frustrated instinctual drives. Scratching was almost constant, but became more intense at certain

---

[2] One might speculate on the ways in which excessive erotism of the skin might develop. A traumatic factor may have influenced the site of the specific erotism, for instance the childhood eczema in Case 1. Excessive punishment on various portions of the skin were mentioned in Deutsch's (10) case. Excessive fondling during early years might also be a factor in sensitizing the skin.

times. It was connected with considerable pleasure, at times reaching orgiastic proportions, as in the case reported by Cormia and Slight (9). A further determinant of the scratching was the wish to exhibit the macerated skin.

It would seem more than a coincidence that the first patient, whose sexual tension expressed itself in the form of exhibitionism and voyeurism, should have his most intense eruption on the face clearly visible to others and easily visible to himself in the mirror. In the second patient, while the psychological origin of the lesions behind the knees and on the feet are not explainable by the material of the analysis, there seems to be some significance in the fact that the hand by which he masturbated, the sexual offender which was associated in his mind with so much guilt and fear of punishment, should be afflicted for all to see.

Appendix

Statistical Study. A statistical analysis has been made of the occurrence of exhibitionistic and voyeuristic trends in the dreams of the two skin cases in comparison with those of 12 other available cases of passive and inhibited types of young men.

The results are as follows:

Case	Manifest Dreams of Looking and/ or Exhibiting	Manifest Dreams of Exhibiting
1. Eczema	62%	29%
2. Neurodermatitis	72%	45%
3. Asthma and Neurodermatitis	57%	16%
4. Bisexual conflict, headache, etc	57%	26%
5. Petit mal	52%	40%
6. Blushing	44%	14%
7. Ulcer	43%	22%
8. Constipation	43%	18%
9. Constipation	39%	13%
10. Work Inhibition	34%	13%
11. MD, passivity, gastrointestinal distress	34%	5%
12. MD, impotence	34%	9%
13. Character neurosis	32%	16%
14. Hypertension, tremor, insomnia	31%	7%

It can be seen that the two skin cases and the case of asthma and neurodermatitis, and the case of petit mal (who had a slight skin outbreak during his analysis), have a comparatively high degree of voyeuristic and exhibitionistic tendencies in their manifest dreams. The markedly inhibited personalities, namely, the patients with blushing, work inhibition, and ulcer, show a considerably lower percentage of these trends—and the manic depressive cases and hypertension cases also were low. However, Case 4, with headache and chronic diarrhea, is a markedly bisexual person with the ability to sublimate his strong exhibitionistic and voyeuristic trends in his daily life. This limited trial study would suggest that the skin cases are not the only ones which show a high degree of exhibitionism in their reported dreams, but they do show it to a comparatively high degree, in their dreams, as well as in their daily life and analytic sessions.

BIBLIOGRAPHY

1. Ackerman, N. Personality factors in neurodermite—a case study. *Psychosom. Med.*, 1939, **1**, 366.
2. Allendy, R. A case of eczema. *Psychoanal. Rev.*, 1932, **19**, 152.
3. Barinbaum, M. Eine kurze Mitteilung über zwei psychotherapeutisch beeinflusste Ekzeme. *Z. Psychother. med. Psychol.*, 1932, **5**, 106.
4. Barinbaum, M. Eine vorläufige Mitteilung über die Bedeutung der Freud'schen Psychoanalyse für die Dermatologie. *Derm. Wschr.*, 1932, **95**, 1066.
5. Bartemeier, L. A psychoanalytic study of a case of chronic exudative dermatitis. *Psychoanal. Quart.*, 1938, **7**, 216.
6. Bernstein, E. Emotional factors in skin disease. *J. nerv. ment. Dist.*, 1938, **87**, 1.
7. Bernstein, E. Skin diseases from an emotional standpoint. *Intern. Clin.*, 1938, **1**, 154.
8. Blaisdell, J. H. Mental allergy. Report of a case of seborrheic eczema with recurrences dependent on emotional background. *N. Y. Arch. Derm. Syph.*, 1932, **25**, 205.
9. Cormia, F., and Slight, D. Psychogenic factors in dermatoses. *Canad. med. Ass. J.*, 1935, **33**, 527.
10. Deutsch, Felix. Emotional factors in asthma and other allergic conditions. Paper read at the meeting of American Association of Medical and Social Workers, New England District, February, 1938.
11. Dunbar, H. F. Syndromes of asthma and hay fever. *Psychoanal. Quart.*, 1938, **7**, 25.
12. French, T. M., Alexander, Franz, and Co-Workers. Psychogenic factors in bronchial asthma. Part I. *Psychosom. Med. Monogr.*, Vol. 1, No. 4. Part II. *Psychosom. Med. Monogr.*, Vol. 2, Nos. 1 and 2.
13. Freud, Sigmund. *Three contributions to the theory of sex.* New York: Nervous & Mental Disease Publishing Co., 1930.
14. Gillespie, R. Psychological aspects of skin diseases. *Brit. J. Derm.*, 1938, **50**, 1.
15. Heise, W.: Ein Beitrag zur Frage des akuten Ekzemes mit psychischer Aetiologie. *Neurol. Zbl.*, 1914, **33**, 492.
16. Jelliffe, S. E., and Evans, E. Psoriasis as hysterical and conversion symbolization. *N. Y. J. Med.*, 1916, **104**, 177.
17. Klauder, J. Psychic hyperhydrosis of the palms and soles. *N. Y. Arch. Derm. Syph.*, 1925, **11**, 694.
18. Mohr, F. *Psychophysische Behandlungsmethoden.* Leipzig: Hirzl, 1925.
19. Pearson, G. H. Some psychological aspects of inflammatory skin lesions. *Psychosom. Med.*, 1940, **2**, 22.
20. Rogerson, C. H. Psychological factors in skin diseases. *Practitioner*, 1939, **142**, 17.
21. Stokes, J. H. The complex of eczema: a diagnostic and aetiologic analysis. *J. Amer. med. Assn.*, 1932, **98**, 1127.

22. STOKES, J. H.   The nervous and mental component in cutaneous disease.   *Penn. med. J.*, 1932, **35**, 229.
23. STOKES, J. H.   The effect on the skin of emotional and nervous states.   Masochism and other sex complexes in the background of neurogenous dermatitis.   *N. Y. Arch. Derm. Syph.*, 1930, **22**, 803.
24. STOKES, J. H., AND BEERMAN, H.   Psychosomatic correlations in allergic conditions: a review of problems and literature.   *Psychosom. Med.*, 1940, **2**, 438.

INCIDENTAL OBSERVATIONS ON
PRURITIS ANI *

By Leon J. Saul, M.D.

During his analysis, a young man complained of occasional attacks of pruritis ani. As the analysis progressed it became evident that the pruritis developed regularly upon occasions when he would be taken out, for example to dinner, by older men who were personally interested in him. The analytic material showed clearly that passive anal homosexual wishes were aroused by these situations. They appeared frankly in the material, and the patient gave a history of having indulged in homosexual practices in childhood with attempts at both the active and passive roles. After adolescence he had a single passive homosexual experience, and had an orgasm at the instant at which his anus was penetrated. He occasionally indulged in anal masturbation and stated that he often used the pruritis merely as an excuse for this indulgence. The regular occurrence of pruritis when his passive anal homosexuality was aroused, as well as the analytic material, left no doubt as to the connection. It is of interest that the pruritis was often relieved following a satisfactory defecation.

Dr. Thomas M. French has told me of a woman patient of his in which the connection between pruritis ani and passive wishes was equally clear. The itching provoked insertion of the finger into the rectum and violent rubbing manipulation, which constituted an unrecognized form of anal masturbation. Her pruritis disappeared as satisfactory genital erotism developed.

It is by no means concluded that passive anal homosexual wishes are regularly connected with pruritis ani, but in these cases they were clearly of etiological importance. In other cases, other causative factors are more prominent; for example local irritation caused by fine fecal particles in the anal folds, a condition which can be cured by cleaning and salves.(1)

There is apparently very little in the psychoanalytic literature on pruritis ani, although itching in general has been discussed, for example, by Abraham. (2) Ferenczi mentions pruritis ani in his

---

* The Psychoanalytic Quarterly VII: 336, 1938.

"Psychoanalysis of Sexual Habits." (3) Schilder mentions it in his "Psycho-physiology of Skin." (4)

BIBLIOGRAPHY

1. LILIENTHAL, HOWARD. Pruritis ani: a simple and efficient treatment. *J. Amer. med. Assn.*, 1938, **90**, 509.
2. ABRAHAM, KARL. *Selected papers.* London: Hogarth Press, 1927.
3. FERENCZI, SÁNDOR. Psychoanalysis of sexual habits. *Int. J. Psycho-Anal.*, 1925, **6**, 381.
4. SCHILDER, PAUL. Psycho-physiology of skin. *Psychoanal. Rev.*, 1936, **23**, 277.

THE EMOTIONAL SETTINGS OF SOME
ATTACKS OF URTICARIA *

By Leon J. Saul, M.D.,
AND
Clarence Bernstein, Jr., M.D.

Introduction

In thinking of "psychogenic" or "psychological" factors in disease, it is well to bear in mind that we mean the production of physical symptoms by the powerful biological urges which motivate our lives —fear, love, hate, and the forces which drive men to the heights of heroism, accomplishment, and love, and to the depths of despair, to murder, suicide, neurosis, and psychosis. These motivations can best be understood at present by studying their manifestations in thought, fantasy, dreams, and behavior. Under certain conditions, particularly intensification of these drives without adequate expression, they can affect the physiology sufficiently to produce symptoms, in, broadly speaking, the cerebral or psychological, the voluntary-muscular, and the vegetative spheres.

The essence of the concept of functional symptoms is that the physiological disturbance is produced, not by any damage to the organ but only by a variation in its operation—a change in the balance of forces. This is like the knock in an automobile engine in perfect condition when the car is forced up too steep a hill in high gear. Erythema can be produced by local injury to structure, and also by functional variations such as response to heat or to certain emotional situations. In certain cases of the latter it is called blushing. It would not be surprising, when embarrassment causes blushing, if stronger emotions might not produce more severe effects of similar nature like urticaria. There is considerable evidence in the literature that these emotional forces play a role in producing urticaria in certain cases. Just what forces or what constellations of them are specifically involved has not been worked out. The present paper is a study of this problem.

* *Psychosomatic Medicine* III: 349-369, 1941.

Review of the Literature

An excellent discussion of aspects of urticaria appears in Sulz-berger's *Dermatologic Allergy*. It is generally accepted that urticaria is a syndrome which comprises various disease entities, probably differing in pathogenesis, some allergic and some not (25). It is differentiated from angioneurotic edema, with which, however, it overlaps. In angioneurotic edema there is more involvement of other organs than the skin (15, 17). There are certain differences between the acute and chronic urticaria. The chief of these is the fact that while specific allergens are usually found as causing the acute urti-carias, it is exceptional to find this etiology in the chronic cases, where a great variety of factors may be operative, among them the psycho-logical and endocrinological, (26). The case herein described is of the chronic type, with occasional swelling of the throat, and with no definitely ascertainable family history of allergic reactions. Sulzberger is skeptical of the psychological factor : "*Psychic and emotional* influ-ences can *perhaps* elicit urticarial attacks, and in many ways, perhaps, even favor the creation of allergic states and the elicitation of allergic reactions. I have never had the opportunity to observe purely *psy-chogenic urticarial attacks,* but their existence is reported by many careful observers, such as J. Jadassohn, Sack, and others in Europe, and, in America, Stokes, Pillsbury, Kulchar and co-workers, in arti-cles which merit careful reading by all interested in the problem of psychogenic and emotional effects in various dermatoses (Stokes, Kulchar, and Pillsbury, *Arch. Derm. Syphil.* April, 1935, 31, 470–499)."

The physiological mechanisms are not entirely clarified. Stokes, et al., review studies of the acid-base equilibrium, the effect of emo-tion on vasomotor responses, the vagus-sympathetic mechanism, the calcium-potassium balance in relation to this mechanism, the impor-tant Lewis "H-substance" theory as a connecting link, the role of the antidromic impulse, and so on.

A digest of the papers on emotional factors in urticaria appears in Dunbar's *Emotions and Bodily Changes* (6) and in the excellent critical review by Stokes, et al., (25). Recently, Stokes and Beerman (24) have published a thorough review of psychosomatic correla-tions in allergic conditions. Extended bibliographies are to be found in these articles and will not be repeated here. In this literature there are reports, not always carefully controlled, of persons developing urticaria by auto- or hypnotic suggestion upon seeing it in others, or upon erroneously believing that they had eaten a food to which they were sensitive. It is common for patients to observe that their attacks are precipitated by emotional disturbances. The case reports show the occurrence of urticarial attacks in a great variety of emotional situations, including anger, overwork, or overexertion, frequently under pressure to excel, and situations in which sexual wishes are aroused but frustrated, and very many other circumstances. For example, quoting a small bit of the literature reviewed by Stokes, et al., (25) : ". . . In Dufke's case, urticaria of the face, neck, and arms developed when silk was hung around the patient's neck. When linen was applied, nothing occurred until she was told that the linen was silk, whereupon the eruption developed. Flandin's three typical cases included that of a medical student in whom urticaria developed with each examination, that of a young man allergically sensitive to strawberries and fish, in whom urticaria also developed with any violent emotion, and that of a woman whose emotional outbursts were followed by asthma and urticaria.

"Kreibich and Sobotka 'suggested' successfully to a patient the appearance of urticaria on the trunk. Mayr observed an English physician who could 'suggest' wheals on any portion of his body. Klauder described a woman who had persistent urticaria under physical and nervous tension, responsive to psychotherapy, and a convict in whom urticaria developed each day when he was locked in his cell at 5 P.M., and who recovered under psychotherapy. Schamberg described urticaria in a manufacturer following emotional shock on watching his factory burn down." There is not sufficient consistency in the many reports to bring out any constant personality type or specific emotional state associated with urticaria. However, a series of 100 cases was studied by Stokes, Kulchar, and Pillsbury, and led the authors to the conclusion that ". . . the driving, high tension, competitive personality, keyed to high pitch and perpetually intent on destination, achieved at no matter what expense, is the urticariogenic personality. . . ." (25).

Turning to the psychoanalytic literature, there are reports of patients seen in interviews, but no analyzed cases. Oberndorf (17) in 1912 published observations on the disappearance of angioneurotic edema after appendectomy. W. C. Menninger and J. Kemp (16) report on a man seen in interview whose urticaria occurred after breaking off with a girl with whom he went for six months, indulging in intimacies, but unable to bring himself to having intercourse. The patient connected the attack with "his sexual continence in the face of the repeated sexual excitement with this girl." Also, at this time his brother became ill and he dreaded the possibility of his having to take the responsibility of his family. He relinquished outdoor athletics, as these stimulated the rash. The authors point out the occurrence of the rash when he was threatened with the necessity to prove his manhood. Lorand's (14) case, seen in interviews, is strikingly similar in psychological structure to the one herein to be reported. Her urticaria occurred following an accident, at the point when she was to leave home for a vacation. The chief similarities are the close, highly sexualized attachment to her father, the keen rivalry with a younger sister whom the mother favored, the very inhibited sexuality, the protracted period of uncertainty about marrying, and the very masochistic dreams, which in this case, however, apparently had a special relationship to the accident. Graf-Best (10) has reported the case of a woman who was in the situation of having remarried and being very jealous of her second husband's deceased wife and of the stepson. The analysis was interrupted after fourteen interviews, by which time the urticaria was gone. So far as I know, no psychoanalyzed case of urticaria has been published. It is hoped, therefore, that through a description of the emotional states of the patient at those times when her urticarial attacks occurred, the following report will contribute something to the understanding of the psycho-dynamics of this common disease of the skin.

Methodology

Urticaria is a symptom of a kind which may well result from tendencies in an individual which are reflected in his personality make-up. But functional organic symptoms are often manifestations of particular emotional tensions in an individual rather than of his total personality make-up (3). The same psychogenic symptoms may occur in individuals with diverse personalities which are similar only insofar as they have in common the one emotional tension or constellation which is manifested in the symptom. Moreover, most patients have a number of symptoms, so that a description of the personality does not of itself yield the specific emotional factor. Because an individual has a particular organic symptom and also certain personality trends, it does not follow that the two are causally related. Such correlations are only significant where a large series is available; for example, the 100 cases of Stokes, Kulchar, and Pillsbury (23). The present study is a detailed investigation of a single case in a search for specific emotional factors. Therefore it will focus not upon the details of the patient's personality structure but upon her emotional states at the time of her urticarial attacks.[1]

---

[1] This method was developed by French in studying asthma (8).

Chief Complaints and Medical History

Miss Q, a pleasant, somewhat obese young woman in her middle twenties, with a persistent, severe, generalized urticaria especially about the face and eyes, gave a history which was not typical of a reaction to any commonly recognized specific allergen, nor was any clue discovered by an exhaustive allergic work-up, including extensive skin tests, elimination diets, allergen free room, eosinophile count, and so on. The following are excerpts from the allergist's report:[2]

The patient reached me through a general physician to whom she was sent because of generalized urticaria, especially about the face and eyes, presumably related to a sinus infection. . . . From our angle there was nothing specifically allergic in her story that could be related to any physical contactant, ingestant, or inhalant.

The physical findings were of little assistance. The temperature was occasionally 99.0. . . . Blood pressure 110 to 120/66 to 70.

Our impression was and has been "psychogenic urticaria." Trial at hospitalization, and later a sojourn in Miami, resulted in unsustained improvement. . . . Other methods were used: ergotamine tartrate, parathormone, thermal baths, and turkish rubs—all to no real avail, and really marking time until analysis could be started.

It was never felt that she was at any time in the "basal state" either for metabolic assay or as regards her skin. However, in order to make our survey complete, the tests were done, intradermally, with the following very DUBIOUS "positives": TWO PLUS, pecan; ozite. ONE PLUS, potato, apple, kapok, rabbit hair, almond, celery, cantaloupe, date, watermelon, cottonseed, broccoli. PLUS-MINUS, oat, cauliflower, house dust, prune.

The laboratory findings are in no way remarkable. She was completely studied during her admission to Michael Reese Hospital. . . . The blood showed no eosinophilia, nor did the nasal smears. The stools were negative for blood and parasites. . . .

On the other hand, she was upset emotionally. Her very incomplete family history gave no evidence of allergies, nor had she had any herself. In her early years, besides the childhood diseases, she had two severe accidents and was enuretic for one year while at an orphan's home. In addition to the urticaria she suffered from migrainous headaches, dysmenorrhea, bulimic tendencies, feelings of incompetence, nightmares, and anxieties. She attributed all her current complaints to her nervousness. The analysis brought out emotional

---

2 Dr. Clarence Bernstein, an allergist, was responsible for the patient's allergic work-up and for following her allergically during her psychoanalysis by Dr. Leon J. Saul who was responsible for the psychological aspects of the case.

connections with these other symptoms but they will not be discussed in this paper.

Life Experiences and Reactions to Them

The patient gave the following history. Her mother divorced in order to marry the father when both were not yet 20. When the patient was one and a half her sister was born, and when she was 2, her mother died, owing, it was rumored, to violence from the father. The father then married a divorcee and the children were placed in separate orphan homes when the patient was 4. A year later, in 1917, he took them back in order to avoid the draft. He was always engaged in illicit or shady enterprises and served several prison terms. The patient was well treated by the stepmother until the age of 6. Then the stepmother began to accuse her of things she had not done, for example, scratching the furniture, and would get the father to force a confession. This he did by cruel treatment with a sexual tinge. He stripped her and burned her with a poker, held her under water in the bathtub, forced her out into the cold scantily clad, and so on. This, she complained, was the only kind of attention she received from him. He never took her on his lap or was otherwise affectionate toward her. As soon as the children could help, they were put to doing charwork in the father's saloon and brothel. They knew abuse and drudgery, and the ostracism of the neighborhood and almost no pleasure. They longed for a good mother and a good father. Exposed to violence and promiscuous sexuality, they were forbidden all companionship with boys by the suspicious parents, who constantly accused them of sexual misbehavior and who threatened to shoot them and any boy they might be seen with. At the age of about 11, the patient made three suicidal attempts.[3] At 12, she succeeded in getting a job in a near-by city. With her first salary she bought ice cream and consumed all she could possibly eat. Through hard work she brought the sister to live with her and helped her through school. The patient did well at secretarial work and helped the sister until the latter's marriage at the age of 22. The patient was then even more miserably lonesome. She was befriended by a girl her own age, Miss N, who took her to live in her own poor and emotionally tense family. About this time the patient began going with a young man her own age upon whom she became dependent for male companion-

---

[3] At least one of these was serious. This was by cutting her arm and wrist necessitating five stitches. Previously she had attempted suicide by drinking hydrogen peroxide, and on another occasion by swallowing a bottle of black pills. At 3, she fell through a trap door fracturing her leg, and still carries a scar of a gash on her leg which occurred when she fell while jumping at the age of 10.

ship, but who made no sexual advances, and who, despite his abilities and his intentions of marriage, was perpetually unable to find a position which would have made the marriage possible.

The patient reacted against her early sordid, sensual environment by constant but only partially successful struggles to rise above it. She daydreamed of fairy princes, love, and dancing at gay restaurants, and strove strenuously, but inhibitedly, to improve herself through night school, dramatics and discussion groups, and the like. But in her dreams she was often back in poverty, being attacked by a cruel man who clearly represented her father. She tried to break completely with her father, but could not. She was dependent on him emotionally, hated, feared, loved, and pitied him. Because of her masochistic dependence on him she was sexually repressed and frigid, and for three years preceding the urticaria, was engaged to the above mentioned boy who made no sexual advances and never succeeded in finding a job which would have enabled them to marry.

Throughout the analysis she had not a single directly sexual dream. Her sexual wishes appeared only in an extremely masochistic and almost never gratified form, such as being chased by a man with a gun or a big stick. The men were usually thinly disguised representatives of the father. Her extreme fear of sexuality was due to the severe repressiveness of her sexual training, to her concept, based on her early experience, of sexuality as something degraded, and more important, to guilt from her own hostilities to her sister, stepmother and father. Moreover, during the analysis, she had not a single dream concerning impregnation. This degree of sexual repression led Dr. Therese Benedek to suspect that she had an infantile uterus—a prediction confirmed by gynecological examination by Dr. Marie Wessels. She identified herself with her sister and covered her hostility to her with an oversolicitous, self-sacrificing helpfulness. She hated her stepmother, but only partially, for she longed for her love—the love of a good mother. Her deepest wish, judging by her frequently recurring dream, which began in earliest childhood, was for a good mother, actually for her concept of her own mother whom she had lost at the age of 2.

The patient's Cinderella-like history reveals a childhood of drudgery and abuse in sordid surroundings, with no pleasure or escape except in daydreams of love and romance. Grown to womanhood, she retained these intense longings of her childhood, but was unable to satisfy them through a normal sexual life because of her fears.

She dreamed of a man with a high hat and a beard, very understanding and helpful, but who could never marry because his legs were paralyzed. And in life she became attached to such a man—one who gave her companionship and understanding and who made no sexual advances. When her perpetually frustrated longings were increased, either internally through the endocrinological changes of her menstrual cycle or externally by some stimulation and disappointment, then she would become upset, frequently eat uncontrollably, be irritable, develop migrainous headaches, and also weep, or else, as we shall see, break out with hives.

Psychological Setting of Major Urticarial Attack

The patient's severe generalized attack of urticaria occurred several years ago just before Christmas, on December the 17th, after mild manifestations for three weeks. She had been overworking and in addition trying to keep up with outside study and dramatic groups. The engagement of Miss N, the girl who had taken the patient into her family, led the patient to leave them at the end of October to take a room alone.[4] Just then her father married a young lady the age of the patient's sister and went to a distant city. Only two human contacts remained for this girl, whose cravings for love were intensified by her loneliness and overexertions. One was her inhibited boy friend who could never find a job. The other was an independent girl at the office upon whom the patient leaned. This girl, Miss A, now decided to leave town to be with her father in a neighboring town, her mother being dead, and invited the patient to come with her for Christmas. The patient envied her intensely for having a good father to go to. Also at this time the patient felt she should no longer wait for her boy friend but should break off with him, despite her dependence upon him. *Thus her last human contacts were threatened.* It was at this point, the end of November, that the first swellings appeared, chiefly on her forehead, eyes, and lips. A few weeks later, after a day of overwork organizing an office party, on the verge of the departure of Miss A., and following a fight with the boy friend, she broke out in a generalized urticaria so severe that she was in the hospital for three weeks and away from work for six months. It thus began *when her extreme cravings for love, intensified by her overexertions, were on the verge of total frustration, through separation from those persons upon whom she was emotionally dependent.*

The patient improved markedly in May when she was referred for analysis and was assured of treatment in the fall, and she returned to

---

[4] This was many weeks before the onset of the urticaria, the course of which was unaffected by changing her living quarters twice. The allergist considered that this ruled out the local environment as a possible source of allergens, particularly since the hives persisted unabated in an allergen-free hospital room.

work a few days after the interview. The urticaria recurred in mild form on and off throughout the summer, along with her severe headaches, and subsided further when her analysis was begun in the fall. Apparently it was mitigated by the prospect of the care of a physician (who, as was seen later, meant to her a substitute for her father who had gone off and married). It disappeared, except for minor recrudescences, upon entering the analytic situation. The following is a description of the emotional settings of these recrudescences.

Urticarial Attacks During Analysis

1. At the first interview (sitting) on October 5th, the patient spoke of how anxious she was for analysis, how she envied other children for having mothers, her expectation of marrying when her fiancé found a job, how inferior she felt about her education and her father's being a bootlegger, and how she hoped for help, having always helped others without thought of reward. The main theme was her thwarted wish for love and help. Practical details concerning analysis were discussed with her, including the fact that an analysis begins with a trial period. The next day she reported that she was very upset for three hours after this interview, and that her face swelled far more than usual and even today was somewhat swollen. She felt she could not free-associate but knew that if she did not she could not be helped. Her worst fear, she said, was that through her incompetence she would lose her job. This was interpreted to her as her reaction toward the analysis. Discussion with her brought out the fact that her expectations toward the analysis were aroused, but that she feared that she would not do well what was expected during the trial period and would be sent away. She felt relieved by this discussion. The urticaria decreased markedly that day and did not recur in severe form until a week later. (These longings of which she spoke, threatened with further frustration by separation from the persons to whom she directed them, is what we observed before the onset of the urticaria the preceding December.)

2. A week later, October 12th, she came in with her upper lip swollen and reported that she found it to be so on awakening. During the night she had *dreamed:* "Father came to the office to say good-bye." She went on to say that she always feared doctors and was ashamed to tell them things. She then told of her father's marriage to the mother, his reputed violence to her, his cruelty toward the patient, at the instigation of the accusing stepmother, to make the patient confess, and his sending her away to an orphanage. From the associations, the dream seems to indicate the patient's

longing for her father, but also her wish for him to leave. She was reacting to the analyst with a pattern she had toward her father, as though the analysis was like the confession situations of childhood. She wanted the analyst's help and love but feared that, like her father, he would punish her and send her away. Again we see that urticaria appeared when her longings and expectations, in this case toward the analyst, were aroused but threatened with frustration.

3. Monday through Wednesday, October 25th to 27th, the first days of her menstrual period, she was away because of severe headaches and an eruption of urticaria all over her body. She came on Thursday, the 28th, her face swollen. She spoke entirely of her dissatisfaction and doubts about her platonic boy friend who, after 3 years, was still unable to find a job and give her the kind of marriage she wanted. She complained that he would not have made a good doctor, thereby implying that she would like to marry a doctor, more specifically that she was dissatisfied with her fiancé and would prefer to marry the analyst. Again the urticaria occurred in a setting of intensified unsatisfied longing, probably increased endocrinologically at this point in her menstrual cycle.

That afternoon (she reported the next day) she wept for hours, and then felt better. At the next session, two days later, she felt fine and her symptoms had disappeared. Her urticaria regularly terminated with weeping, as though the weeping acted as a sort of safety valve. When she wept freely her urticaria subsided.

4. Over a month later, on November 17th, the patient reported that for the preceding weeks she had awakened almost every night sobbing, her pillow drenched with tears. This was always following a repetitive *dream* which recurred since early childhood—a long dream of which she could only remember the endings, that some object she had set her heart on slipped away through her fingers just as she was grasping it, leaving her terribly disappointed. Sometimes it was a figure in a white flowing robe. The object reminded her of her "wishes and ambitions, air castles which had not come true." She thought the figure was her mother, and that this repetitive dream reflected her childhood longing for the maternal affection that she had missed. Now, she said, she again felt that she was reaching for someone she could not get. She then spoke of the intensity of her cravings for romance and their invariable disappointment. At adolescence she saw other girls go out on dates and parties, while the patient was not allowed to, even at 16, although she simply craved to. At 14 she had a bad case of puppy love for a boy of 16, but when he talked to the patient, she ran away. At 14 she yearned to be kissed by a boy she was in love with, but when he tried to she kicked and

scratched, and thought that, if she did, she would be a bad girl and have a baby. Books and movies made her imagination run wild. Her unsatisfied wishes were overly strong, she said, because as a child she never got the affection she craved. It is clear that these internally frustrated sexual wishes were now directed toward the analyst, and that at their nucleus was her yearning for the love and affection of a good mother. She wished to satisfy these yearnings through a sexual relationship with a man, but was unable to because of her fears.

Two days later, November 19th, she said that for the past days she had developed headaches while on the analytic couch, and that after each hour there was some swelling of her face, especially her eyes, and sometimes her lips. Thus nights she wept because of her frustrated wishes while in the analysis she did not weep but developed urticaria. It is interesting and suggestive that she spoke of weeping and of kisses, and the urticaria was chiefly of her eyes and lips. She was puzzled at being worse again, since now she was not very busy at work and was conscious of no emotional upset.

The urticaria persisted for two days longer. It was gone on the third day, Sunday. Later on Sunday she walked out of the home of her boy friend in fury because he lay down after dinner to sleep while she saw the girl next door being taken out for a date in a big car. The boy friend called to her but she would not go back because she would have burst into tears. At home she wept for four hours, and developed a severe headache but no hives.

5. On January 7th she told that she awoke with hives from a *dream* that another girl's work was in a basket with the patient's, and the patient could not tell which was which. The patient said she would help the girl, who was crying, but was so nervous that she was of no real help. In reality, she said, this girl was the new one at the office. She was motherless like the patient, then her father died, leaving her penniless, and now her boy friend had died. The patient sympathized with her completely and tried unsuccessfully to get help for her from one of the women bosses. The patient became angered at this boss for her refusal of help. This dream is a reproach against the analyst for not helping the patient. In it she identifies herself with this other lonely, longing girl and takes the same compensatory protective attitude she had toward her sister. She demands for the girl, and tries unsuccessfully to give her what the patient wants for herself. Her longing and frustration are self-evident from the dream and associations. I wondered why this other girl, capable of evoking such a close identification—their work in the basket was indistinguishable—did not develop urticaria. Inquiry

revealed that when she lost her father and boy friend, she actually was incapacitated by a severe generalized urticaria. This was striking, but it may, of course, be only a coincidence.

6. On January 18th she reported three *dreams:* The first was about a man who was shot. The second was about traveling. The third was her repetitive dream of reaching for something which slipped through her hand. Omitting further material, the dreams showed the patient's anger at her father, now at the analyst, because of her frustrated wishes and her feeling that because of her anger she would be sent away (traveling) and lose him entirely—the satisfaction slipping through her fingers. She awoke not weeping as previously following the repetitive dream, but with hives.

7. On January 19th the patient awoke with a few hives widely distributed. That night she had *dreamed* that Miss A, the girl who the preceding Christmas had invited her to visit her and her father in a neighboring town and whom the patient liked very much, repeated this invitation. The patient was very anxious to go but on the way to the station remembered an engagement with an elderly woman and at the very last minute did not go, and the girl was angry. Again last minute frustration.

After January the patient had no more urticaria until the following fall, although she sometimes itched.

8. On November 3rd, the hour of the preceding day having been canceled by the analyst, the patient had "just a few hives" on her chest and right thigh. She reported that the day before her boy friend had just failed to obtain a position which would have enabled them to marry. All that afternoon the patient was upset, and struggled to keep from crying. She did not cry, but thought she would have felt much better if she had. We again see the urticaria following frustration—by her fiancé and by the analyst. Also there is no weeping, but this time we know there is an impulse to do so, which is suppressed.[5]

---

[5] That these relatively mild frustrations resulted in so severe a reaction can be accounted for by their coming at a time when the patient's desires were heightened endocrinologically in her menstrual cycle. That she was in such a state at this time was concluded entirely independently by Benedek and Rubenstein (4, 5) as she was one of the cases in their series (5). Urticaria occurred during 3 of the 8 menstrual cycles studied by Benedek and Rubenstein in this patient. Each time it occurred just following increased estrone and progesterone production, with parallel heightened heterosexual desire and general longings (as is characteristic of the ovulative period). The frustration of these desires and longings in life was followed by a sharp fall in the hormone level, as they found regularly in other cases. The urticaria occurred at this time of frustration and fall in hormone level, as shown by study of the day by day analytic material and vaginal smears. (75 per cent cornified cells, indicator of hormone production, was the highest observed in this case, i.e., her average hormone level was lower than the average.) The connection between the patient's sexual desires and bulimic episodes, is shown by the following incident. Her craving for food during these bulimic episodes was beyond control and she would often eat candy all day for two days. Being invited to a meal and seeing a table set with food so excited her emotionally that she could barely restrain herself. She was very anxious about

9. On November 9th the patient *dreamed* that she was married to a man who looked like her father. He slit her throat so she could not tell something, threw her down the stairs from the attic to get rid of her, and then ran away as the patient tried to yell. The patient thought that even though dead she would haunt him. At the end of the dream it flashed through the patient's mind that this was a punishment for something that she had never dared tell the analyst, namely, that in childhood she and the little girl next door experimented with each other sexually. We see here that she feared to confess her sexual impulses lest the analyst punish her as her father threatened to do and get rid of her. Interestingly enough, this time the urticarial swelling was in her *throat,* which she dreamed was cut—just as previously, material about weeping and kissing was followed by urticaria of the eyes and lip.

10. On May 23rd, after several days of anticipation, Miss A, who had invited the patient to visit her the Christmas the urticaria began, arrived in town. The patient eagerly anticipated this visit for days and was terribly disappointed that she did not get all the attention from Miss A that she expected. When she retired that night, she wept. Then, she felt her lips to be swollen and got up to find that they were, and her eyes also. This was the only occasion on which weeping and urticaria occurred simultaneously. Possibly the weeping was not adequate as a safety valve.

11. On October 29th the patient's fiancé actually got a position and urged her to marry him. But the position was a very poor and menial one, not at all in line with his ambitions, and in tragic contrast to the patient's dreams and expectations. She would even have to continue working. Urticarial swelling of the right eye occurred that evening and was followed by a *dream* in which she was to marry a young blond man, not her fiancé, but in the end gave him up and was to marry the fiancé. Associating, she said the analyst was not blond, and recalled that the preceding week she had *dreamed* directly that it was the analyst whom she was to marry. Now her marriage meant to her giving up her hopes of marrying the analyst and all the hopes that he had come to symbolize.

12. On January 17th she reported a *dream* in which her fiancé's mother brought her a wool suit in which to be married. The patient

---

having a gynecological examination even by a woman physician, but went through it without feeling emotionally disturbed. After it, she walked down the street thinking how foolish she had been to fear it. Without realizing what she was doing, she entered a restaurant and consumed a large quantity of food. She only realized what she had been doing upon leaving the restaurant. These fugue-like eating episodes often happened to her, she said. That night she *dreamed* of marrying a "well-liked villain" who broke into a store with a key that fitted the door. Thus unable, because of her fears, to satisfy her cravings by genital sexual relations, she relieved them by passionate eating. She indulged excessively orally because she could not indulge genitally.

refused it and went to get the blue street dress she had decided upon for the occasion. But at the shop they did not have the dress and she was terribly disappointed. In associating, she said that she had given up the idea of having a white bridal costume, and felt that she must be satisfied with something practical. She did not like associating to blue because it made her afraid that she was really depressed about the prospect of her marriage, and went on to talk of a friend of hers who married a doctor—a wish of the patient's toward the analyst which now faced frustration.

At times the patient had itching and redness, but no urticaria. This usually occurred the few days or weeks before her period and sometimes during it. The difference between her psychological state during the urticaria as opposed to the itching and erythema may not be only quantitative, since the patient's dreams at these latter times showed slightly less direct frustration and much more prominent exhibitionistic and hostile tendencies than did those connected with the urticaria. The following are examples:

1. On Friday, January the 13th, following severe itching of her back, the patient had a long *nightmare* in which she was nearly attacked by a crowd while eating with her fiancé, and which ended with the patient's pinching the arm of a girl in a white satin dancer's costume who was looking longingly inside of a night club. The patient was very angry at her for trying to show that she was a goody-goody, when really she wanted to enter this place to dance or sing. The repressed and frustrated desires and exhibitionism are clearly seen at the end of the dream.

2. On Thursday, February the 2nd, when the patient was just getting over her menstrual period, she reported that for the past days she had been in a terrible mood, as was usual for her premenstrually. She had been angry at her fiancé, and her skin itched and was irritated. The preceding night she had *dreamed* that as she and her fiancé were singing before an audience, her belt and dress fell off. There was also something about her father's being shot—or only wanting to stay in bed. (The analyst had canceled the hour the day before.) These two dreams show the prominence of the exhibitionism in connection with erythema and itching, but the material is meager and this aspect of the problem has not been systematically studied.

Discussion

General features in this patient's personality, which were more prominent than in the average case, were tension, masochism, repressed exhibitionism, frustrated longings, and repression of sexual wishes. The emotional settings of twelve flare-ups of urticaria have been observed, eight of them with dreams. The patient saw the allergist, Dr. Clarence Bernstein, frequently throughout her analysis, and at no time was he able to discover any specific allergens related to the attacks. On the other hand, the emotional states of the patient at these times were remarkably similar. Every attack of urticaria, without exception, occurred in an identical emotional situation—*when intense longings were aroused but were in the very moment of frustration.* The onset occurred when the patient felt on the verge of frustration in all of her human relations, and, in particular, by the marriage and departure of her father. Attacks not associated with dreams occurred when, at the beginning of the analysis, her hopes and expectations were aroused but she feared that she would not be allowed to continue, when her desires and frustrations were increased in connection with her menstrual cycle, when she did not get all the direct help and gratification she expected, and when her wishes toward the analyst were thwarted by interruptions of the analysis, and by the prospects of an unsatisfying marriage. In all of these situations libidinal wishes were aroused but frustrated. The dreams which occurred in connection with the eight other attacks reveal further details of the patient's emotional state at these times. The main theme in these dreams is also always: "Almost but not quite." Or, "so near but yet so far." In the dreams, father comes, but to say good-bye; as she grasps for mother's love or for romance, it slips through her fingers; a poor girl who has lost her near ones is almost, but not quite, getting helped by her; she is anxious to visit a girl and her father but at the last minute does not; she is married to a man who deserts her; she is to marry the analyst but it is called off; she goes for a blue dress but it is not there. The common element in all of these dreams is readily apparent. They all show the patient in the very moment in which strong libidinal wishes are aroused and frustrated, as in her typical repetitive dream.[6]

Of a total of 94 dreams during her analysis, the non-urticaria dreams were either not frustration dreams or else the frustration was not in just this status. She did not have a single reported dream of just this type which was not associated with either urticaria or weeping. Conversely, she never reported urticaria associated with a different type of dream. For example, when she had a dream that her father returned, this time to stay, she had no urti-

---

[6] So much importance is attached to the dreams because they provide the most intimate sample of the psychic life, analogous to laboratory samples of blood, urine, etc. Once thought to be chaotic, they actually reveal characteristic patterns for each person. See for example Hitschmann (11, 12); also the author (21).

caria. In such work, one is of course dependent upon the patient's reports. She could not have been influenced, however, as I did not discuss the attacks with her until after the analysis.

The following are examples of dreams of different type or status than those described in association with the urticaria attacks. The critical point is the status of the frustration, if present, at the *ending* of the dream.

> *Dream:* Dreamed of father, that they came back, had no money, and stayed with me and my sister, and we all got into a heated argument.
>
> *Dream:* I was chosen to carry out some plot, to kill someone, or something like that.
>
> *Dream:* I was on a bus. There was an older couple, a very fat girl, a nice looking girl, and a fellow. His parents introduced him to the fat girl. I thought that they wanted him to marry the other one—maybe as a test. Then time elapsed. He was going with the fat girl but was going to marry the other girl, and the fat girl was very upset. Then I was going into a grocery store and said it wasn't fair what they were doing to this girl. On the way out he let me take a lot of cookies. I wanted to be thinner but they tasted so good, and I took a whole lot of them. Then I was walking down a dark street.
>
> *Dream:* I was being chased by a man who shot a gun at me and I awoke in terrific fear.
>
> *Dream:* Something about the office—something was wrong about the travel expense accounts.
>
> *Dream:* (a) I was writing a book and was pleased because the words came easily, just flowed, and I wrote and wrote and wrote. (b) I was going to join a group and put on plays. Then I was walking down a road, asking a man about dramatic art in this district, about the instructors, their methods of teaching, etc. Also something about Wednesday, which is Washington's Birthday.

When we use other cases as controls, we find a similarity in the structure and dreams of this case and the asthma series (8), insofar as the longing is prominent. In the asthma cases the underlying longing for the mother was a uniform finding. In contrast are the dreams of, for example, the blood pressure cases which were associated with elevations of the blood pressure (2, 20). In these, although there may be frustration, last-minute frustration is not the central feature. What is central is hostility, fear, and paralysis of action. This, of course, does not mean that an individual with hypertension cannot have urticaria (although it has been noted that allergic symptoms and hypertension do not commonly occur in the same person 22). In such a case one would expect both kinds of dreams, respectively associated with either urticarial attacks or elevations in blood pressure.

The content of the frustrated desires is apparent from the settings of the attacks which have been described. They were of the nature of the longings of a child for the love of its parents. The patient could not satisfy her longings for love by a normal sexual relationship to a man because of the severity of her masochistic fears. When the longings and their frustration were sufficiently exacerbated by external disappointments or by endocrinological increase of these unsatisfied desires, then, if she did not weep, urticaria would develop.

The objection may be raised that the patient had experienced frustrations previously in life without developing urticaria. The answer for the present must be the same as for any functional symptom, namely, the quantitative factor. The tension must reach a certain point before the symptom appears.

At the time of the onset of the urticaria the patient was exerting herself excessively in work and self-improvement. This overexertion has been observed at the time of onset in many cases and is reported in the literature. There is little doubt that it bears some relationship to the urticaria. But the common feature in the settings of the attacks described above was the status of the frustrated longings, and not the exertion. The latter was referred to in only one dream (see attack number 5) and some of the attacks occurred when the patient was taking things quite easy. The overexertion, in this case, was in part itself a symptom of the state of frustration like the urticaria (as a flight into activity to escape her feelings of inadequacy and frustration), and in part bore an etiological relationship to the symptom in that the harder the patient drove herself, the more intense were her longings for the opposite—ease, pleasure, and love. Thus the overexertion increased the longings and feelings of frustration.[7]

It has also been observed that some persons develop urticaria when they become angry. However, in this case the anger was not related to the urticaria directly, but appeared as a reaction to the frustration which was the critical element. (This patient reacted to anger somewhat as she did to overexertion, in that when she became angry she usually did not express it directly but retreated to a passive masochistic attitude.)

The need to excel, noted in the literature, was also a feature of this case, in which it was a reaction not only against her repudiated

---

[7] The physiological mechanism of urticaria is complex and not entirely known. If it is essentially parasympathetic in mediation, being relieved by adrenalin, then the occurrence of urticaria when increased demands are made on the patient would place it in the category of regressive responses, as described by Alexander (1). In these cases, demands for exertion result in discharge of excitation not via the sympatheticoadrenal system as normally, but via the parasympathetics, signifying a retreat from effort.

early social position, but also, and more important, a reaction to her childish masochistic longings. By it she sought at once to escape these, and also to win love, admiration, and acceptance.

Thus those correlations reported in the literature of urticaria with tension, anger, overwork, pressure to excel, masochism, and frustrated sexual wishes were confirmed by the detailed study of this case, all being parts of an emotional constellation in which frustrated longing was central.

It must be especially noted that this frustration was essentially neurotic, that is, internally determined. Whatever frustrations and deprivations this patient was subjected to by external situations beyond her control, in her adult life she caused the major part of them herself. Although an attractive girl, she shunned various eligible young men and became attached to a man who made no sexual advances and for years could not find a job or decide to marry her. And even in her dreams she could not permit herself the gratifications she desired. The chief reason she was so self-frustrated was the common one—guilt. The guilt was due to various causes, chiefly hostilities against her sister and her stepmother, and also her father (Oedipus guilt). It was this which caused her masochism, that is, her deep need to suffer. This was seen in all aspects of her life, in her overwork, her self-denial, her self-sacrifice, her self-depreciation, and her self-frustration. It was seen in her dreams of being attacked. And in connection with the urticaria it was seen in her Tantalus reaction of frustrating herself on the verge of gratification, and even conjuring up this situation in her dreams. Indeed this need for suffering raises the suspicion not only that she provoked many of her cruel punishments in childhood, but that her story of her past brutal treatment may be unconsciously retrospectively colored by her masochism as commonly occurs in such cases, and that her father and stepmother, however cruel, may not have been quite such fiends as she remembers and pictures them. Certainly guilt and consequent masochistic suffering and self-frustration was a central feature of her personality, as it was in a second analyzed case.

Weeping bore a special reciprocal relationship to the urticaria in this case. It relieved the patient's disappointment and anger. When she wept she did not have urticaria, and the attacks usually terminated with weeping. Conversely, when she suppressed her weeping, she developed urticaria. Her repetitive dream would terminate in either weeping or urticaria. She said that the urticarial swelling of her eyes felt as though she "had cried a lot and could cry no more," as though she literally "could feel the tears back there."

This observation led to an illuminating clinical experiment with a girl seen at the Cook County Hospital. This girl of 26 felt unable to get along in Chicago, and longed to return to her home in a distant town. She dared not return, however, because of having an illegitimate child of 3.5 months. She wept during the interview, and when I asked her how long she had been doing so, she replied, to my astonishment, "Three and a half months, since the birth of the child." I suggested to the resident, Dr. Paul Rosenfels, that if she were forbidden to weep she might develop urticaria. A week later he told me the following: that evening he told her that if she wept so much she might be found committable. She stopped entirely, and in the morning she had a generalized urticaria, chiefly of her chest, back, and arms. After several days he told her that a good cry might make her feel better. She replied: "You seem to want me to cry— but I don't feel like it any more." The following morning, he observed that the rash was gone.

Five cases, seen only in interview, provide confirmatory material, although they were apparently of the acute type. One of these warrants mention. A young woman had a generalized urticaria at 17— which was when she left home for the first time to take a position. This was ten years ago, and she had no allergic manifestations in the interim. But recently she awoke with a mild urticarial swelling of her face. Inquiry revealed that she had been *dreaming* as follows: She went to see a man at his home, but when she arrived there he was gone.

Another clear example is the following: A young lady of 16 had had urticaria occasionally in childhood. It was thought to be a reaction to fish. However, it occurred on several occasions when she had not eaten fish, and she sometimes ate fish without having urticaria. She had had no attacks since childhood until the one about to be described. Several months previously she had left her home in Chicago to attend college in the east. This was her first time away from home. At Easter the other girls all received Easter eggs from their parents, but the patient did not receive any. She telephoned home long distance but was hardly able to talk on the telephone. Both of her parents tried to speak with her and later remarked to each other that her difficulty in talking was obviously due to the fact that she was holding back her tears at not having been sent the Easter egg. Two days later they received a letter from her saying that after this phone call, for the first time since childhood, her urticaria had recurred.

Since writing this communication a year and a half ago I have had the opportunity of analyzing a young woman with a severe generalized urticaria which had recurred every few weeks for 13 years. This analysis confirmed the present findings. The patient was closely similar to Miss Q in pertinent respects, including certain personality trends, her state of frustration (she, too, had a boy friend who could not make up his mind to marry her), and the emotional settings of her urticarial attacks. She, too, was seen in the spring when she was given an interpretation of the settings of the attacks. The analysis was begun in the fall. Since that spring, now a year ago, she has had only two very mild urticarial manifestations.

Theoretical

The fact that this patient's urticaria should have occurred consistently and exclusively when her longings were in a particular state of frustration cannot be without significance. But this finding alone is far from a solution of the problem. In the first place, this is only one analyzed case, to which a second has now been added. Despite confirmatory material from cases seen in interview, it may be that detailed analytic study of others will reveal some other emotional situation. In the second place, there remains the important question of why just an urticarial swelling of the skin should be the choice of symptom for the manifestation of this particular emotional tension. Why a wish to be fed should affect the stomach is readily intelligible, but why should frustrated longing result in urticaria? One possibility that suggests itself for the choice of the skin as the site of lesion is the status of the exhibitionism. This was a prominent feature in this case, and even more prominent in the second analyzed case, and has been remarked by Lorand (14) and other authors. It has been particularly noted in the literature in regard to skin disorders with important psychogenic elements. Miss Q, the patient here reported, so repressed her strong exhibitionism that, although she yearned to shine as a dancer, actress, be admired for her conversation, and so on, and these exhibitionistic tendencies appeared clearly in her dreams, yet she was unable to disrobe herself even partially when with even her most intimate girl friends. However, while exhibitionism was prominent in the emotional settings of her few episodes of erythema and itching, as has been reported above, it was by no means a prominent or constant feature in the settings of the attacks of urticaria.

Another suggestion as to the choice of the skin is one which has been made widely in the literature, particularly the psychoanalytic literature. This is a heightened erotism of the skin. In terms of the libido theory, this would then follow the well-known mechanism by which, when longings are aroused but cannot be satisfied through genital sexual activity, the frustrated excitement (whether mediated chemically, nervously, or both) affects the skin. This mechanism appeared explicitly in a young woman who developed a generalized urticaria during her analysis. Her central problem was sexual inhibition. She was chronically frustrated in her intense sexual wishes because of guilt, and came to analysis for relief of this inhibition. Her urticaria developed upon awakening from a dream that she was about to relieve her sexual feelings by masturbation, when her uncle arrived and so she did not. Here the last minute frustration is of desires that are frankly sexual. In the light of the preceding observations it is unlikely that the occurrence of the urticaria at this point was entirely coincidental. Here, as in the case of Miss Q, the genital sexual activity is blocked by the too strong masochism. That masochism may play a role in skin symptoms has been pointed out by Rado (8). The masochism in this case was certainly far more severe than in the average. These considerations would still leave unanswered questions as to whether the heightened erotism of the skin is primary or secondary,[8] and as to what the relationships are between the longings and the skin. Two possible relationships are suggested by the data. The one is through skin erotism, that is, a desire to satisfy these wishes through the skin as an organ, by its being seen or touched; the other is through the concomitant endocrinological changes.

If we are to think biologically, we must not forget the importance of the skin in human sexuality. Our mechanistic training interferes with biological functional thinking and observation. But evidence to date, from the literature and from my own limited experience, indicates that the relationship of the skin to sexuality is an important clue to the etiology of urticarias of this particular type.

As to the second possibility, endocrinological dysfunction has been seriously considered as a cause of urticaria, and certain urticarias are regarded as directly related to the menstrual cycle, to the menopause, and to pregnancy (25). The occurrence in this case of urticaria at points of sharp fall in hormone level confirms this connection. Certainly much light will be shed upon this type of urticaria, as well as upon the relation of the skin to sexual tension, by further knowledge of the endocrines and their chemistry in relation to sexuality.

---

8 Perhaps Miss Q's skin erotism was heightened by the father, through his sexually colored punishments, and possibly through other treatment which does not appear in the history. Dr. Maxwell Gitelson has told me that a woman patient of his, with a heightened skin erotism, had been massaged with alcohol by her father throughout childhood. When sexual feelings entered the transference, she developed urticaria.

From this and other cases sexuality appears to be an important link in the causal chain, but just how is not entirely clear. While genital sexuality exists as an emotional impulse and mechanism, the essential point (at least in the human psychology) is that this mechanism acts as a channel for desires and impulses of various types. According to this concept, the patient with her strong need for love would attempt to gratify this need through the channel of the genital sexual relationship to a man, but would be unable to do so because of her fears of utilizing this channel and would, therefore, be left with intense cravings for love which she could not satisfy through heterosexual activity. Hence these cravings for love would remain permanently unsatisfied and additional frustration would result in urticaria, regardless of whether this frustration was a disappointment in general desires for love, for example, when Miss A came to town and did not pay the patient enough attention; or whether these were more specific wishes for the sexual love of a man, which would be one way of satisfying the general longings. The basic thing would remain the frustrated need for love.

To formulate the explanation slightly differently, this girl is an infantile personality, with an infantile uterus and abnormally low sexual hormone level in her menstrual cycle. The content of her libidinal longings is also infantile, in fact so much so that from it these physiological conditions were predicted. The essence of this content is to have the love of a good and strong father, and, in the deepest layer, of a good mother. Because of the patient's guilt the wish for the strong father is also for a punishing father, as in the dreams of being attacked by a thinly disguised representative of the father. This infantile wish for the father is more or less sexualized. One way the patient seeks to satisfy it is by sexuality, but this is *blocked internally because of the masochistic component* (the wish to be punished) *and so the frustration results.*

Schematically and very tentatively, the situation would be something like this: Longings for love (intensified by early deprivations, present frustrations, and overexertion) → wishes to satisfy these through sexual love (with strong components of being admired, accepted, and perhaps with a special relationship to satisfaction through the skin) → frustration of these desires due to fears of sex → when the longings are sufficiently aroused and frustrated, the urticaria develops.

Urticaria, in this case, did not affect the skin exclusively (25). This patient also had edematous swellings of her throat, and it is not unlikely that her sinusitis was related to a swelling of the mucosa. It is well known that internal organs may also be affected. This leads us, however, into a consideration of the physiology of the vaso-dilatation and away from the main point of the paper which is concerned with the psychological settings rather than the physiological mechanisms of mediation.

Although this report deals with only a single case (confirmed by others), it is worth while to compare the findings with those of the extensive asthma study of the Chicago Institute for Psychoanalysis (8). In brief, conflictful libidinal wishes and the theme of separation are central in both conditions. But in the urticaria the wishes for love are less regressive than in asthma, more manifest and consciously accepted, more sexualized, and, in this case, more directed toward the father, although longings for the mother are clearly evident in the background. The dynamic situation in urticaria is that these longings are in the moment of frustration. On the other hand, in asthma, the wishes are more regressive, as seen in the prominence of dreams and fantasies of returning to the protecting womb ("proto-receptive" as Alexander has called them). These wishes are usually feared and repressed. Also the asthma seems to be a more acute symptom than the urticaria, more of an emergency measure, which is invoked when separation from the mother or loss of her love is suddenly threatened. The asthma attack often seems to replace a repressed cry of the vocal, and in early days, tearless sort. This may be a determinant of the choice of organ. The urticaria, on the other hand, seems in this case to take the place of weeping (repressed), or at least to be related to it. Confession was important in this case of urticaria, as it is in asthma, and this patient's overcompensatory helping, giving attitude was frequent in the asthma series also.

In this case of urticaria in the second analyzed case and in those seen in interviews, and also in the asthma cases, the symptoms were connected with strong longings for love. Such longings were also found to be directly connected with pruritis ani in three cases, and pruritis ani is thought to be an allergic symptom in certain cases. Frustrated longings have also been found to play a role in certain cases of colds (19); and some authors distinguish a group of colds as basically allergic (13). The patient herein reported had flare-ups of sinusitis, which the allergist considered to be secondary to swelling of the mucosae on an allergic basis. The fact that libidinal longings should be found to be directly connected with these different types of allergic symptoms suggests a connection between states of unsatisfied longing and certain states of allergic sensitivity (10). Possibly the states of longing increase the allergic sensitivity.[9]

---

[9] That emotional states may affect allergic sensitivity is not a new suggestion. Stokes and Beerman (24) conclude from their review of the literature "that there is a slow accumu-

The need in every case for a complete medical work-up before analysis is obvious. Amebic dysentery, blood dyscrasias, local skin disease, insect bites, serum sickness, and active focal or general infections must be ruled out. Pathological disturbances may be perceived in waking life (9). It is possible, therefore, that allergic responses might influence dreams, as does thirst, urges to urinate, sexual tension, and so on. It is frequently observed that children during the summer preceding their first hayfever year are restless, irritable, and averse to eating. They lose weight and occasionally become unsociable, but with the onset of frank and overt symptomatology they are apt to become quite themselves again. Of similar interest are two milk-sensitive patients who had distressing nightmares whenever raw milk was ingested. However, few workers in the field report more than a 10 per cent incidence of positive skin tests in this type of chronic urticaria. Furthermore, whatever may be the specific agent, the analysis seems definitely to reduce the number and severity of the attacks without the removal, as far as we are able to ascertain, of any extrinsic factors.

It is, I hope, needless to state that nothing in this discussion is meant to imply that all allergic symptoms are psychogenic, or that the emotional state is of any importance in certain cases. Moreover, the converse question of the possible effects upon the psychological state of allergic responses has not been considered. This paper has focused exclusively upon the emotional factor in cases selected because of the prominence of this factor. It may be, of course, that all allergic individuals show, in varying degrees, a common peculiarity in their personalities as some authors believe. If so, it may be that this peculiarity is largely a reflection of an underlying, unsatisfied longing in a certain status, or of reactions to it. But thus far, only a beginning has been made toward the answer of this fundamental question.

Summary

A young woman with intense longings for love was unable to satisfy these desires by a normal sexual relationship with a man because of her fears and inhibitions. She developed urticaria at times when her longings were especially stimulated and frustrated. Twelve attacks were observed during analysis, and their emotional settings are described. Eight of them occurred in connection with dreams.

lation of evidence for the belief that in the allergic seizures . . . particularly in urticarias and eczema, psychogenic factors . . . are capable of modifying materially the so-called allergic reactivity of the skin." From the material it appears that the more specific emotional state involved is one of libidinal longing.

TABULAR SUMMARY

First Major Attack

Date	Life Situation or Content of Associations	Dream	Urticaria Attack
End of Oct.	Engagement of Miss N., girl in whose family patient was living. Patient leaves the family to room alone. Father married girl age of patient's sister and leaves.		
End of Nov.	Miss A, girl at office upon whom patient is dependent, decides to leave to be with her father. Patient decides to break with her boy friend. These were patient's last contacts in town.		First hives occur at just this point. Few mostly on forehead.
Dec. 17	Overworking at office, managing Christmas party, fight with fiancé, Miss A leaving to be with her father.		That evening severe generalized urticaria, which persisted.
May 24	Accepted for psychoanalysis.		Urticaria clears up.

Attacks Observed During Analysis

1. Oct. 5	First analytic session. Told that all analyses begin with trial period. Fears that after trial period patient will not be accepted for analysis, but will be sent away.		Upset for three hours after the session, with urticarial swelling, chiefly of face, lasting until next day.
2. Oct. 12	Fears that because of what patient will tell in the analysis she will be sent away.	(Night of Oct. 11–12) *Father came to my office to say goodbye.*	Awoke in morning of Oct. 12 with urticarial swelling of upper lip.
3. Oct. 25– 28	Beginning of menstrual period. Disappointment that fiancé cannot find job and marry, with unconscious implication that patient would prefer marrying psychoanalyst.		Severe, generalized urticaria— Oct. 25–28. Wept on afternoon of Oct. 28, urticaria diminished and disappeared the next day.
4.	For several days, up to Nov. 19, unsatisfied cravings for love—unconsciously implying the wish that psychoanalyst satisfy them.	Repetitive dream each night with: "*Some object or person that I set my heart on slipped away out of my grasp.*"	Patient awoke from the dreams weeping profusely. At end of analytic sessions, no weeping, but urticaria, especially of eyes and lips.
5. Jan. 7	Feelings of frustration and plea for more direct help by psychoanalyst.	Night of Jan. 6. "Another girl's work was in a basket with mine. I could not tell which was which. I said I would help the girl, who was crying, but I was so nervous that *though I was trying, I was of no real help to her.*" Associations deal with the patient's identification with this girl, who was terribly lonely because of losing her mother, father, and fiancé.	Patient awakes from this dream with urticaria.
6. Jan. 18	Anger (for not satisfying patient's wishes) at analyst, but fears that if she expresses it she will be sent away.	Night of Jan. 17. Three dreams, the last being patient's repetitive dream, of "*something or someone I yearn for slipping through my grasp.*"	Patient awakes from the last dream, not with weeping, as on previous occasions (see attack Nov. 4, Nov. 19), but with urticaria.

TABULAR SUMMARY—Continued

Date	Life Situation or Content of Associations	Dream	Urticaria Attack

Attacks Observed During Analysis—Continued

Date	Life Situation or Content of Associations	Dream	Urticaria Attack
7. Jan 19	Fears of losing her job due to reorganization of the office.	Night of Jan. 18. "I was invited by Miss A to go with her on a visit to her father in another city. *I was anxious to go* and accepted, but at the station I remembered that I had an engagement with an elderly woman, and *at the very last minute did not go,* and the girl was angry."	Awakes with a few widely distributed hives.
8. Nov. 3	On Nov. 2, fiancé had prospect of good position (which would have made marriage possible) but at the last minute failed to get it. Analytic hour canceled by analyst. (Height of hormone level in menstrual cycle.)	No dream reported.	Urticaria; all afternoon of Nov. 2, patient disappointed, desire to weep which she struggles against. That night she develops urticaria on chest and right thigh.
9. Nov. 9	Fear to tell analyst of her sex play in childhood, and unconsciously of her sexual wishes toward the analyst.	Night of Nov. 8. "I was married to a man who looked like father. He slit my throat so I couldn't tell something and threw me downstairs from the attic *to get rid of me.* Then *he ran away from me* as I tried to yell, although dead I would haunt him."	Awakens with urticarial swelling of throat.
10. May 23	After days of anticipation, Miss A comes to town but pays little attention to patient. Patient terribly disappointed. (Height of hormone level in menstrual cycle.)	No dream reported.	That night, upon retiring, wept, and also urticaria of eyes and lips.
11. Oct. 29	On Oct. 28, fiancé gets very poor position. To marry him means a life of poverty, that patient must continue working and must give up her dreams and expectations.	Night of Oct. 28. "I was to marry a young blond fellow, but in the end *had to give him up* and was to marry my fiancé."	Urticaria occurs in the early evening of Oct. 28, just after fiancé tells patient of getting the position. The dream was that night.
12. Jan. 17	Disappointment in the approaching marriage, which means frustration of patient's dreams of how it would be.	Night of Jan. 16. "My fiancé's mother brought me a wool suit in which to be married. I refused it. I had decided to give up having the white bridal costume I had dreamed of *and went to the store for the blue dress* I had decided on. *But they did not have it and I was terribly disappointed.*"	Urticaria.

These dreams invariably ended on the verge of frustration in an "almost but not quite" situation. Other types of dreams, out of a total of 94, were never followed by urticaria and vice versa, with the exception of a repetitive dream of reaching for an object or person who slipped from the patient's grasp. This dream was followed by weeping, when not by urticaria. The urticaria appeared when weeping was repressed and often terminated when the patient wept.

Some of the observations are somewhat suggestive concerning the choice of sites for the urticaria. The findings were confirmed by a second analyzed case and by a few observations on five cases seen in interview. In connection with other observations, particularly on asthma, they led to the supposition of a possible relationship between certain states of allergic sensitivity and states of intense frustrated longing.

BIBLIOGRAPHY

1. ALEXANDER, FRANZ. Further contributions concerning specific emotional factors in different organ neuroses. A paper read at the annual meeting of the American Psychoanalytic Association, May 8, 1939.
2. ALEXANDER, FRANZ. Psychoanalytic study of a case of essential hypertension. (In this volume, p. 298.)
3. ALEXANDER, FRANZ AND CO-WORKERS. The influence of psychologic factors upon gastrointestinal disturbances: a symposium. *Psychoanal. Quart.,* 1934, 3, 501. (In this volume, p. 103.)
4. BENEDEK, THERESE, AND RUBENSTEIN, B. B. The correlations between ovarian activity and psychodynamic processes: I. The ovulative phase. *Psychosom. Med.,* 1939, 1, 245. II. The menstrual phase. *Psychosom. Med.,* 1939, 1, 461.
5. BENEDEK, THERESE, AND RUBENSTEIN, B. B. The sexual cycle in women. The relation between ovarian function and psychodynamic processes. *Psychosom. Med. Monogr.,* Vol. III, Nos. 1 and 21. Published with the Sponsorship of the Committee on Problems of Neurotic Behavior Division of Anthropology and Psychology, National Research Council, Wash., D. C., 1942.
6. DUNBAR, H. F. *Emotions and bodily changes.* (2nd Ed.) New York: Columbia University Press, 1938.
7. FRENCH, T. M. Psychogenic factors in asthma. *Amer. J. Psychiat.,* 1939, 96, 87.
8. FRENCH, T. M., ALEXANDER, FRANZ, AND CO-WORKERS. Psychogenic factors in bronchial asthma: Part I. *Psychosom. Med. Monogr.,* 1941, 1, No. 4. Psychogenic factors in bronchial asthma: Part II. *Psychosom. Med. Monogr.,* 1941, 2, Nos. 1 and 2.
9. FREUD, SIGMUND. A metapsychological supplement to the theory of dreams. In *Collected papers,* 4, 37. London: Hogarth Press, 1925.
10. GRAF-BEST, A. M., VAN DE. Psychische Behandlung einer Urtikaria. *Psychoanal. Praxis,* 1932, 2, 40.
11. HITSCHMANN, E. Beiträge zu einer Psychopathologie des Traumes: I. *Int. Z. (ärztl.) Psychoanal.,* 1934, 20, 459.
12. HITSCHMANN, E. Beiträge zu einer Psychopathologie des Traumes: II. *Int. Z. (ärztl.) Psychoanal.,* 1935, 21, 430.
13. KERR, W. J. The common cold. *J. Amer. med. Assn.,* 1936, 107, 323.
14. LORAND, S. The psychogenic factors in a case of angioneurotic edema. *J. Mt. Sinai Hosp.,* 1936, 2, No. 5.
15. MACKENZIE, G. M. Angioneurotic edema. In CECIL, R. L. *A textbook of medicine.* Philadelphia: W. B. Saunders Co., 1940.
16. MENNINGER, W. C., AND KEMP, J. E. Psychogenic urticaria. *J. Allergy,* 1935, 6, 467.
17. OBERNDORF, C. P. Disappearance of angioneurotic edema after appendectomy. *J. Amer. med. Assn.,* 1912, 59, 623.
18. RADO, S. Fear of castration in women. *Psychoanal. Quart.,* 1933, 2, 425.

19. SAUL, L. J.   Psychogenic factors in the etiology of the common cold and related symptoms. *Int. J. Psycho-anal.,* 1938, **19,** 451.
20. SAUL, L. J.   Hostility in cases of essential hypertension. *Psychosom. Med.,* 1939, **1,** 153.   (In this volume, p. 345.)
21. SAUL, L. J.   Utilization of early current dreams in formulating psychoanalytical cases. *Psychoanal. Quart.,* 1940, **9,** 453.
22. SAUL, L. J.   Some observations on the relations of emotions and allergy. *Psychosom. Med.,* 1941, **3,** 66.   (In this volume, p. 547.)
23. STOKES, J. H., KULCHAR, G. V., AND PILLSBURY, D.   Effect on the skin of emotional and nervous states. Etiological background of the urticaria with special reference to the psychoneurogenous factor. *N. Y. Arch. Derm. Syph.,* 1935, **31,** 470.
24. STOKES, J. H., AND BEERMAN, H.   Psychosomatic correlations in allergic conditions—a review of problems and literature. *Psychosom. Med.,* 1940, **2,** 438.
25. SULZBERGER, M.   *Dermatologic allergy. An introduction in the form of a series of lectures.*   Springfield: C. C. Thomas, 1940.
26. SULZBERGER, M., AND GOODMAN, J.   Allergy in dermatology. A critical review of recent contributions. *J. Allergy,* 1939, **10,** 481.

PART VII

JOINTS AND SKELETAL MUSCLES

THE PSYCHOGENIC TIC IN EGO DEVELOPMENT *

By MARGARET W. GERARD, M.D.

Although there is a considerable volume of literature upon the subject of tics, only a few papers attempt to explain the production of the symptom from a psychodynamic viewpoint. Many authors describe the varieties of forms of the symptom, or discuss its statistical frequency, or the like.[1] For present purposes I shall attempt to review only those papers of import to a study of the psychodynamic factors involved in the production of the symptom and of the character formations found in tiqueurs.

Ferenczi (3), in 1921, suggested that the tic represents an equivalent of onanism in which the libido connected with genital sensation was transformed into "muscle erotism" and displaced to other parts of the body. This displacement, he stated, resulted in decreased genital potency and an increased pleasure in muscular movement. Beyond the onanistic significance, Ferenczi believed that many tics represented a method of warding off suffering, similar to reflex withdrawal from a stimulus. However he claimed also that some tics inflicted injury upon the self and compared this condition to the extreme self-mutilation of schizophrenics. In the same paper he described several cases of compulsive neurosis in which the patients carried out rituals with a variety of manneristic movements. The individual elements in the ritual were compared with tic movements, and he offered this comparison as evidence that tics were often hard to differentiate from compulsive acts. In attempting to explain the dynamic cause of the symptom, he stated that it was a "narcissistic disorder of a person who is hypersensitive and unable to endure a physical stimulus without a defensive reaction." The narcissism of such a person was described as a constitutional narcissism in which the smallest injury to a part of the body strikes the whole ego, and

* From *Psychoanalytic Study of the Child* II :133-162. New York, International Universities Press, 1947.

[1] Since the writing of this paper a series of articles on tics has appeared in *The Nervous Child* (13). They are interesting and rich in information concerning treatment, parent-child relationships, art expressions, and Rorschach responses of tiqueurs, and they follow the theoretical concepts of Mahler (9, 10, 11) concerning the neurodynamics and psychodynamics of the tic.

which he believed to have resulted from an organic condition. He offered two reasons for the latter conclusion. The first consisted of the fact that in analyzing patients who presented a tic as part of a group of symptoms he was able to cure the patient of other symptoms but the tic remained unaltered. The second reason grew out of his belief that paranoia and schizophrenia, psychoses which often exhibited stereotyped movements, were of organic origin.

In a paper discussing Ferenczi's analysis, Abraham (1), drawing conclusions from one of his own cases, stated that tics could not be differentiated from compulsive obsessive acts except in two respects. In one respect the tiqueur does not attribute any significance to the symptom in his mental life, as does the obsessional patient. In the other respect, the obsessional patient fears disaster from the omission of the compulsive act and experiences anxiety from its suppression, whereas the tiqueur fears no disaster and experiences only discomfort with symptom suppression. Abraham also believed that the tic, like the compulsive act, possesses a hostile component, even though he yielded the possibility of an erotic element as well.

In three papers on the subject, Mahler (9, 10, 11) discussed the tic as a problem related to body motility in general. She defined it as an involuntary, lightning-like, repetitious jerk of a physiological group or groups of muscles; a purposeless motility without logical or rational goal, but the patterns of which in the beginning may have represented purposive and intentional movements. For the one case which she described in detail, as well as for those examined in a statistical study of 33 cases, she formulated the psychodynamics of the tic system as "a resultant of the interaction of instinctual, ego, and socio-environmental factors." She claimed evidence for both erotic and aggressive components in the instinctual forces involved, such that the tic represented provocative erotic aggression toward a mother or father, as well as the defense against the aggressive parent. She hypothesized that in the process of development of a tic "cathexis in the motor sphere" was involved, and this cathexis was caused by a conflict occurring between an increased need for motor activity on the part of the patient and interference in that activity by an environmental agent. She attributed the patient's increased need for motor activity to a secondary environmental factor of excessive restriction and overstimulation, and a possible primary constitutional motor factor, as Ferenczi had suggested earlier. In the detailed case she believed the constitutional factor consisted of "an underlying substratum or organic disease of the central nervous system . . . probably a neurophysiological inferiority," and because of this inferiority she stated that "the prognosis is unfavorable for this disease." However, in the later paper (11) she claimed she had achieved symptom cures through psychotherapeutic approaches.

In the statistical studies Mahler (11) described several interesting similarities both in character and behavior of the patients and in attitudes and behavior of the parents. Of 33 child tiqueurs studied, 79 per cent were boys and only 21 per cent were girls. Many of these children exhibited awkwardness in large body movements, and facility in small muscle coordination as exhibited in mechanical aptitude. Many of them had great ambitions for athletic skill but their athletic achievements were poor. In school the greater number were restless and inattentive, and their achievements were below that expected for their intellectual capacity. All showed evidences of increased body narcissism and a tendency to hypochondriacal self-observation. Parents in many instances held perfectionistic goals for their children's intellectual achievement, and in many cases were overindulgent to the children in the oral stage of emotional relationship; anal and urinary oversolicitude was far less common.

Levy (8) defined the psychogenic tic as a "superfluous, involuntary, brisk, repeated rhythmical movement set off by a mental process," the origin of which is emotional and represents an inhibition of an impulse which is regarded by the individual as dangerous or shameful. In a study of the psychic content of the tic he found every variety of sexual and aggressive impulse inhibited by the fear of consequences. He claimed that the tic was either a partial representation of the original impulsive act or a protective gesture to avert danger. He equated tics with compulsive movements, but also differentiated them from each other by suggesting that a tic represented the motor expression of an act in its initial phase and a compulsive movement in its end phase. Certain repetitive movements found among animals when restrained, such as the head weaving of stalled horses or the rocking movements of caged bears he considered as tics, and compared them to the stereotyped movements of infants restrained in an orphanage who indulged in head rolling, banging, or body swaying. He found that these movements decreased or disappeared when the physical restraint was removed. In this article, however, Levy does not attempt to differentiate dynamically between "tics" which cease with freedom from restraint and those true tics which continue to occur in a great variety of situations in which no physical restraint occurs. Two factors he found to be associated with the symptom were general restlessness of the tiqueurs and compulsive and meticulous behavior in their parents.

A summary analysis of the papers by these authors discloses certain similarities in their conclusions and certain dissimilarities. Both

Mahler and Levy noted similarities in the attitudes of the parents of the patients. Levy mentioned that the parents were compulsive and meticulous, while Mahler describes the parents of her cases as ambitious for intellectual achievement. Abraham, Mahler and Levy found both erotic and hostile aggressive components in the tic, although Ferenczi mentioned only the erotic component. All of them noted the narcissistic orientation of the patient, while Mahler emphasized the muscular cathexis in this narcissism and described for some of her patients hyperactivity, excessive body interest, poor large-muscle coordination and fine-muscle skill.

Both Ferenczi and Levy suggested that the tic served to ward off suffering as well as to express, partially, an impulsive wish.

Ferenczi and Mahler claimed that a constitutional inferiority played a role in the production of the symptom, and consequently suggested a poor prognosis. Mahler offered no evidence for a constitutional factor, but suggested it as a hypothesis. Ferenczi based his claim for a constitutional factor and poor prognosis on his comparison of tics with schizophrenic mannerisms as well as upon his inability to cure the symptom by analysis. If one defines the term "tic" more specifically and excludes schizophrenic mannerisms from the definition, his argument for a constitutional basis and a poor prognosis is not tenable. Mahler based the poor prognosis on a case described in detail, but claimed cures from psychotherapy in a later paper. It is possible that the discrepancy in her claims may have been the result of an error similar to that of Ferenczi, since the description of the behavior of the analyzed case—with multiple mannerisms, hyperactivity, silly, erotic, aggressive behavior, and only slight superego repression—approximates some forms of childhood psychoses more closely than it does forms of behavior found in the other tiqueurs described by her, by other authors, or by this author. If this one case were that of a psychosis and the others described in her statistical studies were true tics, one can readily understand the reason for the unfavorable prognosis in the former instance and the therapeutic successes in the latter cases.

Comparisons with compulsive ritualistic acts were made by both Abraham and Levy. Abraham stated that they differed only in the emotion associated with inhibition of the movement; that is, discomfort with inhibition of the tics and anxiety with inhibition of the compulsive act. Levy differentiated between the two in his statement that the tic represented the initial phase of an act whereas the compulsive movement was its end phase. And, finally, he equated tics with rhythmic movements resulting from artificial restriction of activity, but did not explain why the former continued and the latter ceased upon removal of restriction.

For the present study cases were chosen which presented, as part of the symptom picture, a simple tic which consisted of a rapid contraction of a group or groups of muscles occurring at irregular intervals without evidence of an appropriate purpose.[2] The muscles involved, however, consisted in all instances of voluntary physiological units, such as are found in eye-blinking, lip-pursing, pants-hitching, etc. Although most frequently the movements were not produced voluntarily, the patients were often aware of their occurrence. Although the theoretic conclusions are based upon the analysis of thirteen such cases, three of which were adults, only those in which the circumstances at the time of the onset of the tic were known accurately are discussed in this study. All of the cases were analyzed for a year or longer, and during treatment the character patterns of the patients were well revealed and the dynamic factors involved in the symptom production were exposed. A thorough historical study of the children's cases included, also, an evaluation, through interviews, of the attitudes and the behavior of the parents toward the patient in order to define the role of daily experiences in the symptom choice and in the character development.

The ages of the children ranged from 3 to 10 at the time treatment was undertaken. Except in the case of one 4-year-old girl, the tic had been present for several years and had not been considered as a problem by the parents who brought the child for the treatment of other symptoms. Of the thirteen cases, the number of males was higher than that of females, as in Mahler's studies, i.e., 10 to 3, but there were revealed no marked differences between the males and females in the ego mechanisms concerned in the tic production, in the role of the tic in the total character constellation, or in the attitudes and behavior of their parents toward them.

Although there were variations in the secondary symptoms presented by the children, different events acting as precipitating causes of the tic and considerable variations in motor skill, intellectual ability, and interests, all of them presented important and interesting similarities. In all of the cases the mothers, and in some cases both parents, were ambitious for the child in the realm of intellectual

---

[2] This definition is closer to Mahler (11) than to Levy (8) who includes "rhythmical" in his definition of the movement. Since a ryhthmical sequence is not mentioned in other papers as characteristic of tics, and since my own experience contraindicates any rhythm in tic occurrence, such qualification appears unjustified. The slow movements of schizophrenic mannerisms or other habit reactions such as ear-pulling, masturbation, etc., and compulsive ritualistic acts which some authors correlate with tics, are excluded from this definition since the psychodynamic purpose of the tic is different from these.

achievement and of conformance to nonaggressive behavior. As mentioned, this parental characteristic was noted also by Mahler and Levy. The mothers were affectionate but firm and controlling in their behavior toward the child, friendly and even-tempered in their personal relationships, and efficient and ambitious in work. All the children before treatment were somewhat shy, but had winning manners toward adults and were conforming to adult authority. Fears in one form or another, such as night terrors, fear of separation from a parent, fear of the dark, fear of being injured, etc., were symptoms possessed by all of them. They were more narcissistic than the average child of similar age, as suggested by Mahler (11) and Ferenczi (3). This orientation was exhibited in bragging, selfishness with siblings and playmates, etc., but they also had concomitant fear of failure in a variety of areas and fear of competition with other children.

Of particular importance were the similarities disclosed in relation to the precipitating causes at the time of the onset of the tic and its incorporation into the ego structure as a defense mechanism against anxiety. It is interesting that tics are described in the literature as inappropriate muscular contractions. In the following cases, however, it will be seen that, at its onset, the tic was an appropriate response for the particular child to an overwhelming traumatic experience. Only later the tic continued to occur in other situations fraught with anxiety for the child but in which the movement was no longer an appropriate reaction.

The traumas which preceded the first tic noticed by the parents were all sudden frightening occurrences which would cause, in the majority of children at the same age, violent muscular responses such as crying, running away, temper outbursts, or physical attack. These natural responses were inhibited in these children by a fear of punishment or of loss of love should they react to the trauma with the use of the natural muscular response. In the majority of instances the factors responsible for the inhibition of crying, running away, attack, etc. were the restrictive training and attitude of the parent or parents. In one instance, added to this general parental attitude, was a specific threat to the child at the time of the traumatic experience by the individual responsible for inflicting the trauma. Several factors operated in achieving such marked conformity to parental inhibition of aggressive behavior. The child's wish to conform came from the desire to maintain the love of the mother. As is well known, this wish is present in all young children but operates successfully only when the child actually experiences the pleasures of his mother's love and when he is aware of those activities which the mother will reward with affection versus those which will provoke rejection. Since the mothers of these children were affectionate when the child was "good," i.e., not aggressive, but were firm and consistent in their demands for conformity and disapproving when not obeyed, the child learned early that he could maintain his mother's love by certain restrictions upon his own activity. The conflict which the child must solve in this situation is a typical instinctual conflict described by Alexander (2), in this instance a conflict between the aggressive impulses and the drive for love and dependence.

The ego mechanisms used in the solution of the conflict were inhibitions, substitution of a part of the act, and denial, which are the simplest and earliest learned defense mechanisms (7). A more elaborate mechanism, such as adequate substitution, sublimation, conversion, undoing, projection, etc. was not possible because of two circumstances; one was the immaturity of the prelatency ego and the meager development at this early age of the cognitive process, or intellectual capacity; [3] the other circumstance was the mother's ambitious attitude toward the child, which made unacceptable to her the unskilled attempts at more complete substitution or sublimation of which the child might have been capable in the prelatency years.

As will be demonstrated in the case discussions, the tic at its onset served the same purposes that many neurotic symptoms serve—inhibition of the direct expression of the instinctual wish and partial satisfaction of that wish. In some instances, also, it served to shut out or deny the awareness of the traumatic experience (8). As an example, in Case 1, a 4-year-old boy, following a first view of his father's amputated leg, developed a bilateral blinking tic preceded by a sudden rapid widening of the palpebral fissure. During the treatment of this boy, analysis of the symptom disclosed the widening of the palpebral fissure to be a partial substitute for the wish to see more; the blinking to be a visual denial of the traumatic sight and its implications, and a partial substitute in muscular action of his repressed castrative wishes toward his father. These latter wishes were precipitously aroused from his unconscious, to which they had been previously relegated when he was presented so suddenly with the actuality of his father's injured condition; a symbolic or displaced castration.

Also, common to all the tic cases, as for many varieties of neurotic cases, the symptom followed the "repetition compulsion" phenomenon. The tic was repeated not only to serve as a defense against the specific traumatic experience, if and when it occurred again, but

---

[3] See French's discussion of the role of cognition in ego development (5, 6).

also became generalized and was used as a reaction to every anxiety-producing situation. This phenomenon was the result of isolation, in which the awareness of the traumatic experience was repressed and isolated from the fear and the reaction to the fear (the tic). Fear and tic thus became correlated so that consequently the reaction (the tic) occurred when any kind of fear was felt. This subsequent fate of the symptom accounts for the so-called "inappropriateness" which various authors emphasize as typical of tics.

Of interest also, perhaps, in view of assumptions in the literature of a probable constitutional factor in the use of the neuromuscular system for the production of the neurotic symptom (3, 8, 11), none of my cases presented actual hyperactivity. Parents of most of them did complain of their child's activity. This, when described and observed in detail, was found to be normal for the child's age. The mother's preference for quiet, restrained, conforming children made this normal childish activity unacceptable to them. This is in direct contrast to Mahler's finding of "a progressive general muscular restlessness and hypermotility" (11). However, since her diagnoses were mostly gleaned from histories taken from the parents, it is possible that their evaluation of restlessness was influenced, as in the case of my patients, by their own neurotic attitude toward childish aggressiveness and activity, or that the restlessness was a secondary symptom not always equated with the tic.

Ferenczi (3), as well as Mahler (11), claimed a constitutional factor in tic formation, but Ferenczi based his belief in part on his inability to cure the tic by psychoanalysis, by which he relieved concurrent symptoms. This tenacity of the symptom was not exhibited by the cases presented here nor by the other children with tics who were analyzed but are not discussed in detail in this paper. When the dynamic factors producing the tic were well analyzed, the symptom was discarded and no other abnormal neuromuscular activity ensued during the three or more postanalytic years in which the cases were followed. However, in defense of Ferenczi's conclusions, I have found that, in the treatment of adults who possess tic-like movements as one of their symptoms, analysis has decreased the frequency of the tic but has never cured it completely. Also, in a few child cases, the tic returned from time to time when the parent relapsed to the previous repressive perfectionistic attitude.

This difference between the results in the treatment of children and adults accords with our experiences in the treatment of children in general. If one analyzes a child in the prelatency or latency period and, at the same time, can effect changes in the environment such that the child is no longer exposed to the experiences which produced the symptoms and the distorted character patterns, a much more extensive and permanent cure is effected than in adults who, even after analysis, maintain noticeable remnants of old ego mechanisms within the framework of the modified character pattern which has been achieved through analysis. This difference can be explained by the fact that the young child is still in a developmental stage, and his methods of reaction are much less fixed than are those of the adult. One might compare the child to a sapling which may be bent at an angle by the application of pressure. If this pressure is continued, it produces a bent tree which can be straightened only partially by reverse pressures. Corrective pressure, however, exerted during the growing period, can straighten the sapling so that it becomes a normally straight tree.

Summary of Cases

CASE 1.   John, (age 7½, I.Q. 122), was referred for a learning inhibition which was so severe that he had been unable to learn to read and was repeating the first grade. His difficulty did not include inability to recognize or write letters or numbers, but in putting letters together into words and numbers into combinations. He also exhibited an eye tic which had been present for three years, consisting of a sudden widening of both palpebral fissures immediately followed by a rapid blinking of both eyelids. John was a bright boy with shy but winning manners and a ready smile. He was conforming at home and with other adults, and tended to be a follower with other children of his age; but, if the play became rough, he would withdraw to play by himself. He was oversolicitous and affectionate with his 4-year-old sister and, although he tended to dominate her in their play, he yielded to her easily if she cried. He disliked rough sports but possessed some mechanical skill both in the execution and the planning of a project. He had a fear of dogs and of the dark, as well as frequent nightmares from which he awoke screaming and in some confusion.

Both parents were ambitious for their children's school achievement. The mother was meticulous as to manners and repressive of any aggressive or hostile behavior. She was a tense, active but friendly woman, proud of her domestic perfectionism and of her husband's success. The father was an ambitious and hard worker, successful in his profession but with a tendency to depressive moods. He was frequently irritable at home, particularly when he was suffering from pain in one leg which had been amputated below the knee, following an automobile accident in his youth. He wore an artificial leg which fairly successfully masked the injury of which he was very ashamed. Although he was often affectionate with both children, he frankly favored John's sister and insisted that the boy protect and love her.

Birth was normal and breast-feeding, for five months, was followed by easy weaning to a bottle. There had never been any food difficulties. Excretory training, begun at 4 months for bowel control, was complete at 6 months, and urinary control was complete at 14 months both for night and day. He walked alone at about 12 months and was talking in short sentences by about 18 or 20 months. When he was 1½ his mother had pneumonia, and during her months of hospitalization he was irritable and fearful of the strange nurse who cared for him. A traumatic event occurring during this time was of significance relative to his fears which started then. The nurse had left him alone in a play pen in the yard; she heard him crying, but finished a task before going to him. She found a Great Dane had jumped into the pen and was licking and pawing the baby, who screamed in terror. The onset of his night terrors and fear of dogs followed this experience, and upon the return of the mother he was aggressive and hostile when directed. The mother controlled these outbursts by spanking and by irritation and by praise of any docile acceptance or friendly gestures on his part. Within a few months he became quite conforming but more dependent, clinging tightly to the mother when out of the house and following her around at home. He played less freely, often asking permission of his mother before he started with a toy and begging her to play with him.

When he was 3½ his sister was born. For this he had been prepared enthusiastically by the parents who talked often about the new baby he was going to love and care for. He responded to her arrival with an increase in the frequency of his nightmares, but this gradually decreased as he was allowed to fondle and hold the baby. He was awkward with her, however, and was often scolded if she cried when he was playing with her, and once when he dropped her. When he cried himself, he was scolded for being a baby, but was consistently praised for gentleness and quietness. At about this time the father spent more time with John and urged him to help with tools and woodwork. He developed considerable mechanical skill about which he bragged to his mother and others. She discouraged this bragging, always pointing out his goal of skill equal to the father. His response to this was usually withdrawal to his own room or an exaggerated oversolicitude for the sister and, occasionally, refusal to work with his father but insistence upon making something by himself, with which he was never satisfied.

At about 4 a second important trauma occurred. Awakening from a fearful dream, he ran trembling into his parents' room when they were preparing for bed. Suddenly he stopped moving, with his eyes glued to his father's amputated leg, which he had never seen before because of the father's exaggerated care in hiding what he considered a shameful inadequacy. His father, embarrassed, exploded in a temper and ordered him back to his room; the child went very docilely but was restless and cried out often during the remainder of the night. The next day the eye tic was noticed whenever the father was present. The parents were unable to remember how soon the tic began to occur in situations other than the presence of the father, but within several months the mother had noted its fairly frequent occurrence: when he was scolded, was with strangers, was frustrated, and so on. It was still present when he was referred for treatment.

At about 4½ he was severely scolded by the mother of a neighbor child when she caught him viewing the little girl's genitals in the bathroom. John's mother was embarrassed by the news of this event, and forbade him to play with the girl. His tic became worse after this event. During the next three years the child attended nursery school, kindergarten, and first grade. During these years he continued to be a conforming, fairly passive child, at first playing fairly well in directed groups with other children, but withdrawing, noticeably during first grade, from group activities, preferring to stay in school at recess with the teacher. His nightmares continued but less frequently than at 4. Although he could not learn to read, he liked school and disliked to be absent when ill with colds.

At 7½ he was referred for therapy by the teacher who recognized the neurotic factor in his learning difficulty. He was in treatment for a year with biweekly interviews, and was seen occasionally the following year. Interviews with the mother were maintained in the beginning at monthly intervals in an attempt to help her to understand the correlation of John's difficulties with her restrictive, perfectionistic demand upon him. Insight into her own character difficulties led her to seek treatment for herself with another psychiatrist within about six months. After this time discussions with her concerning John changed from office interviews to occasional telephone conversations.

With the analyst John at first was friendly but withdrawn in his play. For some time his main interest was lining up small cars and pushing them forward to see how far they would run. His only conversation at this time was, "See how good I am," "I make them go farther than the other children," "I'm smart," "I read best in my room," and so on. One day one of the cars hit a chair leg and broke a fender. His tic was very noticeable at this time and he said he would fix the fender. With Duco he mended it very well and commented, "I'm the best fixer in my home—even better than Daddy." This followed a period in which he mended various broken toys in the toy box, bragging as he proceeded. He found one doll with a broken leg which he insisted upon mending, saying, "Mary (his sister) is broken, no, Daddy is broken, no, I am broken." His tic was marked, and at the end of his speech he threw down the doll and said, "Everyone is broken. I can't fix it. The wood won't work." Tears came to his eyes and the analyst said, "Maybe you wonder why Daddy's leg is broken." He jumped up and said, "No, No!" more vehemently than he had ever spoken before. He put his right hand over his genitals and said, "I know. It is because a car ran over him and it hurts him, but he's fixed. He wears a wooden leg. I know it is, he said so. I'm sure it is." After some discussion by the analyst as to how frightened he must have been when he first saw his father's leg, he said, "I can't look at it, it's awful." During this period he became quiet, leaned close to the analyst, and showed no signs of eye-blinking.

Following a series of further interviews during which he was very friendly and played dominoes with the analyst at his own request, he began to peep at the analyst's dominoes before he would play one of his own. Upon the analyst's jokingly saying, "It's fun to peep, it's fun to really know things," he answered with a smile, "I look all over, I look at everything, I know everything." Then, "I used to say I could read, but I can't. I'm dumb like Mary." It was suggested to him that maybe he was afraid to look at things for fear he'd learn something frightening like seeing his father's leg. He blinked and answered excitedly, "I want to break everything up and run and run and run, only I can't do it. Gee, would they kill me if I did!" When it was suggested that perhaps he thought his mother wouldn't love him and would punish him if he was aggressive, he quieted down with, "Dad too; he always takes mother's side and he always sticks up for Mary—Gee they are mean. No, they aren't. Mother's o.k., but I get sore at Dad, he's always butting in. He thinks he's perfect. Someday I'll be better and bigger; that will show them!" He smiled very warmly at this and took a deep breath and relaxed with, "Let's play dominoes again."

In the middle of a play he suddenly said very quietly, "I try to look at the girls in the bathroom"; to the analyst's, "Maybe you want to see how they are made," he answered, "I want to look at their penis." He discussed at some length his belief that girls really had penises, and if he could really look clearly he could see them. Following interviews were concerned with sex instructions during which he was avidly interested in pictures of male and female genitals. At one time he drew a woman, then crossed out the breasts and added a penis, then crossed out the penis and redrew the breasts, then scribbled over it saying, "It is all mixed up now."

As his confusion concerning anatomy and sexual functions were gradually being cleared up, he admitted his own castrative fears, his jealousy of his father, his fears of his own destructive wishes toward his father, and his fears of being injured in retaliation. Within the framework of this discussion, hostile wishes toward the sister, who displaced him, and toward his mother, who controlled and deprived him, were also uncovered gradually as he became able to discuss his fears of retaliation from his mother as well as from his father. During this period also he was able to recall and tell the content of various dreams. These repeated like a theme song situations in which he was about to be attacked by a variety of fearful figures, both male and female, such as witches, robbers, devils, ghosts, and in which he was terrified but "frozen," as he called it, and was unable to move either to attack or to flee. During the whole period the parents noticed a decrease and finally a cessation of the tic. In the treatment hours he became gradually much more friendly and merry. He was active building with blocks and making airplanes. Painting them, he took great pleasure in smearing the paint and camouflaging the planes by painting over and over with various colors. He entered gradually into competitive play at school and became one of the best "batters" in baseball. At first his relationship to his sister changed from oversolicitude to hostile teasing, which gradually gave way to tolerance and neglect of her with only occasional verbal criticism. His interest in reading became quite marked: he began to read and write words, and often in the hour he would ask to read a simple book.

Arrangements were made for tutoring as he evidenced decrease in blocking, and he then progressed rapidly so that he was almost up to grade by the end of the school year. His fear of dogs showed some decrease after he had worked out his own fears of injury as retaliation for his hostile destructive wishes, to both parents and his sister. He differentiated often between dangerous dogs, meaning strange ones, and nice dogs, in which class he placed the analyst's cocker spaniel. At the beginning of the visits he would not enter the analyst's house until he had been assured that the dog was locked up. As he became more aggressive and less fearful, he asked to see the dog, which he approached tentatively at first and at each visit more fearlessly until, toward the end, he would insist on the dog's staying with him during the hour; one day while petting her he said, "I love her; someday I'm going to have one too." At the present time he still shows restraint with strange dogs but no longer evidences any panic upon meeting them.

In this case an analysis of the historical events, plus the material uncovered in therapy, lead to certain theoretical conclusions which offer the most valid explanation for the production and maintenance of the symptoms until therapy resolved the conflicts and made available constructive outlets for his impulse energy. The mother's prohibition and punishment of aggressive activity, taken in conjunction with her rewarding by love and praise of his repression of hostility and competitive strivings, offered a fairly rigid framework within which he could work out his conflicts. By inhibiting his aggressive protests, repressing his rivalrous hostility, and compensating with oversolicitude he was able to gain a maximum of pleasure from his mother's love, but at the expense of his aggressive impulses. These, at first, were offered sublimated channels of expression in his handiwork, but the mother's depreciation of his accomplishments and her emphasis on a too ambitious goal of achievement robbed these sublimations of their satisfactions and inhibited further attempts at thus transforming repressed aggressive energy into constructive activity.

At the time of the traumatic incident when he saw his father's injury, his aggressive impulses had already been repressed so that fear of the expression of his rivalrous hostile impulses toward his father, arising out of the Oedipus phase and the consequent fear of retaliation from the father, produced an unconscious conflict expressed only in his nightmares, in which he was impotent in the face of danger. The view of his father's leg represented a confirmation of the dangerousness of his hostile wishes toward his father; the rage of his father at this time confirmed the retaliative danger from the father. Since repressive training had made an aggressive solution of the conflict impossible, his reaction became denial, a technique he had used previously to solve hostile feelings toward his mother and sister. Denial by word (4) was clearly expressed during the therapeutic hours as he first talked of his father's leg. Denial in act (4) took the form of the eye tic in which he closed his eyes to shut out the view. Such a small-muscle activity was probably preferable to one more grossly aggressive, since the mother had early prohibited gross muscular movement in preference for quiet inoffensive muscular activity. It is interesting, in view of the theory that an impulse can never be completely repressed and that it continues to seek devious symptomatic outlets, that the "wish to see" claimed part of the symptom expression. This was expressed in the palpebral fissure widening which momentarily preceded the eye closing. The vigorousness of the muscular contraction of the lid muscles suggests that the tic condensed, also, into its action a substitute muscular expression for the aggressive hostile wishes.

The use of the symptom to protect himself, at first, from further visual traumas, as in viewing the sex organs of the little girl, and then, later, as a defense against any anxiety-producing experiences, was clear in the subsequent history of its occurrence. This development is in line with our knowledge of the usual course of most neurotic symptoms. The other problem, which was noted only when he went to school, the learning inhibition, correlated directly with the fixation of the mechanism of denial and its elaboration to protect him from learning anything through visual experience. The widening of the field in which denial was used probably grew out of the fallacious reasoning from the specific to the general, such as, "I looked and I learned something dangerous, therefore I must not look and learn." [4]

CASE 2. Robert, (age 10, I.Q. 136), was referred to the analyst because of a generalized anxious behavior. He was a tall sturdily-built boy, shyly friendly, with meticulous manners and a quiet but anxious mien. He exhibited a marked mouth tic in which he pursed his lips tightly together and grunted. According to the mother, his fears reached panic proportions whenever he was expected to be on his own, either at home or in unfamiliar situations. He refused to ride alone on the bus or streetcar or to go to friends' houses to play. The final straw which influenced the parents to seek treatment was his reaction to their leaving him alone in the house for about an hour one afternoon. When they returned, he cried hysterically, was trembling, and was quieted only after he was given a sedative at the doctor's advice.

Although Robert had been for four or five years an anxious child, his fears had increased noticeably in the last five or six months after plans had been made for him to go to camp the ensuing summer. He had been ambivalent about going, afraid that he would be homesick, but he wished to go with his friends who discussed enthusiastically their own camp plans.

Robert's mother was an attractive, excellently groomed woman of 39, who was friendly but aloof. She talked proudly of her well-run routinized home and of her activities in various civic organizations, in which she held executive positions. She emphasized the importance of rules and routine in living and in the bringing up of children.

---

4 See Sylvester and Kunst (12) for an excellent analysis of the psychodynamic factors in some reading inhibitions.

She believed that she had been able to cope with all the problems of child development until Robert's fears had become so severe. Although his tic embarrassed her, she considered it an idiosyncrasy which would gradually disappear with time, since he had learned to control himself so well in other realms. She was ambitious for her children's achievement, already tentatively planning professions for both boys.

The father was a jovial man who worked sporadically in his father's business but, because of an independent income, was able to lead a fairly irresponsible life. Although the mother disapproved, he kept irregular hours and was frequently out of the home. He spent very little time with the children, and demanded immediate obedience and conformity to his wishes when he was with them.

Robert's older brother, Richard, 14 years old, was a conforming boy who was successful in school, independent, with a few close friends. His interests were normal for his age except in that he had not been allowed to enter athletic activities because of his health. He had developed asthma at about 4, and attacks occurred at irregular intervals during the winter months. He frankly rejected Robert, calling him a sissy and a dummy. He had been cruel to him when he was younger, but with the mother's consistent control he gave up his open antagonism and merely ignored and depreciated him. Although the mother claimed that she loved both boys equally, she spoke with pride of Richard's success in school, of his good manners, and of his confidential relationship to her, and she exhibited shame when talking of Robert and his symptoms.

Robert's development had progressed normally in the early years. He was bottle-fed and took solids easily when they were introduced into his diet. Although the mother did not remember the age of excretory training, it was achieved without difficulty by the nurse who cared for him for seven years, after which she left to be married. She was a rigid perfectionistic person who pleased the mother with her insistence upon routine and strict discipline. The mother was proud of the fact that the nurse had prevented the development of any aggressive problems, and that Robert preferred to play quietly instead of roughly and actively. From an early age he had withdrawn from children when they were rough or demanding, and gave in rather than fight for his rights. The mother knew of no incidents of masturbation, but was sure that the nurse would have punished him if she had noted any masturbatory activity. To her knowledge, Robert had never asked any sex questions nor had he been given any sex information.

At 4 he had entered nursery school. For the first few months, each morning as they entered the school, he clung to his nurse, begging her not to leave him. She was firm, insisting that he be a big boy and scolding him if he cried. As he became familiar with the school he accepted attendance, although he never became enthusiastic about it. At 5½ the tic was first noticed consequent to the following experience. Robert had been watching Richard play with his electric train in the basement playroom, when an older boy joined them. Although all the details of the occurrences were not known, it was later learned that the friend had attempted fellatio with Robert, threatening to kill him if he cried or told. That evening Robert had refused to eat, kept whimpering, and when asked what was the trouble all he did was to look apprehensively at his brother. When pressed, Richard finally admitted the fellatio attempt, but insisted that Robert had kept his lips clamped tightly and the boy's penis had not entered his mouth. Both brothers were scolded by the mother for the event, and Robert was told that if he would leave the older boys alone, he would not get into such difficulties. Not only did this experience usher in the tic which persisted, but it also increased Robert's fear of being left alone. Night terrors with incoherent talking in his sleep gradually developed and occurred, according to the mother, whenever the boy was overly tired or had an exciting day or had been anxious. In the following year the only new difficulty which was noted was a slowness in learning, despite his superior ability, which difficulty the teacher explained by his inattentiveness and his tendency to daydream. He was conforming in school and kept up with his grade, but at the bottom of the class instead of at the top where his I.Q. of 136 would place him.

In spite of his shyness, Robert entered into the therapeutic interviews with enthusiasm and frankly admitted his wish to overcome his fears. Occasionally he would ask to play a game of checkers, at which he was adept, but, in general, the sessions, twice a week for a year, were conducted entirely on the verbal level. He revealed a rich fantasy life of which he told shyly, admonishing the analyst not to let his family know. In his fantasies he identified himself with superman, and his exploits included magical control of his enemies, devil-like creatures who wished to destroy him. By his merely looking at them they became frozen to the spot and could move only as he commanded. In one fantasy, which he produced in the hour after discussing his fear and hatred of his brother, he tore off long tails from the devils. When one was gone, another grew in its place, each longer than the other. Finally they were so long that the devils were tangled in the coils of the tails. During this recital he became quite excited, ticking repeatedly, and laughing uproariously. He tore off a rope from a pull toy in the room, jumped on the sofa and said, "See, this is the way it goes." He wrapped the tail around himself and squirmed as if he were trying to free himself. He had tucked one end in the front instead of the back of his trousers and the analyst commented that, starting in front, it looked more like a penis than a tail. For a moment he looked frightened, then said, "Why are penises different? Sometimes they are enormous and stiff. Sometimes like mine." After an explanation that differences of size correlated with differences in age, the analyst said, "I wonder when you have seen large ones?" He sat very stiffly, kept ticking so badly that he could hardly talk, but finally got out, "Lots of times. I've seen Daddy's and Richard's." To the analyst's, "And who else's?" he said, "You know, didn't mother tell you? That time in the basement." To a sympathetic reassurance he asked, "Why does it get so stiff? I know! Richard told me—to make babies; but why doesn't it get bitten?" When asked if he thought intercourse took place through the mouth, he looked surprised and said, "Of course, how else? Richard told me that is the way they make babies." After some sexual information during which he revealed ignorance of the female genitalia, he was able to tell of the fellatio trauma, of his terror, of nightmares in which he was attacked by enormous men trying to push a penis or a club, sometimes a sword, down his throat. He was always alone in the dream and would try to scream for help, but no sound ever came out.

His tic ceased while telling these things to the analyst and he returned to his quiet and confidential mood. At the next interview, he said, "I've been thinking about that silly idea I had that babies were made in the mouth; you know, once I looked at Daddy on purpose to see if he really had a penis still." He giggled at this and laughingly said, "Daddy licked me for breaking into the bathroom. I pretended it was an accident." He was quiet for awhile, then, looking up with his old shy manner, he said, "You know, accidents can't happen in our family." The analyst took this opening to suggest that perhaps his parents were very strict. And with this lead he complained at great length about the things at home that must or must not be done. It was interesting that with each complaint of his mother he countered with praise of her and with a description of the comfort he felt in her presence, definitely exposing the ambivalence in his feelings toward her. The analyst interpreted this ambivalence, emphasizing the fact that because he really loved her he wished to obey her, and it was hard for him to be critical of her. He admitted this, but said he would not dare to disobey her. Interestingly enough, however, soon after this discussion the mother complained of his defiance at home, which irritated her particularly because he refused to wash properly and was irritable when she asked him to do things for her at home which he had previously done automatically. She admitted, however, that the tic had markedly decreased and that he was now independently going to other children's homes to play, although he had not attempted any excursion alone on buses or streetcars. In the interview he bragged of his increasing courage, and his fantasies took on a picture of independence in which he stayed out all night, seeking adventure, while his parents suffered at home from their loss of him.

These fantasies were told with a twinkle and with the reassurance that he would never really do it; and, in the end of the fantasy, he finally returned home to be welcomed like the prodigal son and to relegate the brother to the background. A final dream which seemed to put an end to the tic was frightening to him. He was alone in a large empty room and a frightening figure began to approach him. As the figure put out his arm to grab him, Robert sunk his teeth in the figure's hand and then saw that it was his brother. He was trembling when he awakened, but he remembered saying to himself, "I'd kill him, I'd chew him all up." In retelling the dream he was able to talk quite calmly of his anger at his brother and of how often he had been terrified of him, but of his fear of tattling because "they always took his part." He said, "I can't do anything right. Richard is an expert. I'm a fumbler." He was reminded by the analyst of his fear at the time of the fellatio experience, and it was suggested that perhaps his tic represented a defense against the attack but also a defense against his own hostility which might be expressed in biting. His relaxation after this interpretation and the consequent cessation of the tic indicated the verity of the reconstruction.

In the treatment of this case the mother was seen at infrequent intervals in an attempt to help her relax in her perfectionistic attitude toward Robert. She was able to change only when specific details of handling situations were discussed with her, but on the whole she remained much the same, with only slightly more tolerance for aggressive behavior than previously. However, since Robert became less anxious, he was able to enter into competitive sports with his friends and thus sublimate his aggressive energy with little active hostility or disobedience at home. With a decrease in his fear he was also able to give up much of his distraction during school hours in compensatory superman fantasies, which made possible a marked improvement in school achievement. It was not until he was 12 that he finally went to camp; his adjustment during the two months was a happy one.

In this case, as in the previous one, we find a tic developing in a child inhibited in aggressive outlets by a repressive nurse and a mother who was ambitious for mannerly behavior and too superior achievement. The tic developed following a trauma in which he was unable to protect himself adequately both because of his own fear of his aggression and because of the threat of death. The tic thus represented a substitute for a protective movement, the lip closure, and the grunt, a cry for help. The tic then later became a reaction in other anxiety situations in which it was no longer appropriate. His fear of leaving the family was a protection against the expression of his own aggression and the fear of retaliation in injury, since the traumatic experience had shown him his own inability to defend himself adequately.

CASE 3. Mary, (age 4, I.Q. 117 [5]), was brought to the analyst because of two main difficulties. She performed repeatedly a "sniffing" tic which had been of about a year's duration, consisting of nose-wrinkling accompanied by a rapid inspiration, followed immediately by a noisy expiration. She also had a tenacious constipation, with moments of voluntary holding back of her feces. At these times she would squat on the floor with her knees drawn up, her arms tightly circling her bent legs, and would hold herself rigid, with an anxious look on her face. Then she would suddenly relax and continue her interrupted activity. After about five to seven days of constipation, occasional hard balls of feces would appear in her panties. The mother had noticed that she became increasingly anxious at these times, and that the tic became more frequent. During the constipation period she would never defecate in the toilet, although she was placed there at least twice a day, but after the feces began to appear in her panties she would finally have a large hard stool in her panties. After this she became much more relaxed and ticked less frequently until a new cycle of constipation began and the whole performance was repeated. Other symptoms which were revealed in the first interview with the mother were (a) infrequent night terrors from which she would awake crying and could relax only if she were taken into the mother's bed; and (b) a fear of separation from the mother which made it impossible for the mother to leave the house without her during the day or for her to play outside the house if the mother was not present.

Mary's mother was an attractive, vivacious woman of 35 years with a ready smile and an efficient, intelligent manner. She had been a successful primary-grade school teacher before her marriage, with

---

5 This I.Q. was obtained at the time of a referral, but the precocity both of her development and of her intellectual behavior indicated that she was a superior child, whose performance in the test situation was below her actual capacity probably as a result of neurotic blocking.

a reputation among other teachers, for keeping perfect order in the classroom and for exacting quick obedience. At the same time her pupils seemed very attached to her. She had been eager for children, and Mary was born a year after her marriage. She entered into the care of the child with enthusiasm and an ambition to have a perfect child. She was a meticulous housekeeper and prided herself on the fact that her tasks did not interfere with a rich social life.

The father, ten years older than the mother, was a successful lawyer, devoted to his wife and children, but ambitious for them. He was very disturbed by Mary's symptoms and was so punitive and irritable at each excretory lapse that she had gradually withdrawn from him and appeared fearful in his presence. At these periods he favored a sister of fifteen months—an attractive, friendly baby.

Mary's birth was normal and she was breast-fed on a four-hour schedule. Weaning was accomplished without difficulty at about six months, and she accepted solid foods as they were added gradually to her diet. Bowel training was begun about the fifth month and urinary training about the ninth month. By a year she was completely trained, even for night wetting. The mother was meticulous in maintaining a routine for eating, sleeping, toilet, and playtime. She was firm in discipline and consistently rigid in punishing aggressive behavior, such as hitting, breaking, tempers, etc. She usually isolated Mary but occasionally spanked her for these acts. In general the mother was affectionate and warm, but allowed Mary little free play. During play periods she taught her how to build with blocks, arrange doll furniture in the doll house, and suggested the direction of doll play. By 2, Mary was a very well-behaved obedient child, but already showed hesitancy and anxiety in learning new skills such as tricycle riding, climbing, and the like. After her sister was born, when Mary was 2½, she was eager to play with the baby, but when she tried to poke at the baby's eyes was punished for touching her. The mother took full care of the sister, and Mary was cared for by the baby nurse who stayed on with the family. Mary began to be somewhat stubborn with the nurse and developed some incontinence of urine and feces, for which she was punished by the nurse as well as by her mother.

When she was 3 the mother one day went to waken her from her nap on the nurse's day off and found her smearing feces all over her face. Deeply shocked, the mother slapped her and scrubbed her face vigorously while Mary spluttered and gasped. To further punish her, the mother refused to talk to her the rest of the afternoon, while she cared for the baby. The next day the tic was noticed, and the voluntary constipation started. Her next bowel movement did not occur for six or seven days, and then only after an enema which was prescribed by the doctor. During the following year it was noticed that the tic became worse whenever Mary was anxious, was presented with a task to do, was with strangers, and so on. The nightmares developed during this year, and she clung more and more persistently to her mother, often following her around the house instead of playing. She refused to play with the sister, and when they were left alone Mary made her cry. She became very neat and orderly, arranging her toys in specific order on the toy shelves and looking anxious and protesting when the toys were placed in a different arrangement by the nurse.

In the first interview Mary appeared as a shy, anxious, and unsmiling child who ignored the analyst completely and refused to let the mother leave the room. For play she chose doll furniture and the small dolls. She arranged the furniture meticulously into rooms, looking to the mother for approval at the placing of each piece of furniture. She put the dolls to bed, each in a separate room, and after waking them, washed them thoroughly, dressed them, and placed them in separate chairs in the living room. Then she repeated the undressing, going to bed, getting up and so on, until the hour was over, when she went away holding tightly to the mother's hand. At the next interview, after two days, she allowed the mother to leave the room but frequently looked into the waiting room to see if the mother was still present. In following interviews, once assured that her mother was waiting for her, she played without interruption, but for several of the interviews she looked frequently at the analyst, saying, "Is that all right?" Gradually she played more freely and then began to bring the analyst as a collaborator into the play, asking her to dress the dolls, wash them, and so on. It was remarkable how carefully she handled the toys and how skillfully she could walk among the pieces of furniture without displacing or knocking over any of them. If, as rarely happened, a piece was knocked over, she looked at the analyst anxiously and ticked repeatedly. To the analyst's, "Never mind, here, we can knock them over and put them back easily," she responded by relaxing and continuing with her activities. The play became more detailed and covered most of the events of daily living. One day she made small balls of clay which she called "grunt," her name for feces, and placed them in the panties of the little girl doll. She always spanked and scolded the doll when she found the balls in the panties, pretending to discover them unexpectedly. One day she smeared clay all over the girl doll's bed, became quite excited, ticked as she rubbed it off, and scolded loudly. The analyst said, "Poor Mary, she just wanted to play with the grunt and it was fun. If we pretend it is clay instead of grunt, she can rub it all over everything and no one cares." To this she smiled, for the first time, and began tentatively to rub the clay over the bed, the bed clothes, and finally over the doll. This play continued with increasing abandon and without a noticeable tic for several interviews. Then one day she said, "The baby won't grunt in the toilet. Now sit there until it comes out!" She placed the doll on the toilet seat, made clay balls which she surreptitiously placed in the toilet, then said, "O.K., there it is. You can get off." She wiped the doll vigorously, and then repeated the play many times before putting the dolls to bed. For several interviews she repeated this toilet play and the fourth day changed the routine with, "She's going to grunt by herself now." She put the doll on the toilet, and instead of waiting excitedly, began to get out the other furniture and arrange it into rooms. She put the nurse in the kitchen, the baby in bed, commenting, "She's having a nap," and finally put the mother and father at the dining-room table. Then she took the girl doll off the toilet saying, "She can eat now," and without looking for feces in the toilet or wiping her buttocks she placed her at the table with the parents saying, "Baby is too young to eat, now. She has to finish her nap." It was following this hour that the mother reported that Mary had defecated for the first time in the toilet without telling her mother first, but afterwards she had run to her mother excitedly and had pulled her to the toilet, and, pointing to the feces, said, "Look mummy! Look at all the grunt."

In the following hours, she gradually gave up the toilet play and entered into a routine in which the nurse took the baby out for a walk and the big doll remained with the mother and played and talked with her. To the analyst's, "It is fun to have the baby out of the way," Mary said very solemnly, "She's always in the way. I always have to give her my candy. She's a stinky. I wish mother never borned her." The analyst reassured her that all big sisters were angry when babies got in their way and took mother's time. Following this period Mary entered into much more active play, choosing blocks to build with and laughing uproariously when she knocked them down.

The treatment interviews of this case were held at tri-weekly periods for three months and weekly for another four months. The tic decreased after the first period in which she smeared the clay over the bed, and ceased entirely after the block play had begun. Her constipation continued for about a year but decreased gradually from the seven- to ten-day periods through three- to four-day periods until the stools occurred daily. However, following the first voluntary movement in the toilet at home, she never again soiled her panties. Gradually during this period her play at home became freer, she clung less to the mother and nightmares ceased. Coincident to interviews with the child, weekly visits with the mother were instituted, in which she was offered insight into the causative factors producing the symptoms and was given specific advice as to methods of handling the children to give them greater freedom of expression in activities of their own choice. This mother was able to relax, remarkably well, her perfectionistic attitude and her ambitious pushing of Mary toward achievement beyond her age level. She also learned to handle the sibling rivalry in such a way that she could keep the children from injuring each other, but was able to accept without too great distress their verbal antagonism.

An analysis of the events involved in the production of the tic in this case seems clearly to indicate that psychodynamic factors were involved similar to those of the other cases. The nose-wrinkling expressed denial of the smelling pleasure and probably hostility toward the punishing parent. Such a grimace is used often by children to represent rejection of a person. The short inspiration was a substitute for the pleasurable smelling sensation which is normally achieved through a deep, long inspiration. The expiration expressed a denial and an inhibition of that pleasure. The precipitating trauma was, in this case, punishment by the mother at the moment of the child's indulgence, which was followed by a prolonged rejection by the mother. Inability to protest against the mother's behavior was due to the repression of this child's aggressive and hostile impulses, accomplished through the developmental years by the mother's restrictive training in which she had punished aggressive activity and had rewarded docile conforming behavior by her love. The development of adequate sublimations for aggressive impulses was hampered by the mother's dissatisfaction with the child's performance and her consequent direction of the child's play. This, at the moment of panic, when the child was probably overwhelmed by several conflicting impulses—a hostile retaliation, a wish to continue indulgence in pleasure, and a need to conform—an integration was achieved through a neurotic symptom which partially expressed all wishes and yet did not permit activity which might lead to further danger. The second symptom, constipation, undoubtedly developed as a further protection against dangerous activity. Fear of defecation led to avoidance of the toilet, and occasional involuntary defecation into her panties probably occurred when the physiological need overpowered the protective device. Previous to the traumatic event, the child's conforming behavior had partially broken down. Her regression, as exhibited in the incontinence which began after the birth of her sister, probably resulted from the disillusion she felt at the mother's relegating her to the nurse while she cared for the baby. Incentive for conformity was thereby weakened, and hostile retaliative impulses intensified. This disbalance allowed repressed impulses partially to reappear. It is interesting that there was evidence that this child had begun to defend herself against the uncontrollable act of defecation by a compulsive undoing, as seen in her meticulous orderliness. This is the only case, in my series, in which a compulsive sequela was exhibited. As has been mentioned above, Levy (8) suggested that the tic was the forerunner of a compulsion ritual. This case suggests the circumstances in which such a phenomenon may occur, although there is no evidence that it is an inevitable end result of a tic in all cases.

CASE 4. Charles, (age 9, I.Q. 124), was referred for treatment because of fear of and withdrawal from any aggressive activity. Sports, which were compulsory at his school, he evaded whenever possible. If forced to play, he fumbled balls, ran very poorly and trembled noticeably. He preferred to play with girls and would dress often in his sister's clothes and parade before a mirror. He was afraid of injury and nursed minor cuts and bruises by bandaging them with an antiseptic dressing. In the last two or three years he had developed a phobia of riding in trains and, when in one, insisted on standing up in the middle of a car, in order, he said, "to be more protected in case of accidents." He also had a complicated tic consisting of three rapid movements which occurred simultaneously. He would suddenly ball his right hand into a fist over his genitals and quickly run the fist up the fly of his pants as if hitching them up. At the same time, he jerked his head backward and to the left. His school achievement was average but below his capacity, and his writing and composition were poor.

Charles' mother, of 37 years, was a plain, small woman with a friendly but aggressive manner. She was a portrait painter who had gained a small reputation because of her accuracy in reproduction and the meticulousness of her painting. Like the mothers in the other cases, she was an efficient, methodical woman who maintained an active life. Although she had several maids, she oversaw all the housekeeping and planned the work. As well, she painted and entered into a rich social program. The children had been trained in a rigid routine and, except for the younger daughter, were early inhibited in aggressive or hostile activity. The mother stated that she preferred them to play quietly, and disliked rowdy children. She admitted, smiling, that she had been unable to accomplish the same conformity in her younger daughter that she had produced in the two older children. She had set a high goal of achievement for all of them, and believed that firm, consistent training would teach them habits of work and good manners. She admitted that she pushed them to learn, since she thought that satisfaction with less than the best would lead to carelessness and to lack of ambition. Although she punished carelessness and aggressiveness severely, she was a warm, affectionate mother when the children were "good," to use her own word. This mother revealed a prudishness concerning sex, and when asked about sex instruction she admitted that she would be too embarrassed to offer it. She did not believe that any of the children but Charles had ever masturbated, and he had been severely punished when he had been caught at it when he was about 5 years of age. This incident will be discussed later in detail.

The father, of 40 years, was a short, stocky man who was, like his wife, an efficient and ambitious person. He was a moderately successful business man, but admitted dissatisfaction with the position he had been able to achieve, and hoped that his children, particularly his son, would go farther than he. He was proud of his wife and devoted to her. Although presenting a friendly, even-tempered manner outside the home, he was domineering and critical with the children and, like the mother, urging them always to better achievement. He was particularly critical of Charles for his "sissy" ways, and gave him footballs, trapezes, etc. to encourage "manly" sports. He felt very frustrated when Charles, forced into sports, was awkward and fearful.

Ann, a sister of 12, was an attractive, shy child, very well-mannered, with a few close girl friends. She was the father's favorite. Jane, 6 years of age, was an attractive, tomboyish girl who preferred to play with boys and used her brother's sports equipment in her play with them. She was enuretic, was afraid of the dark, and had occasional nightmares.

Charles' early development was uneventful. Breast-fed until about five months, he was easily weaned and easily took solids as offered. Excretory training was instituted in the third month for bowel control and, about the sixth month, urinary control by day was begun. Night wetting continued until a year of age, when a routine of picking him up at eleven o'clock was instituted. After this he became dry at night. However, by the age of 4 he began to go voluntarily to the toilet during the night.

Any kind of destructive activity was inhibited from the beginning and by three he was already a well-behaved, obedient child who would sit for long periods looking at picture books, quietly scribbling, or playing with his Teddy bear. This latter play consisted mostly of rocking in a small rocker with the animal in his arms. When he was 4 the mother was pleased with his quiet behavior with adults and his excellent social manner. She remembered that with guests he always said "How do you do" and "Good bye" voluntarily, and often repeated the mother's, "It was nice to have you," as the guests left.

When he was 3, and the sister was born, the mother noticed no particular reaction to the baby's coming other than curiosity which he expressed when watching the baby being bathed. Once, the nurse reported, he touched the sister's genitals and said, "All gone?" with a questioning inflection. She spanked his hand, scolded him for touching the baby, and told him to go away, which he did obediently. The mother reported this event to show how easily his sexual curiosity had been curbed. The baby slept in his room until he was about 7, when he was given a room of his own in order to have space for the gym equipment which the father had purchased "to make a man of Charles." His shy, withdrawn behavior was obvious at 5 when he went to kindergarten. In the group he showed a marked preference for the girls and became fearful and clung to the teacher when the children were rough or aggressive. This teacher also noted that he showed little independence in activities, often asking for permission or for direction. The teacher had told the mother that he was "too good and too polite." This incensed the mother, but she admitted to the analyst, when she brought the child at 9, that it was possible that the teacher had been right since he had developed into such a "sissy" and such a fearful child. The teacher had also noticed that he peeped surreptitiously at the little girls when they were in the toilet together.

At 6 a traumatic event occurred. The father, going into his bathroom one afternoon, caught Charles naked in front of a long mirror masturbating. In a rage he slapped Charles so hard that a red mark remained on his cheek. He ordered him to get into his pajamas and to go to bed without his dinner. Charles obeyed without a comment. In the morning the father admonished him again and told him that if he ever masturbated again, the doctor would have to cut the foreskin. While the father was talking Charles put his hand over his pants fly and the father raised his hand to slap him. Charles jerked his head back and looked so frightened that the father restrained himself from hitting him. It was that evening that the mother noticed the tic when the family was eating dinner. It occurred so frequently that Charles had difficulty eating. She sent him to the kitchen to finish the meal. Eating in the kitchen was her usual punishment for carelessness in table manners. Thereafter the tic continued, but in various situations, whether or not the father was present. The mother believed that it became worse when he was tense or anxious. The fear of riding in trains was noticed sometime during the ensuing year and became sufficiently severe to avoid taking him any place on a train unless absolutely necessary. During the following years he became increasingly passive and anxious.

At the first interview Charles appeared as a well-built, slender boy with a noticeable stoop. He was shy and fearful but very polite. Treatment had been explained to him by the mother, at the analyst's suggestion, as help for him in overcoming his fear of trains. When the analyst explained that they would talk and play together so that they could become better acquainted, and that by learning more of his interest she could help him, he said, "Daddy wants me to be strong, too," and he ticked repeatedly. When asked what he might like to play, he answered, "You tell me, I don't know," but he looked at the boxes of airplane parts. With the suggestion from the analyst that they might make one, he said, "If you don't mind." In the next few interviews airplanes and boats were constructed. At first he asked for direction at each move, but by the fourth hour he went along on his own and asked for help in holding glued pieces together while he worked on other parts. He responded to praise with, "I'm not really good." When it was suggested that he feared failure if he did things on his own, he answered, "I can't do anything. Daddy wants me to play football; I can't kick the ball; the boys don't want me to play; they call me 'Butterfingers.'" He ticked repeatedly at this time and stopped working on the plane. The analyst pointed out that he was really a smart boy and had a well-built body, but probably some fear inside him made him anxious and awkward and interfered with his using his strength. Maybe he was afraid of being injured in play, as he was afraid of trains. To this he said, "Don't tell anybody, but I wish I were a girl! They get it much better!" When the analyst said, "I know just how you feel! Then you wouldn't have to play football and get into all those dangerous situations." He relaxed and smiled as if it was the first time anyone had understood him. Then the analyst said, "But, you know, girls have troubles, too. Sometimes they want to be boys." At this he began to giggle so hard that he choked and tears rolled down his cheeks. Finally he said, "That's what Jane wants." He told then, very confidentially, of his love of his sister Ann's clothes, and how he dressed up in them when he dared. At these times he fantasied himself as a beautiful movie actress whom everyone adored.

At the next hour he smiled in a very friendly way and began immediately to bring articles out of his pocket. Among these things was a chocolate bar which he gave to the analyst, saying, "We can eat that together. You break it in two." When this was done and the chocolate eaten, he picked up a comb and a mirror with, "I fluff up my hair like a girl's." Then he took a ribbon and tied it around his hair, saying, "Now, I am a girl!" The analyst complimented his looks and said, "Outside a girl, but underneath, what are you?" With a conspiratorial whisper he said, "There too," hesitated, then blurted out, "I stick my 'pea' between my legs." To the analyst's, "And then you're exactly like a girl?" he looked embarrassed and said, as if disappointed, "No, not really, I just pretend." Then the analyst said, "I think you would really like to know what is the difference between girls and boys." He answered, "I saw Jane, she hasn't any 'pea'." At this he ticked repeatedly. When the analyst offered to give him information he said, "Oh, please do!" With drawings the anatomical differences were explained while Charles sat very quietly and asked no questions.

At the next few hours he asked for repetitions of the explanations, made drawings himself, and compared them with the analyst's drawings asking often, "Is that right?" At one interview during this period he related the following dream from which he awoke frightened and trembling. In the dream he was riding in an automobile with the family. Suddenly there was a terrible crash. Then he was standing at the side of the road looking at the automobile, which was broken in many pieces. In the middle of the pieces his father was lying all bloody. He thought, "He's dead," and started to walk toward the father's body. Suddenly the father stood up; and he was enormous. He came toward Charles with his hand raised menacingly. Trying to run, Charles could only move the top of his body backward. He awoke just as the father reached him. In associating to this dream he said that his father had "terrible tempers," that he was always frightened if he was alone with his father, who admonished him constantly because he was a sissy. He hated sports; sometimes he dreamed he was trying to play football and he was smashed all to pieces and could see the blood all over. Thinking of the wrecked automobile he remembered his fear of trains. He said that he felt sure every time he rode on a train it was going to be wrecked and he would be all maimed. He remembered seeing a man with an arm cut off, and after that he always thought of losing his arm in a wreck. When asked about his father's menacing arm he ticked repeatedly and couldn't answer. The analyst told him that she remembered the time his father had hit him in the bathroom, and sympathized with the terror he might have felt. He relaxed and said, "Daddy said he'd cut off my 'pea'." The analyst then explained that boys often heard that, but assured him that really it never happened. Charles answered, "But he said so!"

After the analyst gave him an explanation about circumcision, which the father had meant, he asked for pictures to explain it and became quite absorbed in the subject. Later he said, "Sometimes I want to touch my penis, but I don't dare it. I put it between my legs and I feel safe." The analyst reminded him of his saying that he pretended to be a girl by this measure, and she suggested that perhaps his wish to be a girl was a wish to be safe; that is, if he had no penis, no injury could occur. To this he confided a fantasy in which he had frequently indulged. He fantasied that his father went away on a trip and never came back. He alternated between the thought that his father was killed in an accident and the thought that he just got lost and didn't know how to get back. The analyst suggested that this fantasy was a good way to get rid of the punishing father, but also it would successfully punish the father for his cruelty to Charles. She interpreted the indecision between the two ways of eliminating the father as due to, first, the fantasied consummation of the death wishes toward him, and then, second, from guilt and fear, the softening of the destructive wish by allowing the father to live but to be lost from the family. Charles seemed relaxed and relieved during this interpretation, but smiled as if he were happy only after the analyst had explained how common such death wishes were in children, and that really he would not kill his father, nor his father kill him, nor cut off his penis. At this point the analyst told him that the way he ran his hand up his trouser fly made her think that he might be protecting his penis unconsciously. He agreed that it could be so, and then said, "I always feel better after I do it. But why do I double up my fist?" It was suggested that the fist could be a wish to protect himself by fighting back, too. He laughed and said, "Gee, would I punch in his face if I hit!" And he began striking out in the air with his fist as if he were boxing.

The next hour he voluntarily commented, "I don't have to jerk around any more. When I think of it I think of beating up John and am I strong!" John, it was revealed, was the popular football player in his class. When asked if he thought he could play games now, he said shyly, "Maybe sometime. But I'm no good at it. I'm no good at anything." Encouraged to elaborate on this he complained about his mother, who always wanted him to do things better than he could. He said, "If I try to do anything, I think of hearing mother say, 'You should do it this way, that isn't good enough,' and then I stop." Further interviews included much repetition of his complaints against his mother, with the accompanying retelling of incidents in which his mother was nice when she kissed him goodnight, brought him candy, and so on. His love for his mother was interpreted to him, as well as his despair of pleasing her. He was encouraged to make models in the hours, for which he was praised by the analyst, and by the mother at the analyst's suggestion. One day he made an elaborate valentine for his mother which he took home with, "I bet she'll like this."

Weekly interviews with the mother to give her insight into the dilemma into which her conforming, ambitious training had led Charles' emotional growth allowed her to relax enough to accept, partially, more aggressive behavior and to give at least verbal praise for his productions and achievements. For greater security in activities with boys, the parents accepted a plan for recreational excursions with a kindly and sympathetic college student, who taught him to play ball, skate, etc. This teaching was casual and began with very simple skills, increasing in difficulty and activity by slow steps.

Symptomatic improvement included cessation of the tic, following Charles' avowal of its uselessness, progressive decrease of his fear of trains during the treatment period, with an increasing lack of interest in feminine dress and activities. Within a year after treatment had ceased he was a fairly normal boy, entering into school sports, but not as enthusiastically as in constructive play and reading.

Reviewing the causative factors of the tic in this case, we note, as in the other cases, that aggressive outlets were denied by Charles' mother, who offered him the satisfaction of her love only for conforming behavior and who discouraged the transformation of energy into sublimated activity by her depreciation of his performance. Thus inhibited, the child's defense against the terrors of his father in the traumatic event involved the use of specific protective muscular movements appropriate for warding off the danger and for partial impulse indulgence. The head movement attempted to avoid the blow; the balled fist expressed an aggressive wish to attack the father who attacked him; the hand moving up the pants fly, covered the endangered penis, and at the same time allowed partial masturbatory sensation. Repetition of these movements in other anxious situations in which the tic was no longer an appropriate protection followed, as in other cases, the dynamic rule of symptom repetition. Feminine identification proved to be a further protection against his destructive fantasies toward his father and the consequent fear of destruction at the hands of his father. Since riding in a train often symbolizes sexual activity, the choice of the train as the dangerous situation may have had sexual significance for Charles, although this was not clarified in the analysis.

Discussion

In these cases summarized above, certain common factors are in evidence, as was indicated in the introduction. The tic, in each instance, followed a traumatic experience which aroused the fear of being injured. The tic became a defensive response of the small muscles which was appropriate at the moment of the trauma, but became inappropriate as it was further used in response to different fears. The small-muscle contractions were substituted for more normal large-muscle aggression because of previous parental prohibition of such activity and the fear of loss of love or fear of punishment which had become equated in the child's mind with such aggressive motion. In other words, previous to the precipitating trauma, the children already were aggression-inhibited youngsters. In the cases of many children brought up with equally strict parents, aggressive energy is transformed gradually into constructive sublimated activity of competitive games, building and carpentry, cooking, sewing, etc. Two factors inhibited adequate sublimations in these children. One which seemed to operate effectively was the ambitious attitude of the parents which led them to depreciate the child's achievement. Withdrawal from such activity, therefore, protected the child from the further pain of the parents' disapproval. The other factor which made successful sublimation impossible was that the child was too young, both in physical and intellectual growth, to be able to turn to a sufficient variety of activities with success.

French (5, 6, 7) has given us clues to the circumstances in which an ego defense mechanism develops instead of an adequate and acceptable expression of the impulse seeking an outlet. According to his theory, the defense mechanism develops when the normal synthetic function of the ego breaks down, interrupting the successful striving toward an integrated goal. This may occur when instinctual tension becomes too great, or when there is too great a gap between instinctual need and opportunity for fulfillment. As a result of these circumstances the ego becomes fixated upon the obstacle which is blocking successful achievement of the goal. Adequacy in overcoming the obstacle is then interfered with by a variety of factors: (a) the intensity of the emotion which confuses the cognitive or thinking process; (b) a poor or inadequate development of the cognitive process; and (c) the struggle for dominance between different goals. Under these circumstances an inadequate substitute solution is achieved, which we term a defense mechanism and which is expressed in the individual by his neurotic symptoms.

If we scrutinize the circumstances present at the time of production of the tics, it is evident that the events satisfy the criteria suggested by French for the development of a neurotic solution with the use of an ego defense mechanism. In these cases the goal toward which the child was striving, that of maintenance of the parents' love by acceptable constrained activity, was interrupted by the sudden traumatic event which stimulated strong hostile defensive impulses. The ego, at this point, was confronted with the task of integrating these two opposing impulses striving toward opposing goals. It was unable to synthesize the two impulses satisfactorily because both were charged with such intense emotion that neither could yield its goal to the other, and also because intellectual development (cognitive process) was not sufficiently advanced to aid in a rational compromise satisfactory to both impulses. The ego was also constricted in choosing a satisfactory solution by the previous inhibitory influence of the parental training which made dangerous many normal childish activities.[6] The ego then became fixated on the obstacle, the traumatic event, and a compromise solution was achieved which satisfied partially the conflicting impulses and expressed partially the associated emotions. The tic warded off danger, was a partial substitution for impulse expression, and maintained parental love by a non-taboo action. Omitted from this solution was the criterion for an adaptive act; that is, the use of the energy for striving toward a constructive goal. As French claims, a neurotic rather than an adaptive solution leads to constriction of the ego. This condition is clearly shown in the tic case, when, as the child develops, the ego reacts to all anxiety-producing experiences with the tic rather than with a reaction fitting to the particular event. Thus, learning to react differently to new situations is restricted by the repetition compulsion, and the character development is retarded. Character development can progress normally again in the child only after a reversal of the process which led to the development of the tic is achieved. This is accomplished through the corrective experience of psychotherapy and of modified parental behavior toward the patient. Within this new environmental framework, the ego, no longer pressed by fear, is able to discard the old method of solution, the tic, to experiment with new and more constructive solutions and thus to widen the ego span.

---

6 The narrowed "integrative field" which French discusses.

BIBLIOGRAPHY

1. ABRAHAM, KARL. Contribution to a discussion on the tic. In *Selected papers*. London: Hogarth Press, 1921.
2. ALEXANDER, FRANZ. The relation of structural and instinctual conflicts. *Psychoanal. Quart.*, 1933, **2**, 181.
3. FERENCZI, SÁNDOR. Psychoanalytic observations on tics. In *Further contributions to the theory and technique of psychoanalysis*. London: Hogarth Press, 1921.
4. FRENCH, T. M. Defense and synthesis in the function of the ego, *Psychoanal. Quart.*, 1938, **7**, 38.
5. FRENCH, T. M. Analysis of the goal concept. *Psychoanal. Rev.*, 1941, **28**, 61.
6. FRENCH, T. M. Goal, mechanism, and integrative field. *Psychosom. Med.*, 1941, **3**, 226.
7. FREUD, ANNA. *The ego and the mechanisms of defence*. London: Hogarth Press, 1937.
8. LEVY, D. M. On the problem of movement restraint. *Amer. J. Orthopsychiat.*, 1944, **45**, 644.
9. MAHLER, M. S. Psychosomatic studies of "maladie des tic." *Psychiat. Quart.*, 1943, **17**, 579.
10. MAHLER, M. S. Tics and impulsions in children: A study of motility. *Psychoanal. Quart.*, 1944, **13**, 430.
11. MAHLER, M. S. ET AL. Clinical follow-up studies of the tic syndrome in children. *Amer. J. Orthopsychiat.*, 1945, **15**, 631.
12. SYLVESTER, E., AND KUNST, M. S. Psychodynamic aspects of the reading problem. *Amer. J. Orthopsychiat.*, 1943, **13**, 69.
13. SYMPOSIUM: Tics in children, *The Nervous Child*, 1944-1945, **4**.

PRELIMINARY REPORT ON A PSYCHO-SOMATIC STUDY OF RHEUMATOID ARTHRITIS *

By ADELAIDE M. JOHNSON, M.D., LOUIS B. SHAPIRO, M.D.,
AND
FRANZ ALEXANDER, M.D.

Introduction

For a long time it has been recognized that emotional factors play a role in rheumatoid arthritis. Nicolson (10) and Williams (17) studied the effects of hypnosis in such patients. Emerson (3), Thomas (15), Pottenger (13), Nisen and Spencer (11), McGregor (9), Cobb et al. (2), and Ripley et al. (14) have contributed important observations on the relationship of psychologic factors to rheumatoid arthritis.

Seeking an understanding of physiologic mechanisms, Wright and Pemberton (19), Kovacs (7), and Wolff and Mittleman (18) studied the relationship between emotional reactions and skin temperature in these arthritics. Patterson et al. (12) were concerned with prolonged circulatory disturbances secondary to emotional factors and their possible influence on the course of the illness. Trommer and Cohen (16), believing that even in a quiescent disease process of the joint there remains a spastic state of the muscles, emphasized the fact that increased comfort could be obtained for patients through the use of neostigmine.

Fenichel reported a female case of MacFarlane's (8) whose arthritic symptoms had a double psychological meaning. Unconsciously it meant for the patient both a punishment for her hostile competitive feelings toward men and an atonement for her favorite activity, dancing, of which her father had disapproved.

Booth (1) and Halliday (5, 6) have reported highly significant observations of the personality traits and psychologic factors in rheumatoid arthritic patients. Groddeck (4) reported analysis of a woman with spinal arthritis in which the disease seemed to be a defense against the heterosexual role.

* Psychosomatic Medicine IX: 295-300, 1947.

This presentation will be restricted to the psychodynamic findings in a study of 33 cases of rheumatoid arthritis; 18 of these were seen in therapeutic sessions; 15 in anamnestic interviews. There were 4 male and 29 female patients. The psychodynamic formulations pertaining to women have accordingly a greater validity at this point. The clinical supervision of our patients has been primarily in the hands of Dr. David Markson; Dr. Harvey Horwitz has cooperated in making many cases available.

The women patients show impressive similarities in nuclear conflict situations and in general personality structure. Although our findings on men are not sufficiently extensive to make generalizations at the present time, our impression is that in the male patients also certain features are recurrent. The conflict common to all the male patients is a defensiveness against a profound passive and feminine wish. In our studies thus far the types of character defenses appear to be multiple.

Overt Personality Features

A conspicuous characteristic of our women patients is a tendency toward bodily activity, manifesting itself in an inclination toward outdoor and competitive sports. In the period of latency and in adolescence they show decidedly tomboyish behavior. In contrast to this active tendency, they show in adult life a strong control of all emotional expression. Booth made similar observations on 45 cases. Halliday stressed this tendency to control and self-restriction.

In the majority of our female cases there is a striking need to be of service to other people. Although their dependence upon persons in the environment is obvious, it is subtly masked by service and activity, overtly masochistic in character. In respect to their children, the patients in our study are generally demanding and exacting. While they worry and do a great deal for their children, at the same time they dominate them. In a very small group the masochism is not a character trend but appears to be restricted more to the concept of the feminine sexual role, against which they defend themselves in the manner of the hysterical woman.

The sexual behavior of all the female cases shows the common feature of an overt and easily recognizable rejection of the feminine role, the so-called masculine protest reaction. They assume certain masculine attitudes, compete with men, and cannot submit to them. The husbands are for the most part compliant and more passive than their wives; several husbands even have physical defects. The husbands readily accept the part of serving their incapacitated wives.

Precipitating Events

On superficial inspection, the precipitating factors of the disease seem to be without any common denominator. They cover a wide range of external and psychologically significant events; indeed, they run the whole gamut of life situations: birth of a child, miscarriage, death in the family, change in occupation, sudden change in marital situation or sexual relationship, a great disappointment in some inter-personal relationship. It is, therefore, not astonishing that such an observant investigator as Halliday found little rhyme or reason in causative factors. If, however, we focus our attention on what these various events mean to the patients, we can reduce the precipitating causes to a few significant psychodynamic factors.

1. The disease process seems to have developed in these women patients when an *unconscious* rebellion and resentment against men increased, as, for instance, when a patient was abandoned by a man with whom she had felt safe, or when a previously compliant man became more assertive, or when a man in whom the patient had invested a great deal disappointed her.

2. The disease may also be precipitated by events which tend to increase hostility and guilt feelings previously latent and adequately handled through the patient's self-sacrifice and service to others. The birth of a child, with consequent reactivation of an old sibling rivalry, may be the disturbing factor. Hostility and guilt may be mobilized because adequate opportunities for self-sacrificing service are thwarted, as in the event of a miscarriage, or of the death of a hated dependent relative, or when circumstances force the patient into a situation where she must accept help beyond her ability to compensate with service.

3. Finally, in a few cases, the process appears to have begun when a masculine protest reaction was intensified in order to serve as a defense against fear of sexual attack. One woman developed an acute arthritis of the hips and knees when exposed to a sexual threat, and a 16-year-old girl suffered an extreme stiffening of the back with arthritis after a sexual assault by the father.

Immediate Unconscious Background

The overt personality features in these women are defenses against their feminine and dependent role in respect to men and children and to society in general. Two outstanding modes of behavior indicate the immediate dynamic situation. (a) All the female cases are classical examples of masculine protest reaction—a rejection of the feminine functions. The defense mechanism utilized by all of them is hostile masculine identification which produces the typical phenomenon of bisexuality. The rejection of the feminine role, the wish to be a man, is in many cases naively and openly expressed. In other cases it shows itself more in derivatives : being head of the house, controlling the environment, and making the decisions. Interest in competitive sports is the most common manifestation of this pattern in earlier life. Some of the patients show their masculine identification in a predilection for the masculine posture in the sexual relationship. In the deeper psychoanalytic material, the masculine identification appears at times through the utilization of the neck or limbs or of the whole body as phallic symbols. This identification has always a hostile connotation and is often linked with castrative impulses both in the form of grabbing with the hands and of oral incorporation. Such a competitive relationship with men serves as one means of discharging hostile feelings. (b) With few exceptions the cases show an excessive masochistic need to do for others, which serves both as a discharge of the hostility and as a denial of their own extreme dependent demands.

The general psychodynamic background of all these patients is a chronic, inhibited, hostile aggressive state relieved by discharge through the two character trends discussed above.

A case illustrative of the first mode of defense is Mrs. S. G., 28 years old, who developed painful, stiff muscles immediately after she found out her husband had had a love affair. After continued pain and stiffness of the muscles for a few months, she developed a fairly generalized arthritis. Her mother was a conscientious, but cold woman; the father had deserted the family when the patient was 2 years old. She was very competitive with an older brother, and spent much of her childhood in outdoor activities. She felt that her mother's role, and the position of women in general, was unbearable, and said openly she would rather die than tell her husband she loved him, *even if* she did. "Then I could never be on top." She refused sexual intercourse for several months after marriage, had never had an orgasm, and agreed infrequently to sex relations. Although her husband had been a prize fighter of sorts, and she was a frail-appearing little woman, she always headed the household and made the decisions directing her three young daughters in assisting her excellent housekeeping. Her husband's infidelity was the first indication of his rebellion and of her inability to compete with him and control him. When frustrated in her competition, the hostility increased, found no outlet, and the muscle soreness and arthritis followed. During analysis she nightly refused to go out for recreation with him, and finally he was unfaithful to her for the second time. This led to an acute exacerbation of the illness.

The masculine protest is far more subtle in such cases as Mrs. T. H., who developed acute arthritis of a severe nature four different times after lovers had abandoned her. Her unconscious hostile identification with men, envy of the brothers, interest in sports, and her competitive relationship to a weak husband were subtly integrated in a complicated character structure. Although she did not have orgasm, she had sexual relationships easily with her lovers as the terminal event in her machinations to overcome and control them. Primitive, destructive tearing, castrative dreams toward men were common, often associated with oral incorporative impulses.

An example of a patient who manifested the second type of character defense, the excessive masochistic need to serve, is Mrs. E. S., 32 years old and mother of three children. She was the eighth of nine siblings. The following statement gives a succinct picture of her personality : "I am very anxious to get over my arthritis so I can finish having my family. If my mother had not had such a large family, I would never have existed." As a young girl she not only did heavy housework and cared for her invalid mother, but she also assisted the father with duties on the farm, although there was a younger brother. All the siblings went to college. After completing high school she went to live with her older sister to care for her and her many children. In her marriage she continued to display the same slavishly serving attitude toward her three daughters and her husband. Reaction to a miscarriage marked the onset of her arthritic symptoms. On entering analysis she said characteristically, "I have no emotional problems but I am glad to do anything for science."

Genetic Reconstruction

In respect to the pronounced bisexual attitude and the masochistic need to serve, associated with a chronic state of hostility, certain family situations have been found typical. There is usually a strong, domineering, demanding mother and commonly a more gentle, compliant father. Booth speaks of his patients having stern parents, and Halliday found that the arthritic had at least one domineering parent, and that self-restriction began early in life. As little girls our patients developed a dependence upon and fear of a cold aggressive mother, and at the same time a great deal of rebellion which they did not dare to express because of that dependence and fear. This relationship with the mother is the source of their intense masochism ;

the female role becomes frightening to them at the oedipal period. Those patients who have brothers express their sibling rivalry in a hostile identification with the males. This attitude is subordinated to their dependent relationship on the mother, since by assuming the masculine role they are more acceptable to her. A further component of their aggressiveness toward men is based on identification with the mother, whose dominating attitude toward a depreciated father they repeat in their own relationship to their husbands. There are indications that in their oral aggressive attitude toward the cold and rejecting mothers lies the earliest basis of the later grasping, aggressive attitude toward men. This often appears in castrative tendencies in dreams. One patient, speaking of jealousy and men, said, "I feel like grabbing what they have . . . I am so grabby, I feel I have to hold on tight." The masochistic, serving attitude stems also from the earliest mother-daughter relationship; it is designed to placate the mother and to resolve the guilt feelings toward her which originated in sibling rivalry and oedipal jealousy. In addition, there is the wish to atone for the resentment against the mother because of her original rejection. The masochistic serving attitude allows the arthritic woman to express the hostility, and at the same time to discharge it in a more acceptable fashion, in serving, but at the same time also dominating the environment. Furthermore, the suffering is aimed to win the mother's love in which the child never was secure.

Discussion

The fact that these patients express and discharge unconscious emotional tendencies through the voluntary muscles puts their symptoms in the category of hysterical conversion. At least the *modus operandi* is the same as in conversion hysteria—namely, the expression of an unconscious conflict by somatic changes in the voluntary muscles. Our present assumption is that these muscle spasms and increased muscle tonus, under certain conditions, may precipitate an arthritic attack.

In the majority of our cases the unconscious tendencies which find expression and discharge in the muscle system are chronic hostile aggressive impulses and the defense against them. Accordingly the character structure is of a compulsive nature. Two cases, for example, had definite washing rituals.

In a few of our cases the actual localization of the arthritic condition is in relation to a current conflict; the affected organs become the focal point in which the patient expresses unconscious tension, as we observed in their dreams. The sexual conflict was expressed in specific representations of the limbs or the whole body as a phallic symbolic defense against the masochistic feminine wishes. In some cases a nonsexual conflict was symbolically related to a specific bodily area.

These findings correspond to Halliday's assertion that arthritic patients show either hysterical or compulsive character structures. However, we question on the one hand Booth's belief that symbolic use of the body is true in all cases, and on the other hand Halliday's assertion that it never occurs.

In the light of these considerations, the arthritis cases we have seen could be described as a series. At one end are those cases in which aggression and defense against attack are handled by discharge into somatic conversion with a symbolic expression of ideational content. In all gradations to the other end of the series we find those cases where the egosyntonic discharge of chronic inhibited hostility through muscle activity, hard work, and sports has been interrupted, and there develops an increased general muscle tonus which may precipitate an arthritic attack. Of the cases closest to conversion hysteria, we cite the following examples: (a) With the mobilization in analytic sessions of strong feelings connected with oral attacks on the mother's breasts, one patient developed an arthritic condition in the sterno-costal joints. (b) Another woman, who had been accused of infidelity by her husband (who finally asserted himself), developed severe arthritis in the ring finger which spread to all the fingers of both hands. Moving toward the other end of the series are such cases as: (a) A young woman, hard working since early childhood, who developed arthritis when a hated, dependent younger sister died. (b) Another patient with a strong masochistic need to serve her children developed arthritis shortly after a spontaneous abortion. Again, if there is an interruption of the usual mode of expressing hostile masculine competitiveness, for example, by the husband's suddenly becoming much more capable and strong, we may see the muscular tension rise and arthritis develop. In quite a few cases the patient cannot be held in analysis. Some women break off and run away because the analysis threatens their intense masculine protest, the loss of which would make their relationship to men intolerable and would throw them back on the dreaded mother.

In all these cases detailed studies of the widely varying precipitating factors of the disease process show in the psychodynamic factors of these patients a common denominator. As the most general psychodynamic formulation which can account for all our observations of precipitating causes and exacerbations, as well as for fundamental etiologic factors, we postulate a general predisposing personality factor which develops as the result of excessively restricting parental (predominantly maternal) attitudes. In the little child the most primitive expression of frustration is random motor discharge. If, through punitive measures, this discharge becomes associated with fear and guilt, in later life whenever fear and guilt arise there results a psychologic strait jacket. These patients try to achieve an equilibrium between aggressive impulses and control. They learn to discharge aggression through muscle activity in ego-syntonic channels: hard work, sports, gardening, actively heading the house. They learn also to relieve the restrictive influence of the conscience by serving others. Whenever this equilibrium is disturbed by specific events which interrupt their adaptive mode of discharging hostility and relieving guilt, the chronic inhibited aggression leads to increased muscle tonus and in some way to arthritis. In the last analysis we always see an increase of dammed-up aggressive impulses resulting either from external obstacles, such as a recalcitrant husband, or an increase of internal inhibition, such as guilt which increases when its atonement through service is interrupted.

In a small number of cases specific sexual conflicts are handled by the typical symbolic conversion mechanism. Whether this is superimposed on the same character structure as in the majority of our cases, or whether this can independently lead to the disease, is an open question. The fact that in some of these latter cases we see a masochistic concept of sexuality rather than masochism in character structure makes the second assumption more probable.

As we progressed in our understanding of the psychodynamics of rheumatoid arthritis, we were able to explain many of the remissions as well as relapses which took place in patients during analysis.

If the old avenue of discharge for hostility is opened up again through sudden compliance on the part of the husband, the arthritis has been observed to subside. A woman with very severe arthritis had to be carried about by her husband. When he died suddenly, she got out of bed, assumed charge of everything, traveled across the country for the funeral, and made an immediate recovery which continued for many months. The recurrence of arthritis when opportunities for masochistic service are diminished has been observed, followed by its subsidence when self-sacrifice is again demanded by family conditions. As the patients become more able to receive help in analysis, the disease diminishes.

In the study of arthritis one must bear in mind the fact that the personality picture of advanced crippled cases is overlaid by a chronic psychologic adaptation of the personality to the state of being crippled. Time does not allow us to go into details of cripple psychology.

Naturally, the preexisting character has an influence on the behavior, but new features dominate the picture. Most authors who have studied such cases were impressed by the secondary features, such as stoicism and optimism. In addition to the self-deceptive wish fulfillment, this type of adaptation can be easily understood by the fact that the diseased condition relieves the patient from guilt feelings and gives him the right to expect attention that was previously withheld or unacceptable. This was most clearly seen in a patient who had had to care for a demanding father for years. When her arthritis became advanced she said, "Now he will have to take care of me."

Preliminary Theoretical Conclusions

In these cases the general psychodynamic background is a chronic inhibited hostile aggressive state as a reaction to the earliest masochistic dependence on the mother that is carried over to the father and all human relationships, including the sexual. The majority of these personalities learn to discharge hostility through masculine competition, physical activity, and serving, and also through domination of the family. When these methods of discharge are interrupted in specific ways, the persistent increased muscle tonus resulting from the inhibited aggression and the defense against it in some way precipitates the arthritis. But these factors—rejection of a masochistically conceived feminine role with its typical defense of masculine protest, increased muscular tension, or spasms due to inhibited hostile aggression—are found so commonly in patients who do not suffer from arthritis that additional etiologic factors, still unknown, must be postulated. The nature of these factors is probably somatic: inherited, traumatic, or infectious. Whether further studies of psychodynamics and physiology will allow the claim that certain cases may develop a pathologic joint change only as a result of chronic muscular tension without any predisposing somatic involvement remains to be seen. Be this as it may, recrudescence of the psychologic conflict situation, according to our view, is largely responsible for relapses; and improvement of the psychologic situation, for remissions.

The view that increased muscular tonus is involved in this disease is further substantiated by the extremely common observation that arthritis patients complain of muscular rigidity and tenseness upon awakening. Some of them report sleeping in overflexed positions. In many cases muscular stiffness and pain were the precursors of the first arthritic attack. We should refer here again to the common use of neostigmine by clinicians who believe relief of muscle spasm and pain can occur even in a burned-out joint. In order to test the validity of this latter hypothesis we have begun a study of muscle tonus in arthritis patients and in control groups, with the help of a special apparatus devised by Dr. Ralph Gerard of the University of Chicago.

BIBLIOGRAPHY

1. Booth, G. C. The psychological approach in therapy of chronic arthritis. *Rheumatism*, 1939, 1, 48.
2. Cobb, S., Bauer, W., and Whiting, I. Environmental factors in rheumatoid arthritis. *J. Amer. med. Assn.*, 1939, 113, 668.
3. Emerson, C. P. The importance of the emotions in the etiology and prognosis of disease. *Bull. N. Y. Acad. Med.*, 1929, 5, 984.
4. Groddeck, G. Klinische Mitteilungen aus einer 20-jährigen psychotherapeutischen Praxis: Allg. ärztl. Kongress. f. Psychotherap. III (1928). (Clinical notes from a 20-year psychotherapeutic practice: Proceedings: third Congress for Psychotherapy), Baden Baden, 1928.
5. Halliday, J. L. Psychological factors in rheumatism: preliminary study. *Brit. med. J.*, 1937, 1, 213, 264.
6. Halliday, J. L. Psychological aspects of rheumatoid arthritis. *Proc. roy. Soc. Med.*, 35, 455.
7. Kovacs, J. The surface temperatures and the minute blood vessels of the skin in arthritis. *J. Amer. med. Assn.*, 1938, 100, 1018.
8. MacFarlane, D. Arthritis and aggressiveness. Reported at the San Francisco Psychoanalytic Society (1942), but not published.
9. McGregor, H. G. The psychological factor in rheumatic disease. *Practitioner*, 1939, 143, 627.
10. Nicolson, N. C. Notes on muscular work during hypnosis. *Bull. Johns Hopkins Hosp.*, 1920, 31, 89.
11. Nissen, A., and Spencer, K. A. The psychogenic problem in chronic arthritis. *New England J. Med.*, 1936, 214, 576.
12. Patterson, R. M., Craig, J. B., Waggoner, R. W., and Freyberg, R. Studies of the relationship between emotional factors and rheumatoid arthritis. *Amer. J. Psychiat.*, 1943, 99, 775.
13. Pottenger, R. T. Constitutional factors with special reference to incidence and role of allergic disease. *Ann. intern. Med.*, 1938, 12, 323.
14. Ripley, H. S., Bohnengel, C., and Milhorat, A. T. Personality factors in patients with muscular disability. *Amer. J. Psychiat.*, 1943, 99, 781.
15. Thomas, G. W. Psychic factors in rheumatoid arthritis. *Amer. J. Psychiat.*, 1936, 93, 693.
16. Trommer, P. R., and Cohen, A. Use of neostigmine in the treatment of muscle spasm. *J. Amer. med. Assn.*, 1944, 124, 1237.
17. Williams, G. W. The effect of hypnosis on muscular fatigue. *J. abnorm. soc. Psychol.*, 1929, 24, 318.
18. Wolff, H. G., and Mittelman, B. Experimental observations on changes in skin temperature associated with induced emotional states. *Trans. Amer. neurol. Assn.*, 1937, 63, 136.
19. Wright, Lillie M., and Pemberton, R. The peripheral surface temperature in arthritis. *Arch. intern. Med.*, 1930, 45, 147.

PART VIII

MISCELLANEOUS STUDIES

ENURESIS: A STUDY IN ETIOLOGY *

By Margaret W. Gerard, M.D.

For all of those persons treating children's difficulties, whether in a child guidance clinic or in private practice, enuresis is an ever-recurring problem. Many theories of etiology have been advanced and various methods of treatment have been used with occasional success, sometimes permanent, but more frequently temporary. We know, also that without treatment and without apparent cause, enuresis may cease for long periods of time or permanently. This is particularly true as the child enters adolescence, and has led to the common attitude expressed as, "Don't worry about his bed wetting. He will stop in puberty."

In literature on the subject, which is voluminous, there are innumerable causes suggested and an equal number of treatment methods recommended. Data offered in support of the theories are frugal and confusing, and one is lead to believe that our real knowledge concerning the cause of the symptom is in reverse proportion to the frequency of its occurrence. Although the majority of authors agree that enuresis is psychological in origin, a few claim an organic etiology. The latter divides into neurological and somatic causes. Homburger (15) claims that it is due to a spina bifida occulta, and that enuretics show mental deficiency and other degenerate symptoms. Karlin (16) contradicts this contention, stating that 54 per cent of normal children evidence spina bifida upon X-ray examination, and that in a study of enuretic children he found it as a cause only in the cases of extensive involvement of the lumbosacral vertebra which evidenced other symptoms of myelodysplasia, such as disturbances in rectal function and in cutaneous sensory perception of the legs and feet. Neurological causes also include Bleyer's (5) suggestion of a defective cerebral control of the bladder reflex, or its disturbance by faulty deep sensation, and Ederer's (10) and Sicard's (23) contention that enuresis is the result of a local spasm due to hypervagatonia. One should also mention here Schachter's (22) and others' theory that enuresis results from inadequate conditioned reflex development. Among somatic causes, thickened bladder mus-

* American Journal of Orthopsychiatry IX: 48-58, 1939.

501

culature is suggested by Esersky (11) and Sturniman (24), who substantiate their conclusions with the fact that enuresis is more frequent in males than females, and with the statement that, anatomically, the male bladder musculature is thicker than that of the female. Campbell (7) found physical causes in two thirds of 300 cases; the most common finding being that of occlusion of the urethra. Fatigue, offered by Mohr (21) as one of a variety of causes, is denied by Christoffel (8) who found, in an extensive study of treatment methods, that tiring the child by active physical exercise in the afternoon markedly decreased the incidence of wetting. Bakwin (3) claims that enuresis is the result of an irritable bladder, and associates it with frequency and urgency. Christoffel (8), on the other hand, found no such correlation, but believes that frequency and urgency are more often associated with diarrhea and represent symptoms of an anxiety neurosis. And, finally, Macciotta (19) maintains that there is a correlation between enuresis and spasmophilia, having noted an increased galvanic response in such cases.

An equal variety of psychological causes is offered. Mohr (21) mentions suggestion among emotional factors. Poor training in certain cases is claimed by Levy (17), Mohr (21), and Bakwin (3), while the last author also includes a wish of a neglected child to gain attention among possible causes. Levy (17) found some cases developing enuresis as a regressive reaction to love loss. This latter is substantiated by Christoffel (8) who found that, often, a cure of the symptom was achieved when a cleanliness routine was given up and affectionate handling of the child was substituted for it; and by Lippman (18), who found an excessive number of cases in foster homes. The symptoms in these cases, he believes, resulted from the wish of the patient to punish the new parents for the loss of his real parents. The revenge motive is also upheld by MacGuinness (20) who claims that wetting is an expression of antagonism against parental domination of children otherwise submissive in their behavior. Both Hamill (14) and Beverly (4) state that it is a conduct disorder due to the child's lack of responsibility. In the psychoanalytic literature we find Freud's (12) early statement that nocturnal enuresis, when not an accompaniment of epilepsy, is a pollution. Levy (17) agrees with the above, offering as evidence the fact that an infant has an erection just before urination, and that enuresis stops at adolescence when urethral eroticism passes into genital eroticism. She also quotes Sadger as claiming an urethral character in enuretics. This is also maintained by Winnicott (25). Christoffel (8) likewise believes in the erotic significance of the act, stating that a beginning orgasm can be lost by a sudden urinary need. Enuresis, as a consequence of conflict between active and passive wishes, occurred in a case described by Bornstein (6), represented an identification of the male with the female in a case of Deutsch (9), and developed as a result of a sexual trauma in Angel's (1) case, while Baudomin (3) found it as a regressive phenomenon, a desire to return to the suckling stage in which wetting is uncontrolled.

It seems obvious from this review of the literature that enuresis is not a clinical entity to which one can ascribe a single cause, and also that there is no consensus as to what can be considered as enuresis. The word is used in many instances to apply to any urination which occurs in places other than designated for it, that is, the toilet, thus discarding the dictionary definition of "involuntary urination." For clarity in this study I shall differentiate between incontinence as a result of physical disease—deliberate wetting—and enuresis or involuntary wetting of psychic origin. The data which I shall discuss in this paper consist of the histories and treatment records of the cases referred to the psychiatric service for wetting over a period of seven years, a total of 72 cases.

In this group are included seven children in whom the wetting was definitely found to be due to physical causes. In one case there were grand mal epileptic attacks and the wetting started two years previously, at the time of onset of the epilepsy. In this case it was found that nocturnal wetting coincided with a convulsion; that day wetting occurred during the attacks, as would be expected, but also in intervals between attacks. Careful observation during the day, however, disclosed that this interval wetting was accompanied by momentary loss of consciousness without convulsions; evidence of the epileptic causation of all the instances of wetting in this case, and also disclosure of the presence of petit mal attacks as part of the total picture, which had not previously been described. In two other cases of petit mal it was found that the wetting was associated with the attacks, and in all three cases control of the epilepsy by luminal also eliminated wetting. Return of the attacks brought a return of involuntary wetting. I classify these epileptic cases in the group of physical etiology, because, even by those who consider the convulsion as possibly psychic in origin, the involuntary soiling is conceded to be a reflex phenomenon. Bladder infections were found to be present in three cases. Two patients started wetting after their return home following a period of hospitalization for acute pyelocystitis. Frequency, urgency, and pain upon urination were associated symptoms, and in each case the patient started for the toilet but wet before arrival. In the one case which was followed in the clinic, wetting ceased when the cystitis was cured. A third case of infective etiology was found to be due to tuberculosis of the bladder. The wetting of this child was in the form of dribbling which occurred night and day. He was aware of the flow but unable to control it, a rather typical finding in tuberculous bladder infections. There was only one case in which spina bifida occulta, with its accompanying nerve agenesis, could be considered as the cause of the wetting. In this case there was diurnal and nocturnal wetting of which the child insisted he was unaware until he found himself wet. He had also occasional incontinence of feces. Physical examination revealed spina bifida occulta as well as a dilated bladder and rectum, suggesting probable imperfect development of the nerves. In none of our cases was there any evidence of a thickened bladder musculature, noninfective bladder irritability, occlusion of the urethra, hypervagatonia, spasmophilia or fatigue.

Of the remaining 65 cases, only four could be ascribed to faulty training; the other 61 showed definite diagnosable psychogenic causation. Of the four untrained cases, two were under 4 years of age. In both, wetting occurred only once during the night in the second or third hours of sleep. Training in the two instances had been started before one year of age by picking the child up at intervals during the night. The time of arousal had never been consistent, and dry nights had only occasionally occurred. In both cases, as in all four, large quantities of fluids were taken at the night meal and the children were put to bed immediately afterwards. The two older cases, brothers, 7 and 9 years old, had been previously trained, but started wetting after a period of hospitalization for scarlet fever. Wetting occurred at about 10 P.M., two hours after retiring. Treatment had consisted of picking up the children a little before 10, which usually resulted in dry beds, but if left until later they were found to be wet. In these cases it was disclosed that, in the hospital, they had been wakened at 10 for temperature recording and for urination. None of these four children evidenced any neurotic or behavior problems, and treatment by reduction of fluids at the evening meal cleared the symptom within a week for the older children and within two weeks for the younger ones. The faulty training in these instances might be ascribed to poorly conditioned reflex development if one wished to so designate it. Wetting occurred at a time when the children had been accustomed to urinate, also, when the bladder was full because of the high fluid intake at the evening meal and during the period of deepest sleep. In deep sleep the cortex is depressed relative to the lower parts of the nervous system. Therefore the increasing stimuli from the filling bladder, which would ordinarily awake the patient before producing reflex evacuation, may then cause reflex emptying before producing wakefulness.

All the remaining cases, 61 in number, presented definite neurotic patterns of which wetting represented one symptom in the syndrome. For five of these, the onset of wetting, both day and night, coincided with the arrival of a sibling in the home. One started wetting five months before the birth of the sibling at a time when the mother was ill, admitted she had been irritable, and had left the patient to the care of a 10-year-old sister. Three others started wetting within the first month after the birth of the sibling, and the last, a 4-year-old adopted child, began to wet after a 2-year-old boy was taken into the home.

All children developed at the same time other regressive symptoms, such as food refusal if not fed by the mother, whining, clinging to the mother and following her around, and in three cases, hostile attacks upon the sibling. Treatment consisted in simple advice to the mother, aiding her to plan her day in such a way as to give more time and attention to the patient and less care to the sibling in the presence of the patient. Two cases did not return to the clinic. The mother of the other three reported cessation of wetting and feeding problems, as well as a redevelopment of the previous more mature attitudes. Eight other cases, all over 5 years of age, were children who had never responded to training, wet nightly, occasionally in the day, and in a few instances also defecated in their clothes or bed. One boy of 7 defecated in a paper and put it into his mother's soiled clothes bag. All of these children evidenced various degrees of stubborn and aggressive behavior. They refused to obey, were critical of, and negativistic toward food, were antagonistic to their siblings, although four of them got on well in school and were devoted and obedient to their teachers. All, during interviews, were verbally antagonistic toward one or both of their parents, and four admitted deliberate soiling, two stating that they did it to make the parent angry, admitting also that they wakened at night but urinated in their beds instead of going to the toilet. Of interest in the determination of factors responsible for the development of this stubborn form of wetting are the frankly admitted attitudes of the parents toward the children. Five mothers openly rejected the children. Three stated that the children had been unwanted in the first place, and the others, that caring for them had been an irritation and a nuisance. These mothers were all dominating characters, nagging, perfectionistic, and unusually punitive and hostile in their disciplinary measures.

In the three other cases of this category, the mothers' attitudes were moderately good, but the fathers were cruelly punitive and undertook the major part of the discipline, occasionally with the mothers' interference but usually with her acquiescence. In all of the cases the children had been restless and irritable from infancy, indicating tension developing early as a response to the rejecting attitude of the parents. Treatment in such instances, as one may easily understand, is difficult, since the symptoms are obviously conscious defense mechanism of the child against the ever-present painful experiences. As long as the experiences continue, the child's immature ego finds no other solution to the problem. Such parents are deeply neurotic, and recognition of the cause of the children's behavior has little effect in changing their real attitude toward them. In only one case was a change of attitude on the part of the parent accomplished, but in this case the gradual cessation of symptoms and the development of a more adequate personality of the child corroborated our etiological diagnosis. Foster home placement of two of the children with tolerant, easy-going, affectionate foster parents effected a salutary change in behavior and a cessation of wetting. These results confirm the statement already made that the conflict in this type of wetting is not deep, and the problems are the result of a conscious reaction to the traumatic environmental situation.

One case is of interest because of the unusual precipitating event, and because of the obvious hysterical nature of the symptom. An 8-year-old boy developed occasional nocturnal wetting, diurnal wetting with urgency and frequency, as well as abdominal pains and generalized anxiety, following the death of his father from carcinoma of the bladder. The symptoms of the father during his illness were similar to those developed by the patient. Upon physical examination the boy evidenced no physical disease. He had been devoted to his father, had been with him much during the latter part of his illness, had witnessed his death, and had reacted with tremendous distress. After the father's death the mother kept her son constantly with her, slept with him, confided her grief to him, and placed much responsibility upon him. During treatment interviews the patient disclosed his close identification with the father and an ensuing anxiety about himself. Following a two-month stay in a good summer camp, where he was able to identify himself with a male counselor as a father substitute, his symptoms disappeared, but unfortunately reappeared after his return to his mother, whose attitude had remained unchanged.

The last group of 46, which makes up by far the largest per cent of our nocturnal enuretic cases, and if one can generalize from our experience, probably represents the most common form of enuresis, presented neuroses, in each of which was found a distinct and similar clinical syndrome and in which the enuresis was only one of the symptoms. Wetting, in these cases, occurred during sleep or unconsciousness, and therefore, according to definition, was true enuresis. In a previous paper (13) I have presented in more detail than I shall here the findings in such cases obtained by psychoanalysis. In this study the six analyzed cases are included, as well as 40 more cases studied less intensively but sufficiently long to discern the neurotic pattern. Of interest is the fact that the manifest attitudes of these children were consistent for the boys and for the girls. But of significance is the finding that these attitudes differed strikingly in the two sexes. The boys' attitudes were passive, retiring, and self-depreciatory. Physical activity, such as rough play or gymnastics, was avoided from fear of physical injury. They were slow and dawdling in their daily activities, as dressing, eating, working in school, and so forth. They demanded more than the normal amount of help and assurance in performing tasks, and indulged in evasive petty lying. In school their achievement was below that expected from their intelligence quotient rating, and their behavior indicated inattentiveness and easy distractibility. In many of the cases teachers reported exhibitionistic activities of a nonaggressive type, such as giggling, grimacing, and so forth.

The girls, on the contrary, appeared much more normal in their manifest behavior. All were active children, the majority leaders among other girls, and they were independent and proficient in performing tasks. In school their achievement correlated with their intelligence quotient rating, and they were attentive, ambitious, and well-behaved. In play they evidenced a strongly competitive attitude toward boys, associated with a verbal depreciation of males in general. And finally they were honest and frank in their relations with other individuals. Although the girls, in contrast to the boys, were fearless in daytime activities, both sexes shared a common anxiety, that of nocturnal fears. In some cases this was evidenced by an undifferentiated fear of the dark without fantasy association. In others, the fear was of attack from some fantasied person, either living or ghostly. Twenty-two of the children had definite nightmares which awakened them and led them to seek solace from one or both parents. In eleven of the cases the dream was recurrent and remembered. The others were aware of having dreamt, but had no memory of the dream content.

In summary the boys behaved as if they were inferior to their fellows, whereas the girls behaved as if they were equal or superior to theirs, but in both sexes a real anxiety expressed itself in nocturnal fear. Besides these manifest attitudes revealed in the case histories of these children the investigation of the individual cases, both of those completely analyzed and of those studied less completely, disclosed neurotic personality patterns which were similar for the boys and for the girls but differed in the two sexes. In the analyzed cases, as one might suspect, the material was more detailed and more obvious than in the cases less completely studied, but in all of them the patterns were evident. The boys disclosed a preponderance of material indicating a fear of women as dangerous persons who could injure or destroy them if they themselves were active. The mechanism for overcoming this fear was an identification with the woman in the form of a passive attitude and an avoidance of the active role of the male.

In the analyzed cases it was found that urination was conceived by them as a passive act. One boy described it as a feeling similar to drifting lazily down a stream in a boat without paddling. Enuresis thus became part of a passive pattern, urine being allowed to flow uncontrolled and without responsibility for the act. Each girl, on the other hand, presented an excessive amount of material which expressed clearly a fear of man as a destructive aggressor who could injure her in his activities. She, in turn, avoided the difficulty by denying men their abilities, eliminating them from her existence in fantasy, and yet identifying with the active male rather than in the passive female. Enuresis in the girl represented an active destructive process rather than a passive flow. As one girl expressed it, "Urine can burn and hurt people. I could use it in a war by flying in a plane and killing the enemy by urinating on them." Of significance, also, was the fact that the majority of both girls and boys admitted pleasant bodily sensations during the act of urination, and also the fact that in none of the cases was masturbation indulged in, nor did they or their parents remember the occurrence of actual masturbation after infancy. This leads me to hypothecate that enuresis in this neurotic type acts as a substitute for masturbation, associated in the male with fantasies of passivity and in the girl with fantasies of activity. This agrees with Freud's original postulate that nocturnal enuresis, when not occurring during an epileptic attack, represents a pollution. It may also explain the reason for the frequent cessation of enuresis during puberty, since, due to the increased sexual development and its resultant stimulation at this time, actual masturbation is usually indulged in in spite of anxiety or guilt associated with the act, and a symptom substitute is no longer necessary. The material presented by these children disclosed the reason for the substitution of actual masturbation by another act. The fantasies which they associated with sexual stimulation were so destructive that masturbation was too dangerous an indulgence. The choice of the substitute act of urination by the girls can be explained by their identification with men, and their concept of the male sexual act as urination. In the boys it is less easily explained, but a hint is given to us by three boys who had witnessed menstruation and conceived of it as an involuntary bloody urination. Thus, involuntary urination became a part of the expression of their feminine identification.

In all of these cases treatment by the usual superficial methods resulted in failure, except for temporary remission of enuresis in some cases and reduction in its frequency in others. The various common methods used were restriction of fluids, awakening the child during the night for urination, star charts, urging responsibility, environmental changes, atropine, salty diet, and so forth. However, of significance is the fact that those cases treated by psychoanalysis were cured of enuresis, but also, and of greater significance, is the fact that they developed character changes which were exhibited in more normal behavior and normal manifest attitudes.

Finding these consistent neurotic patterns in such a large number of our group of cases studied, the question naturally presented itself as to what were experiences of the children which developed these anxieties and which led to such deep emotional conflicts with the attendant pathological solution of the disturbing emotion. With this question in mind I undertook a detailed study of the development experiences of the children and of the attitudes of the persons in the home environment toward the children themselves. Several important factors were disclosed which should aid in explaining the development of the neurosis. For the sake of simplicity in the following discussion of attitudes, I use the word *mother* for the woman caring for the child. In most instances she was the real mother, in other instances she was a grandmother, in some a stepmother, a foster mother, or a housekeeper. Similarly I use *father* for the real father or paternal figure in the home. In the cases of the girls no consistent maternal attitude was disclosed. In some cases the mothers were affectionate, kindly persons, fond of their daughter and tolerant toward her. In other cases they were irritable, semirejecting mothers, but none were as excessively rejecting and punitive as were those found in the cases of the stubborn negativistic type of wetting. A few of the mothers disclosed jealousy toward their daughters because of the obvious affection of the father for the girl. The fathers in these cases, however, presented an exceptionally similar picture. They were fond of their daughters, affectionate toward them, and, in most cases, obviously favored them above the siblings. In eleven of the cases they were punitive as well, alternating between affectionate advances and criticism with occasional whippings during temper explosions. Four of the fathers had been physically seductive, handling the child's genitals in play, while two of this group also exhibited themselves to the patients.

In the cases of the boys the attitudes of the fathers varied as that of the mothers varied toward the girls. Some were easygoing, kindly men, some strict disciplinarians, but the majority were ambitious for their sons, constantly set standards of masculine achievement for them, and were irritated and critical of the boys' passive behavior. The majority of the mothers of these boys, on the other hand, were rejecting persons. However, except for a few who openly rejected their sons, the rejection was less blatant than that exhibited by the parents of those cases described early in this paper in which wetting was a conscious attack upon the rejecting parent. The largest number of mothers of the neurotic enuretic boys were on the whole unconscious of their rejection, but the attitudes were disclosed by their mechanism of overcompensation evidenced in their behavior toward their sons. These women were excessively oversolicitous and fearful of injury of the patient, as well as constantly supervising and directing him in all his activities. In several instances the boy was identified with a consciously rejected husband, and these mothers admitted that they could not love the particular child as much as the others because of the resemblance to the unloved husbands. In two cases no actual rejection was evidenced by the mothers, who seemed devoted to their children. These children, however, during interview expressed the feeling that they were unloved. One gave as a reason for his belief the fact that the mother did not protect him from the father who was rough and often cruel, but usually watched as if she enjoyed the painful play or punishment.

Besides the findings of the seductive attitudes of the fathers in the cases of the girls, and the rejecting attitudes of the mothers in the boys' cases, one other experience of traumatic import appeared with regularity in the case histories, that of a sexual trauma. In the histories of these children, information disclosed the incidence of early actual sexual experiences of a frightening nature in a surprisingly larger percentage of cases than was found in the total number of histories in the clinic. In the majority of instances it had occurred during sex play with other children. Two girls had, at the ages of 2 and 3, been seduced by men to masturbate them, and in four cases already mentioned, the children had been frightened by actual seduction from their fathers. Besides traumatic sexual experiences, a large number of the cases, 28, had slept in their parents' bedroom and were exposed to marital relations, while eleven slept in an adjoining room or an alcove. In such situations it is common knowledge that children see and hear more than their parents suspect, and, as a result, very frequently develop sadistic fantasies and nocturnal fears.

No other experiences could be found in the histories of these cases, or from information from the children during interviews which occurred with any regularity. However, if one correlates the above data and our knowledge of psychic development with the form of the fantasied fear exhibited in the interviews with the children, it is possible to theorize as to the causative factors which could be responsible for the development of the specific anxiety and its resultant symptoms. Psychoanalytic studies of adults and children have given us often repeated proof that in the early years, the child develops a close attachment to the parent of the opposite sex, and a resultant wish to possess the exclusive love of that parent. This wish for exclusiveness creates hostile attitudes toward the rival parent which are expressed in destructive fantasies of injury or death of the rival; the well-known Oedipus complex. In our neurotic enuretic cases we find the concept that sexual intercourse is injurious to the parent of the same sex as the patient. Thus, by a mechanism of projection, the rival is injured or destroyed, not by himself but by his loved parent. In our case histories we find justifiable reasons for the choice of this particular projection, since these children have been exposed, in most instances, to traumatic sexual experiences and have witnessed coitus between the parents. Such a projection, however, leads to a conflict concerning his own relation to this parent. If such a parent is destructive in love expression, the patient may also be destroyed if his wish for exclusive love is consummated. The affectionate attitudes of the fathers toward the girls, then, develop expectant fears of sadistic consequences of such affection, making them withdraw from men and attempt to acquire a semblance of safety by identification with men, as if, they argued, "If I am a man, then I can make the attacks and not be attacked." The boys, in turn, conceiving the female role as dangerous to the man, may accept the mother's rejecting attitudes as corroboration of evil intent, and they attempt to avoid the danger also by identification, but with the woman, not with the man, and by denying their masculinity. In this way they evade any behavior which might stimulate the woman's attacks. Also, because of the child's sadistic sexual concepts, masturbation fantasies become sadistic and the wish to avoid harm is probably responsible for the repression of genital masturbation and its substitution by a safer, unconscious act, i.e., urination.

In summarizing the results of the present study it seems clear that wetting is not a symptom with one etiology similar in all the cases, and which will respond to one form of treatment, but divides itself into several categories. Thus, wetting, both diurnal and nocturnal, occasionally occurred as a result of a physical disorder of the nervous system or of the bladder. Treatment of such cases naturally should be directed toward the disease itself, not toward the relief of the symptom. In only a small number of the cases were faulty training methods found to be responsible for wetting. Etiological factors of an emotional nature were present in the majority of cases. A small number of these could be classified as regressive cases, in which the wetting developed as part of an episode of total personality regression to a more infantile level of behavior. This regression, in turn, was precipitated by jealousy of a new sibling. A few other cases fell into a category which I may, perhaps, designate as revenge response cases. In these the child retaliated by wetting or soiling, as well as by general stubbornness, to a nagging punitive attitude of the mother or person training him. In both of these two types of cases treatment directed toward relieving or eliminating the traumatic daily occurrences was found to result in the cessation of the wetting symptom and in a favorable personality change, thus corroborating the finding that the symptom, here, was not the result of a deeply unconscious conflict, but of a conscious attitude. Its occurrence during consciousness also excludes it from the category of true enuresis if one adheres to the classical definition. Only one case in the series could be designated as an hysterical type of case in which the wetting was one expression of a symptom complex resulting from an hysterical form of identification with the father. Treatment of such a case, naturally, should be directed toward the resolution of the total pathological pattern. And, finally, in the present study, it was found that the largest number of cases of wetting fell into a group which should be classified as true enuresis because wetting occurred during unconsciousness, that is, during sleep. In these cases the enuresis was one symptom of a syndrome which presented a clear-cut neurotic pattern of behavior and neurotic mechanism development. These disclosed a common etiology, fear of harm from persons of the opposite sex. This fear, in turn, probably developed as a result of three factors working together: destructive wishes toward the rival parent, traumatic sexual experiences or information and experiences of parental seduction or rejection, depending upon the sex of the patient. Of importance in terms of treatment of the case, this latter group proved resistant to therapy of a superficial nature because the emotional conflict was deeply repressed and partially solved by unhealthy defense mechanisms.

This analysis of the types of wetting and the resulting classification, based upon etiology rather than upon symptom expression, should be of value in aiding one to determine the specific treatment necessary for an individual case. Thus it should be possible to make treatment causal and logical rather than empirical.

BIBLIOGRAPHY

1. ANGEL, A. Aus der Analyse einer Bettnässerin. *Z. f. psychoanal. Paed.,* 1934, 8, 216.
2. BAKWIN, HARRY. Enuresis in children. *Arch. Ped.,* 1928, 45, 664.
3. BAUDOUIN, C. Ein Fall von Bettnässen. *Z. f. psychoanal. Paed.,* 1928, 3, 29.
4. BEVERLY, B. I. Incontinence in children. *J. Pediatrics.,* 1933, 2, 218.
5. BLEYER, ADRIAN. A clinical study of enuresis. *Amer. J. Dis. Child.,* 1928, 36, 989.
6. BORNSTEIN, BERTA. Enuresis und Kleptomanie als Passageres Symptom. *Z. f. psychoanal. Paed.,* 1934, 8, 229.
7. CAMPBELL, MEREDITH F. A clinical study of persistent enuresis. *N. Y. J. Med.,* 1934, 34, 190.
8. CHRISTOFFEL, VON H. Zur Biologie der Enuresis. *Z. f. Kinderpsych.,* 1934, 1, 104.
9. DEUTSCH, HELENE. *Psychoanalysis of the neurosis.* London: Hogarth Press, 1932.
10. EDERER, S., AND LEDERER, VON E. Zur Pathogenesis der Enuresis. *Jahrb. f. Kinderhlk.,* 1933, 138, 21.
11. ESERSKY, J. M., PLOTITSCHER, A. I., AND FURMANOW, A. M. Probleme der Klinik und der Genese der Enuresis Nocturna beim Kinde. *Z. f. Kinderforsch.,* 1931, 38, 133.
12. FREUD, SIGMUND. *Three contributions to the theory of sex.* New York: Nervous & Mental Disease Publishing Co., 1930.
13. GERARD, M. W. Child analysis as a technique in the investigation of mental mechanisms. *Amer. J. Psychiat.,* 1937, 94, 653.
14. HAMILL, R. C. Enuresis. *J. Amer. med. Assn.,* 1929, 93, 254.
15. HOMBURGER, AUGUST. *Psychopathologie des Kindesalters.* Berlin: Julius Springer, 1926.
16. KARLIN, I. W. Incidence of spina bifida occulta in children with and without enuresis. *Amer. J. Dis. Child.,* 1935, 49, 19.
17. LEVY, KATA. Vom Bettnässen des Kindes. *Z. f. psychoanal. Paed.,* 1934, 8, 178.
18. LIPPMAN, HYMAN. The treatment of enuresis. Address delivered at the Minnesota State Conference of Social Work. September 24, 1932.
19. MACCIOTTA, G. Spasmophilic forms of enuresis in children. *Pediatria,* 38, 1145. (Quoted from *Child. Develpm. Abstr.,* 1931, 5, 46.)
20. MacGUINNESS, AIMS C. The treatment of enuresis in children. *Med. Clin. N. Amer.,* 1935, 19, 286.
21. MOHR, G. J., AND WATERHOUSE, E. H. Enuresis in children. *Amer. J. Dis. Child.,* 1929, 37, 1135.
22. SCHACHTER, M. Die Pathogenese der Enuresis. *Jahrb. f. Kinderhlk.,* 1933, 14, 234.
23. SICARD, J. A. Enuresis. *Annales de méd.,* 8.
24. STURNIMAN, A. *Das erste Erleben des Kindes.* Frauenfeld: Huber & Co., 1933.
25. WINNICOTT, D. W. Enuresis. *Proc. roy. Soc. Med.,* 1930, 23, 255.

AKINESIA AFTER VENTRICULOGRAPHY *

A CONTRIBUTION TO EGO PSYCHOLOGY
AND THE PROBLEM OF SLEEP

By Martin Grotjahn, M.D.,

AND

Thomas M. French, M.D.

In seven of 89 patients upon whom ventriculographies were performed, a state of peculiar and complete akinesia was observed. These observations were made at the Neurological and Psychiatric Clinic of the University of Berlin. The akinesia occurred in a direct causal and temporal relationship with the ventriculography, during which from 140 to 210 cc. of fluid were withdrawn and replaced by air. All seven patients suffered from brain tumors localized in the region around the third ventricle, near the Aqueduct of Sylvius, the splenium septi pellucidi, or in the corpora quadrigemina, and especially in the supra-sellar region.

The similarity of the patients in age, development, and psychological behavior before the onset of the illness, their hypothalmic adiposity, the neurological and X-ray findings, and the later progress of the illness corresponded with the similarity in the clinical reaction to the ventriculography. The patients lay in bed as though they were sleeping with open eyes. They did not move spontaneously, and in most cases there was atonia of high degree in all extremities. The patients stopped not only all voluntary movements but also automatic movements. They seldom moved their eyelids and sometimes they did not move at all for approximately a week. Reactive movements, especially the blinking reflexes, were not obtainable.

In one there was a temporary disappearance of athetoid movements. It was astonishing to observe a patient who for some days had been without any spontaneity of automatic or voluntary movements (described in the record as immobile, "like a corpse" or "a piece of wood") unexpectedly begin to brush flies from his face or pick his nose, only to resume his akinesia. In another patient the akinesia was interrupted by a surprising and short hyperkinesia mani-

* The Psychoanalytic Quarterly VII: 319-328, 1938.

fested by singing loudly without other movement. Every night (without any affect) he sang common children's songs very monotonously. Similar sudden interruptions were seen in patients who felt forced to motor activity without volition. One of the completely akinetic patients, for instance, answered the telephone with a short "hello" after the receiver was put to his ear, and then fell back into his akinesia. The complete discontinuation of movement lasted for weeks and months, and during this time the patients stared straight into space with only half-open eyes. The spontaneous movements of the eyes were the first to reappear. Then the patients began to follow actions in their surroundings with their eyes, but without expression of interest. They still had to be fed by the nurse, as they were unable to feed themselves. When bread or a glass was placed in their hands they would hold it, but they did nothing with it. After a long time they swallowed food placed in their mouths if they were asked to do so.

There was no loss of consciousness. There was no disorientation as to person, time, or place. Recent and remote memory were intact. The akinesia could be interrupted, and it is of great interest that it was possible to establish some contact with the patient. With persistence and patience the patient's lack of initiative could be overcome for a short time. They were usually able to answer commands very slowly, in apparently difficult and forced monosyllables. According to information given by one patient following recovery from akinesia, his conscious and perceptive faculties were not changed during the akinesia. Another patient could give information about the daily occurrences on the ward; she could describe examinations and conversations, report the doctors' questions and her own answers; all her statements confirmed the fact that she was well oriented. There was no insight into the changed motor behavior, and the patients had no feeling regarding their difficulties and their "slowing down." But behind this unawareness of their own akinesia, the knowledge of the nature of the underlying illness, namely the brain tumor or the brain disease, remained unchanged. One patient remarked, "A new head is what I need badly." The face was without expressive movements. There was not even a mask or rigid face, but more the expression of a person peacefully sleeping with open eyes. They appeared to be bored, but this impression was more the observer's reflection than the result of observation; the patients denied having such feeling. They did not cry or complain and they denied headaches and other pain. Subsequent to the akinesia they often stated that they were not depressed, but on the contrary were rather happy, and their remarks during the akinesia permit the conclusion that they were in a somewhat happy, contented, emotional state, although they certainly did not like to be questioned or otherwise disturbed in their rest. They did not object if something happened or if somebody read a book or newspaper aloud before them, but they did not show any interest even though later they could relate the subject matter. It was apparently easier and more convenient for them to follow the reader than to divert their attention. The akinetic behavior of these patients remained unchanged during visits from parents and friends, and even expensive and carefully selected presents did not move them. They remained without motion and emotion.

They usually slept well during the night; some patients rested part of the night with open eyes, apparently not sleeping. They did not feel tired, but slept often because the psychological field did not offer any stimuli. They went to sleep easily and frequently during the day, but they awoke spontaneously. The phenomenological difference between being asleep and being awake was only the difference in the position of the eyes. The vegetative functions continued without change. Temperature and pulse were within normal limits. The blood pressure was in the lower normal range. There was no constipation. Defecation and urination occurred spontaneously, but it was not known whether or not they occurred voluntarily. The patients did not inhibit this automatic process. It was one of the most astonishing observations that all akinetic patients (well-trained children as well as adults) became incontinent during akinesia. They urinated and defecated in bed without notifying the nurse and without apparent embarrassment. Some patients admitted that they had a sensation of wanting to defecate, and yet they were surprised when the bowel movement occurred. In their lack of initiative and their listless attitude they were concerned only with the present and had no expectations, no interest in the future, and could not anticipate coming events.

In the further course of the akinesia the patients regained initiative and tried to clean themselves, but they always acted after it was too late. Only at the end of the akinesia did the patients gradually become able to prepare themselves for the future. From the akinetic life, which was entirely devoted to a motionless rest in the present moment without past or future, they changed to a higher level in which the present moment, as with normal persons, is a connection between the past and the future.

The neurological and the X-ray findings after the ventriculography and one autopsy supported the opinion that the underlying pathological lesion producing the akinesia may be localized in the floor of the third ventricle. Very similar stages of akinesia are observed in encephalitic cases, and the autopsies of these cases gave further proof of the localization of the underlying lesion in the anterior part of the floor of the third ventricle.

The akinesia of these seven patients showed more than a superficial similarity to sleep, and justified speculation about the difference between mental sleep and physical or bodily sleep. There is, of course, only one sleep; namely, the sleep of the person, and to see the sleep from two different points of view does not necessarily mean to see the object double but to see it more clearly.

Akinetic patients do not sleep mentally; that is, they do not have a dreamlike mental state as does a normal sleeping person. On the contrary they are easily differentiated from a sleeping or dreaming person since they have an intact ego with intact perception and reality-testing ability, and the level of consciousness is not lowered. They are in a somewhat euphoric mood, but their intellectual potentialities are not diminished. Their orientation is intact.

The main feature common to both the akinesia and sleep is the complete lack of initiative or will power. These patients showed the same passivity, the same indifference and similar lack of response to stimuli from the outer world, the same expressionless face, the quiet, motionless rest, and the withdrawal of libidinal interest from reality, as does a person in sleep. The complete ignoring of the body by the akinetic person is also very significant and shows how little the bodily ego is cathected with libido.

In strict contrast to the awakening of the normal person, the akinetic person awakes only partially; that is, in the akinetic person the bodily ego feeling, not cathected during sleep, remains without cathexis, the person remaining without bodily ego feeling and without the ability to act.

Akinesia is seldom observed, but if there be such a thing as a difference between a total deep mental sleep and bodily sleep, then some experiences of a similar kind should be expected in the normal person also. The behavior of these seven patients reminds one, for instance, of the behavior of a person who takes a prolonged bath in the morning after a very good, quiet, long, and deep sleep. Persons who have such a habit enjoy this rest with much pleasure and prolong the bath as long as possible. Their behavior is very much like that of the akinetic patient, for they are quiet, hypnotic, and oblivious to time. They seem to think of nothing in particular, but they do not dream and are well oriented. If the telephone rings or something similar occurs and requires their response, they require a great deal of energy to change the original situation and to overcome their lack of initiative.

However, these observations and similar experiences with morphinated patients in the prolonged bath are not the only illustrations which show states between a total deep mental sleep and a partial motor bodily sleep. Neurotics with increased self-observation, or people who are interested in the study of the phenomena of falling asleep, also occasionally observe that the body seems to sleep and cannot be moved but that the mind is still more or less awake. Sometimes awakening offers similar subjective experiences. The cathexis of mental and bodily ego feeling is a combination of psychic and motor processes, and under normal conditions the one process is accompanied by the other. When awakening, the eyes are opened, then the eyeballs move downward and become converged. Sometimes the process of the motor awakening may be experienced in a symbolic expression at the end of a dream. Such observations show the most important influence of the will in the stage between sleeping and being awake. The will appears in the dream as the connection between mental ego feeling and the beginning of physical bodily feeling.

The following dreams, illustrative of this point, were related during an analysis by a man 27 years of age.

> *Dream:* There seems to be a session of the legislature. The meeting is just coming to an end and the members of parliament begin to leave the conference room. One member suddenly has an acute state of delirium. At first the dreamer's interest is "awakened." He tries to look into the man's pupils, and with the convergence and fixation of his eyes in the dream, he then awakes completely.

> *Dream:* Many flowers pass away before the dreamer's eyes. He tries to see the flowers more closely, tries to fixate them, and awakens at the movement of convergence and fixation.

These observations show clearly the psychic and symbolic appearance of the motor phase in the process of awakening. The ego had gained its full cathexis when the dreamer's interest was aroused and had cathected the bodily ego feeling by awakening entirely.

The observations described above offer opportunity for some reflections on the functions and structure of the ego. The most clearly defined function of the ego is the dynamic function of integration and synthesis of conflicting psychological tendencies. This integrating function has two aspects: first, a cognitive one, to understand external and internal reality in order to find satisfactory compromises which will satisfy as many of the conflicting urges as possible; and second, a motor or volitional function to accept and act upon such satisfactory compromises when they are found. Indeed it would probably be more accurate to say that the integrating function of the ego starts with cognition and proceeds by various intermediate stages to volition and voluntary activity.

The first of the two dreams just reported is of particular interest in this connection. Even without associations it is evident from the manifest content that this dream has to do with a conflict concerning the synthetic dynamic function that we ordinarily attribute to the ego. The function of a legislature is to deliberate and make decisions for the nation, much as the ego, in its intellectual capacity, deliberates and makes decisions for the individual. The legislature would seem, therefore, to be a symbol of this dynamic synthetic function of the ego. In confirmation of this suggestion is the fact that just as the meeting is finishing, one member has "an acute state of delirium," signifying that the attempt at a dynamic synthesis is failing. We next see that this threatened failure of synthesis stimulates the synthetic function to renewed activity, for the dreamer's interest is awakened and he looks into the man's eyes, and this time the synthetic effort coincides with his awakening from sleep.

The particular interest of this dream, however, lies in the fact that although the dream is obviously concerned with the synthetic dynamic function that we ordinarily attribute to the ego, nevertheless the dream ego does not acknowledge this effort at synthesis as its own activity. The dream ego recognizes this effort at synthesis only in a projected form. The dreamer projects outside of himself his intrapsychic perception of the attempt at synthesis, and portrays it in the dream as a session of a legislature. The motive for such a rejection of its own synthetic function must be that the dream ego does not wish to be driven, as a result of its "deliberations," to a volitional act. The dreamer prefers to continue sleeping. It is only when the attempt at deliberation threatens to end in "an acute state of delirium" that the dreamer is stimulated to a new effort at synthesis, which this time the patient's ego is willing to recognize as its own; and this new synthetic effort coincides with the patient's awakening and is accompanied by an act of the will. The convergence and fixation of the eyes in the dream obviously corresponds to the active will of the patient to try to understand himself, to try to substitute clear insight for his "delirium."

Thus it would appear, upon the evidence of this dream, that the integrating function may be active without being recognized as an activity of the ego, and may indeed be rejected by the central kernel of the ego and perceived intrapsychically only in a projected form.

In the akinesias that have just been described we seem to see a slightly different sort of dissociation between the cognitive and volitional aspects of the ego's synthetic function. The cognitive function is performed apparently well, but only passively; without participation of the will. The patients grasp only what can be grasped without effort. They make no effort to understand. This corresponds with the fact that the volitional aspect of the synthetic function is for the most part entirely absent. If exercised at all, it apparently has a very high threshhold before it can be aroused to activity. This is illustrated by the fact that the patients' lack of initiative could be overcome for a short time, but only by virtue of persistence and patience upon the part of the physician.

Finally we may ask, what happens to the libido of the akinetic patient? Apparently it is for the most part withdrawn from the external world, as in sleep, and, as in sleep, concentrated perhaps upon the task of neutralizing the destructive processes associated with functional activity. In the akinetic patients it has of course also the additional task of combating the organic lesion.

Summary

Stages of peculiar and complete akinesia occurred in seven patients after the third ventricle had been filled with air. All seven patients had brain tumors localized around the third ventricle. The neurological findings were similar in all the cases and ventriculography revealed internal hydrocephalus of high degree in all of them. The third ventricle was always partially filled with air, the fourth ventricle was never filled. Immediately following the ventriculography, a manifest akinesia occurred. The akinetic patients did not move spontaneously; even the eyes were not moved and the winking reflexes were not obtainable. The patients could not eat unassisted and were incontinent of feces and urine. Yet their consciousness was undisturbed; they were able to answer questions and could give information about their feelings, experiences, and dreams.

Slight atrophy of the frontal lobes was present in all of the seven cases, but this damage alone was not responsible for the occurrence of the akinesia. The akinesia was different from the akinetic syndrome due to extrapyramidal processes. The X-ray findings, the neurological symptoms, other pathological symptoms, and the autopsy of one of the cases support the opinion that the underlying pathological process, which may be considered as being the cause of the akinesia, may be localized in the hypothalamic region. This localization is confirmed by neuropathological studies of encephalitic patients suffering from a similar kind of akinesia.

Akinetic patients have, in common with *waking* persons, clear consciousness and intact reality testing ability. Akinetic persons have, in common with *sleeping* persons, complete lack of initiative and will power, passive attitude and indifference, lack of response to stimuli from the outer world, withdrawal of libidinal interest from reality, and the external picture of quiet, emotionless, and happy rest. The bodily ego feeling is absent, and the akinetic person has no knowledge of the lack of bodily ego feeling. Therefore the akinesia is to be compared with a partial bodily sleep. The two different forms of awakening, mental and bodily, are sometimes observed separately under certain conditions, even in normal persons.

These observations make clear the possibility of dissociations between the cognitive and volitional aspects of the ego's synthetic activity, and should stimulate comparison with other forms of dissociation of the synthetic function of the ego as seen in dreams and in psychotic states. Of particular interest is the relation between such dissociations of the synthetic function and the processes of sleep and awakening.

BIBLIOGRAPHY

1. FEDERN, PAUL. The awakening of the ego in dreams. *Int. J. Psycho-Anal.,* 1934, **15**, 296-301.
2. FEDERN, PAUL. Some variations in ego-feeling. *Int. J. Psycho-Anal.,* 1926, **7**, 434-444.
3. FRENCH, T. M. Reality and the unconscious. *Psychoanal. Quart.,* 1937, **6**, 23-61.
4. FRENCH, T. M. Reality testing in dreams. *Psychoanal. Quart.,* 1937, **6**, 62-77.
5. GROTJAHN, MARTIN. Klinik und Bedeutung akinetischer Zustände nach Luftfüllung des dritten Ventrikels. *Mschr. f. Psych. u. Neur.,* 1936, **93**, 121-139.
6. SADGER, J. *Sleep walking and moon walking.* Washington, D.C.: Nervous & Mental Diseases Publishing Co., 1920.

A CASE OF MIGRAINE *

By ADELAIDE M. JOHNSON, M.D.

It is not the aim of this paper to go into an extensive discussion of migraine and its etiology. The emphasis is rather on the more effective use of the transference in a therapeutic challenge.

In the past ten years there have appeared a fairly large number of excellent papers demonstrating the psychogenic factors in migraine. Contributions from Gutheil, Fromm-Reichmann, Knopf, Selinsky, Touraine and Draper, Slight, Wolberg, and others give a great deal of evidence that conflict situations, such as hostile destructive aims toward a beloved person, set off the migrainous attack. Various concepts of the somatic component have been advanced, constitutional weakness or some physicochemical mechanism serving as the organic vehicle for the acting psychological factors. With some disagreements, clinicians generally describe the sufferers from migraine as frequently of the intellectual type, as conscientious to the point of an exaggerated sense of responsibility. They have a need to be independent; they are ambitious, highly sensitive to criticism, and show, among women especially, considerable sexual maladjustment and a definite trend toward conventionality. Excellent therapeutic results are reported in many cases treated psychologically.

The patient under discussion is a 29-year-old, married, female physician who has suffered from frequent and severe typical migrainous attacks since the age of 15. There was no other presenting complaint. She has been seen about 75 times over a period of 19 months. The treatment is not yet completed, but for the purposes of the paper this is not pertinent.

The migrainous attacks (blurring vision, right hemicrania, nausea and vomiting, with occasional diarrhea) seemed to be related to various emotional stresses. They began at 15 when the patient was expected to take care of her three young stepsisters during the summer vacation, at a time when, because of economic stress, the stepmother had to go to work. The patient had insisted instead on having a vacation with her girl friend, and while on this vacation the

* From *The Proceedings of the Third Psychotherapy Council,* 1946. Chicago, Institute for Psychoanalysis, pp. 69-93.

headache began. At 9 years the patient had had a fall, when she saw stars, and was in bed for two days with vomiting. The findings at that time were negative. Her stepmother had had migraine for years, and during these attacks would have to withdraw to her bedroom for a day or two.

The patient impressed the admission interviewer immediately as being an attractive, flexible, mature woman of considerable brilliance and charm. Her parents were ambitious, professional people who had come to New Hampshire from Austria just before they met and married in this country. When the patient was two, her mother became ill, and after several months' illness died of endocarditis. As she spoke of this the patient felt vaguely that she recalled her mother's illness, but could not be sure. She was confused as to where she lived for a year in New England before she came with her father to a town near Chicago where she lived with a maternal uncle and aunt until her father remarried. The patient was then four. She had been told that she was a feeding problem for a short time after she went to live with her father and stepmother. The patient spoke of her stepmother as "mother," and did so throughout the treatment. She maintained that this kind, warm-hearted, sensitive woman was like one's own mother, and stated that she had always felt that her three stepsisters were like real sisters.

Her fifth birthday was one of her earliest and most delightful memories. The patient recalled no feelings about the first stepsister, who was born when she was six and a half years old. She thought that she took pleasure in the coming of the other two siblings in the next four years. She felt that her stepmother had always been very warm and supportive, and thought of her father as quiet, intelligent, cheerful, and kindly. She recalled crying when she was 12 years old when her father told her that her own mother had died. At the time the patient had cut him short, saying she knew this.

The patient had had excellent group relationships and good intellectual adjustment through her high-school and college years. Although hard-pressed financially, the family had made it possible for her to have an extensive education and had taken pleasure in this, never begrudging it. At the time the patient came to treatment she had many friends of both sexes.

She met her husband in college when she was 18; she married him, a professional man, seven years later. He was said to be brilliant and attractive, but inclined to be a little pessimistic. The couple had many engrossing mutual interests. Their sexual adjustment had been excellent; they were "about to decide to have a child" when her husband had to enter the service and go overseas. He was away when the patient came for treatment. It was decided that for a few exploratory interviews with the psychiatrist the patient was to be seen only once a week, after which a plan of treatment could be made.

In the first hour with the therapist the patient gave much of the above material. She was quietly friendly and talked easily. She stated she had had her worst migraine attack just before coming to the office. After much questioning she recalled she had just spent two days with a woman who acted quite friendly, but whom she suspected of harboring much unconscious hostility toward everyone. She had never thought of resenting this woman until the therapist raised the question. Although the patient had dreamed little of her husband since he went into service, just before she came for treatment she had had two dreams in which she was meeting him as a civilian; details were lost. She had been conscious, too, of wanting him to be home lately. The therapist commented that possibly it was more comfortable to turn to him than to an unknown woman therapist. The patient laughed and went on to say, however, that she had mixed feelings about his return, for she was uneasy that he would ask her to cut down on her work and have babies. She also recognized that this feeling was due to some problem in her, for she was by no means ready to have children.

In the second hour she brought a dream in which her husband was stationed at an airfield near her, but he appeared in a dilapidated old Air Force outfit. The elements in this simple dream give the crux of much of the structure of this case. She associated with this her need for him rather than for women, but she recognized how annoyed she was with him that he had to do menial tasks in the Air Force. She discussed her fears for his emotional and work inadequacies. The therapist asked why she made matters worse for him in the dream by giving him a wretched uniform. She was not clear as to her motives. When it was suggested that possibly a fear of her identification with him in some emotional inadequacy led her to withdraw and depreciate him, the patient realized for the first time how she *had* avoided going to visit him in training camps in this country. Now she began to feel guilty toward him. It was pointed out that although she needed him, she immediately tried in the dream to deny that his strength was important to her.

Thus there appear three fairly definite elements in this patient's character structure: some serious anxiety about turning to women, greater ease in leaning on her husband, but a need to depreciate him. In spite of this, with the therapist the patient showed a real warmth. Since it was felt that too frequent hours would probably have threatened her need for independence in relationship to the therapist, she was given an appointment for one week later.

In the third hour the patient brought a dream in which she was competitive with a woman for an Air Force major; she depreciated the woman. The major was much older than her husband and by far his superior in rank. Associations led to the realization that in the last interview the patient had at first been a little annoyed that the therapist had not let the dream go by as a depreciation of the husband, but later the patient felt she had a wonderful husband after all and she would not give him up to anyone. The therapist replied, "As soon as I question your depreciating him, you feel I may compete with you?" The patient laughed and said, "I hope it's just your theory." The therapist went on to say that since the major was an older man, could there be some deeper significance to the dream? Possibly as a child the patient may have been quite fond of her father and jealous for all his attention. The patient was definite in her denial of this, and added that such theorizing was a little surprising. In the next hour she stated that immediately on leaving the office the week before she had recognized her anger at being asked about jealousy of her father and had realized emotionally that the major in the dream had many likenesses to her father. Upon inquiry with regard to early feelings she recalled that once, at 11, while her stepmother was away, she tried to crawl into her father's bed, but he firmly said she should sleep in her own room. She recalled quite consciously she had felt "snuggly" on this occasion, and had had actual sexual thoughts in her mind that night at the age of 11. She was piqued and angry with him.

The patient then recalled that since the last hour she had had several dreams. These proved to be disguised dreams which, on association, led quickly to sexual fears of very young boys. She went on to say that she had thought for a long time that she would be very uneasy with a young son and had only thought in terms of a daughter. One saw in her fantasies also the same hostility to a son which she may have felt toward her rejecting father. Soon thereafter, in the same hour, the patient expressed fears of a competing daughter also, for if the father had not been firm there would have been trouble. Now the patient voiced the fear that her husband might not be equally firm with a daughter.

Then the patient had her first severe headache in four weeks of treatment. At first she gave superficial explanations, such as just having seen her sister with her fiancé. Associations led to the realization of intense resentment in a competitive situation with a colleague. Now she began to think maybe there *was* some connection between headache and such competition.

The therapist's accumulated impression of the patient, after five interviews, corroborated the original impression: she was an attractive and brilliant young woman, reared in a home of good conventional standards. Discussion of her work and friends made it appear that she had a very good ego. She was not only intellectual, but highly intuitive as well. That she had read widely, and was acquainted intellectually with psychoanalytic theory, was to the therapist an immediate warning that this patient might understand interpretations too readily and seem to accept dynamic explanations without emotional assimilation. All psychoanalysts are aware of the pitfalls in therapy with such patients. To use this patient's understanding, to capitalize on the flexible quality of her ego, and yet to strike at the depths of her feeling, was recognized by the therapist as the challenge in this case. Fortunately the patient was endowed with keen psychological insight and with the capacity to use this insight not only in the presence of the therapist but also during the intervals between interviews. Unconsciously she "worked through" the revelations and interpretations of each hour, producing in the next session deeper and always relevant material with appropriate feelings. Though she showed immediately a defensive attitude toward women, she had sufficient basic warmth to enter a rapport with the therapist, with whom it was easy for her to identify herself. This constituted the beginnings of a workable transference which had to be kept strong enough to bear her defensiveness against women, and yet not so intensive that it would interfere with the analysis of this defense. (The importance of maintaining this equilibrium will be obvious as the therapeutic process unfolds.)

Since the treatment seemed to be moving satisfactorily during these first five sessions, it was decided to continue with weekly interviews for the time being. There was no indication that the treatment should not be conducted with the patient sitting up; indeed, this procedure was found to be highly important as the treatment progressed.

The therapist found it striking in the early material that this young woman, who had never had sexual relations with anyone but her husband, was, as an 11-year-old girl, quite aggressive with her father and actually conscious of sexual feelings at that time. Her father had been firm, but where was the girl's guilt? This was the therapist's first hint of what later turned out to be the traumatic nucleus of her neurosis, namely, some interference with a wholly normal oedipal period through loss of her mother at 2. Yet it was noteworthy that the patient had always had orgasm in her marriage and enjoyed sexual relations. It should be emphasized that these are indications of a much better emotional adjustment than one usually sees in migraine cases.

Following this material, for three sessions the patient produced dreams and associations having to do with jealousy over her siblings. She produced first an actual memory of jealousy of her beautiful stepmother who was able to have and nurse the babies, and later envy of the babies themselves. She recalled noticing especially the beauty of her stepmother's breasts, as well as the feeling of envy for the baby, and she remembered feeling strange and far away from her stepmother at such times. The question was raised, what prompted this strange and distant feeling? During these three weeks the patient was quite depressed but without headache.

At this point, dreams of competing with women on a professional basis (friends and therapist) were common, but when little twists in the dreams were pointed out the patient realized that work competition and masculine identification were pure masks for her jealousy and competition with women. Dreams, as well as expressed resentments in dealing with her female patients, brought to light the patient's homosexual fears in relation to them and to the therapist.

At this time a patient of our patient, a young girl, developed a crush on her. Our patient dreamed that she avoided making a medical examination of her young patient and instead took her to a prayer meeting. As our patient began, in the hour, to realize how cold and abrupt she had been recently with the 15-year-old child, she began to weep and grieve that her problems should hurt her patients. When the therapist suggested the recent anxiety with the girl might be related possibly to some uneasy feelings toward the analyst, the patient became uneasy and said, trying to be flippant, "Let us take it to prayer meeting." Later she said she felt anxious and afraid. When the therapist wondered if her fear did not indicate some guilt or anger, the patient burst out weeping, saying her stepmother was so kind that she could never be angry with her, and then she wished the therapist would be "more mean" to her. The analyst commented, "You wish, possibly, I'd be cold and abrupt, as you were with your young patient—then you would feel less guilty." The patient added quickly, with just a shade of annoyance, "I think, in the end, I make her less depressed," and the therapist replied, "I think you do." Here her competition with the analyst came out on a professional level. Furthermore the patient was feeling she would like to be with the analyst, but not in the position of suffering through an uncovering therapy.

The next defense that appeared was a shifting of her conflict with women in the direction of hostility toward men. First there were dreams of men fighting men. From material that had come into the interviews unwittingly, the therapist felt quite sure the patient's husband and father were kind and considerate men. With this in mind, she raised the question as to whether the patient might be projecting her hostility toward men onto men. This soon was proved by multiple associations and further dreams. The patient realized now that when preconscious hostility to men was interpreted, she would become angry at once, whereas when an interpretation about similar hostility to women was raised, she usually felt depressed.

For the first time the patient realized that, unconsciously, she had frequently been hostile with men in a subtle way. She spoke of competing with them intellectually, and she knew she had unwittingly hurt her husband through frequently telling him of other men. Details related to these episodes showed her hostility to be unmistakable. She was for a time depressed over this. It became increasingly evident that her masculine protest and her profession were a defense against competition with women; that her hostility to men was a defensive intellectual disguise. The headaches became more severe as her resentment and criticism of her husband began to come to light. She finally came to feel warmer toward her husband, and dealt with her young men students with more frankness and fairness. This was due, however, only to partial insight and to the transference effect, namely identification with the therapist, for the emotional insight into the cause of this hostility had not yet emerged. Then President Roosevelt died. The patient felt devastated by a sense of personal loss.

After the President's death an astonishing change was observed. The patient became strikingly more regressive: she had no interest in her work; she would not cook for herself but went to her stepmother's often for meals and felt uneasy and defensive about this; she had no interest in giving to her patients or students. This period had all the signs of a depression with mourning. Accordingly the therapist arranged for two or three extra interviews so that the patient might feel she was receiving something during this distressing period. The therapist finally commented that she believed the patient must have felt much greater than the usual dependence a little girl feels on her father because of her mother's early death, and wondered also if she may have blamed him for the mother's death. This elicited no response from the patient, but that night she had a violent headache. She reported a highly disguised dream in which she hated men for their connection with the birth of a baby. In associating, she said, "Maybe I blame him for my birth to offset any guilt I may have toward my birth and mother's death." With this she associated new memories of the excitement connected with the birth of her first stepsister. She was then in a panic (and is angry now, as she recalls it) because she and an aunt had to take her stepmother to the hospital in the absence of her father. She was terrified that her stepmother would die. Her own unconscious ambivalent wishes here were not suggested, but the therapist felt it important to query again as to whether the patient might have felt that her father was responsible for her own mother's death. This recalled to the patient a dream from the night before in which she had made a nonsensical slip to her father, indicating she was having psychoanalytic treatment. In the dream he looked hurt, and the patient awoke. There followed several weeks of resentment toward her father. "It is his fault—not my mother's—that I am having to have treatment now. I can't tell him I am in treatment because I am so angry at him and am afraid I shall hurt him."

The therapist continued to be impressed with the patient's psychological insight. (Eighteen interviews had now taken place.) Since the transference relationship had mobilized the patient's confidence in the therapist, she continued to focus attention on her problems without too much resistance. It was therefore decided that nothing was to be gained by altering the transference at this point. It is important to emphasize again that although this material has to be greatly condensed, and therefore seems schematic and intellectual, actually this patient recognized and worked with her feelings to an unusual degree. No interpretations were actually given until the patient was obviously dealing with emotions and had given many leading associations.

Since there was evidence that her father and stepmother were really consistently kind and tolerant parents who gave little grounds for resentment, the proposition grew in the therapist's mind that the loss of her mother at 2 years was probably never faced and integrated by the patient and that she was living out a defense against this trauma, unable to receive freely from the good stepmother. It was as if she were saying, "I will have no one but my own mother." The patient tried to lean more on men than women, but seemed to be defensive about this for these reasons: (a) she was blaming Father, not Mother, for Mother's leaving her; (b), if Father really misused Mother, then he would misuse her (men are not to be trusted entirely); (c) also by projecting all the blame on Father, she could avoid facing her own later repressed anger at Mother, which, one speculated, would be terrifying to her. If men are mean, then that explains everything and she could thus avoid thinking of Mother.

About this time the therapist was to leave for a vacation about which the patient had been told some time before. She brought a dream in which she was at a museum looking at four stuffed birds, a mother and three little birds. The little birds came to life, and the patient remarked to someone, "Why don't they fly away?" As soon as the patient finished recounting her dream she said, "Oh, I see at once my guilt toward my siblings; I have them dead. But maybe I have them come to life only to get them out of the picture and away from the mother." Now the patient became depressed. The therapist inquired if even more she were guilty over the dead mother bird? The patient wept a little and commented that she had no such wishes toward her stepmother. The analyst suggested the possibility of exploring why this was a museum. At once the patient replied, "The bird was stuffed—I could go on seeing it, though dead." She was asked if this could in any way be associated with her own mother, and the patient recalled now that the day before the dream a friend had been speaking of *her* dependence on her mother, and at that time the patient had wondered if *she* (patient) were ever dependent on her own mother. In answer to this the analyst said that this was only natural. Since the patient was such a little girl, only 2, when her mother died, she could have seen her mother's leaving only as a desertion. Instantly the patient retorted, "I wonder if I held it against my father," and angrily she said, "We are going in circles, way back to my mother—we are getting no place." "On the other hand," the analyst said, "we might be getting too close to the mother and this upsets you." The patient could see at this time no connection between the therapist's leaving for her vacation and the dream just discussed.

After the analyst returned, for several sessions all the analytic material was defensive—hostile and destructive toward men. Women were always misused by men. The patient continued in this assertion for some time rather than seeing the therapist as misusing her by having left her. Finally the real meaning of the displacement and projection to men of her being misused by women became somewhat clear to her intellectually, but as yet it had not been emotionally assimilated.

After nine months of treatment the patient often dreamed of wanting a baby, but *headache would set in* and she would awaken with pain. In the dreams the patient felt guilty toward her stepmother, but why was not clear. Consciously she did not want a baby, and she felt no competition with women. She insisted she was guilty toward her stepmother over wishes toward her father on the basis of many associations and dreams at this time. The therapist suspected the patient's talking about babies and stepmother and "oedipal material" was actually a defense against her earlier experience with her own mother.

For instance the patient had a dream at this time in which Ginger Rogers was writing comic strips to say that incest is the greatest problem confronting the nation, and in the dream the patient felt that in some way she should help write these scripts. It is obvious that unconsciously the patient was laughing at the therapist and her silly ideas about oedipal conflicts. Still she was trying hard to inject the incest problem into the discussion as the cause of guilt toward mothers, and seemed to want the matter dropped there. Although the therapist felt there was guilt here, it was regarded as a cover for an earlier, greater conflict with the mother. The defense and its guilt, however, had still to be analyzed. The patient again mentioned her overtures to her father at 11 years. To bring out her anger to the therapist it was commented casually that he *was* wise to have handled this matter firmly. The patient looked depressed, flushed, and said, "Now for a headache." A fairly severe one was developing as she left the interview.

She slept through her next appointment and showed her anger against the therapist later in dreams. The patient was unable to express anything but the slightest annoyance, and said that the therapist "did not have to be *so* stuffy and blunt about it." A dull headache developed during this hour. Frightening homosexual dreams then emerged, among them one of extremely eerie quality. In this dream the patient had come stealthily to some public affair in a large park. She and her girl friend were hiding and watching what was going on. Suddenly they were both swept up in a parade of women in black who seemed to be Fascists, and all enemies of the patient. She felt that she should go along with them, since that would be safest. Her associations were interesting. "Does this have to do with spying on my parents? Does this have anything to do with peeking at my mother's death and at the funeral? Could it be that I feel all women are my enemies because I felt they were on mother's side and I was angry at her for leaving. I go along with them and they think I am one of them." The patient became very depressed as she discussed this dream from the point of view of the mother's death. Again we see her mention the *oedipal conflict* before she associates to her *mother's death,* as if any guilt over Mother at the oedipal level were far less painful than something deeper. The therapist's problem was how to get at this suspected conflict with the mother which existed in the pre-oedipal period.

About this time, the patient heard her husband would be home soon. She dreamt of him as a homosexual. This was such an obvious projection that the therapist questioned it at once, wondering about the patient's anxieties about depending on women. In analysis of this projection the therapist brought the conflict into the transference and called to her attention that the patient had hinted before that they would be hard pressed financially for a time when her husband was discharged; that apparently she had not even thought of asking that the therapist might then reduce her fee. The patient confessed she had worried over this, and she was *consciously* relieved when the therapist brought it up and the fee was reduced. Although all along in an inoffensive way, this patient had shown a great need to be independent, it was with conscious relief she accepted this aid. Obviously, however, fear and defensiveness about this would certainly emerge. There followed dreams, highly disguised, that the therapist, not having children of her own, really did not like them and their dependence. It was pointed out that the patient feared greatly any dependence on the therapist lest in the end she would be let down. To this the patient protested, maintaining her strong confidence in the analyst. At last in one of these dreams the patient could see her own pattern of projecting all blame onto men transferred to the therapist. She had the therapist really liking children (and yet there was a twist in this), but the real fault for not having children was the analyst's husband who was too dependent himself to stand such responsibility. Everything is the men's fault, not Mother's or women's. It was clear by now that the patient's main lines of defense against anger and fear, and guilt toward the mother's dying, were, "men are to blame—men misuse me—Mother is not to blame—my guilt toward Mother is oedipal—not terror or anger over her leaving me at 2. Men are homosexual and dependent—I am not."

Just before her menses the patient had the following dream: She and another woman were involved. The patient was extremely anxious in this dream, whereas the other woman was calm, kind, and objective. Before them was a fetal-like baby, crying and red with helplessness and anxiety, all bound up in a fish-net-like covering. The patient was extremely concerned, whereas the other woman was not, and the patient tried to get through the net to help the baby. She saw herself as identified with the baby; the therapist was the woman, in whom unconsciously the patient had much confidence. She wondered if she could have felt anything like this baby in the first year or two of her life when her mother was ill. She was not sure whether her mother was in a sanitarium, or whether the dream related to her mother's death. When asked if she had ever asked her father if her mother were in a sanitarium, she said she had never asked him anything. The therapist was impressed that this ordinarily warm, anything but shallow woman, at this moment spoke flippantly and almost callously. She was pushed for the real reason why she had asked her father nothing and she answered, "I am afraid of what he might think." When asked what he might think the patient said that he would wonder why she wanted to know, and then she stopped, saying she felt "awfully depressed." The therapist commented, "It must be that you have a great fear of learning something, since you cannot ask your father about your mother," and added, "Possibly you are more uneasy in a dependent relationship with women than with men." The patient said she had always been able to ask things of men but not of women.

It soon became clear that the headaches were related specifically to babies or Mother. If her friends mentioned babies or mothers, the patient was certain to have a migraine. "Babies" meant dependent demands on the patient. Once when the patient was depressed, and the therapist asked sympathetically if she felt "sorry for herself," she became incensed. When asked why she had taken this as a criticism, the patient insisted that she should be grown up. The therapist took this up with her sympathetically, picturing what she might have wished, as a little girl losing her mother. This made the patient depressed rather than angry and headachey. From this time, since it was clearer that the loss of her mother was highly significant for the patient, the therapist held her to analysis of the meaning of the mother's death. Resistance to this was intense, as will be seen, with over and over again a flippant callousness or stubbornness that indicated some fear underneath, for such an attitude was completely out of character.

Time after time she tried to elude the problem of her mother with all kinds of projections, fear for her husband's inadequacy instead of her own, men's homosexuality, etc. Any slight sexual inadequacy in her husband led to associations which showed her unconscious terror when she could not lean completely on him. Such a situation left her too aware of her own unsolved dependence. As she brought up these matters the therapist promptly indicated there might be some problems in the husband we should look into later, but that now the patient was only pushing them to the foreground as a defense. This would annoy the patient, and though she laughingly agreed, she showed some sulkiness and developed a headache. The patient maintained strongly that her own mother had utterly no significance for her and that her stepmother was her mother.

About this time it was discussed with the patient how, through accepting her stepmother as her own mother, she could use this as a defense and would thus not have to face the painful fact that there were two mothers. At once the patient became deeply depressed during the hour, and when the therapist persisted in asking her what she was thinking she became stubborn and angry and said she could think of nothing, for she was developing a headache. In this interview the anger was more prominent and the headache not so severe.

For a week there were no headaches, no depression, but feelings of detachment, almost depersonalization. This was a better defense apparently than the headache, since the latter was wearing a little thin. Several authors mention that at times the migrainous patient may faint when the headache as a defense is not sufficient. The therapist decided at this point she would push the patient hereafter to think, regardless of the headache, and not allow her to escape through her migraine. When the analyst pushed her to more expression in one hour, a violent headache, preceded by some anger, developed. The patient said, "I cannot think with such a headache."

In a dream that night a pair of spectacles appeared on a vague woman in the dream. The spectacles seemed the only clear thing. These were associated by the patient with a pair of the mother's that the father had, also a lapel watch of the mother's that the patient said just six months before the father agreed the patient might have. She had not taken the watch, thinking it unattractive. The therapist felt this was an excellent point at which to insist that the patient face emotionally that she felt she was different from her stepsisters. When the patient was asked if she would mind if her father gave the watch to one of the stepsisters, the patient became angry and burst into tears with, "It's mine—she was *my* mother." These were the first tears over her mother. It should be mentioned that this woman had rarely cried in her entire life, that she prided herself on this control.

The analyst now wanted to mobilize more feelings about the mother. These next steps are extremely important. First the analyst could honestly believe this woman's mother had been warm and loving because of the basic warmth she showed through the good positive transference—positive but never hungry. It must be kept in mind that a little child has to be assured of some love from her mother in order to dare face the full extent of her terror and ambivalence about the loss of a mother. The therapist decided to fantasy a little with the patient about the fact that the mother was probably a loving person, since the patient had always seemed so basically warm. This fantasy was mixed with sympathetic comments about how sad and lonely and lost the patient must have felt as such a little girl. The therapist was exceedingly careful not to suggest too much loving by the mother, in order to avoid stirring up too much terror over the loss. It should be remarked here that it was good that the patient was sitting up. To avoid any misinterpretations of the therapist's profound sympathy for the patient, it was helpful that she could observe the analyst's facial expressions. It now seemed wise that the patient should have more frequent interviews—two or three a week. This seemed necessary to intensify the working transference, to enhance the feeling of confidence in the therapist.

The patient's reaction to such fantasying was to sob brokenly but quietly, and finally she recalled that long ago she was told many times that her mother had gotten up from her sick bed to buy a lovely doll for her when she was two. For several sessions the patient just cried brokenly. This weeping from loneliness and feeling sorry for herself, with no anger, was something strange to her. She sobbed many times, "I have never known such loneliness as I feel now —but I must have, at one time." With her husband she realized she was acting like a leaning, lonely little girl and was inarticulate like a child in telling him of her grief. To see her sob in the interviews was extremely pathetic because of the peculiar child-like appearance and quality which came over her. There were no headaches now, and none of the anger formerly associated with them. There was none of the remorse in the sobbing of the depressed guilty patient; it was just the sobbing of a lonely child. Only feelings came up—no content. These were feelings too far back to recall content, but there were many dreams in which there was a vague woman who just seemed to come in and go out. Each dream ended with her going. At this time, sad and lonely as the patient felt, the analyst believed that, since the anger toward the mother had not yet really been mobilized, she should not move too close to the patient in giving comfort through physical contact such as a pressure of the hand lest the patient become too guilty. The analyst's verbal comments and facial expressions, however, were deeply sympathetic.

The patient soon realized, for the first time, that she had always felt a certain defensiveness with her stepmother; she recognized that now she had become much more at ease with her stepmother. She remarked that her stepmother (who had migraine) had lost her mother as a little girl, and that *she* had had a fine stepmother.

For the next three weeks the analyst continued to give the patient two or three interviews a week. For such a hidden mourning, where work and people outside make demands on the mourner, a few hours a week with the analyst seemed pretty barren at best. Much of this time she wept quietly with deep grief, saying very little. Often her only comment was, "I only feel—I can pin it on nothing—just lonely." At first she regarded this as a humiliation, since she was a grown woman. After she was able to accept the fact that it was natural she should feel sorry for herself, she wept in a heartbroken manner. The therapist knew it was then safe to be openly sympathetic with her.

With the patient, the analyst fantasied the little child in an atmosphere of mourning where the adults close to the child are so burdened by their own sorrow that they cannot weep with the child. They withdraw and, of course, the little one withdraws. Having the whole burden of fear and despair to carry alone, the child represses everything. Later, when the less grieved adults try to talk with the child, it is too late.

The patient feared her husband would not understand her if she spoke to him of her grief, and she said if it were not for hurting her stepmother she would feel much more at ease in talking to her; "she would understand." When the therapist commented that this was a real index of the patient's love and confidence in her stepmother's great warmth, she wept even more for her own mother. It was as if the reconciliation were coming first through the stepmother. It should be noted here that so far all the weeping is the patient's sorrow for herself; at no point did she express any sorrow for the mother that had to die. This, it was speculated but not revealed to the patient, meant that the anger toward the mother was still repressed and that no real reconciliation was yet possible. At the end of the hour the patient said, "I wish I could get this straightened out before I leave for Maine for my vacation in three weeks." The therapist said she understood, for she knew that the patient was going to a locality close to the place where the mother was buried. The patient suddenly commented that she had wondered why she had chosen Maine this year. Several times in recent sessions a mention of resentment toward the mother for leaving had been made by the therapist but had elicited no response.

In the next three sessions, when certain slips gave indication of negative feelings toward the analyst, the patient was made aware of this. Such minor resentments soon developed into very frank, sulky, provocative behavior. At this point the therapist responded to the provocative adult with some impatience of tone as she questioned the patient. The patient sulked and said nothing. By the end of the interview she had a moderate headache. She reported next time that as soon as she got outside of the analyst's office she realized she was extremely angry with the therapist; she laughed and cried on her way home, and felt that the therapist did not like her. She realized that she had been more angry than she had been in years, and her headache disappeared almost immediately.

To the next interview the patient came depressed, but with anger close to the surface. When the therapist said nothing, the patient gave a long, angry lecture to the therapist, pointing out that an analyst should never be impatient, that it was a profound disappointment to find the therapist so sharp the last hour, that the therapist lacked subtlety when she failed to realize that the patient cannot talk when she sulks; that this had been true for years. The analyst listened quietly, and finally the patient became uneasy and said, "I feel so scared, just panicky." The therapist, seeing the patient beginning to be tearful and anxious, said that she felt the patient was fearful the therapist no longer liked her. The patient nodded and then began to cry and was obviously in great misery. The therapist told the patient that her anger had been followed by fear that she was unloved, possibly because as a little girl she was terrified and angry that her mother had gone away and had never come back to reassure her that she was safe and loved in spite of the anger. If her mother could have come back, the mother would have realized the child's anger was because of her terror at being alone and would have loved her and not blamed her. This threw the patient into the most desperate suffering. Since she was obviously in great agony, the therapist moved closer to her, patted her on the shoulder, took her hand, and openly sympathized with her.

Now for the first time the patient seemed to be letting go of her great grief with real abandon; she was no longer crying silently. This went on for a long period. The patient was obviously getting an increasing feeling of confidence from the therapist's sympathy and closeness to her. Suddenly she sobbed, "For weeks I have been weeping for myself, and just now I feel so sorry for my poor mother —to die so young." She cried sorrowfully, saying repeatedly, "Poor Mother." When, at the end of the hour, she said that her husband was being very considerate of her lately, the therapist assumed that she would now feel more free about letting him see her grieve. The patient was sad because he would not be home until late that night. At this the therapist asked if the patient took the *New Yorker*. Since she did not, the analyst gave her the copy in which there was a beautiful, subtle story of a young girl who lost her parents. In this story the child's weeping was inhibited by well-meaning relatives, but the relief came when she was allowed to weep by her mother's old Mexican gardener who wept with her. The therapist suggested that the patient in privacy tonight might read this story and mourn with the girl.

We see now the recent phases of the patient's progress. She realized some of the loneliness and loss of her mother in mourning. Then, when she had experienced intense anger toward the therapist, followed by fear that she had lost the analyst, she was assured of understanding and affection. Thus with abreaction of the grief and fear came reassurance and final reconciliation.

Two nights later at her father's home she thought of her mother's watch, wanted it, but did not take it for fear her stepmother might notice and be hurt. In the next session she said, "So many times lately I have wanted to ask my father where the cemetery is, but it is not so easy." The therapist replied, "I know you want to go there, and are you afraid if you speak to your father you will weep, and make him sad?" She stated this was the case and was going to have her husband ask the father.

She still had mentioned no uneasiness in regard to leaving the therapist for three weeks' vacation. When she came in for her last hour, she said, "I don't think of my vacation—I only think of my work starting again." The analyst suggested that the patient seemed to be blotting out the vacation—could this be related to uneasiness regarding separation from the therapist? The patient commented she had not thought of this, but she *had* felt suddenly, two days ago, "When this is over my treatment will stop." The analyst added, "The little 2-year-old girl still feels hurried, doubtful, and fearful that she must take care of herself." Then the patient sobbed desperately, "I want to go to her grave for I know now what I have lost." To this the analyst replied, "And you almost feel, as soon as you find me, I will be lost to you also. You see possibly there is still some fear toward your mother and me—I am not going to die." The patient cried brokenly, suddenly stopped, and said, "I think she is in Richmond." The therapist was amazed and asked what the patient meant. She said, "I think she may be in the family lot in Richmond, Virginia—Oh, no! I know that isn't true. I know she is in New Hampshire. I must still be afraid of her and the loss." The analyst felt the patient should not have to go through this visit to the grave too much alone, so she fantasied this trip and grief with the patient in the hour. The therapist said, "You must recently have visualized yourself often at the grave," and the patient abandoned herself to tears. "Often I have thought of it, and I dread the tangibleness of the loss when I come to the grave." At the end of the hour she said she no longer felt isolated from her husband in this, that he was so kind and tender, and if they could possible make transportation connections she was going to New Hampshire.

Two weeks later a letter came saying that the first few days in Maine she had a dull headache, until one morning she awakened after a dream and felt extremely angry at the therapist for letting her leave. At once the headache subsided and she was very happy. She had never enjoyed a holiday so much with her husband; he thought she was delightful. She wanted to get to New Hampshire if connections could be made without taking too many days of her husband's vacation, since this was his first since he went overseas.

The patient returned from her vacation with the following account. She and her husband had the address of a friend who would show them the grave. The patient allowed a day for this stopover. What occurred was in a sense tragic. The friend had moved. The patient finally reached him on the phone from the station as the conductor was shouting, "All aboard." She heard from him that the cemetery was across from the railroad station, and she barely made her train. As she sat down in the moving train, the cemetery came into view. She was very sad for a time, but consoled herself with her husband's assurance they would return some time. There was no headache.

She returned from her trip, radiant. She had never found her husband so tender and kind, and he seemed delighted with her more casual serene dependence on him. She laughed, "My talk about his inadequacy was nonsense." She went on, "A few months ago when you pressed me to talk of my mother I felt that had nothing to do with me; in a few months a new world has come to light." With regard to further treatment the patient said, "In my last session with you I was feeling I would be thrown out soon—now I feel relaxed and know that you will give me what time I need. Right now I don't know what it could be, but I feel I at least have time to mull it over." This soon led to a discussion of babies and her fears. It became apparent that she had fused the idea of babies with the death of the mother and her own fears of death at childbirth. When the analyst commented that because of her great fear of loving and losing she might hesitate to love a baby, the patient had a sudden emotional release. She talked rapidly of loving children of her friends, pets of her sisters, wanting to play with them, but always managing to remain an onlooker. She had dreaded seeing her sisters mourn over the death of pets.

Periods of sadness and mourning for her mother and longing to ask her father about her continued for some time. It was interesting to see the shifting and reintegration of new attitudes in the reworking of the oedipal conflict as a living experience and not just a defense.

Her warmth and interest in babies became obvious. She now told people frankly she wanted a baby. She began to plan her career in such a manner as best to allow for the coming of a baby, and for a long period to be given to the infant's care. Her husband did not push her, but joined eagerly in her thinking.

When an interruption of the analysis was suggested, the patient became depressed and worked through considerable fear and resentment toward the therapist for abandoning her. She had a severe generalized headache when her husband spoke somewhat impatiently of his wife's dependence on the analyst. Instead of facing her anger toward him immediately, she, contrary to her recent attempts to analyze her reactions, simply abandoned herself for a time to a pounding general headache. Later she responded to him with great anger and the headache subsided.

The interruption of treatment is now in progress, and when she returns the degree of relapse can be determined.

Discussion

The discussion of this psychotherapy falls under three headings: (1) the structure of the case, (2) therapeutic accomplishment, (3) speculations with regard to the future.

1. *The structure of the case.* We see in this case the effects of a serious trauma to a little child before there was much power of verbalization. It is believed that this basically warm woman was really loved as a little child and that she herself loved before the loss. Undoubtedly the child was terrified without her mother, and with her fear came angry frustration. There was no return of the mother to relieve the terror and appease and forgive the anger. Gradually the intensity of such feelings must have been repressed. This left the patient unable to dare to receive fully the love from the really good stepmother—such loving and sudden loss and terror should never be risked again. Her great fear was fear of loss, associated, of course, with the inherent frustration and anger.

Since she was unable to relate herself to the stepmother as a mother, it would appear that the oedipal period did not have normal progress. Since there seems to have been no seductive permissiveness by the parents, we can only account for the 11-year-old girl's lack of guilt for her sexual feelings toward her father by the fact that she had never lived through the oedipal situation with an emotionally *accepted* mother.

Her headache developed in adolescence when demands were made on her for the first time to give to the younger siblings. Since her own receiving had been interrupted at two years, she could not give later without mobilizing that *early trauma* which was too painful to bear. An extension of this conflict is, "Babies lose their mothers by death, and therefore babies are frightening. One dare not love babies too much, for they might die and the loss would be unbearable."

We see this basically warm child later making an excellent social, scholastic, and marital adjustment, certainly not just superficially. Although this patient had a character neurosis with migraine as a defense against mobilization of the painful trauma, still the character involvement was far from a profound and crippling one. Sexual and group adjustments were good; this is not true in many cases of migraine, which usually show serious sexual maladjustments. The question is, why was her character not more dominated by the early trauma?

Counteracting factors were the thoroughly kind and consistent father and stepmother. Had the stepmother been less kind, the patient's trauma might have become less encapsulated, and more negative behavior might have come out toward the substitute mother, with less inclination toward migraine but with a less healthy integration of the personality. The encapsulation of the trauma was further maintained by certain definite lines of defense:

(a) "I will never allow myself to expect or to depend too much on a woman." We saw all through this woman's life a pseudoindependence which, however, was subtle and never offensive to those about her.

(b) The other outstanding defense was the attempt to lean on father and husband. This, however, was far from totally satisfactory, and she had a need to depreciate them subtly for the following reasons: someone or something finally had to become responsible for the mother's leaving, since it was too frightening to make the mother responsible and too guilt-producing to go on hating her. Thus the father was to blame. Mothers are innocent, but fathers misuse women. Yet for two years the little girl was left more or less alone with her father. She had to be dependent on him whom she mistrusted. Here again, to atone for her guilt toward him and to convince herself that she was self-sufficient, she depreciated what her father and husband did for her. Inadequacy was attributed to the men; hostility toward men was turned into hostility between men— the final projection of her problem with the mother to men. Still, leaning on men was far safer than turning to women. The remarkable thing, and this speaks for the kindness and strength of the men in her life, was that somehow this woman had been able to have a satisfactory sexual relationship with her husband.

2. *What was accomplished in the treatment?* During the process of analyzing these defenses, the patient gradually lived through such a reintegration of her fears of loss and her hostile impulses that the migraine began to subside. But far more important are the character changes. Gradually, in treatment, the patient had observed that the analyst had understood her terror at the loss of the mother and accepted the small degree of the patient's annoyance. The final great burst of anger toward the analyst terrified the patient, for she felt she had lost the therapist, since "no one had ever returned to forgive me." Some real continuity with the past and reconciliation were brought about, ending with sorrow for the mother herself and the wish to go to the grave. The corrective emotional experience had at last come through her relation to the analyst who stayed by her and forgave her. The patient feels a new security and serenity in depending upon her husband, who she finds is equal to it and delighted with it. Her relation to her stepmother, which she *had* thought was perfect, is now—surprising to the patient—more relaxed and warm. She says she no longer has the old anxiety about children, nor the feeling that people, and her husband particularly, are pressing her to have a baby. At last she feels she can take her time and do this when she wishes, and the wish is increasingly prominent.

Why was this case suitable for treatment on the basis described? First, this woman's character was not completely dominated by her early trauma, which seemed fairly well encapsulated. Although early in treatment the reasons for it were not clear, still one could see a good, workable transference develop in this patient, though she was seen at weekly intervals. The optimal degree of the working transference is the ideal of any therapy. Although defensive against her good mother, she showed early an identification with the woman analyst, who in many ways represented to her an ego-ideal—her forgotten mother. Furthermore this patient had a remarkable capacity to continue the therapeutic work between sessions through this identification with the analyst. She did not just sit back and drift. Every therapist must sense and gauge the correct balance between the problem to be mobilized and how much transference feeling is necessary to do this. In many cases, however, the cure can only be effected by fostering a more intensive transference neurosis.

Although the therapist could not know it until later in the treatment, the patient usually worked in relation to the analyst as if underneath she felt that women (mothers) were good—"I will do my best and the analyst will do her best." And because otherwise it would have been too painful, she went along in fairly good faith.

The analyst worked quite actively and consciously toward mobilizing her fear of loss and hostility; otherwise a much longer time and a more intensive transference neurosis might have been necessary. The activity in thinking and feeling by the therapist makes the patient feel less frustrated and angry toward the analysis itself.

3. *What is to be expected in the future?* The analyst can only speculate (and this will be interesting for discussion), since by the time the proceedings are published we shall no doubt have substantiation or disproof for some of our speculations. The therapist's feeling is that this woman needs some time at last to catch her breath and not feel rushed toward termination.

The real test will come when this patient must decide whether to become a mother means life or death, and becomes pregnant. This would involve any unresolved fear of her death, as a mother, and her fear of loving a baby, since the patient could not at one time risk the possibility of ever losing such a beloved object. When she can accept motherhood with equanimity she will be cured without a doubt. No abrupt termination would be so effective as possibly a few interruptions for two or three months in order to allow more abreaction of the separation. In this way one can see how much anger recurs.

Although she will not be my patient at such a future date, still it would be interesting to speculate how she will handle her children during their oedipal period. It was to be expected that some unconscious shifting in the ego structure would come about with her reconciliation to her mother, and this was observed. When she has a son or daughter she would be able to guide them through the oedipal period without undue permission or anxiety.

During the interruption the patient developed a severe headache. In a dream she saw herself as a very small baby "perfectly formed and healthy—not like that squalling, terrified, little, red monster caught in a net in one of my earlier analytic dreams." It was obvious that although her condition was greatly improved, she felt that "even though the baby was doing so well, it should not yet be left on its own." She reported that she had felt fairly intense anger and irritability with her family and her work and associates during the interruption. Such prolonged conscious anger was new to her. Furthermore she had felt angry with the analyst and doubtful of her ability. She voiced this frankly when she returned to treatment. These reactions to the therapist are now undergoing further analysis. A follow-up report on this case will be given at the next Council meeting.

A CLINICAL NOTE ON A MECHANISM OF PSYCHOGENIC BACK PAIN *

By Leon J. Saul, M.D.

In his article Fetterman (3) has emphasized the exaggeration of back pain for neurotic reasons. One point is worthy of further stress in this connection, namely that back pain, like many other psychosomatic symptoms, may result from an actual local physical condition which is exacerbated or possibly entirely caused by emotional tensions. It has been noted that emotional tensions produce physical effects, often during sleep, such as nocturnal teeth grinding, (4). Of a number of analyzed patients with back pain, one recently showed such a mechanism in especially clear form. This patient was a young man whose extreme ambitious competitiveness was largely a reaction to strong underlying dependence. He developed severe back pain with tenderness in the 4th–5th lumbar region on just four occasions, each of which was when the analysis was temporarily interrupted. He reacted with rage which, however, was repressed. At these times it appeared in his dreams which were filled with violence and muscular activity. For example:

Dream 1: I race a man and run very fast.
Dream 2: I am pounding something down into a barrel.
Dream 3: I come at a man with a heavy knife and split him in half.
Dream 4: I lead some people over a very difficult path, carrying a load on my back. It is a test. I awake with legs crossed and rigidly tense.

At other times in the analysis, when the patient was not acutely angry and had no back pain, his dreams were much quieter. For example:

Dream 1: I am appointed to an important position.
Dream 2: I am in a locker room. It is almost time for some game I am to play in, to begin, but I cannot find my clothes.

At the periods of repressed rage and dreams of extreme violence and activity, the patient noticed that when he awoke during the night

* Psychosomatic Medicine III: 190-191, 1941.

544

or in the morning his body musculature was so tensed that he was "rigid as a board." His legs would be rigidly extended, often with his ankles locked together and pulling against each other. If he retired without removing his wrist watch, he would find in the morning that his movements during sleep had forced the stem of the watch into the back of his hand, making his hand bleed.

Such muscular contractions during sleep, as in epileptoid conditions, can be of great force. It is difficult for most people who grind their teeth at night to do it as loudly when awake. The observations in the case here mentioned indicate that such contractions of the trunk muscles during sleep either caused the local back condition or exacerbated a condition which had been present. The orthopedist in the case could find no evidence of local pathology and rejected a diagnosis of slipped disc. The patient's repressed rage caused muscle contractions during sleep which caused the back pain and tenderness. If this is the case, the symptom would have no direct psychological "meaning," but would be only the end result of a process initiated by the emotional tensions, just like peptic ulcer as the incidental end result of gastric dysfunction due to emotional disturbance (1). But the muscular contractions which cause the back condition are a result of emotional tension (in this case primarily rage) and may have a symbolic meaning (5) (6). It may be only accidental that the pain is localized in the back. Arm and leg muscles were also contracted in this case, but perhaps anatomical conditions in the extremities are not such as to result in soreness as readily as in the back. On the other hand it may be that there are some specific psychological factors in the choice of the back. In this connection Fetterman makes a very interesting suggestion, namely, that this localization may have to do with the upright posture, implying adulthood with all its responsibilities and exertions. There was some evidence for this in the case herein mentioned as exemplified by Dream 4. Another factor which has been prominent in the five cases I have seen analytically is the sexual tension. These patients, like the young man here described, tended to drain their anger sexually also, and so when under emotional tension were in a highly excitable sexual state with orgasms during sleep, suggesting that pelvic congestion from this source might play a role in the back pain.

At any rate this is a fundamental psychosomatic mechanism. Particular biological impulses, in a specific constellation and status aroused by some life situation whether they are emotionally perceived or repressed by the patient himself, give rise to dreams and stimulate specific physiological responses. These may be mostly evident during sleep, and eventuate in the specific symptom.

BIBLIOGRAPHY

1. ALEXANDER, FRANZ. The influence of psychologic factors upon gastrointestinal disturbances: a symposium. *Psychoanal. Quart.*, 1934, **3**, 501.
2. DUNBAR, F. Character and symptom formation. *Psychoanal. Quart.*, 1939, **8**, 18.
3. FETTERMAN, J. L. Vertebral neuroses. *Psychosom. Med.*, 1940, **2**, 265.
4. SAUL, L. J. A note on the psychogenesis of organic symptoms. *Psychoanal. Quart.*, 1935, **4**, 476.
5. WEISS, E. A contribution to the psychological explanation of the arc de cercle. *Int. J. Psychoanal.*, 1925, **6**, 323.
6. WILSON, G. The transition from organ neurosis to conversion hysteria. *Int. J. Psycho-anal.*, 1938, **19**, 23.

SOME OBSERVATIONS ON THE RELATIONS
OF EMOTIONS AND ALLERGY *

By Leon J. Saul, M.D.

In his paper, Dr. George Wilson (8) has confined himself to a study of the psychological features in his analyzed cases of hay fever. He has deliberately avoided becoming involved in a question which cannot be adequately answered at the present time, namely, the relationship between the emotions and allergic sensitivity. His findings clearly demonstrate the importance of the patient's emotional state for the development of the hay fever symptoms. At the same time the importance of pollens and other irritants for the production of the same symptom is generally recognized and fully established. It may be that the hay fever is only a symptom which may have a number of entirely unrelated causes, of which allergic sensitivity is one and the emotional state may be another. On the other hand, should a constant emotional factor of a certain kind be found in a large series of recognized allergic cases, then the supposition would be justified that at least in these cases there was some relationship between this regularly found emotional factor and the sensitivity to allergens. From the present literature, and my own experience with psychoanalyzed allergic cases, it seems to me that such a constant emotional factor is present. This conclusion was further supported by the material presented by Wilson, particularly the case of the one girl described by him in detail who showed a very strong passive attachment to her mother. In the following discussion I shall depart from the excellent example of caution set by Wilson and advance a general summary of my experience with allergic cases, and a preliminary theory as to the relationship of the emotional and allergic factors.

Three patients analyzed by the author presented material which confirms the findings of Wilson that a factor in the production of the symptoms of hay fever is libidinal desire which is repressed and which affects the nasal mucosa.

CASE A is one of those reported in the monograph on asthma (3). This was a young man of 32 who had a severe seasonal hay fever since the age of 11 and, in addition, asthma since his early twenties. He

* Psychosomatic Medicine III: 66-71, 1941.

had been dominated by his mother, who was also seductive and had him sleep with her until he was 11 years old. This was discontinued because one night he touched her breasts. It was at the age of 11 when he no longer slept with her and left her for the first time to go to camp that his severe hay fever developed. This immediately suggested a connection between his hay fever and longings of a sexual nature for his mother (in addition to the possibility of new allergens at the camp). He had had coryza, colds, and bronchitis more severe than the average, and apparently allergic in nature, since very early infancy. His mother opposed his marriage. The patient repeated toward his wife the dependent attachment he had to his mother and when he came to the analysis, although 32 years of age, he was still going to school and being supported by his wife toward whom he repeated with great exactness many of the attitudes he had toward his mother, including sleeping in the same position. He felt that he did not have a normal potent adult masculine sexual attitude toward her, but was really her little boy. This was his main problem.

The next patient, Mr. B, a middle-aged man and a lifelong sufferer from moderately severe seasonal hay fever, was first spoiled and then severely neglected by his mother. He turned to his father but felt disappointed by him also. He reacted with the attitude, "I don't want anything from her anyway," but went through life with the attitude, "If I expect nothing from anyone I won't be disappointed," and was bitter and cynical because people always made demands upon him, not giving him all the personal interest and affection which he craved. He dreamt repeatedly of his mother. Although he tried to show himself as independent, hard-boiled, and masculine, if he heard of someone going out of his way to do something for another person, even if only in a movie or on the radio, tears would stream down his cheeks. He saw a play in which the wife waited on the husband, having his slippers out for him, holding his coat, and so on. This tremendously impressed the patient. He resented his wife's desires for attention, affection, and sexual satisfaction from him, and longed for a maternal woman who would only give love and care and personal warmth to him. This longing for his mother and her love, with bitterness at its frustration and at the demands of life, was his central emotional problem.

In the third case, that of Mr. C, the hay fever was perennial rather than seasonal, although, like the other patients, this young man of 30 showed the usual sensitivity on skin test to the ragweed and tree pollen groups and to a number of foods. In this case, also, the attachment to the mother was the central problem, with turning to the father which was very conflictual. The mother had been dominating, restrictive, and extremely overprotective.

Thus in these three hay fever cases the basic problem was the longing which originated in the relationship to the mother. The importance of just this component of the sexuality for the nasal congestion and secretion is indicated by a review of those situations in which the symptoms occurred. The 32-year-old man, Mr. A, had one of his most severe periods of hay fever at a time when he had to finance an operation for his wife and was forcing himself to work about sixteen hours a day. This lasted through the heat of the summer and the patient's hay fever continued in extremely severe form, rather than being relieved, as usual, between hay fever seasons. One of his severest periods was at the age of about 13. It occurred just when the patient stopped going with his gang of fellows and got a job in a drugstore at which he worked very hard, while at the same time he had three or four boys working for him taking care of lawns.

The occurrence of the hay fever symptoms in these situations suggests that it was related to the patient's wish to escape from the excessive demands upon him. In the background was the wish to go to his good indulging mother. In any difficulty this patient would run to his mother. For example, when in late adolescence a girl tried to seduce him, he ran to his mother to confess and to reassure himself of her love. He felt that fighting was masculine, but when, on a few occasions, he would force himself to fight and actually did very well, his nose would run and tears would stream down his cheeks.

This patient developed hay fever symptoms out of season, in December, during a visit to his employer and the employer's wife, just when the latter crossed her legs so that the patient could momentarily see her step-ins. The role of the sexuality in this example is clear, and in the patient's psychology the employer's wife was in a mother relationship to him. This incident shows the mechanism described by Wilson, the hay fever following the inhibition of the looking. He developed hay fever at the end of March when the termination of his analysis was discussed with him. This was well before the time his hay fever, which was strictly seasonal, usually occurred. His reaction was that if the analysis was to be terminated that spring he would go home immediately after it to visit his mother. He was unconsciously very angry at the prospect of being pushed out of the analytic situation in which for an hour a day someone was exclusively concerned with him and his problems, and felt that if he could no longer get this from the analyst he would go to his mother. His pride and the insight gained from the analysis prevented him from taking such a dependent receptive attitude toward his wife, and incidentally later weaned him pretty well from his excessive attachment to his mother. The point is that he developed hay fever symptoms at times when demands were made on him and when he wished to escape from them. The direction of his escape was toward his mother, for whom his longing was increased at these times.

Three attacks of hay fever in Case B, the middle-aged man who was rejected by his mother and dreamed of and longed for maternal buxom women, will illustrate the same mechanism in a different individual. One evening in the middle of March the patient's wife refused sexual relations which the patient wanted and the patient developed hay fever symptoms at that point. He turned over and went to sleep and dreamed that he was in bed with his wife, and practiced fellatio, for which he was ashamed while the neighbors looked in, and after that a large maternal woman with a shopping bag of food over her arm came in. This all occurred in his home town. He immediately associated the maternal woman with his mother. In his typical fashion he reacted to difficulties with his wife by wanting to go home to mother. The scoptophilia is seen here also. He had come to the analysis as a last resort, to save his marriage, for he wanted to leave his wife in the hope of finding a woman who would be more maternal and so satisfy him better. In other dreams his wife was regularly equated with his mother. On May 5 he developed hay fever just following a squabble with his wife, associated with wishes to go to another woman whom he had recently met and who he thought would be more maternal. Another attack, on April 30, occurred when the patient found that he had to make another business trip and could not go off for a vacation alone with his wife as he had wanted. Thus, in this case also, the patient, when faced with problems, difficulties, and demands, wished to escape from them to a maternal bosom. This protest against meeting the problems and difficulties, and the wish to escape to mother, were not conscious but repressed and denied by the patients as incompatible with their ideals of independence and masculinity. It was in these settings that the hay fever occurred.

The same was true of Mr. C, the last case mentioned. Attacks occurred regularly when the patient was in situations in which demands were made upon him which he felt obligated to meet but from which he emotionally wished to escape to his mother. When he forced himself against his wishes, the hay fever symptoms would develop.

A combination of these observations with other available data suggests a hypothesis as to the mechanism of operation of emotional factors in hay fever and in allergy in general. The author has reported observations upon the occurrence of common colds in patients in analysis (4). The colds occurred in situations in which the patients suffered intensification and frustration of passive receptive wishes, usually with a prominent oral component (that is, in which the wishes for love, attention, care, help from others were represented in the dreams and associations largely in the form of being taken to dinner, receiving gifts of candy, of being bought drinks, and otherwise being fed). These colds sometimes disappeared dramatically with insight or with the alleviation of the frustration, for example the return of a person upon whom the patient was dependent. This suggested that these colds were not primarily infectious, but that they were perhaps of allergic nature, related to the coryza of hay fever. The author's experience during the past years has amply confirmed this thesis. I have repeatedly observed the occurrence of colds in patients when their analyses have had to be temporarily interrupted, for example by the absence of the analyst for a week or so. I have also observed colds to occur regularly in several patients, who were very passive dependent persons, when they forced themselves to sustained work. In this they approximate the hay fever mechanism above described.

The next group of data is provided by observations on 27 psychoanalyzed asthma patients. In this study (3) it was found that the close attachment to the mother was the central feature. The asthma occurred regularly when this was suddenly threatened.

Two young women, both with severe prolonged generalized urticaria, have been analyzed by the author. In both of these cases the central feature was deprivation of parental, but primarily of maternal, love, in childhood, with consequent strong, masochistic attachment to the father. In the one case (5) the mother died when the patient was two, and the patient was exploited by the father and the stepmother, and received almost no love or regard from them. The other girl's parents overtly preferred the other children and treated her as the ugly duckling or Cinderella of the family. The attacks of generalized urticaria occurred regularly and exclusively when the first patient's longings for love were intensified and frustrated. The second patient has had no attacks since being observed (six months), but her past attacks were under just these conditions. In these cases the longings for love were expressed in the dreams largely in the form of wishes to be admired, to be beautiful, and to have fine clothes. Both parents wanted to be dancers; the first acted in amateur theatricals and the second modeled for artists. The meager evidence suggests that where the wishes for love are in the form of exhibitionistic desires and relate to the skin, and where there is a heightened skin erotism, this operates as one determinant of the skin as a site for the symptom. Wilson's paper has discussed the choice of the nose as the site of the symptom of hay fever as determined by repressed olfactory sexual curiosity. The hypothesis as to the site of the symptom in asthma, as described in the asthma study, is that the asthma attack replaces a cry which is stimulated by the threatened loss of the mother's love or by the separation from her, but which is repressed. In the urticaria cases, weeping relieved the attacks and apparently could replace them, it being an alternative mode of expression for the feelings of frustration.

This leads to a general theory as to the mechanism of emotional factors in allergy. In all of these studies of symptoms of an allergic nature in which emotional actors were found to play a role, the central emotion related to the symptom was a strong longing for love, basically for the mother's. *This suggests that intense, unsatisfied longing for love affects the individual's allergic sensitivity.* This longing is of the infantile dependent kind of the child for its mother. It further suggests as a hypothesis to be tested, that when this longing is especially intensified and frustrated, or threatened with frustration, the allergic sensitivity is increased and the symptoms appear.

Of course such longings are important in everyone, but they apparently bear a special relationship to the allergic symptoms when in a certain status. In contrast to this allergic group, for example, are the functional cardiac cases which serve as a control group. Studies of emotional factors in essential hypertension indicate as the chief emotional tendencies related to the symptoms, not libidinal longings, as in these allergic cases, but hostility and struggle with an unsolved conflict situation (1, 6, 7). This difference in the emotional background of the allergic symptoms, as opposed to essential hypertension, may be of significance for the fact that these two conditions are generally believed to occur only very infrequently in the same individual (2).

The situation appears, then, to be as follows: The emotional factor which is important for the allergic symptoms in these particular cases is libidinal longing, probably basically of the nature of the child's for the mother. This longing must, of course, come to expression in specific ways and involve specific body sites in each case. The choice of these particular sites must be determined by specific psychological and biological factors. There is nothing mutually exclusive about these, for allergic individuals usually present symptoms in different organs at one time or another. The specific factors determining the site of the symptoms in the asthma cases are apparently (a) the sudden threat to the attachment to the mother and (b) the repression of the consequent tendency to cry out. Further study may reveal further specific elements. The specific factors in cases of the common cold, of the type described above, have not been worked out in detail, but the evidence suggests that one of these is the frustration of the oral components of the longing. Wilson's paper has demonstrated the specific factors involved in localizing the libidinal longings in his hay fever cases to the nose, namely, the suppression of the olfactory sexual curiosity, which was found to express not an adult genital sexuality but an immature, dependent, demanding attitude. Not enough cases of urticaria have been studied to reveal the specific elements of the skin as the site for the symptom, but the three analyzed cases all showed a relationship to the repressed longing which did not achieve genital sexual expression and which apparently resulted in a high degree of erotization of the skin (as seen in strong exhibitionistic tendencies). In all these allergic cases in which the emotions appear to play a role in the production of the symptoms, the central factor related to the symptoms was intense, libidinal longing and certain specific factors involving the status of the longing. Its manner of frustration and mode of expression determined the bronchi, upper respiratory passages, or skin as the particular sites for the symptoms.

The observation of the relationship of intense, repressed, frustrated longing to allergic sensitivity provides a theory which takes account of both the psychological factors and the pollen sensitivity, for according to this concept the one complements the other. The situation is this very simple one, that the emotional state leads to physiological changes which either (a) imitate the allergic symptoms, or (b) render the tissues more sensitive to allergens, or (c) do both; and conversely, an individual who is allergically sensitive on presumably an entirely organic basis might conceivably through the very fact of this sensitivity more readily produce symptoms which are psychologically determined. For example, a patient may have seasonal attacks of hay fever due to pollen sensitivity, entirely apart from his emotional state. However, if his longings increase, his hay fever may become more severe. Further, if the repressed frustrated longing becomes sufficiently intense, then the symptoms may appear on this basis alone. An individual in whom certain tissues are constantly stimulated and sensitive because of his emotional state (like a congestion of the nose from a chronic tendency to cry for mother, or of the skin from a chronic tendency to blush) may well be more sensitive in these tissues to irritating allergens. Conversely, it is easily conceivable that an individual whose tissues are irritated by allergens will react more sensitively in these particular sites to emotional stimuli.

It must not be forgotten in all these discussions that when we refer to psychogenic factors we do not mean certain intellectual ideas of the patient, but, on the contrary, the emotions, which are powerful and eminently biological. The child's longing for the parent, its anxiety when left alone are deeply biological; they are concerned with the individual's very existence, and when such deep seated emotions are aroused, they produce far-reaching biological changes.

Summary

On the basis of studies now available on the role of emotions in allergic symptoms, the working hypothesis is presented that states of repressed, intense, frustrated longing are of central importance. This was found in studies of certain cases of common cold, asthma, hay fever, and urticaria. The choice of sites for the symptoms seems to be determined by more specific factors. But whatever the factors in the choice of site for the symptom, the repressed longing, basically for the mother, frustrated or threatened with frustration, plays a central role. The longing is only one factor in the production of the symptoms. It operates in some cases independently of, and in other cases together with, specific allergic sensitivities. It is related to allergic sensitivity perhaps through increasing this sensitivity in the individual. It also operates apart from allergens by producing similar symptoms. It is a biological factor which apparently influences and complements allergic sensitivity, at least in certain cases.

BIBLIOGRAPHY

1. ALEXANDER, FRANZ. Emotional factors in essential hypertension. *Psychosom. Med.*, 1939, **1**, 173.
2. COCA, A. F., WALZER, MATTHEW, AND THOMMEN, A. A. *Asthma and hay fever.* Baltimore: Charles C. Thomas, 1931.
3. FRENCH, T. M., AND ALEXANDER, FRANZ. Psychogenic problems in bronchial asthma. *Psychosom. Med. Monogr.*
4. SAUL, L. J. Psychogenic factors in the etiology of the common cold and related symptoms. *Int. J. Psycho-Anal.*, 1938, **19**, 451.
5. SAUL, L. J. Psychological situations concomitant with urticarial attacks. A paper read at the annual meeting of the Southern Psychiatric Association, Louisville, October 9, 1939.
6. SAUL, L. J. Hostility in cases of essential hypertension. *Psychosom. Med.*, 1939, **1**, 153.
7. SAUL, L. J. Utilization of early current dreams in formulating psychoanalytic cases. *Psychoanal. Quart.*, 1940, **9**, 453.
8. WILSON, GEORGE. A study of structural and instinctual conflicts in cases of hay fever. *Psychosom. Med.*, 1941, **3**, 51. (In this volume, p. 266.)

GLAUCOMA *

Every year in the United States glaucoma causes 20,000 citizens to become totally blind and 100,000 to lose the sight of one eye. The cause of acute primary glaucoma has puzzled ophthalmologists for a long time. It is known that the rise of intraocular tension, when persistent, damages the retina, and that this increased tension is caused by interference with the drainage of the fluid from the anterior chamber. Interference with drainage has been thought to be due to the effects of the sympathetic system on the small vessels in the anterior chamber.

Attacks of primary glaucoma have been known to be precipitated by emotional upsets. Schoenberg [1] cited cases in which the attack seemed to be connected with accidents or death of a member of the patient's family, worry over ill health, or financial losses. Inman,[2] of London, has referred to primary glaucoma as an organ neurosis and proposed the term "angioneurotic edema of the anterior eye."

As a cooperative undertaking with the Illinois State Eye and Ear Clinic, under the direction of Dr. Harry Gradle, the Institute made a psychological survey of a series of 36 glaucoma patients. The psychiatric interviews were conducted by Dr. Gerhart Piers. In 24 patients, Piers found a close connection between glaucoma attacks and specific emotional events to which these individuals were especially sensitive. In nine out of 24 glaucoma cases, the original attack was precipitated by witnessing an accident resulting in injury or death to someone with whom the patient had intense emotional ties. In the majority of the other cases, where such acutely traumatic upsets did not occur, there nevertheless were found chronic emotional conflicts involving the patient and one or more of his dependents. The glaucoma patients interviewed all came from large families, averaging six or seven siblings for each patient, and had a conspicuously overconscientious attitude which made them spend much of their time and energy "providing" for dependent relatives. It was also noted that frequently a history of blindness from causes

* From The Ten-Year Report, 1932-1942. Chicago, Institute for Psychoanalysis, pp. 32-33.

1 Schoenberg, M. Role of states of anxiety in pathogenesis of primary glaucoma. Arch. Ophthal., 1940, 23, 76.

2 Inman, W. Emotions and acute glaucoma. Lancet, 1929, 2, 118.

other than glaucoma was present in the family or among close friends.

Difficulties were encountered, however, in finding patients willing to start psychoanalytic treatment. Eventually a 44-year-old woman, who had had an operation for glaucoma on one eye, was studied psychoanalytically at first by Miller and later by McLean. A daily chart of the eye tension was kept; later biweekly readings of the ocular tension were made. From the beginning of the psychoanalysis it was obvious that the patient was laboring under intense anxiety. The anxiety was not bound by the pathological condition in the eye, but instead was increased by the glaucoma with its accompanying fear of loss of vision. A relation was found to exist between ocular tension and emotional tension. The ocular pressure rose whenever aggressive, hostile feelings with the concomitant anxiety were intensified, and fell during periods of relative freedom from anxiety. In later publications we shall suggest the specific psychodynamic situation which may be related to the increased ocular tension and which, in association with constitutional factors, may lead to glaucoma.

All the patients studied anamnestically and the one patient studied psychoanalytically were found to be visually-minded to an unusual degree. Particularly vivid were their visual images of imagined, predicted, or recalled accidents. It is too early to say whether it will be advisable to study psychoanalytically any other patients with glaucoma. Information gained from psychiatric interviews has been extremely fruitful. Such interviews, in combination with a modified psychoanalytic treatment, may yield even more cogent material.

INDEX OF NAMES

Wilder, J., 360, 383
Wilhelmy, C. M., 219, 223
Williams, G. W., 489, 498
Wilson, A. T. M., 222
Wilson, D. C., 208
Wilson, G. W., 125, 127, 134, 148-160, 223, 224-239, 225, 238, 259-264, 266-286, 286, 335, 343, 344, 546, 547, 552, 553, 554
Wilson, M., 208
Winkelstein, A., 118, 132, 220, 223
Winnicott, D. W., 502, 513

Wislocki, C. B., 50, 84
Wittkower, E., 245, 248, 333, 335, 343, 344
Wolberg, L. R., 522
Wolf, H. G., 12, 489, 498
Wolfe, T. P., 12, 291, 294, 297, 344, 356
Woodyatt, R. T., 384
Wright, L. M., 489, 498

Yaskis, M., 69, 82

Zitman, I. H., 10, 362, 383

SUBJECT INDEX

Akinesia,
after ventriculography, 514-521
ego in, 520
lesion causing, 517
libido in, 520
and sleep, 517, 518
Alcoholism, 23-24, 304
Allergy, 547-554 (See also Asthma, Hay
fever, Neurodermatitis, Urticaria)
in children, 405
and hypertension, 552
role of emotions in, 552-554
specificity of, 553
American culture, 32
Anal character, 192
Anal-erotism, 123
Anal-sadistic impulses, in cases of constipation, 126-127, 193
Anger (See Rage)
Angioneurotic edema, 425
"Antagonistic cooperation," 32
Anxiety, 80
Arthritic pain, 38
Arthritis, rheumatoid, 489-498
cases of, 489-498
as hysterical conversion, 229, 234, 494-
495
and increased muscle tonus, 497
and interruption of hostile expression,
495, 496, 497
and "masculine protest," 490, 491, 492,
494
and masochism, 492, 494
personality features in, 490
precipitating events, 491
psychodynamic factors in, 495-497
review of the literature, 489
typical family situation in, 493-494
unconscious factors in, 491-493
Asthenic syndrome, 359, 363
Asthma, bronchial, 35, 44-45, 551
attacks interrupted in analysis, 246
attitude of parents in, 244
case of, 252-258
causes of attacks of, 247
character structure in, 246
in children, 243-248
confession in, 249-250
constitutional factor in, 247
as a conversion symptom, 8
and crying, 246
and fear of separation from the mother,
245-246
and maternal rejection, 248

Asthma, bronchial—*Continued*
psychogenic causes of, 245-248
psychotherapy in, 244, 249-258
situations causing, 245-246
specificity of, 247
and urticaria, 446
Autonomic nervous system (See also
Parasympathetic nervous system and
Vegetative neuroses)
and emotion, 54
and fear, 60
functions of, 54
and homeostasis, 60
and the hypothalamus, 54-55
and rage, 60
role of in peptic ulcer, 218-219

Back pain, 544-546
as a conversion symptom, 229, 234
and repressed rage, 544, 545
and sexual tension, 545
Behavior, physiology of, 37-45
Biochemistry, and the psychological approach, 29
Blood pressure (See also Hypertension)
in control cases, 328-329
in depression, 321-323, 326-327
and emotional tension, 310-315
and inhibited aggression in psychotics,
316-332
in mania, 316-317
in melancholia, 316-317
in paranoid cases, 319-321, 325-326
in schizophrenia, 323-324, 327-328
Blood sugar level,
and hypoglycemia, 382
in neurasthenia, 361
Bulimia, 140
as a conversion symptom, 8

Carbohydrate metabolism (See also Diabetes mellitus)
and emotional tendencies, 388-392, 395-
396
Cardiac neuroses (See Heart disease,
functional)
Character development, 487
Chemotherapy, 18
Chicago Institute for Psychoanalysis, 10,
44, 95, 103, 107, 161, 192, 200, 206,
249, 298, 344, 446
Choice of neurosis (See Specificity)
Colds, emotional factors in, 87, 88, 227,
551

Racial factors (See Cultural factors)
Rage, 80
  and the autonomic nervous system, 60
  effect of, 381
  and the hypothalamus, 58
Regression, 77
Research, psychosomatic (See Psycho-
  somatic research)
Respiratory system (See Asthma, Colds,
  Coughing, Hay fever)
Retaining tendencies, 108-109, 130

Schizophrenia, 25, 29
  blood pressure in, 323-324, 327-328
  constipation in, 200-201
  constitutional factor in, 26
  electroencephalogram in, 72
  homeostasis in, 72
  and the hypothalamus, 71-72
Schizophrenia, paranoid,
  attitude toward defecation, 201-203
  attitude toward food, 201-203
Scientific method, 14-15
Sexuality, 32
Shock therapy, 29-30
Skin disorders, 8, 401-402 (See also
  Neurodermatitis and Urticaria)
Sleep,
  and akinesia, 517, 518
  role of the hypothalamus in, 58-60
Smell, sense of (See Olfaction)
Specificity, v-vi, 10-11, 37-45, 42, 44, 85-
  90, 98
  of allergy, 553
  of asthma, 247
  of hypertension, 99, 294
  of hypoglycemic fatigue, 376
  of peptic ulcer, 99, 119-120
  of urticaria, 443-444
Stability principle (See Homeostasis)
Stuttering, and constipation, 264
Superego, and the hypothalamus, 80
Symptoms, treatment of, 97-98

Teeth, grinding of, 86-87, 89
Testicle, pain in, 90
Therapy (See Psychotherapy)
Tic, 264, 455-488
  and compulsive-obsessive acts, 456, 458
  as a defense mechanism, 460, 461
  as a defensive reaction, 455, 456, 457,
  458
  definition of, 459
  as denial of aggression, 468, 469, 470,
  485
  as erotic aggression, 456, 458
  and inhibition of aggression, 473
  as inhibition of impulse, 457, 460
  and "isolation" of fear, 462
  and movement restraint, 457, 458
  and muscle coordination, 457
  and narcissism, 455-456, 460
  as onanism, 455
  precipitating causes of, 460

Tic—Continued
  psychodynamics of, 460-461, 486
  purpose of, 461, 487
  as repetition compulsion, 461-462
  review of the literature, 455-459
  and traumatic event, 468
Tic, cases of, 463-469, 469-474, 474-479,
  479-486
  attitudes of parents, 458, 459-460
  conflict in, 461
  personality of, 460
  prognosis in, 456, 458
Training principles in psychosomatic
  medicine, 34-36
Transference, 98
  control of, 526
  use of in therapy, 542

Ulcer (See Peptic ulcer)
Urticaria, 424-451, 551-552
  and angioneurotic edema, 425
  and asthma, 496
  case of, 428-451
  and crying, 441, 442
  dreams in, 432-439, 448-449
  and endocrine dysfunction, 444-445
  and exhibitionism, 443
  and fear of separation, 431
  and frustrated desires for love, 438,
  440, 441, 445
  and guilt, 445
  masochism in, 441, 444, 445
  and overexertion, 440
  psychodynamics of, 443-447
  psychological settings of attacks, 431,
  438, 448-449
  review of the literature on, 425-427
  and sexual frustration, 443-444, 445
  specificity of, 443-444
  as a vegetative neurosis, 8
  and wish for love, 431

Vector theory (Alexander), 108-109,
  130
Vegetative neuroses (See also Organ
  neuroses)
  and conversion symptoms, 6-10, 105-
  106
  as physiological concomitants, 6-7
Vegetative response to emotions, vi, vii
"Vegetative retreat,"
  in hypoglycemic fatigue, 382
  in peptic ulcer, 10
Ventriculography, akinesia after, 514-
  521
Vertigo, 137
Voluntary behavior, vi
Vomiting and diarrhea, a case of, 168-
  172
Vomiting, psychogenic, 106

"Working through," 93, 95

Zest,
  lack of in hypoglycemia, 359-381
  and rage and fear, 381-382

hèques

I